Undergraduate Texts in Mathematics

 MyCopy

Dear MyCopy Customer,

This printed, personal Springer eBook is a unique service that is available at a low cost, only on link.springer.com because your library purchased at least one Springer eBook subject collection. This book is an exact, monochrome copy of the eBook on SpringerLink.

MyCopy books are strictly for individual use only, and not available for resale. You can cite this book by referencing the bibliographic data and/or the DOI (Digital Object Identifier) found in the front matter.

MyCopy is the ideal format for anyone who wants a physical copy for page-by-page study.

My Book, MyCopy.
Enjoy reading.

Springer Science+Business Media, LLC

Undergraduate Texts in Mathematics

Undergraduate Texts in Mathematics are generally aimed at third- and fourth-year undergraduate mathematics students at North American universities. These texts strive to provide students and teachers with new perspectives and novel approaches. The books include motivation that guides the reader to an appreciation of interrelations among different aspects of the subject. They feature examples that illustrate key concepts as well as exercises that strengthen understanding.

Jerry Shurman

Calculus and Analysis in Euclidean Space

 Springer

Jerry Shurman
Department of Mathematics
Reed College
Portland, OR
USA

ISSN 0172-6056   ISSN 2197-5604   (electronic)
Undergraduate Texts in Mathematics
DOI 10.1007/978-3-319-49314-5

Printed on acid-free paper

This Springer imprint is published by Springer Nature
The registered company is Springer International Publishing AG
The registered company address is: Gewerbestrasse 11, 6330 Cham, Switzerland
(www.springer.com/mycopy)

Contents

Part II Multivariable Integral Calculus

Preface

This book came into being as lecture notes for a course at Reed College on multivariable calculus and analysis. The setting is n-dimensional Euclidean space, with the material on differentiation culminating in the inverse function theorem and its consequences, and the material on integration culminating in the general fundamental theorem of integral calculus (often called Stokes's theorem) and some of its consequences in turn. The prerequisite is a proof-based course in one-variable calculus and analysis. Some familiarity with the complex number system and complex mappings is occasionally assumed as well, but the reader can get by without it.

The book's aim is to use multivariable calculus to teach mathematics as a blend of reasoning, computing, and problem-solving, doing justice to the structure, the details, and the scope of the ideas. To this end, I have tried to write in an informal style that communicates intent early in the discussion of each topic rather than proceeding coyly from opaque definitions. Also, I have tried occasionally to speak to the pedagogy of mathematics and its effect on the process of learning the subject. Most importantly, I have tried to spread the weight of exposition among figures, formulas, and words. The premise is that the reader is eager to do mathematics resourcefully by marshaling the skills of

- geometric intuition (the visual cortex being quickly instinctive)
- algebraic manipulation (symbol-patterns being precise and robust)
- and incisive use of natural language (slogans that encapsulate central ideas enabling a large-scale grasp of the subject).

Thinking in these ways renders mathematics coherent, inevitable, and fluid.

In my own student days I learned this material from books by Apostol, Buck, Rudin, and Spivak, books that thrilled me. My debt to those sources pervades these pages, and there are many other fine books on the subject as well. Indeed, nothing in these notes is claimed as new. Whatever effectiveness this exposition has acquired over time is due to innumerable ideas from my students, and from discussion with colleagues, especially Joe Buhler, Paul

Garrett, Ray Mayer, and Tom Wieting. After many years of tuning my presentation of this subject matter to serve the needs in my classroom, I hope that now this book can serve other teachers and their students too. I welcome suggestions for improving it, especially because some of its parts are more tested than others. Comments and corrections should be sent to `jerry@reed.edu`.

By way of a warmup, Chapter 1 reviews some ideas from one-variable calculus, and then covers the one-variable Taylor's theorem in detail.

Chapters 2 and 3 cover what might be called multivariable precalculus, introducing the requisite algebra, geometry, analysis, and topology of Euclidean space, and the requisite linear algebra, for the calculus to follow. A pedagogical theme of these chapters is that mathematical objects can be better understood from their characterizations than from their constructions. Vector geometry follows from the intrinsic (coordinate-free) algebraic properties of the vector inner product, with no reference to the inner product formula. The fact that passing a closed and bounded subset of Euclidean space through a continuous mapping gives another such set is clear once such sets are characterized in terms of sequences. The multiplicativity of the determinant and the fact that the determinant indicates whether a linear mapping is invertible are consequences of the determinant's characterizing properties. The geometry of the cross product follows from its intrinsic algebraic characterization. Furthermore, the only possible formula for the (suitably normalized) inner product, or for the determinant, or for the cross product, is dictated by the relevant properties. As far as the theory is concerned, the only role of the formula is to show that an object with the desired properties exists at all. The intent here is that the student who is introduced to mathematical objects via their characterizations will see quickly how the objects work, and that how they work makes their constructions inevitable.

In the same vein, Chapter 4 characterizes the multivariable derivative as a well-approximating linear mapping. The chapter then solves some multivariable problems that have one-variable counterparts. Specifically, the multivariable chain rule helps with change of variable in partial differential equations, a multivariable analogue of the max/min test helps with optimization, and the multivariable derivative of a scalar-valued function helps to find tangent planes and trajectories.

Chapter 5 uses the results of the three chapters preceding it to prove the inverse function theorem, then the implicit function theorem as a corollary, and finally the Lagrange multiplier criterion as a consequence of the implicit function theorem. Lagrange multipliers help with a type of multivariable optimization problem that has no one-variable analogue, optimization with constraints. For example, given two curves in space, what pair of points—one on each curve—are closest to each other? Not only does this problem have six variables (the three coordinates of each point), but furthermore, they are not fully independent: the first three variables must specify a point on the first curve, and similarly for the second three. In this problem, x_1 through x_6

vary though a subset of six-dimensional space, conceptually a two-dimensional subset (one degree of freedom for each curve) that is bending around in the ambient six dimensions, and we seek points of this subset where a certain function of x_1 through x_6 is optimized. That is, optimization with constraints can be viewed as a beginning example of calculus on curved spaces.

For another example, let n be a positive integer, and let $e_1, \ldots, e_n$ be positive numbers with $e_1 + \cdots + e_n = 1$. Maximize the function

$$f(x_1, \ldots, x_n) = x_1^{e_1} \cdots x_n^{e_n}, \quad x_i \geq 0 \text{ for all } i,$$

subject to the constraint that

$$e_1 x_1 + \cdots + e_n x_n = 1.$$

As in the previous paragraph, since this problem involves one condition on the variables x_1 through x_n, it can be viewed as optimizing over an $(n-1)$-dimensional space inside n dimensions. The problem may appear unmotivated, but its solution leads quickly to a generalization of the arithmetic–geometric mean inequality $\sqrt{ab} \leq (a+b)/2$ for all nonnegative a and b,

$$a_1^{e_1} \cdots a_n^{e_n} \leq e_1 a_1 + \cdots + e_n a_n \quad \text{for all nonnegative } a_1, \ldots, a_n.$$

Moving to integral calculus, Chapter 6 introduces the integral of a scalar-valued function of many variables, taken over a domain of its inputs. When the domain is a box, the definitions and the basic results are essentially the same as for one variable. However, in multivariable calculus we want to integrate over regions other than boxes, and ensuring that we can do so takes a little work. After this is done, the chapter proceeds to two main tools for multivariable integration: Fubini's theorem and the change of variable theorem. Fubini's theorem reduces one n-dimensional integral to n one-dimensional integrals, and the change of variable theorem replaces one n-dimensional integral with another that may be easier to evaluate. Using these techniques, one can show, for example, that the ball of radius r in n dimensions has volume

$$\operatorname{vol}(B_n(r)) = \frac{\pi^{n/2}}{(n/2)!} r^n, \quad n = 1, 2, 3, 4, \ldots.$$

The meaning of the $(n/2)!$ in the display when n is odd is explained by a function called the gamma function. The sequence begins

$$2r, \quad \pi r^2, \quad \frac{4}{3}\pi r^3, \quad \frac{1}{2}\pi^2 r^4, \quad \ldots.$$

Chapter 7 discusses the fact that continuous functions, or differentiable functions, or twice-differentiable functions, are well approximated by smooth functions, meaning functions that can be differentiated endlessly. The approximation technology is an integral called the convolution. One point here is that the integral is useful in ways far beyond computing volumes. The second point is that with approximation by convolution in hand, we feel free to assume in the sequel that functions are smooth. The reader who is willing to grant this assumption in any case can skip Chapter 7.

Chapter 8 introduces parametrized curves as a warmup for Chapter 9 to follow. The subject of Chapter 9 is integration over k-dimensional parametrized surfaces in n-dimensional space, and parametrized curves are the special case $k = 1$. Aside from being one-dimensional surfaces, parametrized curves are interesting in their own right. Chapter 8 focuses on the local description of a curve in an intrinsic coordinate system that continually adjusts itself as it moves along the curve, the Frenet frame.

Chapter 9 presents the integration of differential forms. This subject poses the pedagogical dilemma that fully describing its structure requires an investment in machinery untenable for students who are seeing it for the first time, whereas describing it purely operationally is unmotivated. The approach here begins with the integration of functions over k-dimensional surfaces in n-dimensional space, a natural tool to want, with a natural definition suggesting itself. For certain such integrals, called flow and flux integrals, the integrand takes a particularly workable form consisting of sums of determinants of derivatives. It is easy to see what other integrands—including integrands suitable for n-dimensional integration in the sense of Chapter 6, and including functions in the usual sense—have similar features. These integrands can be uniformly described in algebraic terms as objects called differential forms. That is, differential forms assemble the smallest coherent algebraic structure encompassing the various integrands of interest to us. The fact that differential forms are algebraic makes them easy to study without thinking directly about the analysis of integration. The algebra leads to a general version of the fundamental theorem of integral calculus that is rich in geometry. The theorem subsumes the three classical vector integration theorems: Green's theorem, Stokes's theorem, and Gauss's theorem, also called the divergence theorem.

The following two exercises invite the reader to start engaging with some of the ideas in this book immediately.

Exercises

0.0.1. (a) Consider two surfaces in space, each surface having at each of its points a tangent plane and therefore a normal line, and consider pairs of points, one on each surface. Conjecture a geometric condition, phrased in terms of tangent planes and/or normal lines, about the closest pair of points.

(b) Consider a surface in space and a curve in space, the curve having at each of its points a tangent line and therefore a normal plane, and consider pairs of points, one on the surface and one on the curve. Make a conjecture about the closest pair of points.

(c) Make a conjecture about the closest pair of points on two curves.

0.0.2. (a) Assume that the factorial of a half-integer makes sense, and grant the general formula for the volume of a ball in n dimensions. Explain why it follows that $(1/2)! = \sqrt{\pi}/2$. Further assume that the half-integral factorial function satisfies the relation

$$x! = x \cdot (x-1)! \quad \text{for } x = 3/2, 5/2, 7/2, \ldots.$$

Subject to these assumptions, verify that the volume of the ball of radius r in three dimensions is $\frac{4}{3}\pi r^3$ as claimed. What is the volume of the ball of radius r in five dimensions?

(b) The ball of radius r in n dimensions sits inside a circumscribing box with sides of length $2r$. Draw pictures of this configuration for $n = 1, 2, 3$. Determine what portion of the box is filled by the ball in the limit as the dimension n gets large. That is, find

$$\lim_{n \to \infty} \frac{\text{vol}\left(B_n(r)\right)}{(2r)^n}.$$

The original version of the book was revised: The Author's later corrections have been incorporated. The corrected book is available at https://doi.org/10.1007/978-3-319-49314-5_10

1

Results from One-Variable Calculus

We begin with a quick review of some ideas from one-variable calculus. The material of Sections 1.1 and 1.2 in assumed to be familiar. Section 1.3 discusses Taylor's theorem at greater length, not assuming that the reader has already seen it.

1.1 The Real Number System

We assume that there is a **real number system**, a set $\mathbb{R}$ that contains two distinct elements 0 and 1 and is endowed with the algebraic operations of addition,

$$+ : \mathbb{R} \times \mathbb{R} \longrightarrow \mathbb{R},$$

and multiplication,

$$\cdot : \mathbb{R} \times \mathbb{R} \longrightarrow \mathbb{R}.$$

The sum $+(a,b)$ is written $a + b$, and the product $\cdot(a,b)$ is written $a \cdot b$ or simply ab.

Theorem 1.1.1 (Field axioms for $(\mathbb{R}, +, \cdot)$). *The real number system, with its distinct 0 and 1 and with its addition and multiplication, is assumed to satisfy the following set of axioms.*

(a1) *Addition is associative:* $(x + y) + z = x + (y + z)$ *for all* $x, y, z \in \mathbb{R}$.
(a2) *0 is an additive identity:* $0 + x = x$ *for all* $x \in \mathbb{R}$.
(a3) *Existence of additive inverses: for each* $x \in \mathbb{R}$ *there exists* $y \in \mathbb{R}$ *such that* $y + x = 0$.
(a4) *Addition is commutative:* $x + y = y + x$ *for all* $x, y \in \mathbb{R}$.
(m1) *Multiplication is associative:* $(xy)z = x(yz)$ *for all* $x, y, z \in \mathbb{R}$.
(m2) *1 is a multiplicative identity:* $1x = x$ *for all* $x \in \mathbb{R}$.
(m3) *Existence of multiplicative inverses: for each nonzero* $x \in \mathbb{R}$ *there exists* $y \in \mathbb{R}$ *such that* $yx = 1$.
(m4) *Multiplication is commutative:* $xy = yx$ *for all* $x, y \in \mathbb{R}$.

© Springer International Publishing AG 2016
J. Shurman, *Calculus and Analysis in Euclidean Space*,
Undergraduate Texts in Mathematics, DOI 10.1007/978-3-319-49314-5_1

(d1) *Multiplication distributes over addition:* $(x+y)z = xz+yz$ *for all* $x, y, z \in$ $\mathbb{R}$.

All of basic algebra follows from the field axioms. Additive and multiplicative inverses are unique, the cancellation law holds, $0 \cdot x = 0$ for all real numbers x, and so on.

Subtracting a real number from another is defined as adding the additive inverse. In symbols,

$$- : \mathbb{R} \times \mathbb{R} \longrightarrow \mathbb{R}, \qquad x - y = x + (-y) \quad \text{for all } x, y \in \mathbb{R}.$$

We also assume that $\mathbb{R}$ is an **ordered** field. That is, we assume that there is a subset $\mathbb{R}^+$ of $\mathbb{R}$ (the **positive** elements) such that the following axioms hold.

Theorem 1.1.2 (Order axioms).

(o1) *Trichotomy axiom: for every real number x, exactly one of the following conditions holds:*

$$x \in \mathbb{R}^+, \qquad -x \in \mathbb{R}^+, \qquad x = 0.$$

(o2) *Closure of positive numbers under addition: for all real numbers x and y, if $x \in \mathbb{R}^+$ and $y \in \mathbb{R}^+$ then also $x + y \in \mathbb{R}^+$.*

(o3) *Closure of positive numbers under multiplication: for all real numbers x and y, if $x \in \mathbb{R}^+$ and $y \in \mathbb{R}^+$ then also $xy \in \mathbb{R}^+$.*

For all real numbers x and y, define

$$x < y$$

to mean

$$y - x \in \mathbb{R}^+.$$

The usual rules for inequalities then follow from the axioms.

Finally, we assume that the real number system is **complete**. Completeness can be phrased in various ways, all logically equivalent. One version of completeness is phrased in terms of set-bounds.

Theorem 1.1.3 (Completeness as a set-bound criterion). *Every nonempty subset of $\mathbb{R}$ that is bounded above has a least upper bound.*

This statement of completeness is an existence statement.

A subset S of $\mathbb{R}$ is **inductive** if

(i1) $0 \in S$,

(i2) For all $x \in \mathbb{R}$, if $x \in S$ then $x + 1 \in S$.

Every intersection of inductive subsets of $\mathbb{R}$ is again inductive. The set of **natural numbers**, denoted $\mathbb{N}$, is the intersection of all inductive subsets of $\mathbb{R}$, i.e., $\mathbb{N}$ is the smallest inductive subset of $\mathbb{R}$. There is no natural number between 0 and 1 (because if there were then deleting it from $\mathbb{N}$ would leave a smaller inductive subset of $\mathbb{R}$), and so

$$\mathbb{N} = \{0, 1, 2, \dots\}.$$

A **proposition** is a statement P that is either true or false. A **proposition form defined over** $\mathbb{N}$ is an expression $P(n)$, with n a formal symbol, that becomes a proposition when any particular natural number is substituted for n. For instance, the proposition form $P(n) = $ "n is even" becomes the true proposition "0 is even" when 0 is substituted for n, and it becomes the false proposition "1 is even" when 1 is substituted for n.

Theorem 1.1.4 (Induction theorem). *Let $P(n)$ be a proposition form defined over* $\mathbb{N}$. *Suppose that*

- $P(0)$ *is true.*
- *For all $n \in \mathbb{N}$, if $P(n)$ is true then so is $P(n+1)$.*

Then $P(n)$ is true for all natural numbers n.

Indeed, the hypotheses of the theorem say that $P(n)$ is true for a subset of $\mathbb{N}$ that is inductive, and so the theorem follows from the definition of $\mathbb{N}$ as the smallest inductive subset of $\mathbb{R}$.

The **Archimedean property** of the real number system states that the subset $\mathbb{N}$ of $\mathbb{R}$ is not bounded above. Equivalently, the sequence $\{1, \frac{1}{2}, \frac{1}{3}, \dots\}$ converges to 0: there are no infinitesimal real numbers greater than 0 but less than every reciprocal positive integer. The Archimedean property follows from the assumption that $\mathbb{R}$ satisfies the set-bound criterion for completeness.

A second version of completeness is phrased in terms of monotonic sequences. Again it is an existence statement.

Theorem 1.1.5 (Completeness as a monotonic sequence criterion). *Every bounded monotonic sequence in $\mathbb{R}$ converges to a unique limit.*

This version of completeness follows from the first one. However, it does not imply the first one unless we also assume the Archimedean property.

The set of **integers**, denoted $\mathbb{Z}$, is the union of the natural numbers and their additive inverses,

$$\mathbb{Z} = \{0, \pm 1, \pm 2, \dots\}.$$

Exercises

1.1.1. Referring only to the field axioms, show that $0x = 0$ for all $x \in \mathbb{R}$.

1.1.2. Prove that in every ordered field, 1 is positive. Prove that the complex number field $\mathbb{C}$ cannot be made an ordered field.

1.1.3. Use a completeness property of the real number system to show that 2 has a positive square root.

1.1.4. (a) Prove by induction that

$$\sum_{i=1}^{n} i^2 = \frac{n(n+1)(2n+1)}{6} \quad \text{for all } n \in \mathbb{Z}^+.$$

(b) (**Bernoulli's inequality**) For every real number $r \geq -1$, prove that

$$(1+r)^n \geq 1 + rn \quad \text{for all } n \in \mathbb{N}.$$

(c) For what positive integers n is $2^n > n^3$?

1.1.5. (a) Use the induction theorem to show that for every natural number m, the sum $m+n$ and the product mn are again natural for every natural number n. Thus $\mathbb{N}$ is closed under addition and multiplication, and consequently so is $\mathbb{Z}$.
(b) Which of the field axioms continue to hold for the natural numbers?
(c) Which of the field axioms continue to hold for the integers?

1.1.6. For every positive integer n, let $\mathbb{Z}/n\mathbb{Z}$ denote the set $\{0, 1, \ldots, n-1\}$ with the usual operations of addition and multiplication carried out taking remainders on division by n. That is, add and multiply in the usual fashion but subject to the additional condition that $n = 0$. For example, in $\mathbb{Z}/5\mathbb{Z}$ we have $2 + 4 = 1$ and $2 \cdot 4 = 3$. For what values of n does $\mathbb{Z}/n\mathbb{Z}$ form a field?

1.2 Foundational and Basic Theorems

This section reviews the foundational theorems of one-variable calculus. The first two theorems are not theorems of calculus at all, but rather are theorems about continuous functions and the real number system. The first theorem says that under suitable conditions, an optimization problem is guaranteed to have a solution.

Theorem 1.2.1 (Extreme value theorem). *Let I be a nonempty closed and bounded interval in $\mathbb{R}$, and let $f : I \longrightarrow \mathbb{R}$ be a continuous function. Then f takes a minimum value and a maximum value on I.*

The second theorem says that under suitable conditions, every value trapped between two output values of a function must itself be an output value.

Theorem 1.2.2 (Intermediate value theorem). *Let I be a nonempty interval in $\mathbb{R}$, and let $f : I \longrightarrow \mathbb{R}$ be a continuous function. Let y be a real number, and suppose that*

$$f(x) < y \quad \text{for some } x \in I$$

and

$$f(x') > y \quad \text{for some } x' \in I.$$

Then

$$f(c) = y \quad \text{for some } c \in I.$$

The mean value theorem relates the derivative of a function to values of the function itself with no reference to the fact that the derivative is a limit, but at the cost of introducing an unknown point.

Theorem 1.2.3 (Mean value theorem). *Let a and b be real numbers with $a < b$. Suppose that the function $f : [a,b] \longrightarrow \mathbb{R}$ is continuous and that f is differentiable on the open subinterval (a,b). Then*

$$\frac{f(b) - f(a)}{b - a} = f'(c) \quad \text{for some } c \in (a,b).$$

The fundamental theorem of integral calculus quantifies the idea that integration and differentiation are inverse operations. In fact, two different results are both called the fundamental theorem, one a result about the derivative of the integral and the other a result about the integral of the derivative. "Fundamental theorem of calculus," unmodified, usually refers to the second of the next two results.

Theorem 1.2.4 (Fundamental theorem of integral calculus I). *Let I be a nonempty interval in $\mathbb{R}$, let a be a point of I, and let $f : I \longrightarrow \mathbb{R}$ be a continuous function. Define a second function,*

$$F : I \longrightarrow \mathbb{R}, \quad F(x) = \int_a^x f(t)\, \mathrm{d}t.$$

Then F is differentiable on I with derivative $F'(x) = f(x)$ for all $x \in I$.

Theorem 1.2.5 (Fundamental theorem of integral calculus II). *Let I be a nonempty interval in $\mathbb{R}$, and let $f : I \longrightarrow \mathbb{R}$ be a continuous function. Suppose that the function $F : I \longrightarrow \mathbb{R}$ has derivative f. Then for every closed and bounded subinterval $[a,b]$ of I,*

$$\int_a^b f(x)\, \mathrm{d}x = F(b) - F(a).$$

Exercises

1.2.1. Use the intermediate value theorem to show that 2 has a positive square root.

1.2.2. Let $f : [0, 1] \longrightarrow [0, 1]$ be continuous. Use the intermediate value theorem to show that $f(x) = x$ for some $x \in [0, 1]$.

1.2.3. Let a and b be real numbers with $a < b$. Suppose that $f : [a, b] \longrightarrow \mathbb{R}$ is continuous and that f is differentiable on the open subinterval (a, b). Use the mean value theorem to show that if $f' > 0$ on (a, b) then f is strictly increasing on $[a, b]$. (Note: The quantities called a and b in the mean value theorem when you cite it to solve this exercise will not be the a and b given here. It may help to review the definition of "strictly increasing.")

1.2.4. For the extreme value theorem, the intermediate value theorem, and the mean value theorem, give examples to show that weakening the hypotheses of the theorem gives rise to examples for which the conclusion of the theorem fails.

1.3 Taylor's Theorem

Let $I \subset \mathbb{R}$ be a nonempty open interval, and let $a \in I$ be any point. Let n be a nonnegative integer. Suppose that the function $f : I \longrightarrow \mathbb{R}$ has n continuous derivatives,

$$f, f', f'', \ldots, f^{(n)} : I \longrightarrow \mathbb{R}.$$

Suppose further that we know the values of f and its derivatives at a, the $n + 1$ numbers

$$f(a), \quad f'(a), \quad f''(a), \quad \ldots, \quad f^{(n)}(a).$$

(For instance, if $f : \mathbb{R} \longrightarrow \mathbb{R}$ is the cosine function, and $a = 0$ and n is even, then the numbers are 1, 0, −1, 0, . . . , $(-1)^{n/2}$.)

Question 1 (Existence and uniqueness): Is there a polynomial p of degree n that mimics the behavior of f at a in the sense that

$$p(a) = f(a), \quad p'(a) = f'(a), \quad p''(a) = f''(a), \quad \ldots, \quad p^{(n)}(a) = f^{(n)}(a)?$$

Is there only one such polynomial?

Question 2 (Accuracy of approximation, granting existence and uniqueness): How well does $p(x)$ approximate $f(x)$ for $x \neq a$?

Question 1 is easy to answer. Consider a polynomial of degree n expanded about $x = a$,

$$p(x) = a_0 + a_1(x - a) + a_2(x - a)^2 + a_3(x - a)^3 + \cdots + a_n(x - a)^n.$$

The goal is to choose the coefficients $a_0, \ldots, a_n$ to make p behave like the original function f at a. Note that $p(a) = a_0$. We want $p(a)$ to equal $f(a)$, so set

$$a_0 = f(a).$$

Differentiate p to obtain

$$p'(x) = a_1 + 2a_2(x - a) + 3a_3(x - a)^2 + \cdots + na_n(x - a)^{n-1},$$

so that $p'(a) = a_1$. We want $p'(a)$ to equal $f'(a)$, so set

$$a_1 = f'(a).$$

Differentiate again to obtain

$$p''(x) = 2a_2 + 3 \cdot 2a_3(x - a) + \cdots + n(n - 1)a_n(x - a)^{n-2},$$

so that $p''(a) = 2a_2$. We want $p''(a)$ to equal $f''(a)$, so set

$$a_2 = \frac{f''(a)}{2}.$$

Differentiate again to obtain

$$p'''(x) = 3 \cdot 2a_3 + \cdots + n(n - 1)(n - 2)a_n(x - a)^{n-3},$$

so that $p'''(a) = 3 \cdot 2a_3$. We want $p'''(a)$ to equal $f'''(a)$, so set

$$a_3 = \frac{f''(a)}{3 \cdot 2}.$$

Continue in this fashion to obtain $a_4 = f^{(4)}(a)/4!$ and so on up to $a_n = f^{(n)}(a)/n!$. That is, the desired coefficients are

$$a_k = \frac{f^{(k)}(a)}{k!} \quad \text{for } k = 0, \ldots, n.$$

Thus the answer to the existence part of Question 1 is yes. Furthermore, since the calculation offered us no choices en route, these are the only coefficients that can work, and so the approximating polynomial is unique. It deserves a name.

Definition 1.3.1 (nth-degree Taylor polynomial). *Let $I \subset \mathbb{R}$ be a nonempty open interval, and let a be a point of I. Let n be a nonnegative integer. Suppose that the function $f : I \longrightarrow \mathbb{R}$ has n continuous derivatives. Then the* **nth-degree Taylor polynomial** *of f at a is*

$$T_n(x) = f(a) + f'(a)(x - a) + \frac{f''(a)}{2}(x - a)^2 + \cdots + \frac{f^{(n)}(a)}{n!}(x - a)^n.$$

In more concise notation,

$$T_n(x) = \sum_{k=0}^{n} \frac{f^{(k)}(a)}{k!}(x - a)^k.$$

For example, if $f(x) = e^x$ and $a = 0$ then it is easy to generate the following table:

k	$f^{(k)}(x)$	$\dfrac{f^{(k)}(0)}{k!}$
0	e^x	1
1	e^x	1
2	e^x	$\dfrac{1}{2}$
3	e^x	$\dfrac{1}{3!}$
$\vdots$	$\vdots$	$\vdots$
n	e^x	$\dfrac{1}{n!}$

From the table we can read off the nth-degree Taylor polynomial of f at 0,

$$T_n(x) = 1 + x + \frac{x^2}{2} + \frac{x^3}{3!} + \cdots + \frac{x^n}{n!} = \sum_{k=0}^{n} \frac{x^k}{k!} \, .$$

Recall that the second question is how well the polynomial $T_n(x)$ approximates $f(x)$ for $x \neq a$. Thus it is a question about the difference $f(x) - T_n(x)$. Giving this quantity its own name is useful.

Definition 1.3.2 (nth-degree Taylor remainder). *Let $I \subset \mathbb{R}$ be a non-empty open interval, and let a be a point of I. Let n be a nonnegative integer. Suppose that the function $f : I \longrightarrow \mathbb{R}$ has n continuous derivatives. Then the* **nth-degree Taylor remainder of f at a** *is*

$$R_n(x) = f(x) - T_n(x).$$

So the second question is to estimate the remainder $R_n(x)$ for points $x \in I$. The method to be presented here for doing so proceeds very naturally but it is perhaps a little surprising, because although the Taylor polynomial $T_n(x)$ is expressed in terms of derivatives, as is the expression to be obtained for the remainder $R_n(x)$, we obtain the expression by using the fundamental theorem of integral calculus repeatedly.

The method requires a calculation, and so, guided by hindsight, we first carry it out so that then the ideas of the method itself will be uncluttered. For every positive integer k and every $x \in \mathbb{R}$ define a k-fold nested integral,

$$I_k(x) = \int_{x_1=a}^{x} \int_{x_2=a}^{x_1} \cdots \int_{x_k=a}^{x_{k-1}} \mathrm{d}x_k \cdots \mathrm{d}x_2 \, \mathrm{d}x_1.$$

This nested integral is a function only of x because a is a constant and x_1 through x_k are dummy variables of integration. That is, I_k depends only on the upper limit of integration of the outermost integral. Although I_k may appear daunting, it unwinds readily if we start from the simplest case. We interpret the empty nested integral $I_0(x)$ to be identically 1. Next,

$$I_1(x) = \int_{x_1=a}^{x} dx_1 = x_1 \Big|_{x_1=a}^{x} = x - a.$$

Move one layer out and use this result to get

$$I_2(x) = \int_{x_1=a}^{x} \int_{x_2=a}^{x_1} dx_2\, dx_1 = \int_{x_1=a}^{x} I_1(x_1)\, dx_1$$

$$= \int_{x_1=a}^{x} (x_1 - a)\, dx_1 = \frac{1}{2}(x_1 - a)^2 \Big|_{x_1=a}^{x} = \frac{1}{2}(x - a)^2.$$

Again move out and quote the previous calculation,

$$I_3(x) = \int_{x_1=a}^{x} \int_{x_2=a}^{x_1} \int_{x_3=a}^{x_2} dx_3\, dx_2\, dx_1 = \int_{x_1=a}^{x} I_2(x_1)\, dx_1$$

$$= \int_{x_1=a}^{x} \frac{1}{2}(x_1 - a)^2\, dx_1 = \frac{1}{3!}(x_1 - a)^3 \Big|_{x_1=a}^{x} = \frac{1}{3!}(x - a)^3.$$

The method and pattern are clear, and the answer in general is

$$I_k(x) = \frac{1}{k!}(x - a)^k, \quad k = 0, 1, 2, \dots.$$

Note that this is part of the kth term $(f^{(k)}(a)/k!)(x - a)^k$ of the Taylor polynomial, the part that makes no reference to the function f. That is, $f^{(k)}(a)I_k(x)$ is the kth term of the Taylor polynomial for $k = 0, 1, 2, \dots$.

With the formula for $I_k(x)$ in hand, we return to using the fundamental theorem of integral calculus to study the remainder $R_n(x)$, the function $f(x)$ minus its nth-degree Taylor polynomial $T_n(x)$. According to the fundamental theorem,

$$f(x) = f(a) + \int_{a}^{x} f'(x_1)\, dx_1.$$

That is, $f(x)$ is equal to the constant term of the Taylor polynomial plus an integral,

$$f(x) = T_0(x) + \int_{a}^{x} f'(x_1)\, dx_1.$$

By the fundamental theorem again, the integral is in turn

$$\int_{a}^{x} f'(x_1)\, dx_1 = \int_{a}^{x} \left(f'(a) + \int_{a}^{x_1} f''(x_2)\, dx_2 \right) dx_1.$$

The first term of the outer integral is $f'(a)I_1(x)$, giving the first-order term of the Taylor polynomial and leaving a doubly nested integral,

$$\int_{a}^{x} f'(x_1)\, dx_1 = f'(a)(x - a) + \int_{a}^{x} \int_{a}^{x_1} f''(x_2)\, dx_2\, dx_1.$$

In other words, the calculation so far has shown that

$$f(x) = f(a) + f'(a)(x-a) + \int_a^x \int_a^{x_1} f''(x_2)\, dx_2\, dx_1$$
$$= T_1(x) + \int_a^x \int_a^{x_1} f''(x_2)\, dx_2\, dx_1.$$

Once more by the fundamental theorem, the doubly nested integral is

$$\int_a^x \int_a^{x_1} f''(x_2)\, dx_2\, dx_1 = \int_a^x \int_a^{x_1} \left(f''(a) + \int_a^{x_2} f'''(x_3)\, dx_3 \right) dx_2\, dx_1,$$

and the first term of the outer integral is $f''(a)I_2(x)$, giving the second-order term of the Taylor polynomial and leaving a triply nested integral,

$$\int_a^x \int_a^{x_1} f''(x_2)\, dx_2\, dx_1 = \frac{f''(a)}{2}(x-a)^2 + \int_a^x \int_a^{x_1} \int_a^{x_2} f'''(x_3)\, dx_3\, dx_2\, dx_1.$$

So now the calculation so far has shown that

$$f(x) = T_2(x) + \int_a^x \int_a^{x_1} \int_a^{x_2} f'''(x_3)\, dx_3\, dx_2\, dx_1.$$

Continuing this process through n iterations shows that $f(x)$ is $T_n(x)$ plus an $(n+1)$-fold iterated integral,

$$f(x) = T_n(x) + \int_a^x \int_a^{x_1} \cdots \int_a^{x_n} f^{(n+1)}(x_{n+1})\, dx_{n+1} \cdots dx_2\, dx_1.$$

In other words, the remainder is the integral,

$$R_n(x) = \int_a^x \int_a^{x_1} \cdots \int_a^{x_n} f^{(n+1)}(x_{n+1})\, dx_{n+1} \cdots dx_2\, dx_1. \qquad (1.1)$$

Note that we now are assuming that f has $n+1$ continuous derivatives.

For simplicity, assume that $x > a$. Since $f^{(n+1)}$ is continuous on the closed and bounded interval $[a, x]$, the extreme value theorem says that it takes a minimum value m and a maximum value M on the interval. That is,

$$m \le f^{(n+1)}(x_{n+1}) \le M, \quad x_{n+1} \in [a, x].$$

Integrate these two inequalities $n+1$ times to bound the remainder integral (1.1) on both sides by multiples of the integral that we have evaluated,

$$mI_{n+1}(x) \le R_n(x) \le MI_{n+1}(x),$$

and therefore by the precalculated formula for $I_{n+1}(x)$,

$$m\frac{(x-a)^{n+1}}{(n+1)!} \le R_n(x) \le M\frac{(x-a)^{n+1}}{(n+1)!}. \qquad (1.2)$$

Recall that m and M are particular values of $f^{(n+1)}$. Define an auxiliary function that will therefore assume the sandwiching values in (1.2),

$$g : [a, x] \longrightarrow \mathbb{R}, \quad g(t) = f^{(n+1)}(t) \frac{(x-a)^{n+1}}{(n+1)!}.$$

That is, since there exist values t_m and t_M in $[a, x]$ such that $f^{(n+1)}(t_m) = m$ and $f^{(n+1)}(t_M) = M$, the result (1.2) of our calculation can be rephrased as

$$g(t_m) \le R_n(x) \le g(t_M).$$

The inequalities show that the remainder is an intermediate value of g. And g is continuous, so by the intermediate value theorem, there exists some point $c \in [a, x]$ such that $g(c) = R_n(x)$. In other words, $g(c)$ is the desired remainder, the function minus its Taylor polynomial. We have proved the following theorem.

Theorem 1.3.3 (Taylor's theorem). *Let $I \subset \mathbb{R}$ be a nonempty open interval, and let $a \in I$. Let n be a nonnegative integer. Suppose that the function $f : I \longrightarrow \mathbb{R}$ has $n + 1$ continuous derivatives. Then for each $x \in I$,*

$$f(x) = T_n(x) + R_n(x)$$

where

$$R_n(x) = \frac{f^{(n+1)}(c)}{(n+1)!} (x-a)^{n+1} \quad \textit{for some c between a and x.}$$

We have proved Taylor's theorem only when $x > a$. It is trivial for $x = a$. If $x < a$, then rather than repeat the proof while keeping closer track of signs, with some of the inequalities switching direction, we may define

$$\tilde{f} : -I \longrightarrow \mathbb{R}, \quad \tilde{f}(-x) = f(x).$$

Since $\tilde{f} = f \circ \mathrm{neg}$, where neg is the negation function, a small exercise with the chain rule shows that

$$\tilde{f}^{(k)}(-x) = (-1)^k f^{(k)}(x), \quad \text{for } k = 0, \ldots, n+1 \text{ and } -x \in -I.$$

If $x < a$ in I then $-x > -a$ in $-I$, and so we know by the version of Taylor's theorem that we have already proved that

$$\tilde{f}(-x) = \tilde{T}_n(-x) + \tilde{R}_n(-x)$$

where

$$\tilde{T}_n(-x) = \sum_{k=0}^{n} \frac{\tilde{f}^{(k)}(-a)}{k!} (-x - (-a))^k$$

and

$$\widetilde{R}_n(-x) = \frac{\tilde{f}^{(n+1)}(-c)}{(n+1)!}(-x - (-a))^{n+1} \quad \text{for some } -c \text{ between } -a \text{ and } -x.$$

But $\tilde{f}(-x) = f(x)$, and $\widetilde{T}_n(-x)$ is precisely the desired Taylor polynomial $T_n(x)$,

$$\widetilde{T}_n(-x) = \sum_{k=0}^{n} \frac{\tilde{f}^{(k)}(-a)}{k!}(-x - (-a))^k$$

$$= \sum_{k=0}^{n} \frac{(-1)^k f^{(k)}(a)}{k!}(-1)^k(x-a)^k = \sum_{k=0}^{n} \frac{f^{(k)}(a)}{k!}(x-a)^k = T_n(x),$$

and similarly $\widetilde{R}_n(-x)$ works out to the desired form of $R_n(x)$,

$$\widetilde{R}_n(-x) = \frac{f^{(n+1)}(c)}{(n+1)!}(x-a)^{n+1} \quad \text{for some } c \text{ between } a \text{ and } x.$$

Thus we obtain the statement of Taylor's theorem in the case $x < a$ as well.

Whereas our proof of Taylor's theorem relies primarily on the fundamental theorem of integral calculus, and a similar proof relies on repeated integration by parts (Exercise 1.3.6), many proofs rely instead on the mean value theorem. Our proof neatly uses three different mathematical techniques for the three different parts of the argument:

- To find the Taylor polynomial $T_n(x)$, we differentiated repeatedly, using a substitution at each step to determine a coefficient.
- To get a precise (if unwieldy) expression for the remainder $R_n(x) = f(x) - T_n(x)$, we integrated repeatedly, using the fundamental theorem of integral calculus at each step to produce a term of the Taylor polynomial.
- To express the remainder in a more convenient form, we used the extreme value theorem and then the intermediate value theorem once each. These foundational theorems are not results from calculus but (as we will discuss in Section 2.4) from an area of mathematics called *topology*.

The expression for $R_n(x)$ given in Theorem 1.3.3 is called the **Lagrange form** of the remainder. Other expressions for $R_n(x)$ exist as well. Whatever form is used for the remainder, it should be something that we can estimate by bounding its magnitude.

For example, we use Taylor's theorem to estimate $\ln(1.1)$ by hand to within $1/500\,000$. Let $f(x) = \ln(1+x)$ on $(-1, \infty)$, and let $a = 0$. Compute the following table:

k	$f^{(k)}(x)$	$\dfrac{f^{(k)}(0)}{k!}$
0	$\ln(1+x)$	0
1	$\dfrac{1}{(1+x)}$	1
2	$-\dfrac{1}{(1+x)^2}$	$-\dfrac{1}{2}$
3	$\dfrac{2}{(1+x)^3}$	$\dfrac{1}{3}$
4	$-\dfrac{3!}{(1+x)^4}$	$-\dfrac{1}{4}$
$\vdots$	$\vdots$	$\vdots$
n	$\dfrac{(-1)^{n-1}(n-1)!}{(1+x)^n}$	$\dfrac{(-1)^{n-1}}{n}$
$n+1$	$\dfrac{(-1)^n n!}{(1+x)^{n+1}}$	

Next, read off from the table that for $n \geq 1$, the nth-degree Taylor polynomial is

$$T_n(x) = x - \frac{x^2}{2} + \frac{x^3}{3} - \cdots + (-1)^{n-1}\frac{x^n}{n} = \sum_{k=1}^{n}(-1)^{k-1}\frac{x^k}{k},$$

and the remainder is

$$R_n(x) = \frac{(-1)^n x^{n+1}}{(1+c)^{n+1}(n+1)} \quad \text{for some } c \text{ between } 0 \text{ and } x.$$

This expression for the remainder may be a bit much to take in, because it involves three variables: the point x at which we are approximating the logarithm, the degree n of the Taylor polynomial that is providing the approximation, and the unknown value c in the error term. But we are interested in $x = 0.1$ in particular (since we are approximating $\ln(1.1)$ using $f(x) = \ln(1+x)$), so that the Taylor polynomial specializes to

$$T_n(0.1) = (0.1) - \frac{(0.1)^2}{2} + \frac{(0.1)^3}{3} - \cdots + (-1)^{n-1}\frac{(0.1)^n}{n},$$

and we want to bound the remainder in absolute value, so we write

$$|R_n(0.1)| = \frac{(0.1)^{n+1}}{(1+c)^{n+1}(n+1)} \quad \text{for some } c \text{ between } 0 \text{ and } 0.1.$$

Now the symbol x is gone. Next, note that although we don't know the value of c, the *smallest* possible value of the quantity $(1+c)^{n+1}$ in the denominator of the absolute remainder is 1, because $c \geq 0$. And since this value occurs in the denominator, it lets us write the *greatest* possible value of the absolute remainder with no reference to c. That is,

$$|R_n(0.1)| \le \frac{(0.1)^{n+1}}{(n+1)},$$

and the symbol c is gone as well. The only remaining variable is n, and the goal is to approximate $\ln(1.1)$ to within $1/500\,000$. Set $n = 4$ in the previous display to get

$$|R_4(0.1)| \le \frac{1}{500\,000}.$$

That is, the fourth-degree Taylor polynomial

$$T_4(0.1) = \frac{1}{10} - \frac{1}{200} + \frac{1}{3000} - \frac{1}{40000},$$

which numerically is

$$\begin{aligned}
T_4(0.1) &= 0.10000000\ldots \\
&-0.00500000\ldots \\
&+0.00033333\ldots \\
&-0.00002500\ldots \\
&= 0.09530833\ldots,
\end{aligned}$$

agrees with $\ln(1.1)$ to within $0.00000200\ldots$, so that

$$0.09530633\cdots \le \ln(1.1) \le 0.09531033\ldots.$$

Any computer should confirm this. The point here is not that we have obtained impressively many digits of $\ln(1.1)$, or that we would want to continue carrying out such calculations by hand, but that we see how Taylor's theorem guarantees correct computation to a specified accuracy using only basic arithmetic.

Continuing to work with the function $f(x) = \ln(1+x)$ for $x > -1$, set $x = 1$ instead to get that for $n \ge 1$,

$$T_n(1) = 1 - \frac{1}{2} + \frac{1}{3} - \cdots + (-1)^{n-1}\frac{1}{n},$$

and

$$|R_n(1)| = \left| \frac{1}{(1+c)^{n+1}(n+1)} \right| \quad \text{for some } c \text{ between 0 and 1.}$$

Thus $|R_n(1)| \le 1/(n+1)$, and this goes to 0 as $n \to \infty$. Therefore $\ln(2)$ is expressible as an infinite series,

$$\ln(2) = 1 - \frac{1}{2} + \frac{1}{3} - \frac{1}{4} + \cdots.$$

This example illustrates an important general principle:

To check whether the Taylor polynomial $T_n(x)$ converges to $f(x)$ as n grows, i.e., to check whether the infinite Taylor series

$$T(x) = \lim_{n \to \infty} T_n(x) = \sum_{k=0}^{\infty} \frac{f^{(k)}(a)}{k!}(x - a)^k$$

reproduces $f(x)$, check whether the remainder $R_n(x)$ converges to 0. To show that the remainder $R_n(x)$ converges to 0, estimate $|R_n(x)|$ in a way that gets rid of the unknown c and then show that the estimate goes to 0.

To repeat a formula from before, the nth-degree Taylor polynomial of the function $\ln(1 + x)$ is

$$T_n(x) = x - \frac{x^2}{2} + \frac{x^3}{3} - \cdots + (-1)^{n-1}\frac{x^n}{n} = \sum_{k=1}^{n}(-1)^{k-1}\frac{x^k}{k}.$$

The graphs of the natural logarithm $\ln(x)$ and the first five Taylor polynomials $T_n(x - 1)$ are plotted from 0 to 2 in Figure 1.1. (The switch from $\ln(1 + x)$ to $\ln(x)$ places the logarithm graph in its familiar position, and then the switch from $T_n(x)$ to $T_n(x-1)$ is forced in consequence to fit the Taylor polynomials through the repositioned function.) A good check of your understanding is to see whether you can determine which graph is which in the figure.

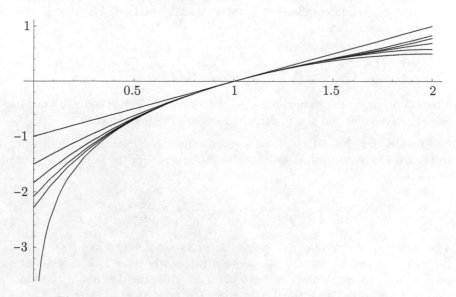

Figure 1.1. The natural logarithm and its Taylor polynomials

For another example, return to the exponential function $f(x) = e^x$ and let $a = 0$. For every x, the difference between $f(x)$ and the nth-degree Taylor polynomial $T_n(x)$ satisfies

$$|R_n(x)| = \left| e^c \frac{x^{n+1}}{(n+1)!} \right| \quad \text{for some } c \text{ between 0 and } x.$$

If $x \geq 0$ then e^c could be as large as e^x, while if $x < 0$ then e^c could be as large as e^0. The worst possible case is therefore

$$|R_n(x)| \leq \max\{1, e^x\} \frac{|x|^{n+1}}{(n+1)!}.$$

As $n \to \infty$ (while x remains fixed, albeit arbitrary) the right side goes to 0, because the factorial growth of $(n+1)!$ dominates the exponential growth of $|x|^{n+1}$, and so we have in the limit that e^x is expressible as a power series,

$$e^x = 1 + x + \frac{x^2}{2!} + \frac{x^3}{3!} + \cdots + \frac{x^n}{n!} + \cdots = \sum_{k=0}^{\infty} \frac{x^k}{k!}.$$

The power series here can be used to *define* e^x, but then obtaining the properties of e^x depends on the technical fact that a power series can be differentiated term by term in its open interval (or disk if we are working with complex numbers) of convergence.

The power series in the previous display also allows a small illustration of the utility of quantifiers. Since it is valid for every real number x, it is valid with x^2 in place of x,

$$e^{x^2} = 1 + x^2 + \frac{x^4}{2!} + \frac{x^6}{3!} + \cdots + \frac{x^{2n}}{n!} + \cdots = \sum_{k=0}^{\infty} \frac{x^{2k}}{k!} \quad \text{for every } x \in \mathbb{R}.$$

There is no need here to introduce the function $g(x) = e^{x^2}$, then work out its Taylor polynomial and remainder, then analyze the remainder.

We end this chapter by sketching two cautionary examples. First, work from earlier in the section shows that the Taylor series for the function $\ln(1+x)$ at $a = 0$ is

$$T(x) = x - \frac{x^2}{2} + \frac{x^3}{3} - \cdots + (-1)^{n-1}\frac{x^n}{n} + \cdots = \sum_{k=1}^{\infty} (-1)^{k-1}\frac{x^k}{k}.$$

The ratio test shows that this series converges absolutely when $|x| < 1$, and the nth-term test shows that the series diverges when $x > 1$. The series also converges at $x = 1$, as observed earlier. Thus, while the domain of the function $\ln(1+x)$ is $(-1, \infty)$, the Taylor series has no chance to match the function outside of $(-1, 1]$. As for whether the Taylor series matches the function on $(-1, 1]$, recall the Lagrange form of the remainder,

$$R_n(x) = \frac{(-1)^n x^{n+1}}{(1+c)^{n+1}(n+1)} \quad \text{for some } c \text{ between 0 and } x.$$

Consequently, the absolute value of the Lagrange form of the remainder is

$$|R_n(x)| = \frac{1}{n+1}\left(\frac{|x|}{1+c}\right)^{n+1} \quad \text{for some } c \text{ between 0 and } x.$$

From the previous display, noting that $|x|$ is the distance from 0 to x while $1+c$ is the distance from -1 to c, we see that:

- If $0 \le x \le 1$ then $|x| \le 1 \le 1+c$, and so $R_n(x)$ goes to 0 as n gets large.
- If $-1/2 \le x < 0$ then $|x| \le 1/2 \le 1+c$, and so again $R_n(x)$ goes to 0 as n gets large.
- But if $-1 < x < -1/2$ then possibly $1+c < |x|$, and so possibly $R_n(x)$ does not go to 0 as n gets large.

That is, we have shown that

$$\ln(1+x) = T(x) \quad \text{for } x \in [-1/2, 1],$$

but the Lagrange form does not readily show that the equality in the previous display also holds for $x \in (-1, -1/2)$. Figure 1.1 suggests why: the Taylor polynomials are converging more slowly to the original function the farther left we go on the graph. However, a different form of the remainder, given in Exercise 1.3.6, proves that indeed the equality holds for all $x \in (-1, 1]$. Also, the geometric series relation

$$\frac{1}{1+x} = 1 - x + x^2 - x^3 + \cdots, \quad -1 < x < 1$$

gives the relation $\ln(1+x) = T(x)$ for $x \in (-1, 1)$ upon integrating termwise and then setting $x = 0$ to see that the resulting constant term is 0; but this argument's invocation of the theorem that a power series can be integrated termwise within its interval (or disk) of convergence is nontrivial.

For the last example, define $f : \mathbb{R} \longrightarrow \mathbb{R}$ by

$$f(x) = \begin{cases} e^{-1/x^2} & \text{if } x \ne 0, \\ 0 & \text{if } x = 0. \end{cases}$$

It is possible to show that f is infinitely differentiable and that every derivative of f at 0 is 0. That is, $f^{(k)}(0) = 0$ for $k = 0, 1, 2, \ldots$. Consequently, the Taylor series for f at 0 is

$$T(x) = 0 + 0x + 0x^2 + \cdots + 0x^n + \cdots.$$

That is, the Taylor series is the zero function, which certainly converges for all $x \in \mathbb{R}$. But the only value of x for which it converges to the original function f is $x = 0$. In other words, although this Taylor series converges everywhere, it fails catastrophically to equal the function it is attempting to match. The problem is that the function f decays exponentially, and since exponential behavior dominates polynomial behavior, any attempt to discern f using polynomials will fail to see it. Figures 1.2 and 1.3 plot f to display its rapid decay. The first plot is for $x \in [-25, 25]$ and the second is for $x \in [-1/2, 1/2]$.

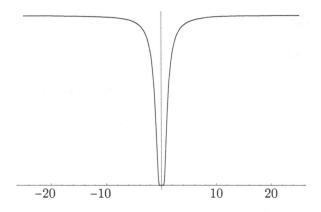

Figure 1.2. Rapidly decaying function, wide view

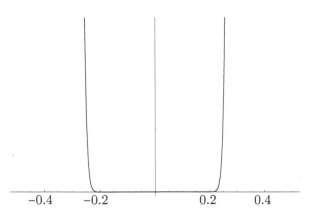

Figure 1.3. Rapidly decaying function, zoom view

Exercises

1.3.1. (a) Let $n \in \mathbb{N}$. What is the $(2n+1)$st-degree Taylor polynomial $T_{2n+1}(x)$ for the function $f(x) = \sin x$ at 0? (The reason for the strange indexing here is that every second term of the Taylor polynomial is 0.) Prove that $\sin x$ is equal to the limit of $T_{2n+1}(x)$ as $n \to \infty$, similarly to the argument in the text for e^x. Also find $T_{2n}(x)$ for $f(x) = \cos x$ at 0, and explain why the argument for sin shows that $\cos x$ is the limit of its even-degree Taylor polynomials as well.

(b) Many years ago, the author's high-school physics textbook asserted, bafflingly, that the approximation $\sin x \approx x$ is good for x up to $8°$. Deconstruct.

1.3.2. What is the nth-degree Taylor polynomial $T_n(x)$ for the following functions at 0?

(a) $f(x) = \arctan x$. (This exercise is not just a matter of routine mechanics. One way to proceed involves the geometric series, and another makes use of the factorization $1 + x^2 = (1 - ix)(1 + ix)$.)

(b) $f(x) = (1 + x)^\alpha$ where $\alpha \in \mathbb{R}$. (Although the answer can be written in a uniform way for all α, it behaves differently when $\alpha \in \mathbb{N}$. Introduce the generalized binomial coefficient symbol

$$\binom{\alpha}{k} = \frac{\alpha(\alpha - 1)(\alpha - 2)\cdots(\alpha - k + 1)}{k!}, \quad k \in \mathbb{N}$$

to help produce a tidy answer.)

1.3.3. (a) Further tighten the numerical estimate of $\ln(1.1)$ from this section by reasoning as follows. As n increases, the Taylor polynomials $T_n(0.1)$ add terms of decreasing magnitude and alternating sign. Therefore $T_4(0.1)$ underestimates $\ln(1.1)$. Now that we know this, it is useful to find the smallest possible value of the remainder (by setting $c = 0.1$ rather than $c = 0$ in the formula). Then $\ln(1.1)$ lies between $T_4(0.1)$ plus this smallest possible remainder value and $T_4(0.1)$ plus the largest possible remainder value, obtained in the section. Supply the numbers, and verify by machine that the tighter estimate of $\ln(1.1)$ is correct.

(b) In Figure 1.1, identify the graphs of T_1 through T_5 and the graph of ln near $x = 0$ and near $x = 2$.

1.3.4. Working by hand, use the third-degree Taylor polynomial for $\sin(x)$ at 0 to approximate a decimal representation of $\sin(0.1)$. Also compute the decimal representation of an upper bound for the error of the approximation. Bound $\sin(0.1)$ between two decimal representations.

1.3.5. Use a second-degree Taylor polynomial to approximate $\sqrt{4.2}$. Use Taylor's theorem to find a guaranteed accuracy of the approximation and thus to find upper and lower bounds for $\sqrt{4.2}$.

1.3.6. (a) Another proof of Taylor's Theorem uses the fundamental theorem of integral calculus once and then integrates by parts repeatedly. Begin with the hypotheses of Theorem 1.3.3, and let $x \in I$. By the fundamental theorem,

$$f(x) = f(a) + \int_a^x f'(t)\, dt.$$

Let $u = f'(t)$ and $v = t - x$, so that the integral is $\int_a^x u\, dv$, and integrating by parts gives

$$f(x) = f(a) + f'(a)(x - a) - \int_a^x f''(t)(t - x)\, dt.$$

Let $u = f''(t)$ and $v = \frac{1}{2}(t - x)^2$, so that again the integral is $\int_a^x u\, dv$, and integrating by parts gives

$$f(x) = f(a) + f'(a)(x-a) + f''(a)\frac{(x-a)^2}{2} + \int_a^x f'''(t)\frac{(t-x)^2}{2}\,dt.$$

Show that after n steps, the result is

$$f(x) = T_n(x) + (-1)^n \int_a^x f^{(n+1)}(t)\frac{(t-x)^n}{n!}\,dt.$$

Whereas the expression for $f(x) - T_n(x)$ in Theorem 1.3.3 is called the **Lagrange form** of the remainder, this exercise has derived the **integral form** of the remainder. Use the extreme value theorem and the intermediate value theorem to derive the Lagrange form of the remainder from the integral form.

(b) Use the integral form of the remainder to show that

$$\ln(1+x) = T(x) \quad \text{for } x \in (-1,1].$$

Part I

Multivariable Differential Calculus

2

Euclidean Space

Euclidean space is a mathematical construct that encompasses the line, the plane, and three-dimensional space as special cases. Its elements are called *vectors*. Vectors can be understood in various ways: as arrows, as quantities with magnitude and direction, as displacements, or as points. However, along with a sense of what vectors are, we also need to emphasize how they interact. The axioms in Section 2.1 capture the idea that vectors can be added together and can be multiplied by scalars, with both of these operations obeying familiar laws of algebra. Section 2.2 expresses the geometric ideas of length and angle in Euclidean space in terms of vector algebra. Section 2.3 discusses continuity for functions (also called *mappings*) whose inputs and outputs are vectors rather than scalars. Section 2.4 introduces a special class of sets in Euclidean space, the *compact* sets, and shows that compact sets are preserved under continuous mappings.

2.1 Algebra: Vectors

Let n be a positive integer. The set of all ordered n-tuples of real numbers,

$$\mathbb{R}^n = \{(x_1, \ldots, x_n) : x_i \in \mathbb{R} \text{ for } i = 1, \ldots, n\},$$

constitutes n-**dimensional Euclidean space**. When $n = 1$, the parentheses and subscript in the notation (x_1) are superfluous, so we simply view the elements of $\mathbb{R}^1$ as real numbers x and write $\mathbb{R}$ for $\mathbb{R}^1$. Elements of $\mathbb{R}^2$ and of $\mathbb{R}^3$ are written (x, y) and (x, y, z) to avoid needless subscripts. These first few Euclidean spaces, $\mathbb{R}$, $\mathbb{R}^2$, and $\mathbb{R}^3$, are conveniently visualized as the line, the plane, and space itself. (See Figure 2.1.)

Elements of $\mathbb{R}$ are called **scalars**, of $\mathbb{R}^n$, **vectors**. The **origin** of $\mathbb{R}^n$, denoted **0**, is defined to be

$$\mathbf{0} = (0, \ldots, 0).$$

© Springer International Publishing AG 2016

J. Shurman, *Calculus and Analysis in Euclidean Space*,

Undergraduate Texts in Mathematics, DOI 10.1007/978-3-319-49314-5_2

Figure 2.1. The first few Euclidean spaces

Sometimes the origin of $\mathbb{R}^n$ will be denoted $\mathbf{0}_n$ to distinguish it from other *origins* that we will encounter later.

In the first few Euclidean spaces $\mathbb{R}$, $\mathbb{R}^2$, $\mathbb{R}^3$, one can visualize a vector as a point x or as an arrow. The arrow can have its tail at the origin and its head at the point x, or its tail at any point p and its head correspondingly translated to $p + x$. (See Figure 2.2. Most illustrations will depict $\mathbb{R}$ or $\mathbb{R}^2$.)

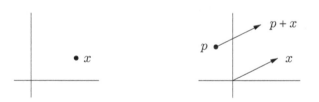

Figure 2.2. Various ways to envision a vector

To a mathematician, the word *space* doesn't connote volume but instead refers to a set endowed with some structure. Indeed, Euclidean space $\mathbb{R}^n$ comes with two algebraic operations. The first is **vector addition**,

$$+ : \mathbb{R}^n \times \mathbb{R}^n \longrightarrow \mathbb{R}^n,$$

defined by adding the scalars at each component of the vectors,

$$(x_1, \ldots, x_n) + (y_1, \ldots, y_n) = (x_1 + y_1, \ldots, x_n + y_n).$$

For example, $(1, 2, 3) + (4, 5, 6) = (5, 7, 9)$. Note that the meaning of the "+" sign is now overloaded: on the left of the displayed equality, it denotes the new operation of vector addition, whereas on the right side it denotes the old addition of real numbers. The multiple meanings of the plus sign shouldn't cause problems, because the meaning of "+" is clear from context, i.e., the meaning of "+" is clear from whether it sits between vectors or scalars. (An expression such as "$(1, 2, 3) + 4$," with the plus sign between a vector and a scalar, makes no sense according to our grammar.)

The interpretation of vectors as arrows gives a geometric description of vector addition, at least in $\mathbb{R}^2$. To add the vectors x and y, draw them as arrows starting at $\mathbf{0}$ and then complete the parallelogram P that has x and y as two of its sides. The diagonal of P starting at $\mathbf{0}$ is then the arrow depicting the vector $x + y$. (See Figure 2.3.) The proof of this is a small argument with similar triangles, left to the reader as Exercise 2.1.2.

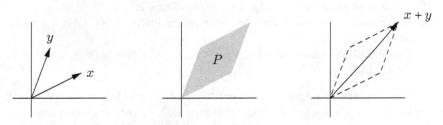

Figure 2.3. The parallelogram law of vector addition

The second operation on Euclidean space is **scalar multiplication**,

$$\cdot : \mathbb{R} \times \mathbb{R}^n \longrightarrow \mathbb{R}^n,$$

defined by

$$a \cdot (x_1, \ldots, x_n) = (ax_1, \ldots, ax_n).$$

For example, $2 \cdot (3, 4, 5) = (6, 8, 10)$. We will almost always omit the symbol "$\cdot$" and write ax for $a \cdot x$. With this convention, juxtaposition is overloaded as "+" was overloaded above, but again this shouldn't cause problems.

Scalar multiplication of the vector x (viewed as an arrow) by a also has a geometric interpretation: it simply stretches (i.e., scales) x by a factor of a. When a is negative, ax turns x around and stretches it in the other direction by $|a|$. (See Figure 2.4.)

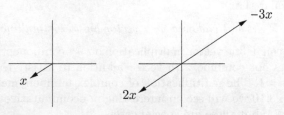

Figure 2.4. Scalar multiplication as stretching

With these two operations and distinguished element $\mathbf{0}$, Euclidean space satisfies the following algebraic laws.

Theorem 2.1.1 (Vector space axioms).

(A1) *Addition is associative:* $(x + y) + z = x + (y + z)$ *for all* $x, y, z \in \mathbb{R}^n$.

(A2) $\mathbf{0}$ *is an additive identity:* $\mathbf{0} + x = x$ *for all* $x \in \mathbb{R}^n$.

(A3) *Existence of additive inverses: for each* $x \in \mathbb{R}^n$ *there exists* $y \in \mathbb{R}^n$ *such that* $y + x = \mathbf{0}$.

(A4) *Addition is commutative:* $x + y = y + x$ *for all* $x, y \in \mathbb{R}^n$.

(M1) *Scalar multiplication is associative:* $a(bx) = (ab)x$ *for all* $a, b \in \mathbb{R}$, $x \in \mathbb{R}^n$.

(M2) 1 *is a multiplicative identity:* $1x = x$ *for all* $x \in \mathbb{R}^n$.

(D1) *Scalar multiplication distributes over scalar addition:* $(a + b)x = ax + bx$ *for all* $a, b \in \mathbb{R}$, $x \in \mathbb{R}^n$.

(D2) *Scalar multiplication distributes over vector addition:* $a(x + y) = ax + ay$ *for all* $a \in \mathbb{R}$, $x, y \in \mathbb{R}^n$.

All of these are consequences of how "$+$" and "$\cdot$" and $\mathbf{0}$ are defined for $\mathbb{R}^n$ in conjunction with the fact that the real numbers, in turn endowed with "$+$" and "$\cdot$" and containing 0 and 1, satisfy the field axioms (see Section 1.1). For example, to prove that $\mathbb{R}^n$ satisfies (M1), take any scalars $a, b \in \mathbb{R}$ and any vector $x = (x_1, \ldots, x_n) \in \mathbb{R}^n$. Then

$$
\begin{aligned}
a(bx) &= a(b(x_1, \ldots, x_n)) && \text{by definition of } x \\
&= a(bx_1, \ldots, bx_n) && \text{by definition of scalar multiplication} \\
&= (a(bx_1), \ldots, a(bx_n)) && \text{by definition of scalar multiplication} \\
&= ((ab)x_1, \ldots, (ab)x_n) && \text{by } n \text{ applications of (m1) in } \mathbb{R} \\
&= (ab)(x_1, \ldots, x_n) && \text{by definition of scalar multiplication} \\
&= (ab)x && \text{by definition of } x.
\end{aligned}
$$

The other vector space axioms for $\mathbb{R}^n$ can be shown similarly, by unwinding vectors to their coordinates, quoting field axioms coordinatewise, and then bundling the results back up into vectors (see Exercise 2.1.3). Nonetheless, the vector space axioms do not perfectly parallel the field axioms, and you are encouraged to spend a little time comparing the two axiom sets to get a feel for where they are similar and where they are different (see Exercise 2.1.4). Note in particular that

For $n > 1$, $\mathbb{R}^n$ is not endowed with vector-by-vector multiplication.

Although one can define vector multiplication on $\mathbb{R}^n$ componentwise, this multiplication does not combine with vector addition to satisfy the field axioms except when $n = 1$. The multiplication of complex numbers makes $\mathbb{R}^2$ a field, and in Section 3.10 we will see an interesting noncommutative multiplication of vectors for $\mathbb{R}^3$, but these are special cases.

One benefit of the vector space axioms for $\mathbb{R}^n$ is that they are phrased **intrinsically,** meaning that they make no reference to the scalar coordinates of the vectors involved. Thus, once you use coordinates to establish the vector space axioms, your vector algebra can be intrinsic thereafter, making it lighter and more conceptual. Also, in addition to being intrinsic, the vector space axioms are general. While $\mathbb{R}^n$ is the prototypical set satisfying the vector space axioms, it is by no means the only one. In coming sections we will encounter other sets V (whose elements may be, for example, functions) endowed with their own addition, multiplication by elements of a field F, and distinguished element $\mathbf{0}$. If the vector space axioms are satisfied with V and F replacing $\mathbb{R}^n$ and $\mathbb{R}$ then we say that V is a **vector space over** F.

The pedagogical point here is that although the similarity between vector algebra and scalar algebra may initially make vector algebra seem uninspiring, in fact the similarity is exciting. It makes mathematics easier, because familiar algebraic manipulations apply in a wide range of contexts. The same symbol-patterns have more meaning. For example, we use intrinsic vector algebra to prove a result from Euclidean geometry, that the three medians of a triangle intersect. (A median is a segment from a vertex to the midpoint of the opposite edge.) Consider a triangle with vertices x, y, and z, and form the average of the three vertices,

$$p = \frac{x + y + z}{3}.$$

This algebraic average will be the **geometric center** of the triangle, where the medians meet. (See Figure 2.5.) Indeed, rewrite p as

$$p = x + \frac{2}{3}\left(\frac{y + z}{2} - x\right).$$

The displayed expression for p shows that it is two-thirds of the way from x along the line segment from x to the average of y and z, i.e., that p lies on the triangle median from vertex x to side yz. (Again see the figure. The idea is that $(y + z)/2$ is being interpreted as the midpoint of y and z, each of these viewed as a point, while on the other hand, the little mnemonic

head minus tail

helps us to remember quickly that $(y + z)/2 - x$ can be viewed as the arrow-vector from x to $(y + z)/2$.) Since p is defined symmetrically in x, y, and z, and it lies on one median, it therefore lies on the other two medians as well. In fact, the vector algebra has shown that it lies two-thirds of the way along each median. (As for how a person might find this proof, it is a matter of hoping that the geometric center $(x + y + z)/3$ lies on the median by taking the form $x + c((y + z)/2 - x)$ for some c and then seeing that indeed $c = 2/3$ works.)

The **standard basis** of $\mathbb{R}^n$ is the set of vectors

$$\{e_1, e_2, \ldots, e_n\}$$

where

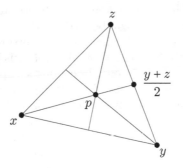

Figure 2.5. Three medians of a triangle

$$e_1 = (1, 0, \ldots, 0), \quad e_2 = (0, 1, \ldots, 0), \quad \ldots, \quad e_n = (0, 0, \ldots, 1).$$

(Thus each e_i is itself a vector, not the ith scalar entry of a vector.) Every vector $x = (x_1, x_2, \ldots, x_n)$ (where the x_i are scalar entries) decomposes as

$$\begin{aligned}
x &= (x_1, x_2, \ldots, x_n) \\
&= (x_1, 0, \ldots, 0) + (0, x_2, \ldots, 0) + \cdots + (0, 0, \ldots, x_n) \\
&= x_1(1, 0, \ldots, 0) + x_2(0, 1, \ldots, 0) + \cdots + x_n(0, 0, \ldots, 1) \\
&= x_1 e_1 + x_2 e_2 + \cdots + x_n e_n,
\end{aligned}$$

or more succinctly,

$$x = \sum_{i=1}^{n} x_i e_i. \tag{2.1}$$

Note that in equation (2.1), x and the e_i are vectors, while the x_i are scalars. The equation shows that every $x \in \mathbb{R}^n$ is expressible as a **linear combination** (sum of scalar multiples) of the standard basis vectors. The expression is unique, for if also $x = \sum_{i=1}^{n} x_i' e_i$ for some scalars $x_1', \ldots, x_n'$ then the equality says that $x = (x_1', x_2', \ldots, x_n')$, so that $x_i' = x_i$ for $i = 1, \ldots, n$.

(The reason that the geometric-sounding word *linear* is used here and elsewhere in this chapter to describe properties having to do with the algebraic operations of addition and scalar multiplication will be explained in Chapter 3.)

The standard basis is handy in that it is a finite set of vectors from which each of the infinitely many vectors of $\mathbb{R}^n$ can be obtained in exactly one way as a linear combination. But it is not the only such set, nor is it always the optimal one.

Definition 2.1.2 (Basis). *A set of vectors $\{f_i\}$ is a **basis** of $\mathbb{R}^n$ if every $x \in \mathbb{R}^n$ is uniquely expressible as a linear combination of the f_i.*

For example, the set $\{f_1, f_2\} = \{(1,1), (1,-1)\}$ is a basis of $\mathbb{R}^2$. To see this, consider an arbitrary vector $(x, y) \in \mathbb{R}^2$. This vector is expressible as a linear combination of f_1 and f_2 if and only if there are scalars a and b such that

$$(x, y) = af_1 + bf_2.$$

Since $f_1 = (1,1)$ and $f_2 = (1,-1)$, this vector equation is equivalent to a pair of scalar equations,

$$x = a + b,$$
$$y = a - b.$$

Add these equations and divide by 2 to get $a = (x + y)/2$, and similarly $b = (x - y)/2$. In other words, we have found that

$$(x, y) = \frac{x+y}{2}(1, 1) + \frac{x-y}{2}(1, -1),$$

and the coefficients $a = (x + y)/2$ and $b = (x - y)/2$ on the right side of the equation are the only possible coefficients a and b for the equation to hold. That is, scalars a and b exist to express the vector (x, y) as a linear combination of $\{f_1, f_2\}$, and the scalars are uniquely determined by the vector. Thus $\{f_1, f_2\}$ is a basis of $\mathbb{R}^2$, as claimed.

The set $\{g_1, g_2\} = \{(1,3), (2,6)\}$ is not a basis of $\mathbb{R}^2$, because every linear combination $ag_1 + bg_2$ takes the form $(a + 2b, 3a + 6b)$, with the second entry equal to three times the first. The vector $(1,0)$ is therefore not a linear combination of g_1 and g_2.

Nor is the set $\{h_1, h_2, h_3\} = \{(1,0), (1,1), (1,-1)\}$ a basis of $\mathbb{R}^2$, because $h_3 = 2h_1 - h_2$, so that h_3 is a nonunique linear combination of the h_j.

See Exercises 2.1.9 and 2.1.10 for practice with bases.

Exercises

2.1.1. Write down any three specific nonzero vectors u, v, w from $\mathbb{R}^3$ and any two specific nonzero scalars a, b from $\mathbb{R}$. Compute $u+v$, aw, $b(v+w)$, $(a+b)u$, $u + v + w$, abw, and the additive inverse to u.

2.1.2. Working in $\mathbb{R}^2$, give a geometric proof that if we view the vectors x and y as arrows from $\mathbf{0}$ and form the parallelogram P with these arrows as two of its sides, then the diagonal z starting at $\mathbf{0}$ is the vector sum $x+y$ viewed as an arrow.

2.1.3. Verify that $\mathbb{R}^n$ satisfies vector space axioms (A2), (A3), (D1).

2.1.4. Are all the field axioms used in verifying that Euclidean space satisfies the vector space axioms?

2.1.5. Show that $\mathbf{0}$ is the unique additive identity in $\mathbb{R}^n$. Show that each vector $x \in \mathbb{R}^n$ has a unique additive inverse, which can therefore be denoted $-x$. (And it follows that vector subtraction can now be defined,

$$-: \mathbb{R}^n \times \mathbb{R}^n \longrightarrow \mathbb{R}^n, \qquad x - y = x + (-y) \quad \text{for all } x, y \in \mathbb{R}^n.)$$

Show that $0x = \mathbf{0}$ for all $x \in \mathbb{R}^n$.

2.1.6. Repeat the previous exercise, but with $\mathbb{R}^n$ replaced by an arbitrary vector space V over a field F. (Work with the axioms.)

2.1.7. Show the uniqueness of the additive identity and the additive inverse using only (A1), (A2), (A3). (This is tricky; the opening pages of some books on group theory will help.)

2.1.8. Let x and y be noncollinear vectors in $\mathbb{R}^3$. Give a geometric description of the set of all linear combinations of x and y.

2.1.9. Which of the following sets are bases of $\mathbb{R}^3$?

$$S_1 = \{(1,0,0),(1,1,0),(1,1,1)\},$$
$$S_2 = \{(1,0,0),(0,1,0),(0,0,1),(1,1,1)\},$$
$$S_3 = \{(1,1,0),(0,1,1)\},$$
$$S_4 = \{(1,1,0),(0,1,1),(1,0,-1)\}.$$

How many elements do you think a basis for $\mathbb{R}^n$ must have? Give (without proof) geometric descriptions of all bases of $\mathbb{R}^2$, of $\mathbb{R}^3$.

2.1.10. Recall the field $\mathbb{C}$ of complex numbers. Define **complex n-space** $\mathbb{C}^n$ analogously to $\mathbb{R}^n$:

$$\mathbb{C}^n = \{(z_1, \ldots, z_n) : z_i \in \mathbb{C} \text{ for } i = 1, \ldots, n\},$$

and endow it with addition and scalar multiplication defined by the same formulas as for $\mathbb{R}^n$. You may take for granted that under these definitions, $\mathbb{C}^n$ satisfies the vector space axioms with scalar multiplication by scalars from $\mathbb{R}$, and also $\mathbb{C}^n$ satisfies the vector space axioms with scalar multiplication by scalars from $\mathbb{C}$. That is, using language that was introduced briefly in this section, $\mathbb{C}^n$ can be viewed as a vector space over $\mathbb{R}$ and also, separately, as a vector space over $\mathbb{C}$. Give a basis for each of these vector spaces.

Brief Pedagogical Interlude

Before continuing, a few comments about how to work with these notes may be helpful.

The subject-matter of Chapters 2 through 5 is largely cumulative, with the main theorem of Chapter 5 being proved with main results of Chapters 2, 3, and 4. Each chapter is largely cumulative internally as well. To acquire detailed command of so much material and also a large-scale view of how it fits together, the trick is to focus on each section's techniques while studying that section and working its exercises, but thereafter to use the section's ideas freely by reference. Specifically, after the scrutiny of vector algebra in the previous section, one's vector manipulations should be fluent from now on, freeing one to concentrate on vector geometry in the next section, after which the geometry should also be light while one is concentrating on the analytical ideas of the following section, and so forth.

Admittedly, the model that one has internalized all the prior material before moving on is idealized. For that matter, so is the model that a body of interplaying ideas is linearly cumulative. In practice, focusing entirely on the details of whichever topics are currently active while using previous ideas by reference isn't always optimal. One might engage with the details of previous ideas because one is coming to understand them better, or because the current ideas showcase the older ones in a new way. Still, the paradigm of technical emphasis on the current ideas and fluent use of the earlier material does help a person who is navigating a large body of mathematics to conserve energy and synthesize a larger picture.

2.2 Geometry: Length and Angle

The geometric notions of length and angle in $\mathbb{R}^n$ are readily described in terms of the algebraic notion of inner product.

Definition 2.2.1 (Inner product). *The* **inner product** *is a function from pairs of vectors to scalars,*

$$\langle \ , \ \rangle : \mathbb{R}^n \times \mathbb{R}^n \longrightarrow \mathbb{R},$$

defined by the formula

$$\langle (x_1, \ldots, x_n), (y_1, \ldots, y_n) \rangle = \sum_{i=1}^{n} x_i y_i.$$

For example,

$$\langle (1, 1, \ldots, 1), (1, 2, \ldots, n) \rangle = \frac{n(n+1)}{2},$$

$\langle x, e_j \rangle = x_j$ where $x = (x_1, \ldots, x_n)$ and $j \in \{1, \ldots, n\}$,

$\langle e_i, e_j \rangle = \delta_{ij}$ (this means 1 if $i = j$, 0 otherwise).

Proposition 2.2.2 (Inner product properties).

(IP1) *The inner product is positive definite:* $\langle x, x \rangle \geq 0$ *for all* $x \in \mathbb{R}^n$, *with equality if and only if* $x = \mathbf{0}$.

(IP2) *The inner product is symmetric:* $\langle x, y \rangle = \langle y, x \rangle$ *for all* $x, y \in \mathbb{R}^n$.

(IP3) *The inner product is bilinear:*

$$\langle x + x', y \rangle = \langle x, y \rangle + \langle x', y \rangle, \quad \langle ax, y \rangle = a\langle x, y \rangle,$$
$$\langle x, y + y' \rangle = \langle x, y \rangle + \langle x, y' \rangle, \quad \langle x, by \rangle = b\langle x, y \rangle$$

for all $a, b \in \mathbb{R}$, $x, x', y, y' \in \mathbb{R}^n$.

Proof. Exercise 2.2.4.   □

The reader should be aware that:

In general, $\langle x + x', y + y' \rangle$ *does not equal* $\langle x, y \rangle + \langle x', y' \rangle$.

Indeed, expanding $\langle x + x', y + y' \rangle$ carefully with the inner product properties shows that the cross-terms $\langle x, y' \rangle$ and $\langle x', y \rangle$ are present in addition to $\langle x, y \rangle$ and $\langle x', y' \rangle$.

Like the vector space axioms, the inner product properties are phrased intrinsically, although they need to be proved using coordinates. As mentioned in the previous section, intrinsic methods are neater and more conceptual than using coordinates. More importantly:

The rest of the results of this section are proved by reference to the inner product properties, with no further reference to the inner product formula.

The notion of an inner product generalizes beyond Euclidean space—this will be demonstrated in Exercise 2.3.4, for example—and thanks to the displayed sentence, once the properties (IP1) through (IP3) are established for any inner product, all of the pending results in the section will follow automatically with no further work. (But here a slight disclaimer is necessary. In the displayed sentence, the word *results* does not refer to the pending graphic figures. The fact that the length and angle to be defined in this section will agree with prior notions of length and angle in the plane, or in three-dimensional space, does depend on the specific inner product formula. In Euclidean space, the inner product properties do not determine the inner product formula uniquely. This point will be addressed in Exercise 3.5.1.)

Definition 2.2.3 (Modulus). *The* **modulus** (*or* **absolute value**) *of a vector* $x \in \mathbb{R}^n$ *is defined as*

$$|x| = \sqrt{\langle x, x \rangle}.$$

Thus the modulus is defined in terms of the inner product, rather than by its own formula. The inner product formula shows that the modulus formula is

$$|(x_1, \ldots, x_n)| = \sqrt{x_1^2 + \cdots + x_n^2},$$

so that some particular examples are

$$|(1, 2, \ldots, n)| = \sqrt{\frac{n(n+1)(2n+1)}{6}},$$

$$|e_i| = 1.$$

However, the definition of the modulus in terms of inner product combines with the inner product properties to show, with no reference to the inner product formula or the modulus formula, that the modulus satisfies the following properties (Exercise 2.2.5).

Proposition 2.2.4 (Modulus properties).

(Mod1) *The modulus is positive:* $|x| \geq 0$ *for all* $x \in \mathbb{R}^n$, *with equality if and only if* $x = \mathbf{0}$.

(Mod2) *The modulus is absolute-homogeneous:* $|ax| = |a||x|$ *for all* $a \in \mathbb{R}$ *and* $x \in \mathbb{R}^n$.

Like other symbols, the absolute value signs are now overloaded, but their meaning can be inferred from context, as in property (Mod2). When n is 1, 2, or 3, the modulus $|x|$ gives the distance from $\mathbf{0}$ to the point x, or the length of x viewed as an arrow. (See Figure 2.6.)

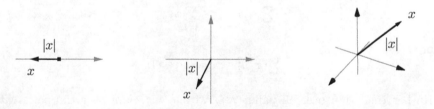

Figure 2.6. Modulus as length

The following relation between inner product and modulus will help to show that distance in $\mathbb{R}^n$ behaves as it should, and that angle in $\mathbb{R}^n$ makes sense. Since the relation is not obvious, its proof is a little subtle.

Theorem 2.2.5 (Cauchy–Schwarz inequality). *For all* $x, y \in \mathbb{R}^n$,

$$|\langle x, y \rangle| \leq |x| |y|,$$

with equality if and only if one of x, y *is a scalar multiple of the other.*

Note that the absolute value signs mean different things on each side of the Cauchy–Schwarz inequality. On the left side, the quantities x and y are vectors, their inner product $\langle x, y \rangle$ is a scalar, and $|\langle x, y \rangle|$ is its scalar absolute value, while on the right side, $|x|$ and $|y|$ are the scalar absolute values of vectors, and $|x|\,|y|$ is their product. That is, the Cauchy–Schwarz inequality says:

The size of the product is at most the product of the sizes.

The Cauchy–Schwarz inequality can be written out in coordinates if we temporarily abandon the principle that we should avoid reference to formulas,

$$(x_1 y_1 + \cdots + x_n y_n)^2 \le (x_1^2 + \cdots + x_n^2)(y_1^2 + \cdots + y_n^2).$$

And this inequality can be proved unconceptually as follows (the reader is encouraged only to skim the following computation). Rewrite the desired inequality as

$$\left(\sum_i x_i y_i \right)^2 \le \sum_i x_i^2 \cdot \sum_j y_j^2,$$

where the indices of summation run from 1 to n. Expand the square to get

$$\sum_i x_i^2 y_i^2 + \sum_{\substack{i,j \\ i \neq j}} x_i y_i x_j y_j \le \sum_{i,j} x_i^2 y_j^2,$$

and canceling the terms common to both sides reduces it to

$$\sum_{i \neq j} x_i y_i x_j y_j \le \sum_{i \neq j} x_i^2 y_j^2,$$

or

$$\sum_{i \neq j} (x_i^2 y_j^2 - x_i y_i x_j y_j) \ge 0.$$

Rather than sum over all pairs (i, j) with $i \neq j$, sum over the pairs with $i < j$, collecting the (i, j)-term and the (j, i)-term for each such pair, and the previous inequality becomes

$$\sum_{i < j} (x_i^2 y_j^2 + x_j^2 y_i^2 - 2 x_i y_j x_j y_i) \ge 0.$$

Thus the desired inequality has reduced to a true inequality,

$$\sum_{i < j} (x_i y_j - x_j y_i)^2 \ge 0.$$

So the main proof is done, although there is still the question of when equality holds.

But surely the previous paragraph is not the graceful way to argue. The computation draws on the minutiae of the formulas for the inner product and the modulus, rather than using their properties. It is uninformative, making the Cauchy–Schwarz inequality look like a low-level accident. It suggests that larger-scale mathematics is just a matter of bigger and bigger formulas. To prove the inequality in a way that is enlightening and general, we should work intrinsically, keeping the scalars $\langle x, y \rangle$ and $|x|$ and $|y|$ notated in their concise forms, and we should use properties, not formulas. The idea is that the calculation in coordinates reduces to the fact that squares are nonnegative. That is, the Cauchy–Schwarz inequality is somehow *quadratically hard*, and its verification amounted to completing many squares. The argument to be given here is guided by this insight to prove the inequality by citing facts about quadratic polynomials, facts established by completing one square back in high-school algebra at the moment that doing so was called for. Thus we eliminate redundancy and clutter. So the argument to follow will involve an auxiliary object, a judiciously chosen quadratic polynomial, but in return it will become coherent.

Proof. The result is clear when $x = \mathbf{0}$, so assume $x \neq \mathbf{0}$. For every $a \in \mathbb{R}$,

$$
\begin{aligned}
0 &\leq \langle ax - y, ax - y \rangle && \text{by positive definiteness} \\
&= a\langle x, ax - y \rangle - \langle y, ax - y \rangle && \text{by linearity in the first variable} \\
&= a^2 \langle x, x \rangle - a\langle x, y \rangle - a\langle y, x \rangle + \langle y, y \rangle && \text{by linearity in the second variable} \\
&= a^2 |x|^2 - 2a\langle x, y \rangle + |y|^2 && \text{by symmetry, definition of modulus.}
\end{aligned}
$$

View the right side as a quadratic polynomial in the scalar variable a, where the scalar coefficients of the polynomial depend on the generic but fixed vectors x and y,

$$
f(a) = |x|^2 a^2 - 2\langle x, y \rangle a + |y|^2.
$$

We have shown that $f(a)$ is always nonnegative, so f has at most one root. Thus by the quadratic formula its discriminant is nonpositive,

$$
4\langle x, y \rangle^2 - 4|x|^2 |y|^2 \leq 0,
$$

and the Cauchy–Schwarz inequality $|\langle x, y \rangle| \leq |x| |y|$ follows. Equality holds exactly when the quadratic polynomial $f(a) = |ax - y|^2$ has a root a, i.e., exactly when $y = ax$ for some $a \in \mathbb{R}$.   □

Geometrically, the condition for equality in Cauchy–Schwarz is that the vectors x and y, viewed as arrows at the origin, are parallel, though perhaps pointing in opposite directions. A geometrically conceived proof of Cauchy–Schwarz is given in Exercise 2.2.15 to complement the algebraic argument that has been given here.

The Cauchy–Schwarz inequality shows that the modulus function satisfies the *triangle inequality*.

Theorem 2.2.6 (Triangle inequality). *For all $x, y \in \mathbb{R}^n$,*

$$
|x + y| \leq |x| + |y|,
$$

with equality if and only if one of x, y is a nonnegative scalar multiple of the other.

Proof. To show this, compute

$$\begin{aligned}
|x+y|^2 &= \langle x+y, x+y \rangle \\
&= |x|^2 + 2\langle x,y \rangle + |y|^2 \quad \text{by bilinearity} \\
&\leq |x|^2 + 2|x||y| + |y|^2 \quad \text{by Cauchy–Schwarz} \\
&= (|x|+|y|)^2,
\end{aligned}$$

proving the inequality. Equality holds exactly when $\langle x,y \rangle = |x||y|$, or equivalently when $|\langle x,y \rangle| = |x||y|$ and $\langle x,y \rangle \geq 0$. These hold when one of x, y is a scalar multiple of the other and the scalar is nonnegative. □

While the Cauchy–Schwarz inequality says that the size of the product is at most the product of the sizes, the triangle inequality says:

The size of the sum is at most the sum of the sizes.

The triangle inequality's name is explained by its geometric interpretation in $\mathbb{R}^2$. View x as an arrow at the origin, y as an arrow with tail at the head of x, and $x+y$ as an arrow at the origin. These three arrows form a triangle, and the assertion is that the lengths of two sides sum to at least the length of the third. (See Figure 2.7.)

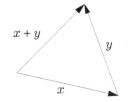

Figure 2.7. Sides of a triangle

The **full triangle inequality** says that for all $x, y \in \mathbb{R}^n$,

$$\big||x| - |y|\big| \leq |x \pm y| \leq |x| + |y|.$$

The proof is Exercise 2.2.7.

A small argument, which can be formalized as induction if one is painstaking, shows that the basic triangle inequality extends from two vectors to any finite number of vectors. For example,

$$|x+y+z| \leq |x+y| + |z| \leq |x| + |y| + |z|.$$

The only obstacle to generalizing the basic triangle inequality in this fashion is notation. The argument can't use the symbol n to denote the number of vectors, because n already denotes the dimension of the Euclidean space where we are working; and furthermore, the vectors can't be denoted with subscripts since a subscript denotes a component of an individual vector. Thus, for now we are stuck writing something like

$$|x^{(1)} + \cdots + x^{(k)}| \le |x^{(1)}| + \cdots + |x^{(k)}| \quad \text{for all } x^{(1)}, \ldots, x^{(k)} \in \mathbb{R}^n,$$

or

$$\left| \sum_{i=1}^{k} x^{(i)} \right| \le \sum_{i=1}^{k} |x^{(i)}|, \quad x^{(1)}, \ldots, x^{(k)} \in \mathbb{R}^n.$$

As our work with vectors becomes more intrinsic, vector entries will demand less of our attention, and we will be able to denote vectors by subscripts. The notation-change will be implemented in the next section.

For every vector $x = (x_1, \ldots, x_n) \in \mathbb{R}^n$, useful bounds on the modulus $|x|$ in terms of the scalar absolute values $|x_i|$ are as follows.

Proposition 2.2.7 (Size bounds). *For every $j \in \{1, \ldots, n\}$,*

$$|x_j| \le |x| \le \sum_{i=1}^{n} |x_i|.$$

The proof (by quick applications of the Cauchy–Schwarz inequality and the triangle inequality) is Exercise 2.2.8.

The modulus gives rise to a distance function on $\mathbb{R}^n$ that behaves as distance should. Define

$$d : \mathbb{R}^n \times \mathbb{R}^n \longrightarrow \mathbb{R}$$

by

$$d(x, y) = |y - x|.$$

For example, $d(e_i, e_j) = \sqrt{2}(1 - \delta_{ij})$.

Theorem 2.2.8 (Distance properties).

(D1) *Distance is positive: $d(x, y) \ge 0$ for all $x, y \in \mathbb{R}^n$, and $d(x, y) = 0$ if and only if $x = y$.*

(D2) *Distance is symmetric: $d(x, y) = d(y, x)$ for all $x, y \in \mathbb{R}^n$.*

(D3) *Triangle inequality: $d(x, z) \le d(x, y) + d(y, z)$ for all $x, y, z \in \mathbb{R}^n$.*

(D1) and (D2) are clearly desirable as properties of a distance function. Property (D3) says that you can't shorten your trip from x to z by making a stop at y.

Proof. Exercise 2.2.9.   □

The Cauchy–Schwarz inequality also lets us define the angle between two nonzero vectors in terms of the inner product. If x and y are nonzero vectors in $\mathbb{R}^n$, define their angle $\theta_{x,y}$ by the condition

$$\cos\theta_{x,y} = \frac{\langle x, y\rangle}{|x||y|}, \quad 0 \le \theta_{x,y} \le \pi. \tag{2.2}$$

The condition is sensible because $-1 \le \frac{\langle x,y\rangle}{|x||y|} \le 1$ by the Cauchy–Schwarz inequality. For example, $\cos\theta_{(1,0),(1,1)} = 1/\sqrt{2}$, and so $\theta_{(1,0),(1,1)} = \pi/4$. In particular, two nonzero vectors x and y are **orthogonal** when $\langle x, y\rangle = 0$. Naturally, we would like $\theta_{x,y}$ to correspond to the usual notion of angle, at least in $\mathbb{R}^2$, and indeed it does—see Exercise 2.2.10. For convenience, define *any* two vectors x and y to be orthogonal if $\langle x, y\rangle = 0$, thus making $\mathbf{0}$ orthogonal to all vectors.

Rephrasing geometry in terms of intrinsic vector algebra not only extends the geometric notions of length and angle uniformly to any dimension, it also makes some low-dimensional geometry easier. For example, vectors show in a natural way that the three altitudes of every triangle must meet. Let x and y denote two sides of the triangle, making the third side $x - y$ by the *head minus tail* mnemonic. Let q be the point where the altitudes to x and y meet. (See Figure 2.8, which also shows the third altitude.) Thus

$$q - y \perp x \quad \text{and} \quad q - x \perp y.$$

We want to show that q also lies on the third altitude, i.e., that

$$q \perp x - y.$$

To rephrase matters in terms of inner products, we want to show that

$$\left.\begin{cases} \langle q - y, x\rangle = 0 \\ \langle q - x, y\rangle = 0 \end{cases}\right\} \implies \langle q, x - y\rangle = 0.$$

Since the inner product is linear in each of its arguments, a further rephrasing is that we want to show that

$$\left.\begin{cases} \langle q, x\rangle = \langle y, x\rangle \\ \langle q, y\rangle = \langle x, y\rangle \end{cases}\right\} \implies \langle q, x\rangle = \langle q, y\rangle.$$

And this is immediate because the inner product is symmetric: $\langle q, x\rangle$ and $\langle q, y\rangle$ both equal $\langle x, y\rangle$, and so they equal each other as desired. The point q where the three altitudes meet is called the **orthocenter** of the triangle. In general, the orthocenter of a triangle is not the geometric center that we considered in the previous section.

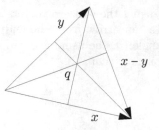

Figure 2.8. Three altitudes of a triangle

Exercises

2.2.1. Let $x = (\frac{\sqrt{3}}{2}, -\frac{1}{2}, 0)$, $y = (\frac{1}{2}, \frac{\sqrt{3}}{2}, 1)$, $z = (1, 1, 1)$. Compute $\langle x, x \rangle$, $\langle x, y \rangle$, $\langle y, z \rangle$, $|x|, |y|, |z|, \theta_{x,y}, \theta_{y,e_1}, \theta_{z,e_2}$.

2.2.2. Show that the points $x = (2, -1, 3, 1)$, $y = (4, 2, 1, 4)$, $z = (1, 3, 6, 1)$ form the vertices of a triangle in $\mathbb{R}^4$ with two equal angles.

2.2.3. Explain why for all $x \in \mathbb{R}^n$, $x = \sum_{j=1}^{n} \langle x, e_j \rangle e_j$.

2.2.4. Prove the inner product properties.

2.2.5. Use the inner product properties and the definition of the modulus in terms of the inner product to prove the modulus properties.

2.2.6. In the text, the modulus is defined in terms of the inner product. Prove that this can be turned around by showing that for every $x, y \in \mathbb{R}^n$,

$$\langle x, y \rangle = \frac{|x + y|^2 - |x - y|^2}{4}.$$

2.2.7. Prove the full triangle inequality: for every $x, y \in \mathbb{R}^n$,

$$\big| |x| - |y| \big| \leq |x \pm y| \leq |x| + |y|.$$

Do not do this by writing three more variants of the proof of the triangle inequality, but by substituting suitably into the basic triangle inequality, which is already proved.

2.2.8. Let $x = (x_1, \ldots, x_n) \in \mathbb{R}^n$. Prove the size bounds: for every $j \in \{1, \ldots, n\}$,

$$|x_j| \leq |x| \leq \sum_{i=1}^{n} |x_i|.$$

(One approach is to start by noting that $x_j = \langle x, e_j \rangle$ and recalling equation (2.1).) When can each "$\leq$" be an "$=$"?

2.2.9. Prove the distance properties.

2.2.10. Working in $\mathbb{R}^2$, depict the nonzero vectors x and y as arrows from the origin and depict $x - y$ as an arrow from the endpoint of y to the endpoint of x. Let θ denote the angle (in the usual geometric sense) between x and y. Use the law of cosines to show that

$$\cos\theta = \frac{\langle x, y \rangle}{|x||y|},$$

so that our notion of angle agrees with the geometric one, at least in $\mathbb{R}^2$.

2.2.11. Prove that for every nonzero $x \in \mathbb{R}^n$, $\sum_{i=1}^{n} \cos^2 \theta_{x,e_i} = 1$.

2.2.12. Prove that two nonzero vectors x, y are orthogonal if and only if $|x + y|^2 = |x|^2 + |y|^2$.

2.2.13. Use vectors in $\mathbb{R}^2$ to show that the diagonals of a parallelogram are perpendicular if and only if the parallelogram is a rhombus.

2.2.14. Use vectors to show that every angle inscribed in a semicircle is right.

2.2.15. Let x and y be vectors, with x nonzero. Define the **parallel** component of y along x and the **normal** component of y to x to be

$$y_{(\|x)} = \frac{\langle x, y \rangle}{|x|^2}x \qquad \text{and} \qquad y_{(\perp x)} = y - y_{(\|x)}.$$

(a) Show that $y = y_{(\|x)} + y_{(\perp x)}$; show that $y_{(\|x)}$ is a scalar multiple of x; show that $y_{(\perp x)}$ is orthogonal to x. Show that the decomposition of y as a sum of vectors parallel and perpendicular to x is unique. Draw an illustration.
   (b) Show that

$$|y|^2 = |y_{(\|x)}|^2 + |y_{(\perp x)}|^2.$$

What theorem from classical geometry does this encompass?
   (c) Explain why it follows from (b) that

$$|y_{(\|x)}| \le |y|,$$

with equality if and only if y is a scalar multiple of x. Use this inequality to give another proof of the Cauchy–Schwarz inequality. This argument gives the geometric content of Cauchy–Schwarz: *the parallel component of one vector along another is at most as long as the original vector.*
   (d) The proof of the Cauchy–Schwarz inequality in part (c) refers to parts (a) and (b), part (a) refers to orthogonality, orthogonality refers to an angle, and as explained in the text, the fact that angles make sense depends on the Cauchy–Schwarz inequality. And so the proof in part (c) apparently relies on circular logic. Explain why the logic is in fact not circular.

2.2.16. Given nonzero vectors $x_1, x_2, \ldots, x_n$ in $\mathbb{R}^n$, the **Gram–Schmidt process** is to set

$$x'_1 = x_1$$
$$x'_2 = x_2 - (x_2)_{(\|x'_1\|)}$$
$$x'_3 = x_3 - (x_3)_{(\|x'_2\|)} - (x_3)_{(\|x'_1\|)}$$
$$\vdots$$
$$x'_n = x_n - (x_n)_{(\|x'_{n-1}\|)} - \cdots - (x_n)_{(\|x'_1\|)}.$$

(a) What is the result of applying the Gram–Schmidt process to the vectors $x_1 = (1, 0, 0)$, $x_2 = (1, 1, 0)$, and $x_3 = (1, 1, 1)$?

(b) Returning to the general case, show that $x'_1, \ldots, x'_n$ are pairwise orthogonal and that each x'_j has the form

$$x'_j = a_{j1}x_1 + a_{j2}x_2 + \cdots + a_{j,j-1}x_{j-1} + x_j.$$

Thus every linear combination of the new $\{x'_j\}$ is also a linear combination of the original $\{x_j\}$. The converse is also true and will be shown in Exercise 3.3.13.

2.3 Analysis: Continuous Mappings

A **mapping** from $\mathbb{R}^n$ to $\mathbb{R}^m$ is some rule that assigns to each point x in $\mathbb{R}^n$ a point in $\mathbb{R}^m$. Generally, mappings will be denoted by letters such as f, g, h. When $m = 1$, we usually say *function* instead of mapping.

For example, the mapping

$$f : \mathbb{R}^2 \longrightarrow \mathbb{R}^2$$

defined by

$$f(x, y) = (x^2 - y^2, 2xy)$$

takes the real and imaginary parts of a complex number $z = x + iy$ and returns the real and imaginary parts of z^2. By the nature of multiplication of complex numbers, this means that each output point has modulus equal to the square of the modulus of the input point and has angle equal to twice the angle of the input point. Make sure that you see how this is shown in Figure 2.9.

Mappings expressed by formulas may be undefined at certain points (e.g., $f(x) = 1/|x|$ is undefined at $\mathbf{0}$), so we need to restrict their domains. For a given dimension n, a given set $A \subset \mathbb{R}^n$, and a second dimension m, let $\mathcal{M}(A, \mathbb{R}^m)$ denote the set of all mappings $f : A \longrightarrow \mathbb{R}^m$. This set forms a vector space over $\mathbb{R}$ (whose *points* are functions) under the operations

$$+ : \mathcal{M}(A, \mathbb{R}^m) \times \mathcal{M}(A, \mathbb{R}^m) \longrightarrow \mathcal{M}(A, \mathbb{R}^m),$$

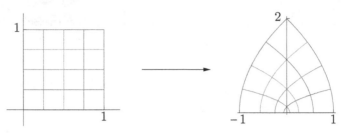

Figure 2.9. The complex square as a mapping from $\mathbb{R}^2$ to $\mathbb{R}^2$

defined by

$$(f+g)(x) = f(x) + g(x) \quad \text{for all } x \in A,$$

and

$$\cdot : \mathbb{R} \times \mathcal{M}(A, \mathbb{R}^m) \longrightarrow \mathcal{M}(A, \mathbb{R}^m),$$

defined by

$$(a \cdot f)(x) = a \cdot f(x) \quad \text{for all } x \in A.$$

As usual, "+" and "·" are overloaded: on the left they denote operations on $\mathcal{M}(A, \mathbb{R}^m)$, while on the right they denote the operations on $\mathbb{R}^m$ defined in Section 2.1. Also as usual, the "·" is generally omitted. The origin in $\mathcal{M}(A, \mathbb{R}^m)$ is the **zero mapping**, $\mathbf{0} : A \longrightarrow \mathbb{R}^m$, defined by

$$\mathbf{0}(x) = \mathbf{0}_m \quad \text{for all } x \in A.$$

For example, to verify that $\mathcal{M}(A, \mathbb{R}^m)$ satisfies (A1), consider any mappings $f, g, h \in \mathcal{M}(A, \mathbb{R}^m)$. For every $x \in A$,

$$
\begin{aligned}
((f+g)+h)(x) &= (f+g)(x) + h(x) && \text{by definition of "+" in } \mathcal{M}(A, \mathbb{R}^m) \\
&= (f(x) + g(x)) + h(x) && \text{by definition of "+" in } \mathcal{M}(A, \mathbb{R}^m) \\
&= f(x) + (g(x) + h(x)) && \text{by associativity of "+" in } \mathbb{R}^m \\
&= f(x) + (g+h)(x) && \text{by definition of "+" in } \mathcal{M}(A, \mathbb{R}^m) \\
&= (f + (g+h))(x) && \text{by definition of "+" in } \mathcal{M}(A, \mathbb{R}^m).
\end{aligned}
$$

Since x is arbitrary, $(f+g)+h = f+(g+h)$.

Let A be a subset of $\mathbb{R}^n$. A **sequence in** A is an infinite list of vectors $\{x_1, x_2, x_3, \dots\}$ in A, often written $\{x_\nu\}$. (The symbol n is already in use, so its Greek counterpart ν—pronounced nu—is used as the index-counter.) Since a vector has n entries, each vector x_ν in the sequence takes the form $(x_{1,\nu}, \dots, x_{n,\nu})$.

Definition 2.3.1 (Null Sequence). *The sequence $\{x_\nu\}$ in $\mathbb{R}^n$ is **null** if for every $\varepsilon > 0$ there exists some ν_0 such that*

$$\text{if } \nu > \nu_0 \text{ then } |x_\nu| < \varepsilon.$$

That is, a sequence is null if for every $\varepsilon > 0$, all but finitely many terms of the sequence lie within distance ε of $\mathbf{0}_n$.

Quickly from the definition, if $\{x_\nu\}$ is a null sequence in $\mathbb{R}^n$ and $\{y_\nu\}$ is a sequence in $\mathbb{R}^n$ such that $|y_\nu| \le |x_\nu|$ for all ν then also $\{y_\nu\}$ is null.

Let $\{x_\nu\}$ and $\{y_\nu\}$ be null sequences in $\mathbb{R}^n$, and let c be a scalar. Then the sequence $\{x_\nu + y_\nu\}$ is null because $|x_\nu + y_\nu| \le |x_\nu| + |y_\nu|$ for each ν, and the sequence $\{cx_\nu\}$ is null because $|cx_\nu| = |c||x_\nu|$ for each ν. These two results show that the set of null sequences in $\mathbb{R}^n$ forms a vector space.

For every vector $x \in \mathbb{R}^n$ the absolute value $|x|$ is a nonnegative scalar, and so no further effect is produced by taking the scalar absolute value in turn,

$$||x|| = |x|, \quad x \in \mathbb{R}^n,$$

and so a vector sequence $\{x_\nu\}$ is null if and only if the scalar sequence $\{|x_\nu|\}$ is null.

Lemma 2.3.2 (Componentwise nature of nullness). *The vector sequence $\{(x_{1,\nu}, \dots, x_{n,\nu})\}$ is null if and only if each of its component scalar sequences $\{x_{j,\nu}\}$ ($j \in \{1, \dots, n\}$) is null.*

Proof. By the observation just before the lemma, it suffices to show that $\{|(x_{1,\nu}, \dots, x_{n,\nu})|\}$ is null if and only if each $\{|x_{j,\nu}|\}$ is null. The size bounds give for every $j \in \{1, \dots, n\}$ and every ν,

$$|x_{j,\nu}| \le |(x_{1,\nu}, \dots, x_{n,\nu})| \le \sum_{i=1}^n |x_{i,\nu}|.$$

If $\{|(x_{1,\nu}, \dots, x_{n,\nu})|\}$ is null then by the first inequality, so is each $\{|x_{j,\nu}|\}$. On the other hand, if each $\{|x_{j,\nu}|\}$ is null then so is $\{\sum_{i=1}^n |x_{i,\nu}|\}$, and thus by the second inequality, $\{|(x_{1,\nu}, \dots, x_{n,\nu})|\}$ is null as well. $\quad\square$

We define the convergence of vector sequences in terms of null sequences.

Definition 2.3.3 (Sequence convergence, sequence limit). *Let A be a subset of $\mathbb{R}^n$. Consider a sequence $\{x_\nu\}$ in A and a point $p \in \mathbb{R}^n$. The sequence $\{x_\nu\}$ converges to p (or has limit p), written $\{x_\nu\} \to p$, if the sequence $\{x_\nu - p\}$ is null. When the limit p is a point of A, the sequence $\{x_\nu\}$ converges in A.*

If a sequence $\{x_\nu\}$ converges to p and also converges to p' then the constant sequence $\{p' - p\}$ is the difference of the null sequences $\{x_\nu - p\}$ and $\{x_\nu - p'\}$, hence null, forcing $p' = p$. Thus a sequence cannot converge to two distinct values.

Many texts define convergence directly rather than by reference to nullness, the key part of the definition being if $\nu > \nu_0$ then $|x_\nu - p| < \varepsilon$.

In particular, a null sequence is a sequence that converges to $\mathbf{0}_n$. However, in contrast to the situation for null sequences, for $p \neq \mathbf{0}_n$ it is emphatically false that if $\{|x_\nu|\}$ converges to $|p|$ then necessarily $\{x_\nu\}$ converges to p or even converges at all. Also, for every nonzero p, the sequences that converge to p do not form a vector space.

Vector versions of the sum rule and the constant multiple rule for convergent sequences follow immediately from the vector space properties of null sequences:

Proposition 2.3.4 (Linearity of convergence). *Let $\{x_\nu\}$ be a sequence in $\mathbb{R}^n$ converging to p, let $\{y_\nu\}$ be a sequence in $\mathbb{R}^n$ converging to q, and let c be a scalar. Then the sequence $\{x_\nu + y_\nu\}$ converges to $p + q$, and the sequence $\{cx_\nu\}$ converges to cp.*

Similarly, since a sequence $\{x_\nu\}$ converges to p if and only if $\{x_\nu - p\}$ is null, we have the following corollary in consequence of the componentwise nature of nullness (Exercise 2.3.5):

Proposition 2.3.5 (Componentwise nature of convergence). *The vector sequence $\{(x_{1,\nu}, \ldots, x_{n,\nu})\}$ converges to the vector $(p_1, \ldots, p_n)$ if and only if each component scalar sequence $\{x_{j,\nu}\}$ $(j = 1, \ldots, n)$ converges to the scalar p_j.*

Continuity, like convergence, is typographically indistinguishable in $\mathbb{R}$ and $\mathbb{R}^n$.

Definition 2.3.6 (Continuity). *Let A be a subset of $\mathbb{R}^n$, let $f : A \longrightarrow \mathbb{R}^m$ be a mapping, and let p be a point of A. Then f is **continuous at** p if for every sequence $\{x_\nu\}$ in A converging to p, the sequence $\{f(x_\nu)\}$ converges to $f(p)$. The mapping f is **continuous on** A (or just **continuous** when A is clearly established) if it is continuous at each point $p \in A$.*

For example, the modulus function

$$| \; | : \mathbb{R}^n \longrightarrow \mathbb{R}$$

is continuous on $\mathbb{R}^n$. To see this, consider any point $p \in \mathbb{R}^n$ and consider any sequence $\{x_\nu\}$ in $\mathbb{R}^n$ that converges to p. We need to show that the sequence $\{|x_\nu|\}$ in $\mathbb{R}$ converges to $|p|$. But by the full triangle inequality,

$$\big| |x_\nu| - |p| \big| \leq |x_\nu - p|.$$

Since the right side is the νth term of a null sequence, so is the left, giving the result.

For another example, let $a \in \mathbb{R}^n$ be any fixed vector and consider the function defined by taking the inner product of this vector with other vectors,

$$T : \mathbb{R}^n \longrightarrow \mathbb{R}, \qquad T(x) = \langle a, x \rangle.$$

This function is also continuous on $\mathbb{R}^n$. To see this, again consider any $p \in \mathbb{R}^n$ and any sequence $\{x_\nu\}$ in $\mathbb{R}^n$ converging to p. Then the definition of T, the bilinearity of the inner product, and the Cauchy–Schwarz inequality combine to show that

$$|T(x_\nu) - T(p)| = |\langle a, x_\nu \rangle - \langle a, p \rangle| = |\langle a, x_\nu - p \rangle| \le |a| \, |x_\nu - p|.$$

Since $|a|$ is a constant, the right side is the νth term of a null sequence, whence so is the left, and the proof is complete. We will refer to this example in Section 3.1. Also, note that as a special case of this example we may take any $j \in \{1, \ldots, n\}$ and set the fixed vector a to e_j, showing that the jth **coordinate function map**,

$$\pi_j : \mathbb{R}^n \longrightarrow \mathbb{R}, \qquad \pi_j(x_1, \ldots, x_n) = x_j,$$

is continuous.

Proposition 2.3.7 (Vector space properties of continuity). *Let A be a subset of $\mathbb{R}^n$, let $f, g : A \longrightarrow \mathbb{R}^m$ be continuous mappings, and let $c \in \mathbb{R}$. Then the sum and the scalar multiple mappings*

$$f + g, \ cf : A \longrightarrow \mathbb{R}^m$$

are continuous. Thus the set of continuous mappings from A to $\mathbb{R}^m$ forms a vector subspace of $\mathcal{M}(A, \mathbb{R}^m)$.

The vector space properties of continuity follow immediately from the linearity of convergence and from the definition of continuity. Another consequence of the definition of continuity is as follows.

Proposition 2.3.8 (Persistence of continuity under composition). *Let A be a subset of $\mathbb{R}^n$, and let $f : A \longrightarrow \mathbb{R}^m$ be a continuous mapping. Let B be a superset of $f(A)$ in $\mathbb{R}^m$, and let $g : B \longrightarrow \mathbb{R}^\ell$ be a continuous mapping. Then the composition mapping*

$$g \circ f : A \longrightarrow \mathbb{R}^\ell$$

is continuous.

The proof is Exercise 2.3.7.

Let A be a subset of $\mathbb{R}^n$. Every mapping $f : A \longrightarrow \mathbb{R}^m$ decomposes as m functions $f_1, \ldots, f_m$, with each $f_i : A \longrightarrow \mathbb{R}$, by the formula

$$f(x) = (f_1(x), \ldots, f_m(x)).$$

For example, if $f(x, y) = (x^2 - y^2, 2xy)$ then $f_1(x, y) = x^2 - y^2$ and $f_2(x, y) = 2xy$. The decomposition of f can also be written

$$f(x) = \sum_{i=1}^{m} f_i(x)e_i,$$

or equivalently, the functions f_i are defined by the condition

$$f_i(x) = f(x)_i \quad \text{for } i = 1, \dots, m.$$

Conversely, given m functions $f_1, \dots, f_m$ from A to $\mathbb{R}$, each of the preceding three displayed formulas assembles a mapping $f : A \longrightarrow \mathbb{R}^m$. Thus, each mapping f determines and is determined by its **component functions** $f_1, \dots, f_m$. Conveniently, to check continuity of the vector-valued mapping f we only need to check its scalar-valued component functions.

Theorem 2.3.9 (Componentwise nature of continuity). *Let $A \subset \mathbb{R}^n$, let $f : A \longrightarrow \mathbb{R}^m$ have component functions $f_1, \dots, f_m$, and let p be a point in A. Then*

$$f \text{ is continuous at } p \iff \text{each } f_i \text{ is continuous at } p.$$

The componentwise nature of continuity follows from the componentwise nature of convergence and is left as Exercise 2.3.6.

Let A be a subset of $\mathbb{R}^n$, let f and g be continuous functions from A to $\mathbb{R}$, and let $c \in \mathbb{R}$. Then the familiar sum rule, constant multiple rule, product rule, and quotient rule for continuous functions hold. That is, the sum $f + g$, the constant multiple cf, the product fg, and the quotient f/g (at points $p \in A$ such that $g(p) \neq 0$) are again continuous. The first two of these facts are special cases of the vector space properties of continuity. The proofs of the other two are typographically identical to their one-variable counterparts. With the various continuity results obtained thus far in hand, it is clear that a function such as

$$f : \mathbb{R}^3 \longrightarrow \mathbb{R}, \qquad f(x, y, z) = \frac{\sin(\sqrt{x^2 + y^2 + z^2})}{e^{xy+z}}$$

is continuous. The continuity of such functions, and of mappings with such functions as their components, will go without comment from now on.

However, the continuity of functions of n variables also has new, subtle features when $n > 1$. In $\mathbb{R}$, a sequence $\{x_\nu\}$ can approach the point p in only two essential ways: from the left and from the right. But in $\mathbb{R}^n$ for $n \geq 2$, $\{x_\nu\}$ can approach p along a line from infinitely many directions, or not approach along a line at all, and so the convergence of $\{f(x_\nu)\}$ can be trickier. For example, consider the function $f : \mathbb{R}^2 \longrightarrow \mathbb{R}$ defined by

$$f(x, y) = \begin{cases} \dfrac{2xy}{x^2 + y^2} & \text{if } (x, y) \neq 0, \\ b & \text{if } (x, y) = 0. \end{cases}$$

Can the constant b be specified to make f continuous at 0?

It can't. Take a sequence $\{(x_\nu, y_\nu)\}$ approaching $\mathbf{0}$ along the line $y = mx$ of slope m. For every point (x_ν, y_ν) of this sequence,

$$f(x_\nu, y_\nu) = f(x_\nu, mx_\nu) = \frac{2x_\nu m x_\nu}{x_\nu^2 + m^2 x_\nu^2} = \frac{2m x_\nu^2}{(1 + m^2) x_\nu^2} = \frac{2m}{1 + m^2}.$$

Thus, as the sequence of inputs $\{(x_\nu, y_\nu)\}$ approaches $\mathbf{0}$ along the line of slope m, the corresponding sequence of outputs $\{f(x_\nu, y_\nu)\}$ holds steady at $2m/(1 + m^2)$, and so $f(\mathbf{0})$ needs to take this value for continuity. Taking input sequences $\{(x_\nu, y_\nu)\}$ that approach $\mathbf{0}$ along lines of different slope shows that $f(\mathbf{0})$ needs to take different values for continuity, and hence f cannot be made continuous at $\mathbf{0}$. The graph of f away from $\mathbf{0}$ is a sort of spiral staircase, and no height over $\mathbf{0}$ is compatible with all the stairs. (See Figure 2.10. The figure displays only the portion of the graph for slopes between 0 and 1 in the input plane.) The reader who wants to work a virtually identical example can replace the formula $2xy/(x^2 + y^2)$ in f by $(x^2 - y^2)/(x^2 + y^2)$ and run the same procedure as in this paragraph.

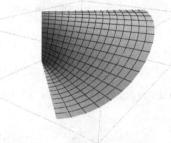

Figure 2.10. A spiral staircase

The previous example was actually fairly simple in that we only needed to study $f(x, y)$ as (x, y) approached $\mathbf{0}$ along straight lines. Consider the function $g : \mathbb{R}^2 \longrightarrow \mathbb{R}$ defined by

$$g(x, y) = \begin{cases} \dfrac{x^2 y}{x^4 + y^2} & \text{if } (x, y) \neq \mathbf{0}, \\ b & \text{if } (x, y) = \mathbf{0}. \end{cases}$$

For a nonzero slope m, take a sequence $\{(x_\nu, y_\nu)\}$ approaching $\mathbf{0}$ along the line $y = mx$. Compute that for each point of this sequence,

$$g(x_\nu, y_\nu) = g(x_\nu, mx_\nu) = \frac{m x_\nu^3}{x_\nu^4 + m^2 x_\nu^2} = \frac{m x_\nu}{x_\nu^2 + m^2}.$$

This quantity tends to 0 as x_ν goes to 0. That is, as the sequence of inputs $\{(x_\nu, y_\nu)\}$ approaches $\mathbf{0}$ along the line of slope m, the corresponding sequence of outputs $\{g(x_\nu, y_\nu)\}$ approaches 0, and so $g(\mathbf{0})$ needs to take the value 0 for continuity. Since g is 0 at the nonzero points of either axis in the (x, y)-plane, this requirement extends to the cases that $\{(x_\nu, y_\nu)\}$ approaches $\mathbf{0}$ along a horizontal or vertical line. However, next consider a sequence $\{(x_\nu, y_\nu)\}$ approaching $\mathbf{0}$ along the parabola $y = x^2$. For each point of this sequence,

$$g(x_\nu, y_\nu) = g(x_\nu, x_\nu^2) = \frac{x_\nu^4}{x_\nu^4 + x_\nu^4} = \frac{1}{2}.$$

Thus, as the sequence of inputs $\{(x_\nu, y_\nu)\}$ approaches $\mathbf{0}$ along the parabola, the corresponding sequence of outputs $\{g(x_\nu, y_\nu)\}$ holds steady at $1/2$, and so $g(\mathbf{0})$ needs to be $1/2$ for continuity as well. Thus g cannot be made continuous at $\mathbf{0}$, even though approaching $\mathbf{0}$ only along lines suggests that it can. The reader who wants to work a virtually identical example can replace the formula $x^2 y/(x^4 + y^2)$ in g by $x^3 y/(x^6 + y^2)$ and run the same procedure as in this paragraph but using the curve $y = x^3$.

Thus, given a function $f : \mathbb{R}^2 \longrightarrow \mathbb{R}$, letting $\{(x_\nu, y_\nu)\}$ approach $\mathbf{0}$ along lines can disprove continuity at $\mathbf{0}$, but it can only suggest continuity at $\mathbf{0}$, not prove it. To prove continuity, the size bounds may be helpful. For example, let

$$h(x, y) = \begin{cases} \dfrac{x^3}{x^2 + y^2} & \text{if } (x, y) \neq \mathbf{0}, \\ b & \text{if } (x, y) = \mathbf{0}. \end{cases}$$

Can b be specified to make h continuous at $\mathbf{0}$? The estimate $|x| \leq |(x, y)|$ gives for every $(x, y) \neq \mathbf{0}$,

$$0 \leq |h(x, y)| = \frac{|x^3|}{x^2 + y^2} = \frac{|x|^3}{|(x, y)|^2} \leq \frac{|(x, y)|^3}{|(x, y)|^2} = |(x, y)|,$$

so as a sequence $\{(x_\nu, y_\nu)\}$ of nonzero input vectors converges to $\mathbf{0}$, the corresponding sequence of outputs $\{h(x_\nu, y_\nu)\}$ is squeezed to 0 in absolute value and hence converges to 0. Setting $b = 0$ makes h continuous at $\mathbf{0}$. The reader who wants to work a virtually identical example can replace the formula $x^3/(x^2 + y^2)$ in h by $x^2 y^2/(x^4 + y^2)$ and run the same procedure as in this paragraph but applying the size bounds to vectors (x_ν^2, y_ν).

Returning to the spiral staircase example,

$$f(x, y) = \begin{cases} \dfrac{2xy}{x^2 + y^2} & \text{if } (x, y) \neq \mathbf{0}, \\ b & \text{if } (x, y) = \mathbf{0}, \end{cases}$$

the size bounds show that that for every $(x, y) \neq \mathbf{0}$,

$$0 \leq |f(x, y)| = \frac{2|x||y|}{|(x, y)|^2} \leq \frac{2|(x, y)|^2}{|(x, y)|^2} = 2.$$

The display tells us only that as a sequence of inputs $\{(x_\nu, y_\nu)\}$ approaches $\mathbf{0}$, the sequence of outputs $\{f(x_\nu, y_\nu)\}$ might converge to some limit between -2 and 2. The outputs needn't converge to 0 (or converge at all), but according to this diagnostic they possibly could. Thus the size bounds tell us only that f *could* be discontinuous at $(0,0)$, but they give no conclusive information.

In sum, these examples illustrate three ideas.

- The straight line test can prove that a limit does not exist, or it can determine the only candidate for the value of the limit, but it cannot prove that the candidate value is the limit.
- When the straight line test determines a candidate value of the limit, approaching along a curve can further support the candidate, or it can prove that the limit does not exist by determining a different candidate as well.
- The size bounds can prove that a limit does exist, but they can only suggest that a limit does not exist.

The next proposition is a handy encoding of an intuitively plausible property of continuous mappings. The result is so natural that it often is tacitly taken for granted, but it is worth stating and proving carefully.

Proposition 2.3.10 (Persistence of inequality). *Let A be a subset of $\mathbb{R}^n$ and let $f : A \longrightarrow \mathbb{R}^m$ be a continuous mapping. Let p be a point of A, let b be a point of $\mathbb{R}^m$, and suppose that $f(p) \neq b$. Then there exists some $\varepsilon > 0$ such that*

$$\text{for all } x \in A \text{ such that } |x - p| < \varepsilon, \ f(x) \neq b.$$

Proof. Assume that the displayed statement in the proposition fails for every $\varepsilon > 0$. Then in particular, it fails for $\varepsilon = 1/\nu$ for $\nu = 1, 2, 3, \ldots$. So there is a sequence $\{x_\nu\}$ in A such that

$$|x_\nu - p| < 1/\nu \quad \text{and} \quad f(x_\nu) = b, \quad \nu = 1, 2, 3, \ldots.$$

Since f is continuous at p, this condition shows that $f(p) = b$. But in fact $f(p) \neq b$, and so our assumption that the displayed statement in the proposition fails for every $\varepsilon > 0$ leads to a contradiction. Therefore the statement holds for some $\varepsilon > 0$, as desired. □

Exercises

2.3.1. For $A \subset \mathbb{R}^n$, partially verify that $\mathcal{M}(A, \mathbb{R}^m)$ is a vector space over $\mathbb{R}$ by showing that it satisfies vector space axioms (A4) and (D1).

2.3.2. Define multiplication $* : \mathcal{M}(A, \mathbb{R}) \times \mathcal{M}(A, \mathbb{R}) \longrightarrow \mathcal{M}(A, \mathbb{R})$. Is $\mathcal{M}(A, \mathbb{R})$ a field with "+" from the section and this multiplication? Does it have a subspace that is a field?

2.3.3. For $A \subset \mathbb{R}^n$ and $m \in \mathbb{Z}^+$ define a subspace of the space of mappings from A to $\mathbb{R}^m$,

$$\mathcal{C}(A, \mathbb{R}^m) = \{f \in \mathcal{M}(A, \mathbb{R}^m) : f \text{ is continuous on } A\}.$$

Briefly explain how this section has shown that $\mathcal{C}(A, \mathbb{R}^m)$ is a vector space.

2.3.4. Define an inner product and a modulus on $\mathcal{C}([0,1], \mathbb{R})$ by

$$\langle f, g \rangle = \int_0^1 f(t)g(t)\,dt, \quad |f| = \sqrt{\langle f, f \rangle}.$$

Do the inner product properties (IP1), (IP2), and (IP3) (see Proposition 2.2.2) hold for this inner product on $\mathcal{C}([0,1], \mathbb{R})$? How much of the material from Section 2.2 on the inner product and modulus in $\mathbb{R}^n$ carries over to $\mathcal{C}([0,1], \mathbb{R})$? Express the Cauchy–Schwarz inequality as a relation between integrals.

2.3.5. Use the definition of convergence and the componentwise nature of nullness to prove the componentwise nature of convergence. (The argument is short.)

2.3.6. Use the definition of continuity and the componentwise nature of convergence to prove the componentwise nature of continuity.

2.3.7. Prove the persistence of continuity under composition.

2.3.8. Define $f : \mathbb{Q} \longrightarrow \mathbb{R}$ by the rule

$$f(x) = \begin{cases} 1 & \text{if } x^2 < 2, \\ 0 & \text{if } x^2 > 2. \end{cases}$$

Is f continuous?

2.3.9. Which of the following functions on $\mathbb{R}^2$ can be defined continuously at $\mathbf{0}$?

$$f(x,y) = \begin{cases} \dfrac{x^4 - y^4}{(x^2 + y^2)^2} & \text{if } (x,y) \neq \mathbf{0}, \\ b & \text{if } (x,y) = \mathbf{0}, \end{cases} \qquad g(x,y) = \begin{cases} \dfrac{x^2 - y^3}{x^2 + y^2} & \text{if } (x,y) \neq \mathbf{0}, \\ b & \text{if } (x,y) = \mathbf{0}, \end{cases}$$

$$h(x,y) = \begin{cases} \dfrac{x^3 - y^3}{x^2 + y^2} & \text{if } (x,y) \neq \mathbf{0}, \\ b & \text{if } (x,y) = \mathbf{0}, \end{cases} \qquad k(x,y) = \begin{cases} \dfrac{xy^2}{x^2 + y^6} & \text{if } (x,y) \neq \mathbf{0}, \\ b & \text{if } (x,y) = \mathbf{0}. \end{cases}$$

2.3.10. Let $f(x,y) = g(xy)$, where $g : \mathbb{R} \longrightarrow \mathbb{R}$ is continuous. Is f continuous?

2.3.11. Let $f, g \in \mathcal{M}(\mathbb{R}^n, \mathbb{R})$ be such that $f + g$ and fg are continuous. Are f and g necessarily continuous?

2.4 Topology: Compact Sets and Continuity

The extreme value theorem from one-variable calculus states:

> *Let I be a nonempty closed and bounded interval in $\mathbb{R}$, and let f : $I \longrightarrow \mathbb{R}$ be a continuous function. Then f takes a minimum value and a maximum value on I.*

This section generalizes the theorem from scalars to vectors. That is, we want a result that if A is a set in $\mathbb{R}^n$ with certain properties, and if $f : A \longrightarrow \mathbb{R}^m$ is a continuous mapping, then the output set $f(A)$ will also have certain properties. The questions are, for what sorts of properties do such statements hold, and when they hold, how do we prove them?

The one-variable theorem hypothesizes two data, the nonempty closed and bounded interval I and the continuous function f. Each of these is described in its own terms—I takes the readily recognizable but static form $[a, b]$ where $a \le b$, while the continuity of f is a dynamic assertion about convergence of sequences. Because the two data have differently phrased descriptions, a proof of the extreme value theorem doesn't suggest itself immediately: no ideas at hand bear obviously on all the given information. Thus the work of this section is not only to define the sets to appear in the pending theorem, but also to describe them in terms of sequences, compatibly with the sequential description of continuous mappings. The theorem itself will then be easy to prove. Accordingly, most of the section will be spent describing sets in two ways—in terms that are easy to recognize, and in sequential language that dovetails with continuity.

We begin with a little machinery to quantify the intuitive notion of nearness.

Definition 2.4.1 (ε-ball). *For every point $p \in \mathbb{R}^n$ and every positive real number $\varepsilon > 0$, the ε-ball centered at p is the set*

$$B(p, \varepsilon) = \{x \in \mathbb{R}^n : |x - p| < \varepsilon\}.$$

(See Figure 2.11.)

Figure 2.11. Balls in various dimensions

With ε-balls it is easy to describe the points that are approached by a set A.

Definition 2.4.2 (Limit point). *Let A be a subset of $\mathbb{R}^n$, and let p be a point of $\mathbb{R}^n$. The point p is a **limit point** of A if every ε-ball centered at p contains some point $x \in A$ such that $x \neq p$.*

A limit point of A need not belong to A (Exercise 2.4.2). On the other hand, a point in A need not be a limit point of A (Exercise 2.4.2 again); such a point is called an **isolated point** of A. Equivalently, p is an isolated point of A if $p \in A$ and there exists some $\varepsilon > 0$ such that $B(p, \varepsilon) \cap A = \{p\}$. The next lemma justifies the nomenclature of the previous definition: limit points of A are precisely the (nontrivial) limits of sequences in A.

Lemma 2.4.3 (Sequential characterization of limit points). *Let A be a subset of $\mathbb{R}^n$, and let p be a point of $\mathbb{R}^n$. Then p is the limit of a sequence $\{x_\nu\}$ in A with each $x_\nu \neq p$ if and only if p is a limit point of A.*

Proof. ($\Longrightarrow$) If p is the limit of a sequence $\{x_\nu\}$ in A with each $x_\nu \neq p$ then every ε-ball about p contains an x_ν (in fact, infinitely many), so p is a limit point of A.

($\Longleftarrow$) Conversely, if p is a limit point of A then $B(p, 1/2)$ contains some $x_1 \in A$, $x_1 \neq p$. Let $\varepsilon_2 = |x_1 - p|/2$. The ball $B(p, \varepsilon_2)$ contains some $x_2 \in A$, $x_2 \neq p$. Let $\varepsilon_3 = |x_2 - p|/2$ and continue defining a sequence $\{x_\nu\}$ in this fashion with $|x_\nu - p| < 1/2^\nu$ for all ν. This sequence converges to p, and $x_\nu \neq p$ for each x_ν. $\square$

The lemma shows that Definition 2.4.2 is more powerful than it appears—every ε-ball centered at a limit point of A contains not only one but *infinitely many* points of A.

Definition 2.4.4 (Closed set). *A subset A of $\mathbb{R}^n$ is **closed** if it contains all of its limit points.*

For example, the x_1-axis is closed as a subset of $\mathbb{R}^n$, because every point off the axis is surrounded by a ball that misses the axis—that is, every point off the axis is not a limit point of the axis, i.e., the axis is not missing any of its limit points, i.e., the axis contains all of its limit points. The interval $(0, 1)$ is not closed because it does not contain the limit points at its ends. These examples illustrate the fact that with a little practice it becomes easy to recognize quickly whether a set is closed. Loosely speaking, a set is closed when it contains all the points that it seems to want to contain.

Proposition 2.4.5 (Sequential characterization of closed sets). *Let A be a subset of $\mathbb{R}^n$. Then A is closed if and only if every sequence in A that converges in $\mathbb{R}^n$ in fact converges in A.*

Proof. ($\Longrightarrow$) Suppose that A is closed, and let $\{x_\nu\}$ be a sequence in A converging in $\mathbb{R}^n$ to p. If $x_\nu = p$ for some ν then $p \in A$ because $x_\nu \in A$; and if $x_\nu \neq p$ for all ν then p is a limit point of A by " $\Longrightarrow$ " of Lemma 2.4.3, and so $p \in A$ because A is closed.

($\Longleftarrow$) Conversely, suppose that every convergent sequence in A has its limit in A. Then all limit points of A are in A by " $\Longleftarrow$ " of Lemma 2.4.3, and so A is closed. □

The proposition equates an easily recognizable condition that we can understand intuitively (a set being closed) with a sequential characterization that we can use in further arguments. Note that the sequential characterization of a closed set A refers not only to A but also to the ambient space $\mathbb{R}^n$ in which A lies. We will return to this point later in this section.

Closed sets do not necessarily have good properties under continuous mappings. So next we describe another class of sets, the bounded sets. Boundedness is again an easily recognizable condition that also has a characterization in terms of sequences. The sequential characterization will turn out to be complementary to the sequential characterization of closed sets, foreshadowing that the properties of being closed and bounded will work well together.

Definition 2.4.6 (Bounded set). *A set A in $\mathbb{R}^n$ is **bounded** if $A \subset B(\mathbf{0}, R)$ for some $R > 0$.*

Thus a bounded set is enclosed in some finite corral centered at the origin, possibly a very big one. For example, every ball $B(p, \varepsilon)$, not necessarily centered at the origin, is bounded, by a nice application of the triangle inequality (Exercise 2.4.5). On the other hand, the Archimedean property of the real number system says that $\mathbb{Z}$ is an unbounded subset of $\mathbb{R}$. The size bounds show that a subset of $\mathbb{R}^n$ is bounded if and only if the jth coordinates of its points form a bounded subset of $\mathbb{R}$ for each $j \in \{1, \ldots, n\}$. The geometric content of this statement is that a set sits inside a ball centered at the origin if and only if it sits inside a box centered at the origin.

Blurring the distinction between a sequence and the set of its elements allows the definition of boundedness to apply to sequences. That is, a sequence $\{x_\nu\}$ is bounded if there is some $R > 0$ such that $|x_\nu| < R$ for all $\nu \in \mathbb{Z}^+$. The proof of the next fact in $\mathbb{R}^n$ is symbol-for-symbol the same as in $\mathbb{R}$ (or in $\mathbb{C}$), so it is only sketched.

Proposition 2.4.7 (Convergence implies boundedness). *If the sequence $\{x_\nu\}$ converges in $\mathbb{R}^n$ then it is bounded.*

Proof. Let $\{x_\nu\}$ converge to p. Then there exists a starting index ν_0 such that $x_\nu \in B(p, 1)$ for all $\nu > \nu_0$. Consider any real number R such that

$$R > \max\{|x_1|, \ldots, |x_{\nu_0}|, |p| + 1\}.$$

Then clearly $x_\nu \in B(\mathbf{0}, R)$ for $\nu = 1, \ldots, \nu_0$, and the triangle inequality shows that also $x_\nu \in B(\mathbf{0}, R)$ for all $\nu > \nu_0$. Thus $\{x_\nu\} \subset B(\mathbf{0}, R)$ as a set. □

Definition 2.4.8 (Subsequence). *A **subsequence** of the sequence $\{x_\nu\}$ is a sequence consisting of some (possibly all) of the original terms, in ascending order of indices.*

Since a subsequence of $\{x_\nu\}$ consists of terms x_ν only for some values of ν, it is often written $\{x_{\nu_k}\}$, where now k is the index variable. For example, given the sequence

$$\{x_1, x_2, x_3, x_4, x_5, \ldots\},$$

a subsequence is

$$\{x_2, x_3, x_5, x_7, x_{11}, \ldots\},$$

with $\nu_1 = 2$, $\nu_2 = 3$, $\nu_3 = 5$, and generally $\nu_k = $ the kth prime.

Lemma 2.4.9 (Persistence of convergence). *Let $\{x_\nu\}$ converge to p. Then every subsequence $\{x_{\nu_k}\}$ also converges to p.*

Proof. The hypothesis that $\{x_\nu\}$ converges to p means that for every given $\varepsilon > 0$, only finitely many sequence-terms x_ν lie outside the ball $B(p, \varepsilon)$. Consequently, only finitely many subsequence-terms x_{ν_k} lie outside $B(p, \varepsilon)$, which is to say that $\{x_{\nu_k}\}$ converges to p. $\qquad\square$

The sequence property that characterizes bounded sets is called the **Bolzano–Weierstrass** property. Once it is proved in $\mathbb{R}$, the result follows in $\mathbb{R}^n$ by arguing one component at a time.

Theorem 2.4.10 (Bolzano–Weierstrass property in R). *Let A be a bounded subset of $\mathbb{R}$. Then every sequence in A has a convergent subsequence.*

Proof. Let $\{x_\nu\}$ be a sequence in A. Call a term x_ν of the sequence a max-point if it is at least as big as all later terms, i.e., $x_\nu \geq x_\mu$ for all $\mu > \nu$. (For visual intuition, draw a graph plotting x_ν as a function of ν, with line segments connecting consecutive points. A max-point is a peak of the graph at least as high as all points to its right.) If there are infinitely many max-points in $\{x_\nu\}$ then these form a decreasing sequence. If there are only finitely many max-points then $\{x_\nu\}$ has an increasing sequence starting after the last max-point—this follows almost immediately from the definition of max-point. In either case, $\{x_\nu\}$ has a monotonic subsequence that, being bounded, converges because the real number system is complete. $\qquad\square$

Theorem 2.4.11 (Bolzano–Weierstrass property in $\mathbb{R}^n$: sequential characterization of bounded sets). *Let A be a subset of $\mathbb{R}^n$. Then A is bounded if and only if every sequence in A has a subsequence that converges in $\mathbb{R}^n$.*

Proof. ($\implies$) Suppose that A is bounded. Consider any sequence $\{x_\nu\}$ in A, written as $\{(x_{1,\nu}, \ldots, x_{n,\nu})\}$. The real sequence $\{x_{1,\nu}\}$ takes values in a bounded subset of $\mathbb{R}$ and thus has a convergent subsequence, $\{x_{1,\nu_k}\}$. The subscripts are getting out of hand, so keep only the ν_kth terms of the original sequence and relabel it. In other words, we may as well assume that the sequence of first components, $\{x_{1,\nu}\}$, converges. The real sequence of second components, $\{x_{2,\nu}\}$, in turn has a convergent subsequence, and by

Lemma 2.4.9 the corresponding subsequence of first components, $\{x_{1,\nu}\}$, converges too. Relabeling again, we may assume that $\{x_{1,\nu}\}$ and $\{x_{2,\nu}\}$ both converge. Continuing in this fashion $n-2$ more times exhibits a subsequence of $\{x_\nu\}$ that converges at each component.

($\Longleftarrow$) Conversely, suppose that A is not bounded. Then there is a sequence $\{x_\nu\}$ in A with $|x_\nu| > \nu$ for all ν. This sequence has no bounded subsequence, and hence it has no convergent subsequence by Proposition 2.4.7.   □

Note how the sequential characterizations in Proposition 2.4.5 and in the Bolzano–Weierstrass property complement each other. The proposition characterizes every closed set in $\mathbb{R}^n$ by the fact that if a sequence converges in the ambient space then it converges in the set. The Bolzano–Weierstrass property characterizes every bounded set in $\mathbb{R}^n$ by the fact that every sequence in the set has a subsequence that converges in the ambient space but not necessarily in the set. Both the sequential characterization of a closed set and the sequential characterization of a bounded set refer to the ambient space $\mathbb{R}^n$ in which the set lies. We will return to this point once more in this section.

Definition 2.4.12 (Compact set). *A subset K of $\mathbb{R}^n$ is* **compact** *if it is closed and bounded.*

Since the static notions of closed and bounded are reasonably intuitive, we can usually recognize compact sets on sight. But it is not obvious from how compact sets look that they are related to continuity. So our program now has two steps: first, combine Proposition 2.4.5 and the Bolzano–Weierstrass property to characterize compact sets in terms of sequences, and second, use the characterization to prove that compactness is preserved by continuous mappings.

Theorem 2.4.13 (Sequential characterization of compact sets). *Let K be a subset of $\mathbb{R}^n$. Then K is compact if and only if every sequence in K has a subsequence that converges in K.*

Proof. ($\Longrightarrow$) We show that the sequential characterizations of closed and bounded sets together imply the claimed sequential characterization of compact sets. Suppose that K is compact and $\{x_\nu\}$ is a sequence in K. Then K is bounded, so by " $\Longrightarrow$ " of the Bolzano–Weierstrass property, $\{x_\nu\}$ has a convergent subsequence. But K is also closed, so by " $\Longrightarrow$ " of Proposition 2.4.5, this subsequence converges in K.

($\Longleftarrow$) Conversely, we show that the claimed sequential characterization of compact sets subsumes the sequential characterizations of closed and bounded sets. Thus, suppose that every sequence in K has a subsequence that converges in K. Then in particular, every sequence in K that converges in $\mathbb{R}^n$ has a subsequence that converges in K. By Lemma 2.4.9 the limit of the sequence is the limit of the subsequence, so the sequence converges in K. That is, every sequence in K that converges in $\mathbb{R}^n$ converges in K, and hence K is closed by " $\Longleftarrow$ " of Proposition 2.4.5. Also in consequence of the claimed sequential property of compact sets, every sequence in K has a subsequence that converges in $\mathbb{R}^n$. Thus K is bounded by " $\Longleftarrow$ " of the Bolzano–Weierstrass Property. $\square$

By contrast to the sequential characterizations of a closed set and of a bounded set, the sequential characterization of a compact set K makes no reference to the ambient space $\mathbb{R}^n$ in which K lies. A set's property of being compact is innate in a way that a set's property of being closed or of being bounded is not.

The next theorem is the main result of this section. Now that all of the objects involved are described in the common language of sequences, its proof is natural.

Theorem 2.4.14 (The continuous image of a compact set is compact). *Let K be a compact subset of $\mathbb{R}^n$ and let $f : K \longrightarrow \mathbb{R}^m$ be continuous. Then $f(K)$, the image set of K under f, is a compact subset of $\mathbb{R}^m$.*

Proof. Let $\{y_\nu\}$ be any sequence in $f(K)$; by " $\Longleftarrow$ " of Theorem 2.4.13, it suffices to exhibit a subsequence converging in $f(K)$. Each y_ν has the form $f(x_\nu)$, and this defines a sequence $\{x_\nu\}$ in K. By " $\Longrightarrow$ " of Theorem 2.4.13, since K is compact, $\{x_\nu\}$ necessarily has a subsequence $\{x_{\nu_k}\}$ converging in K, say to p. By the continuity of f at p, the sequence $\{f(x_{\nu_k})\}$ converges in $f(K)$ to $f(p)$. Since $\{f(x_{\nu_k})\}$ is a subsequence of $\{y_\nu\}$, the proof is complete. $\square$

Again, the sets in Theorem 2.4.14 are defined with no direct reference to sequences, but the theorem is proved entirely using sequences. The point is that with the theorem proved, we can easily see that it applies in particular contexts without having to think any longer about the sequences that were used to prove it.

A corollary of Theorem 2.4.14 generalizes the theorem that was quoted to begin the section:

Theorem 2.4.15 (Extreme value theorem). *Let K be a nonempty compact subset of $\mathbb{R}^n$ and let the function $f : K \longrightarrow \mathbb{R}$ be continuous. Then f takes a minimum and a maximum value on K.*

Proof. By Theorem 2.4.14, $f(K)$ is a compact subset of $\mathbb{R}$. As a nonempty bounded subset of $\mathbb{R}$, $f(K)$ has a greatest lower bound and a least upper bound by the completeness of the real number system. Each of these bounds is an isolated point or a limit point of $f(K)$, since otherwise some ε-ball about it would be disjoint from $f(K)$, giving rise to greater lower bounds or lesser upper bounds of $f(K)$. Because $f(K)$ is also closed, it contains its limit points, so in particular it contains its greatest lower bound and its least upper bound. This means precisely that f takes a minimum and a maximum value on K. $\square$

Even when $n = 1$, Theorem 2.4.15 generalizes the extreme value theorem from the beginning of the section. In the theorem here, K can be a finite union of closed and bounded intervals in $\mathbb{R}$ rather than only one interval, or K can be a more complicated set, provided only that it is compact.

A *topological property* of sets is a property that is preserved under continuity. Theorem 2.4.14 says that compactness is a topological property. Neither the property of being closed nor the property of being bounded is in itself topological. That is, the continuous image of a closed set need not be closed, and the continuous image of a bounded set need not be bounded; for that matter, the continuous image of a closed set need not be bounded, and the continuous image of a bounded set need not be closed (Exercise 2.4.8).

The nomenclature *continuous image* in the slogan-title of Theorem 2.4.14 and in the previous paragraph is, strictly speaking, inaccurate: the image of a mapping is a set, and the notion of a set being continuous doesn't even make sense according to our grammar. As stated correctly in the body of the theorem, *continuous image* is short for *image under a continuous mapping*.

The property that students often have in mind when they call a set continuous is in fact called *connectedness*. Loosely, a set is connected if it has only one piece, so that a better approximating word from everyday language is *contiguous*. To define connectedness accurately, we would have to use methodology exactly opposite that of this section: rather than relate sets to continuous mappings by characterizing the sets in terms of sequences, the idea is to turn the whole business around and characterize continuous mappings in terms of sets, specifically in terms of open balls. However, the process of doing so, and then characterizing compact sets in terms of open balls as well, is trickier than characterizing sets in terms of sequences; and so we omit it because we do not need connectedness. Indeed, the remark after Theorem 2.4.15 points out that connectedness is unnecessary even for the one-variable extreme value theorem.

However, it deserves passing mention that connectedness is also a topological property: again using language loosely, the continuous image of a connected set is connected. This statement generalizes another theorem that underlies one-variable calculus, the intermediate value theorem. For a notion related to connectedness that is easily shown to be a topological property, see Exercise 2.4.10.

The ideas of this section readily extend to broader environments. The first generalization of Euclidean space is a *metric space*, a set with a well-behaved distance function. Even more general is a *topological space*, a set with some of its subsets designated as closed. Continuous functions, compact sets, and connected sets can be defined meaningfully in these environments, and the theorems remain the same: the continuous image of a compact set is compact, and the continuous image of a connected set is connected.

Exercises

2.4.1. Are the following subsets of $\mathbb{R}^n$ closed, bounded, compact?
  (a) $B(\mathbf{0}, 1)$,
  (b) $\{(x, y) \in \mathbb{R}^2 : y - x^2 = 0\}$,
  (c) $\{(x, y, z) \in \mathbb{R}^3 : x^2 + y^2 + z^2 - 1 = 0\}$,
  (d) $\{x : f(x) = \mathbf{0}_m\}$, where $f \in \mathcal{M}(\mathbb{R}^n, \mathbb{R}^m)$ is continuous (this generalizes
(b) and (c)),
  (e) $\mathbb{Q}^n$ where $\mathbb{Q}$ denotes the rational numbers,
  (f) $\{(x_1, \ldots, x_n) : x_1 + \cdots + x_n > 0\}$.

2.4.2. Give a set $A \subset \mathbb{R}^n$ and limit point b of A such that $b \notin A$. Give a set $A \subset \mathbb{R}^n$ and a point $a \in A$ such that a is not a limit point of A.

2.4.3. Let A be a closed subset of $\mathbb{R}^n$ and let $f \in \mathcal{M}(A, \mathbb{R}^m)$. Define the **graph** of f to be
$$G(f) = \{(a, f(a)) : a \in A\},$$
a subset of $\mathbb{R}^{n+m}$. Show that if f is continuous then its graph is closed.

2.4.4. Prove the closed set properties: (1) the empty set $\varnothing$ and the full space $\mathbb{R}^n$ are closed subsets of $\mathbb{R}^n$; (2) every intersection of closed sets is closed; (3) every finite union of closed sets is closed.

2.4.5. Prove that every ball $B(p, \varepsilon)$ is bounded in $\mathbb{R}^n$.

2.4.6. Show that A is a bounded subset of $\mathbb{R}^n$ if and only if for each $j \in \{1, \ldots, n\}$, the jth coordinates of its points form a bounded subset of $\mathbb{R}$.

2.4.7. Show by example that a closed set need not satisfy the sequential characterization of bounded sets, and that a bounded set need not satisfy the sequential characterization of closed sets.

2.4.8. Show by example that the continuous image of a closed set need not be closed, that the continuous image of a closed set need not be bounded, that the continuous image of a bounded set need not be closed, and that the continuous image of a bounded set need not be bounded.

2.4.9. A subset A of $\mathbb{R}^n$ is called **discrete** if each of its points is isolated. (Recall that the term *isolated* was defined in this section.) Show or take for granted the (perhaps surprising at first) fact that every mapping whose domain is discrete must be continuous. Is discreteness a topological property? That is, need the continuous image of a discrete set be discrete?

2.4.10. A subset A of $\mathbb{R}^n$ is called **path-connected** if for every two points $x, y \in A$, there is a continuous mapping
$$\gamma : [0, 1] \longrightarrow A$$
such that $\gamma(0) = x$ and $\gamma(1) = y$. (This γ is the path that connects x and y.) Draw a picture to illustrate the definition of a path-connected set. Prove that path-connectedness is a topological property.

3

Linear Mappings and Their Matrices

The basic idea of differential calculus is to approximate smooth-but-curved objects in the small by straight ones. To prepare for doing so, this chapter studies the multivariable analogues of lines. With one variable, lines are easily manipulated by explicit formulas (e.g., the point–slope form is $y = mx + b$), but with many variables we want to use the language of mappings. Section 3.1 gives an algebraic description of "straight" mappings, the *linear* mappings, proceeding from an intrinsic definition to a description in coordinates. Each linear mapping is described by a box of numbers called a *matrix*, so Section 3.2 derives mechanical matrix manipulations corresponding to the natural ideas of adding, scaling, and composing linear mappings. Section 3.3 discusses in matrix terms the question whether a linear mapping has an *inverse*, i.e., whether there is a second linear mapping such that each undoes the other's effect. Section 3.5 discusses the *determinant*, an elaborate matrix-to-scalar function that extracts from a linear mapping a single number with remarkable properties:

- (Linear invertibility theorem) The mapping is invertible if and only if the determinant is nonzero.
- An explicit formula for the inverse of an invertible linear mapping can be written using the determinant (Section 3.7).
- The factor by which the mapping magnifies volume is the absolute value of the determinant (Section 3.8).
- The mapping preserves or reverses orientation according to the sign of the determinant (Section 3.9). Here orientation is an algebraic generalization of clockwise versus counterclockwise in the plane and of right-handed versus left-handed in space.

Finally, Section 3.10 defines the cross product (a vector-by-vector multiplication special to three dimensions) and uses it to derive formulas for lines and planes in space.

© Springer International Publishing AG 2016
J. Shurman, *Calculus and Analysis in Euclidean Space*,
Undergraduate Texts in Mathematics, DOI 10.1007/978-3-319-49314-5_3

3.1 Linear Mappings

The simplest interesting mappings from $\mathbb{R}^n$ to $\mathbb{R}^m$ are those whose output is proportional to their input, the *linear mappings*. Proportionality means that a linear mapping should take a sum of inputs to the corresponding sum of outputs,

$$T(x + y) = T(x) + T(y) \quad \text{for all } x, y \in \mathbb{R}^n, \tag{3.1}$$

and a linear mapping should take a scaled input to the correspondingly scaled output,

$$T(\alpha x) = \alpha T(x) \quad \text{for all } \alpha \in \mathbb{R}, \, x \in \mathbb{R}^n. \tag{3.2}$$

(Here we use the symbol α because a will be used heavily in other ways during this chapter.) More formally, the definition of a linear mapping is as follows.

Definition 3.1.1 (Linear mapping). *The mapping* $T : \mathbb{R}^n \longrightarrow \mathbb{R}^m$ *is linear if*

$$T\left(\sum_{i=1}^{k} \alpha_i x_i\right) = \sum_{i=1}^{k} \alpha_i T(x_i)$$

for all positive integers k, all real numbers α_1 through α_k, and all vectors x_1 through x_k.

The reader may find this definition discomfiting. It does not say what form a linear mapping takes, and this raises some immediate questions. How are we to recognize linear mappings when we encounter them? Or are we supposed to think about them without knowing what they look like? For that matter, are there even any linear mappings to encounter? Another troublesome aspect of Definition 3.1.1 is semantic: despite the geometric sound of the word *linear*, the definition is in fact algebraic, describing how T behaves with respect to the algebraic operations of vector addition and scalar multiplication. (Note that on the left of the equality in the definition, the operations are set in $\mathbb{R}^n$, while on the right they are in $\mathbb{R}^m$.) So what is the connection between the definition and actual lines? Finally, how exactly do conditions (3.1) and (3.2) relate to the condition in the definition?

On the other hand, Definition 3.1.1 has the virtue of illustrating the principle that *to do mathematics effectively we should characterize our objects rather than construct them*. The characterizations are admittedly guided by hindsight, but there is nothing wrong with that. Definition 3.1.1 says how a linear mapping behaves. It says that whatever form linear mappings will turn out to take, our reflex should be to think of them as mappings through which we can pass sums and constants. (This idea explains why one of the inner product properties is called *bilinearity*: the inner product is linear as a function of either of its two vector variables when the other variable is held fixed.) The definition of linearity tells us how to use linear mappings once we know what they are, or even before we know what they are. Another virtue of Definition 3.1.1 is that it is intrinsic, making no reference to coordinates.

Some of the questions raised by Definition 3.1.1 have quick answers. The connection between the definition and actual lines will quickly emerge from our pending investigations. Also, an induction argument shows that (3.1) and (3.2) are equivalent to the characterization in the definition, despite appearing weaker (Exercise 3.1.1). Thus, to verify that a mapping is linear, we only need to show that it satisfies the easier-to-check conditions (3.1) and (3.2); but to derive properties of mappings that are known to be linear, we may want to use the more powerful condition in the definition. As for finding linear mappings, the definition suggests a two-step strategy: first, derive the form that a linear mapping necessarily takes in consequence of satisfying the definition; and second, verify that the mappings of that form are indeed linear, i.e., show that the necessary form of a linear mapping is also sufficient for a mapping to be linear. We now turn to this.

The easiest case to study is linear mappings from $\mathbb{R}$ to $\mathbb{R}$. Following the strategy, first we assume that we have such a mapping and determine its form, obtaining the mappings that are candidates to be linear. Second, we show that all the candidates are indeed linear mappings. Thus suppose that some mapping $T : \mathbb{R} \longrightarrow \mathbb{R}$ is linear. The mapping determines a scalar, $a = T(1)$. And then for every $x \in \mathbb{R}$,

$$
\begin{aligned}
T(x) &= T(x \cdot 1) &&\text{since } x \cdot 1 = x \\
&= xT(1) &&\text{by (3.2)} \\
&= xa &&\text{by definition of } a \\
&= ax &&\text{since multiplication in } \mathbb{R} \text{ commutes.}
\end{aligned}
$$

Thus, T is simply multiplication by a, where $a = T(1)$. But to reiterate, this calculation does not show that any mapping is linear. Rather, it tells us what form a mapping must necessarily have if it is assumed or known to be linear, and therefore it gives us all candidate linear mappings. But we don't yet know that any linear mappings exist at all.

So the next thing to do is show that conversely, every mapping of the derived form is indeed linear—the necessary condition is also sufficient. Fix a real number a and define a mapping $T : \mathbb{R} \longrightarrow \mathbb{R}$ by $T(x) = ax$. Then the claim is that T is linear and $T(1) = a$. Let's partially show this by verifying that T satisfies (3.2). For every $\alpha \in \mathbb{R}$ and every $x \in \mathbb{R}$,

$$
\begin{aligned}
T(\alpha x) &= a\alpha x &&\text{by definition of } T \\
&= \alpha a x &&\text{since multiplication in } \mathbb{R} \text{ commutes} \\
&= \alpha T(x) &&\text{by definition of } T,
\end{aligned}
$$

as needed. You can check (3.1) similarly, and the calculation that $T(1) = a$ is immediate. These last two paragraphs combine to prove the following result.

Proposition 3.1.2 (Description of linear mappings from scalars to scalars). *The linear mappings $T : \mathbb{R} \longrightarrow \mathbb{R}$ are precisely the mappings*

$$T(x) = ax$$

where $a \in \mathbb{R}$. That is, each linear mapping $T : \mathbb{R} \longrightarrow \mathbb{R}$ is multiplication by a unique $a \in \mathbb{R}$ and conversely.

The slogan encapsulating the formula $T(x) = ax$ (read "T of x equals a times x") in the proposition is:

For scalar input and scalar output, linear OF is scalar TIMES.

That is, given $x \in \mathbb{R}$, the effect of a linear mapping $T : \mathbb{R} \longrightarrow \mathbb{R}$ on x is simply to multiply x by a scalar $a \in \mathbb{R}$ associated with T. This may seem trivial, but the issue is that at times our methodology will be to study a linear mapping by its defining properties, i.e., the rules $T(x+y) = T(x) + T(y)$ and $T(\alpha x) = \alpha T(x)$, while at other times we will profit from studying a linear mapping computationally, i.e., as a mapping that simply multiplies its inputs by something—by a scalar here, but by a vector or by a matrix later in this section. The slogan displayed just above, as well as its two variants to follow below, gives the connection between the two ways to think about a linear mapping.

Also, the proposition explains the term *linear:* the graphs of linear mappings from $\mathbb{R}$ to $\mathbb{R}$ are lines through the origin. (Mappings $f(x) = ax + b$ with $b \neq 0$ are not linear according to our definition even though their graphs are also lines. However, see Exercises 3.1.15 and 3.2.6.) For example, a typical linear mapping from $\mathbb{R}$ to $\mathbb{R}$ is $T(x) = (1/2)x$. Figure 3.1 shows two ways of visualizing this mapping. The left half of the figure plots the domain axis and the codomain axis orthogonally to each other in one plane, the familiar way to graph a function. The right half of the figure plots the axes separately, using the spacing of the dots to describe the mapping instead. The uniform spacing along the rightmost axis depicts the fact that $T(x) = xT(1)$ for all $x \in \mathbb{Z}$, and the spacing is half as big because the multiplying factor is $1/2$. Figures of this second sort can generalize up to three dimensions of input and three dimensions of output, whereas figures of the first sort can display at most three dimensions of input and output combined.

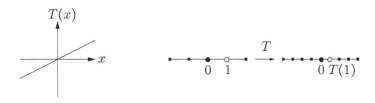

Figure 3.1. A linear mapping from $\mathbb{R}$ to $\mathbb{R}$

Next consider a linear mapping $T : \mathbb{R}^n \longrightarrow \mathbb{R}$. Recall the standard basis vectors of $\mathbb{R}^n$,

$$e_1 = (1, 0, \ldots, 0), \quad \ldots, \quad e_n = (0, 0, \ldots, 1).$$

Take the n real numbers

$$a_1 = T(e_1), \quad \ldots, \quad a_n = T(e_n),$$

and define the vector $a = (a_1, \ldots, a_n) \in \mathbb{R}^n$. Every $x \in \mathbb{R}^n$ can be written

$$x = (x_1, \ldots, x_n) = \sum_{i=1}^{n} x_i e_i, \quad \text{each } x_i \in \mathbb{R}.$$

(So here each x_i is a scalar entry of the vector x, whereas in Definition 3.1.1, each x_i was itself a vector. The author does not know any graceful way to avoid this notation collision, the systematic use of boldface or arrows to adorn vector names being heavyhanded, and the systematic use of the Greek letter ξ rather than its Roman counterpart x to denote scalars being alien. Since mathematics involves finitely many symbols and infinitely many ideas, the reader will in any case eventually need the skill of discerning meaning from context, a skill that may as well start receiving practice now.) Returning to the main discussion, since $x = \sum_{i=1}^{n} x_i e_i$ and T is linear, Definition 3.1.1 shows that

$$T(x) = T\left(\sum_{i=1}^{n} x_i e_i\right) = \sum_{i=1}^{n} x_i T(e_i) = \sum_{i=1}^{n} x_i a_i = \langle x, a \rangle = \langle a, x \rangle.$$

Again, the only possibility for the linear mapping is multiplication by an element a, where now $a = (T(e_1), \ldots, T(e_n))$ is a vector and the multiplication is an inner product, but we don't yet know that such a mapping is linear. However, fix a vector $a = (a_1, \ldots, a_n)$ and define the corresponding mapping $T : \mathbb{R}^n \longrightarrow \mathbb{R}$ by $T(x) = \langle a, x \rangle$. Then it is straightforward to show that indeed T is linear and $T(e_j) = a_j$ for $j = 1, \ldots, n$ (Exercise 3.1.3). Thus we have the following proposition.

Proposition 3.1.3 (Description of linear mappings from vectors to scalars). *The linear mappings* $T : \mathbb{R}^n \longrightarrow \mathbb{R}$ *are precisely the mappings*

$$T(x) = \langle a, x \rangle$$

where $a \in \mathbb{R}^n$. *That is, each linear mapping* $T : \mathbb{R}^n \longrightarrow \mathbb{R}$ *is multiplication by a unique* $a \in \mathbb{R}^n$ *and conversely.*

The slogan encapsulating the formula $T(x) = \langle a, x \rangle$ of the proposition is:

For vector input and scalar output, linear OF is vector TIMES.

In light of the proposition, you should be able to recognize linear mappings from $\mathbb{R}^n$ to $\mathbb{R}$ on sight. For example, the mapping $T : \mathbb{R}^3 \longrightarrow \mathbb{R}$ given by $T(x, y, z) = \pi x + ey + \sqrt{2} z$ is linear, being multiplication by the vector $(\pi, e, \sqrt{2})$.

In the previous chapter, the second example after Definition 2.3.6 showed that every linear mapping $T : \mathbb{R}^n \longrightarrow \mathbb{R}$ is continuous. You are encouraged to reread that example now before continuing.

A depiction of a linear mapping from $\mathbb{R}^2$ to $\mathbb{R}$ can again plot the domain plane and the codomain axis orthogonally to each other or separately. See Figures 3.2 and 3.3 for examples of each type of plot. The first figure suggests that the graph forms a plane in $\mathbb{R}^3$ and that a line of inputs is taken to the output value 0. The second figure shows more clearly how the mapping compresses the plane into the line. As in the right half of Figure 3.1, the idea is that $T(x,y) = xT(1,0) + yT(0,1)$ for all $x, y \in \mathbb{Z}$. The compression is that although $(1,0)$ and $(0,1)$ lie on separate input axes, $T(1,0)$ and $T(0,1)$ lie on the same output axis.

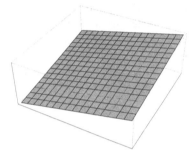

Figure 3.2. The graph of a linear mapping from $\mathbb{R}^2$ to $\mathbb{R}$

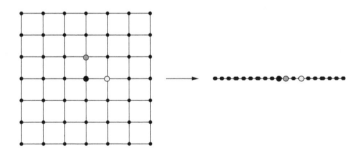

Figure 3.3. Second depiction of a linear mapping from $\mathbb{R}^2$ to $\mathbb{R}$

The most general mapping is $T : \mathbb{R}^n \longrightarrow \mathbb{R}^m$. Such a mapping decomposes as $T = (T_1, \ldots, T_m)$ where each $T_i : \mathbb{R}^n \longrightarrow \mathbb{R}$ is the ith component function of T. The next proposition reduces the linearity of such T to the linearity of its components T_i, which we already understand.

Proposition 3.1.4 (Componentwise nature of linearity). *The vector-valued mapping* $T = (T_1, \ldots, T_m) : \mathbb{R}^n \longrightarrow \mathbb{R}^m$ *is linear if and only if each scalar-valued component function* $T_i : \mathbb{R}^n \longrightarrow \mathbb{R}$ *is linear.*

Proof. For every $x, y \in \mathbb{R}^n$,

$$T(x + y) = \big(T_1(x + y), \quad \ldots, \quad T_m(x + y)\big)$$

and

$$T(x) + T(y) = \big(T_1(x), \ldots, T_m(x)\big) \quad + \quad \big(T_1(y), \ldots, T_m(y)\big)$$
$$= \big(T_1(x) + T_1(y), \quad \ldots, \quad T_m(x) + T_m(y)\big).$$

But T satisfies (3.1) exactly when the left sides are equal, the left sides are equal exactly when the right sides are equal, and the right sides are equal exactly when each T_i satisfies (3.1). A similar argument with (3.2), left as Exercise 3.1.5, completes the proof. □

The componentwise nature of linearity combines with the fact that scalar-valued linear mappings are continuous (as observed after Proposition 3.1.3) and with the componentwise nature of continuity to show that all linear mappings are continuous. Despite being so easy to prove, this fact deserves a prominent statement.

Theorem 3.1.5 (Linear mappings are continuous). *Let the mapping* $T : \mathbb{R}^n \longrightarrow \mathbb{R}^m$ *be linear. Then* T *is continuous.*

By the previous proposition, a mapping $T : \mathbb{R}^n \longrightarrow \mathbb{R}^m$ is linear if and only if each T_i determines n real numbers $a_{i1}, \ldots, a_{in}$ as just discussed. Putting all mn numbers a_{ij} into a box with m rows and n columns gives a **matrix**

$$A = \begin{bmatrix} a_{11} & a_{12} & \cdots & a_{1n} \\ a_{21} & a_{22} & \cdots & a_{2n} \\ \vdots & \vdots & & \vdots \\ a_{m1} & a_{m2} & \cdots & a_{mn} \end{bmatrix} \tag{3.3}$$

whose ith row is the vector determined by T_i, and whose (i, j)th entry (this means ith row, jth column) is thus given by

$$a_{ij} = T_i(e_j). \tag{3.4}$$

Sometimes one saves writing by abbreviating the right side of (3.3) to $[a_{ij}]_{m \times n}$, or even just $[a_{ij}]$ when m and n are firmly established.

The set of all $m \times n$ matrices (those with m rows and n columns) of real numbers is denoted $\mathrm{M}_{m,n}(\mathbb{R})$. The $n \times n$ square matrices are denoted $\mathrm{M}_n(\mathbb{R})$. Euclidean space $\mathbb{R}^n$ is often identified with $\mathrm{M}_{n,1}(\mathbb{R})$ and vectors written as columns,

$$(x_1, \ldots, x_n) = \begin{bmatrix} x_1 \\ \vdots \\ x_n \end{bmatrix}.$$

This typographical convention may look odd, but it is useful. The idea is that a vector in parentheses is merely an ordered list of entries, not inherently a row or a column; but when a vector—or, more generally, a matrix—is enclosed by square brackets, the distinction between rows and columns is significant.

To make the linear mapping $T : \mathbb{R}^n \longrightarrow \mathbb{R}^m$ be multiplication by its matrix $A \in \mathrm{M}_{m,n}(\mathbb{R})$, we need to *define* multiplication of an $m \times n$ matrix A by an $n \times 1$ vector x appropriately. That is, the only sensible definition is as follows.

Definition 3.1.6 (Matrix-by-vector multiplication). *Let $A \in \mathrm{M}_{m,n}(\mathbb{R})$ and let $x \in \mathbb{R}^n$. The product $Ax \in \mathbb{R}^m$ is defined to be the vector whose ith entry is the inner product of A's ith row and x,*

$$Ax = \begin{bmatrix} a_{11} & a_{12} & \cdots & \cdots & a_{1n} \\ a_{21} & a_{22} & \cdots & \cdots & a_{2n} \\ \vdots & \vdots & & & \vdots \\ a_{m1} & a_{m2} & \cdots & \cdots & a_{mn} \end{bmatrix} \begin{bmatrix} x_1 \\ x_2 \\ \vdots \\ \vdots \\ x_n \end{bmatrix} = \begin{bmatrix} a_{11}x_1 + \cdots + a_{1n}x_n \\ a_{21}x_1 + \cdots + a_{2n}x_n \\ \vdots \\ a_{m1}x_1 + \cdots + a_{mn}x_n \end{bmatrix}.$$

For example,

$$\begin{bmatrix} 1 & 2 & 3 \\ 4 & 5 & 6 \end{bmatrix} \begin{bmatrix} 7 \\ 8 \\ 9 \end{bmatrix} = \begin{bmatrix} 1 \cdot 7 + 2 \cdot 8 + 3 \cdot 9 \\ 4 \cdot 7 + 5 \cdot 8 + 6 \cdot 9 \end{bmatrix} = \begin{bmatrix} 50 \\ 122 \end{bmatrix}.$$

Definition 3.1.6 is designed to give the following theorem, which encompasses Propositions 3.1.2 and 3.1.3 as special cases.

Theorem 3.1.7 (Description of linear mappings from vectors to vectors). *The linear mappings $T : \mathbb{R}^n \longrightarrow \mathbb{R}^m$ are precisely the mappings*

$$T(x) = Ax$$

where $A \in \mathrm{M}_{m,n}(\mathbb{R})$. That is, each linear mapping $T : \mathbb{R}^n \longrightarrow \mathbb{R}^m$ is multiplication by a unique $A \in \mathrm{M}_{m,n}(\mathbb{R})$ and conversely.

The slogan encapsulating the formula $T(x) = Ax$ of the proposition is:

For vector input and vector output, linear OF is matrix TIMES.

Recall the meaning of the rows of a matrix A that describes a corresponding linear mapping T:

The ith row of A describes T_i, the ith component function of T.

The columns of A also have a description in terms of T. Indeed, the jth column is

$$\begin{bmatrix} a_{1j} \\ \vdots \\ a_{mj} \end{bmatrix} = \begin{bmatrix} T_1(e_j) \\ \vdots \\ T_m(e_j) \end{bmatrix} = T(e_j).$$

That is:

The jth column of A is $T(e_j)$, i.e., is T of the jth standard basis vector.

For an example using this last principle, let $r : \mathbb{R}^2 \longrightarrow \mathbb{R}^2$ be the mapping that rotates the plane counterclockwise through the angle $\pi/6$. It is geometrically evident that r is linear: rotating the parallelogram P with sides x_1 and x_2 (and thus with diagonal $x_1 + x_2$) by $\pi/6$ yields the parallelogram $r(P)$ with sides $r(x_1)$ and $r(x_2)$, so the diagonal of $r(P)$ is equal to both $r(x_1 + x_2)$ and $r(x_1) + r(x_2)$. Thus r satisfies (3.1). The geometric verification of (3.2) is similar. (See Figure 3.4.)

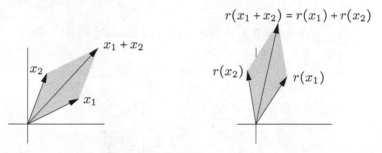

Figure 3.4. The rotation mapping is linear

To find the matrix A of r, simply compute that its columns are

$$r(e_1) = r(1,0) = \begin{bmatrix} \sqrt{3}/2 \\ 1/2 \end{bmatrix}, \qquad r(e_2) = r(0,1) = \begin{bmatrix} -1/2 \\ \sqrt{3}/2 \end{bmatrix},$$

and thus

$$A = \begin{bmatrix} \sqrt{3}/2 & -1/2 \\ 1/2 & \sqrt{3}/2 \end{bmatrix}.$$

So now we know r, because the rows of A describe its component functions,

$$r(x,y) = \begin{bmatrix} \sqrt{3}/2 & -1/2 \\ 1/2 & \sqrt{3}/2 \end{bmatrix} \begin{bmatrix} x \\ y \end{bmatrix} = \begin{bmatrix} \frac{\sqrt{3}}{2}x - \frac{1}{2}y \\ \frac{1}{2}x + \frac{\sqrt{3}}{2}y \end{bmatrix} = \left(\frac{\sqrt{3}}{2}x - \frac{1}{2}y, \frac{1}{2}x + \frac{\sqrt{3}}{2}y \right).$$

Figures 3.5 through 3.8 show more depictions of linear mappings between spaces of various dimensions. Note that although these mappings stretch and torque their basic input grids, the grids still get taken to configurations of

Figure 3.5. A linear mapping from $\mathbb{R}$ to $\mathbb{R}^2$

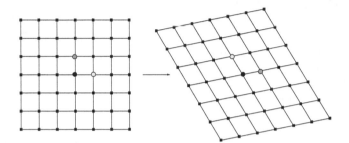

Figure 3.6. A linear mapping from $\mathbb{R}^2$ to $\mathbb{R}^2$

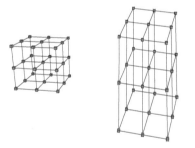

Figure 3.7. A linear mapping from $\mathbb{R}^3$ to $\mathbb{R}^3$

straight lines. Contrast this to how the nonlinear mapping of Figure 2.9 bends the basic grid lines into curves.

We end this section by returning from calculations to intrinsic methods. The following result could have come immediately after Definition 3.1.1, but it has been deferred to this point for the sake of presenting some of the objects more explicitly first, to make them familiar. However, it is most easily proved intrinsically.

Let $\mathcal{L}(\mathbb{R}^n, \mathbb{R}^m)$ denote the set of all linear mappings from $\mathbb{R}^n$ to $\mathbb{R}^m$. Not only does this set sit inside the vector space $\mathcal{M}(\mathbb{R}^n, \mathbb{R}^m)$, it is a vector space in its own right:

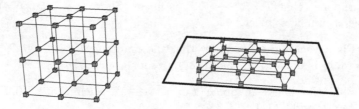

Figure 3.8. A linear mapping from $\mathbb{R}^3$ to $\mathbb{R}^2$

Proposition 3.1.8 ($\mathcal{L}(\mathbb{R}^n, \mathbb{R}^m)$ forms a vector space). *Suppose that $S, T :$* $\mathbb{R}^n \longrightarrow \mathbb{R}^m$ *are linear and that $a \in \mathbb{R}$. Then the mappings*

$$S + T,\, aS : \mathbb{R}^n \longrightarrow \mathbb{R}^m$$

are also linear. Consequently, the set of linear mappings from $\mathbb{R}^n$ to $\mathbb{R}^m$ forms a vector space.

Proof. The mappings S and T satisfy (3.1) and (3.2). We must show that $S + T$ and aS do the same. Compute for $x, y \in \mathbb{R}^n$,

$$
\begin{aligned}
(S + T)(x + y) \\
= S(x + y) + T(x + y) & \quad \text{by definition of ``+'' in } \mathcal{M}(\mathbb{R}^n, \mathbb{R}^m) \\
= S(x) + S(y) + T(x) + T(y) & \quad \text{since } S \text{ and } T \text{ satisfy (3.1)} \\
= S(x) + T(x) + S(y) + T(y) & \quad \text{since addition in } \mathbb{R}^m \text{ commutes} \\
= (S + T)(x) + (S + T)(y) & \quad \text{by definition of ``+'' in } \mathcal{M}(\mathbb{R}^n, \mathbb{R}^m).
\end{aligned}
$$

Thus $S + T$ satisfies (3.1). The other three statements about $S + T$ and aS satisfying (3.1) and (3.2) are similar and are left as Exercise 3.1.12. Once those are established, the rest of the vector space axioms in $\mathcal{L}(\mathbb{R}^n, \mathbb{R}^m)$ are readily seen to be inherited from $\mathcal{M}(\mathbb{R}^n, \mathbb{R}^m)$. $\qquad\square$

Also, linearity is preserved under composition. That is, if $S : \mathbb{R}^n \longrightarrow \mathbb{R}^m$ and $T : \mathbb{R}^p \longrightarrow \mathbb{R}^n$ are linear then so is $S \circ T : \mathbb{R}^p \longrightarrow \mathbb{R}^m$ (Exercise 3.1.13).

Exercises

3.1.1. Prove that $T : \mathbb{R}^n \longrightarrow \mathbb{R}^m$ is linear if and only if it satisfies (3.1) and (3.2). (It may help to rewrite (3.1) with the symbols x_1 and x_2 in place of x and y. Then prove one direction by showing that (3.1) and (3.2) are implied by the defining condition for linearity, and prove the other direction by using induction to show that (3.1) and (3.2) imply the defining condition. Note that as pointed out in the text, one direction of this argument has a bit more substance than the other.)

3.1.2. Suppose that $T : \mathbb{R}^n \longrightarrow \mathbb{R}^m$ is linear. Show that $T(0_n) = 0_m$. (An intrinsic argument is nicer.)

3.1.3. Fix a vector $a \in \mathbb{R}^n$. Show that the mapping $T : \mathbb{R}^n \longrightarrow \mathbb{R}$ given by $T(x) = \langle a, x \rangle$ is linear, and that $T(e_j) = a_j$ for $j = 1, \ldots, n$.

3.1.4. Find the linear mapping $T : \mathbb{R}^3 \longrightarrow \mathbb{R}$ such that $T(0, 1, 1) = 1$, $T(1, 0, 1) = 2$, and $T(1, 1, 0) = 3$.

3.1.5. Complete the proof of the componentwise nature of linearity.

3.1.6. Carry out the matrix-by-vector multiplications

$$\begin{bmatrix} 1 & 0 & 0 \\ 1 & 1 & 0 \\ 1 & 1 & 1 \end{bmatrix} \begin{bmatrix} 1 \\ 2 \\ 3 \end{bmatrix}, \quad \begin{bmatrix} a & b \\ c & d \\ e & f \end{bmatrix} \begin{bmatrix} x \\ y \end{bmatrix}, \quad \begin{bmatrix} x_1 & \cdots & x_n \end{bmatrix} \begin{bmatrix} y_1 \\ \vdots \\ y_n \end{bmatrix}, \quad \begin{bmatrix} 1 & -1 & 0 \\ 0 & 1 & -1 \\ -1 & 0 & 1 \end{bmatrix} \begin{bmatrix} 1 \\ 1 \\ 1 \end{bmatrix}.$$

3.1.7. Prove that the identity mapping $id : \mathbb{R}^n \longrightarrow \mathbb{R}^n$ is linear. What is its matrix? Explain.

3.1.8. Let θ denote a fixed but generic angle. Argue geometrically that the mapping $R : \mathbb{R}^2 \longrightarrow \mathbb{R}^2$ given by counterclockwise rotation by θ is linear, and then find its matrix.

3.1.9. Show that the mapping $Q : \mathbb{R}^2 \longrightarrow \mathbb{R}^2$ given by reflection through the x-axis is linear. Find its matrix.

3.1.10. Show that the mapping $P : \mathbb{R}^2 \longrightarrow \mathbb{R}^2$ given by orthogonal projection onto the diagonal line $x = y$ is linear. Find its matrix. (See Exercise 2.2.15.)

3.1.11. Draw the graph of a generic linear mapping from $\mathbb{R}^2$ to $\mathbb{R}^3$.

3.1.12. Continue the proof of Proposition 3.1.8 by proving the other three statements about $S + T$ and aS satisfying (3.1) and (3.2).

3.1.13. If $S \in \mathcal{L}(\mathbb{R}^n, \mathbb{R}^m)$ and $T \in \mathcal{L}(\mathbb{R}^p, \mathbb{R}^n)$, show that $S \circ T : \mathbb{R}^p \longrightarrow \mathbb{R}^m$ lies in $\mathcal{L}(\mathbb{R}^p, \mathbb{R}^m)$.

3.1.14. (a) Let $S \in \mathcal{L}(\mathbb{R}^n, \mathbb{R}^m)$. Its **transpose** is the mapping

$$S^\mathsf{T} : \mathbb{R}^m \longrightarrow \mathbb{R}^n$$

defined by the characterizing condition

$$\langle x, S^\mathsf{T}(y) \rangle = \langle S(x), y \rangle \quad \text{for all } x \in \mathbb{R}^n \text{ and } y \in \mathbb{R}^m.$$

Granting that indeed a unique such S^T exists, use the characterizing condition to show that

$$S^\mathsf{T}(y + y') = S^\mathsf{T}(y) + S^\mathsf{T}(y') \quad \text{for all } y, y' \in \mathbb{R}^m$$

by showing that

$$\langle x, S^{\mathsf{T}}(y + y')\rangle = \langle x, S^{\mathsf{T}}(y) + S^{\mathsf{T}}(y')\rangle \quad \text{for all } x \in \mathbb{R}^n \text{ and } y, y' \in \mathbb{R}^m.$$

A similar argument (not requested here) shows that $S^{\mathsf{T}}(\alpha y) = \alpha S^{\mathsf{T}}(y)$ for all $\alpha \in \mathbb{R}$ and $y \in \mathbb{R}^m$, and so the transpose of a linear mapping is linear.

(b) Keeping S from part (a), now further introduce $T \in \mathcal{L}(\mathbb{R}^p, \mathbb{R}^n)$, so that also $S \circ T \in \mathcal{L}(\mathbb{R}^p, \mathbb{R}^m)$. Show that the transpose of the composition is the composition of the transposes in reverse order,

$$(S \circ T)^{\mathsf{T}} = T^{\mathsf{T}} \circ S^{\mathsf{T}},$$

by showing that

$$\langle x, (S \circ T)^{\mathsf{T}}(z)\rangle = \langle x, (T^{\mathsf{T}} \circ S^{\mathsf{T}})(z)\rangle \quad \text{for all } x \in \mathbb{R}^p \text{ and } z \in \mathbb{R}^m.$$

3.1.15. A mapping $f : \mathbb{R}^n \longrightarrow \mathbb{R}^m$ is called **affine** if it has the form $f(x) = T(x) + b$, where $T \in \mathcal{L}(\mathbb{R}^n, \mathbb{R}^m)$ and $b \in \mathbb{R}^m$. State precisely and prove: the composition of affine mappings is affine.

3.1.16. Let $T : \mathbb{R}^n \longrightarrow \mathbb{R}^m$ be a linear mapping. Note that since T is continuous and since the absolute value function on $\mathbb{R}^m$ is continuous, the composite function

$$|T| : \mathbb{R}^n \longrightarrow \mathbb{R}$$

is continuous.

(a) Let $S = \{x \in \mathbb{R}^n : |x| = 1\}$. Explain why S is a compact subset of $\mathbb{R}^n$. Explain why it follows that $|T|$ takes a maximum value c on S.

(b) Show that $|T(x)| \le c|x|$ for all $x \in \mathbb{R}^n$. This result is the **linear magnification boundedness lemma**. We will use it in Chapter 4.

3.1.17. Let $T : \mathbb{R}^n \longrightarrow \mathbb{R}^m$ be a linear mapping.

(a) Explain why the set $D = \{x \in \mathbb{R}^n : |x| = 1\}$ is compact.

(b) Use part (a) of this exercise and part (b) of the preceding exercise to explain why therefore the set $\{|T(x)| : x \in D\}$ has a maximum. This maximum is called the **norm** of T and is denoted $\|T\|$.

(c) Explain why $\|T\|$ is the smallest value K that satisfies the condition from part (b) of the preceding exercise, $|T(x)| \le K|x|$ for all $x \in \mathbb{R}^n$.

(d) Show that for every $S, T \in \mathcal{L}(\mathbb{R}^n, \mathbb{R}^m)$ and every $a \in \mathbb{R}$,

$$\|S + T\| \le \|S\| + \|T\| \quad \text{and} \quad \|aT\| = |a| \|T\|.$$

Define a distance function

$$d : \mathcal{L}(\mathbb{R}^n, \mathbb{R}^m) \times \mathcal{L}(\mathbb{R}^n, \mathbb{R}^m) \longrightarrow \mathbb{R}, \quad d(S, T) = \|T - S\|.$$

Show that this function satisfies the distance properties of Theorem 2.2.8.

(e) Show that for every $S \in \mathcal{L}(\mathbb{R}^n, \mathbb{R}^m)$ and every $T \in \mathcal{L}(\mathbb{R}^p, \mathbb{R}^n)$,

$$\|ST\| \le \|S\| \|T\|.$$

3.2 Operations on Matrices

Having described abstract objects, the linear mappings $T \in \mathcal{L}(\mathbb{R}^n, \mathbb{R}^m)$, with explicit ones, the matrices $A \in \mathrm{M}_{m,n}(\mathbb{R})$ with (i,j)th entry $a_{ij} = T_i(e_j)$, we naturally want to study linear mappings via their matrices. The first step is to develop rules for matrix manipulation corresponding to operations on mappings. Thus if

$$S, T : \mathbb{R}^n \longrightarrow \mathbb{R}^m$$

are linear mappings having matrices

$$A, B \in \mathrm{M}_{m,n}(\mathbb{R}),$$

and if a is a real number, then the matrices for the linear mappings

$$S + T : \mathbb{R}^n \longrightarrow \mathbb{R}^m \qquad \text{and} \qquad aS : \mathbb{R}^n \longrightarrow \mathbb{R}^m$$

naturally should be denoted

$$A + B \in \mathrm{M}_{m,n}(\mathbb{R}) \qquad \text{and} \qquad aA \in \mathrm{M}_{m,n}(\mathbb{R}).$$

So "+" and "." (or juxtaposition) are about to acquire new meanings yet again,

$$+ : \mathrm{M}_{m,n}(\mathbb{R}) \times \mathrm{M}_{m,n}(\mathbb{R}) \longrightarrow \mathrm{M}_{m,n}(\mathbb{R})$$

and

$$\cdot : \mathbb{R} \times \mathrm{M}_{m,n}(\mathbb{R}) \longrightarrow \mathrm{M}_{m,n}(\mathbb{R}).$$

To define the sum, fix j between 1 and n. Then

$$\begin{aligned} \text{the } j\text{th column of } A + B &= (S + T)(e_j) \\ &= S(e_j) + T(e_j) \\ &= \text{the sum of the } j\text{th columns of } A \text{ and } B. \end{aligned}$$

And since vector addition is simply coordinatewise scalar addition, it follows that for every i between 1 and m and every j between 1 and m, the (i,j)th entry of $A + B$ is the sum of the (i,j)th entries of A and B. (One can reach the same conclusion in a different way by thinking about rows rather than columns.) Thus the definition for matrix addition must be as follows.

Definition 3.2.1 (Matrix addition).

If $A = [a_{ij}]_{m \times n}$ and $B = [b_{ij}]_{m \times n}$ then $A + B = [a_{ij} + b_{ij}]_{m \times n}$.

For example,

$$\begin{bmatrix} 1 & 2 \\ 3 & 4 \end{bmatrix} + \begin{bmatrix} -1 & 0 \\ 2 & 1 \end{bmatrix} = \begin{bmatrix} 0 & 2 \\ 5 & 5 \end{bmatrix}.$$

A similar argument shows that the appropriate definition to make for scalar multiplication of matrices is as follows.

Definition 3.2.2 (Scalar-by-matrix multiplication).

If $\alpha \in \mathbb{R}$ and $A = [a_{ij}]_{m \times n}$ then $\alpha A = [\alpha a_{ij}]_{m \times n}$.

For example,

$$2 \begin{bmatrix} 1 & 2 \\ 3 & 4 \end{bmatrix} = \begin{bmatrix} 2 & 4 \\ 6 & 8 \end{bmatrix}.$$

The **zero matrix** $0_{m,n} \in M_{m,n}(\mathbb{R})$, corresponding to the zero mapping in $\mathcal{L}(\mathbb{R}^n, \mathbb{R}^m)$, is the obvious one, with all entries 0. The operations in $M_{m,n}(\mathbb{R})$ precisely mirror those in $\mathcal{L}(\mathbb{R}^n, \mathbb{R}^m)$, giving the following result.

Proposition 3.2.3 ($M_{m,n}(\mathbb{R})$ forms a vector space). *The set $M_{m,n}(\mathbb{R})$ of $m \times n$ matrices forms a vector space over $\mathbb{R}$.*

The remaining important operation on linear mappings is composition. As shown in Exercise 3.1.13, if

$$S : \mathbb{R}^n \longrightarrow \mathbb{R}^m \quad \text{and} \quad T : \mathbb{R}^p \longrightarrow \mathbb{R}^n$$

are linear then their composition

$$S \circ T : \mathbb{R}^p \longrightarrow \mathbb{R}^m$$

is linear as well. Suppose that S and T respectively have matrices

$$A \in M_{m,n}(\mathbb{R}) \quad \text{and} \quad B \in M_{n,p}(\mathbb{R}).$$

Then the composition $S \circ T$ has a matrix in $M_{m,p}(\mathbb{R})$ that is naturally defined as the matrix-by-matrix product

$$AB \in M_{m,p}(\mathbb{R}),$$

the order of multiplication being chosen for consistency with the composition. Under this specification,

$$\begin{aligned}
(A \text{ times } B)\text{'s } j\text{th column} &= (S \circ T)(e_j) \\
&= S(T(e_j)) \\
&= A \text{ times } (B\text{'s } j\text{th column}).
\end{aligned}$$

And A times (B's jth column) is a matrix-by-vector multiplication, which we know how to carry out: the result is a column vector whose ith entry for $i = 1, \ldots, m$ is the inner product of the ith row of A and the jth column of B. In sum, the rule for matrix-by-matrix multiplication is as follows.

Definition 3.2.4 (Matrix multiplication). *Given two matrices*

$$A \in M_{m,n}(\mathbb{R}) \quad and \quad B \in M_{n,p}(\mathbb{R})$$

such that A has as many columns as B has rows, their product,

$$AB \in M_{m,p}(\mathbb{R}),$$

has for its (i,j)th entry (for every $(i,j) \in \{1,\ldots,m\} \times \{1,\ldots,p\}$) the inner product of the ith row of A and the jth column of B. In symbols,

$$(AB)_{ij} = \langle i\text{th row of } A, j\text{th column of } B \rangle,$$

or, at the level of individual entries,

$$\text{If } A = [a_{ij}]_{m \times n} \text{ and } B = [b_{ij}]_{n \times p} \text{ then } AB = \left[\sum_{k=1}^{n} a_{ik}b_{kj} \right]_{m \times p}.$$

Inevitably, matrix-by-matrix multiplication subsumes matrix-by-vector multiplication, with vectors viewed as one-column matrices. Also, once we have the definition of matrix-by-matrix multiplication, we can observe that in complement to the already-established rule that for every $j \in \{1,\ldots,n\}$,

$(A \text{ times } B)$'s jth column   equals A times $(B$'s jth column$)$,

also, for every $i \in \{1,\ldots,m\}$,

ith row of $(A \text{ times } B)$ equals $(i$th row of $A)$ times B.

Indeed, both quantities in the previous display are the $1 \times p$ vector whose jth entry is the inner product of the ith row of A and the jth column of B.

For example, consider the matrices

$$A = \begin{bmatrix} 1 & 2 & 3 \\ 4 & 5 & 6 \end{bmatrix}, \qquad B = \begin{bmatrix} 1 & -2 \\ 2 & -3 \\ 3 & -4 \end{bmatrix}, \qquad C = \begin{bmatrix} 4 & 5 \\ 6 & 7 \end{bmatrix},$$

$$D = \begin{bmatrix} 1 & 1 & 1 \\ 0 & 1 & 1 \\ 0 & 0 & 1 \end{bmatrix}, \qquad E = \begin{bmatrix} a & b & c \end{bmatrix}, \qquad F = \begin{bmatrix} x \\ y \\ z \end{bmatrix}.$$

Some products among these (verify!) are

$$AB = \begin{bmatrix} 14 & -20 \\ 32 & -47 \end{bmatrix}, \qquad BC = \begin{bmatrix} -8 & -9 \\ -10 & -11 \\ -12 & -13 \end{bmatrix}, \qquad AD = \begin{bmatrix} 1 & 3 & 6 \\ 4 & 9 & 15 \end{bmatrix},$$

$$DB = \begin{bmatrix} 6 & -9 \\ 5 & -7 \\ 3 & -4 \end{bmatrix}, \qquad AF = \begin{bmatrix} x + 2y + 3z \\ 4x + 5y + 6z \end{bmatrix}, \qquad FE = \begin{bmatrix} ax & bx & cx \\ ay & by & cy \\ az & bz & cz \end{bmatrix},$$

$$EF = ax + by + cz.$$

Matrix multiplication is not commutative. Indeed, when the product AB is defined, the product BA may not be, or it may be but have different dimensions from AB; cf. EF and FE above. Even when A and B are both $n \times n$, so that AB and BA are likewise $n \times n$, the products need not agree. For example,

$$\begin{bmatrix} 0 & 1 \\ 0 & 0 \end{bmatrix} \begin{bmatrix} 0 & 0 \\ 1 & 0 \end{bmatrix} = \begin{bmatrix} 1 & 0 \\ 0 & 0 \end{bmatrix}, \qquad \begin{bmatrix} 0 & 0 \\ 1 & 0 \end{bmatrix} \begin{bmatrix} 0 & 1 \\ 0 & 0 \end{bmatrix} = \begin{bmatrix} 0 & 0 \\ 0 & 1 \end{bmatrix}.$$

Of particular interest is the matrix associated with the identity mapping,

$$id : \mathbb{R}^n \longrightarrow \mathbb{R}^n, \quad id(x) = x.$$

Naturally, this matrix is called the **identity matrix**; it is written I_n. Since $id_i(e_j) = \delta_{ij}$,

$$I_n = [\delta_{ij}]_{n \times n} = \begin{bmatrix} 1 & 0 & \cdots & 0 \\ 0 & 1 & \cdots & 0 \\ \vdots & \vdots & & \vdots \\ 0 & 0 & \cdots & 1 \end{bmatrix}.$$

Although matrix multiplication fails to commute, it does have the following properties.

Proposition 3.2.5 (Properties of matrix multiplication). *Matrix multiplication is associative,*

$$A(BC) = (AB)C \quad \text{for } A \in \mathrm{M}_{m,n}(\mathbb{R}), \ B \in \mathrm{M}_{n,p}(\mathbb{R}), \ C \in \mathrm{M}_{p,q}(\mathbb{R}).$$

Matrix multiplication distributes over matrix addition,

$$A(B + C) = AB + AC \quad \text{for } A \in \mathrm{M}_{m,n}(\mathbb{R}), \ B, C \in \mathrm{M}_{n,p}(\mathbb{R}),$$
$$(A + B)C = AC + BC \quad \text{for } A, B \in \mathrm{M}_{m,n}(\mathbb{R}), \ C \in \mathrm{M}_{n,p}(\mathbb{R}).$$

Scalar multiplication passes through matrix multiplication,

$$\alpha(AB) = (\alpha A)B = A(\alpha B) \quad \text{for } \alpha \in \mathbb{R}, \ A \in \mathrm{M}_{m,n}(\mathbb{R}), \ B \in \mathrm{M}_{n,p}(\mathbb{R}).$$

The identity matrix is a multiplicative identity,

$$I_m A = A = A I_n \quad \text{for } A \in \mathrm{M}_{m,n}(\mathbb{R}).$$

Proof. The right way to prove these is intrinsic, by recalling that addition, scalar multiplication, and multiplication of matrices precisely mirror addition, scalar multiplication, and composition of mappings. For example, if A, B, C are the matrices of the linear mappings $S \in \mathcal{L}(\mathbb{R}^n, \mathbb{R}^m)$, $T \in \mathcal{L}(\mathbb{R}^p, \mathbb{R}^n)$, and $U \in \mathcal{L}(\mathbb{R}^q, \mathbb{R}^p)$, then $(AB)C$ and $A(BC)$ are the matrices of $(S \circ T) \circ U$ and $S \circ (T \circ U)$. But these two mappings are the same, because the composition of mappings (mappings in general, not only linear mappings) is associative. To verify the associativity, we cite the definition of four different binary compositions to show that the ternary composition is independent of parentheses, as follows. For every $x \in \mathbb{R}^q$,

$$
\begin{aligned}
((S \circ T) \circ U)(x) &= (S \circ T)(U(x)) && \text{by definition of } R \circ U \text{ where } R = S \circ T \\
&= S(T(U(x))) && \text{by definition of } S \circ T \\
&= S((T \circ U)(x)) && \text{by definition of } T \circ U \\
&= (S \circ (T \circ U))(x) && \text{by definition of } S \circ V \text{ where } V = T \circ U.
\end{aligned}
$$

So indeed $((S \circ T) \circ U) = (S \circ (T \circ U))$, and consequently $(AB)C = A(BC)$.

Alternatively, one can verify the equalities elementwise by manipulating sums. Adopting the notation M_{ij} for the (i,j)th entry of a matrix M, we have

$$
\begin{aligned}
(A(BC))_{ij} &= \sum_{k=1}^{n} A_{ik}(BC)_{kj} = \sum_{k=1}^{n} A_{ik} \sum_{\ell=1}^{p} B_{k\ell}C_{\ell j} = \sum_{k=1}^{n}\sum_{\ell=1}^{p} A_{ik}B_{k\ell}C_{\ell j} \\
&= \sum_{\ell=1}^{p}\sum_{k=1}^{n} A_{ik}B_{k\ell}C_{\ell j} = \sum_{\ell=1}^{p}(AB)_{i\ell}C_{\ell j} = ((AB)C)_{ij}.
\end{aligned}
$$

The steps here are not explained in detail because the author finds this method as grim as it is gratuitous: the coordinates work because they must, but their presence only clutters the argument. The other equalities are similar.   □

Composing mappings is most interesting when all the mappings in question take a set S to the same set S, for the set of such mappings is closed under composition. In particular, $\mathcal{L}(\mathbb{R}^n, \mathbb{R}^n)$ is closed under composition. The corresponding statement about matrices is that $M_n(\mathbb{R})$ is closed under multiplication.

Exercises

3.2.1. Justify Definition 3.2.2 of scalar multiplication of matrices.

3.2.2. Carry out the matrix multiplications

$$
\begin{bmatrix} a & b \\ c & d \end{bmatrix}\begin{bmatrix} d & -b \\ -c & a \end{bmatrix}, \quad
\begin{bmatrix} x_1 & x_2 & x_3 \end{bmatrix}\begin{bmatrix} a_1 & b_1 \\ a_2 & b_2 \\ a_3 & b_3 \end{bmatrix}, \quad
\begin{bmatrix} 0 & 1 & 0 & 0 \\ 0 & 0 & 1 & 0 \\ 0 & 0 & 0 & 1 \\ 0 & 0 & 0 & 0 \end{bmatrix}^e \quad (e = 2, 3, 4),
$$

$$
\begin{bmatrix} 1 & 1 & 1 \\ 0 & 1 & 1 \\ 0 & 0 & 1 \end{bmatrix}\begin{bmatrix} 1 & 0 & 0 \\ 1 & 1 & 0 \\ 1 & 1 & 1 \end{bmatrix}, \quad
\begin{bmatrix} 1 & 0 & 0 \\ 1 & 1 & 0 \\ 1 & 1 & 1 \end{bmatrix}\begin{bmatrix} 1 & 1 & 1 \\ 0 & 1 & 1 \\ 0 & 0 & 1 \end{bmatrix}.
$$

3.2.3. Prove more of Proposition 3.2.5, that $A(B + C) = AB + AC$, $(\alpha A)B = A(\alpha B)$, and $I_m A = A$ for suitable matrices A, B, C and any scalar α.

3.2.4. (If you have not yet worked Exercise 3.1.14 then do so before working this exercise.) Let $A = [a_{ij}] \in \mathrm{M}_{m,n}(\mathbb{R})$ be the matrix of $S \in \mathcal{L}(\mathbb{R}^n, \mathbb{R}^m)$. Its **transpose** $A^\mathsf{T} \in \mathrm{M}_{n,m}(\mathbb{R})$ is the matrix of the transpose mapping S^T. Since S and S^T act respectively as multiplication by A and A^T, the characterizing property of S^T from Exercise 3.1.14 gives

$$\langle x, A^\mathsf{T} y \rangle = \langle Ax, y \rangle \quad \text{for all } x \in \mathbb{R}^n \text{ and } y \in \mathbb{R}^m.$$

Make specific choices of x and y to show that the transpose $A^\mathsf{T} \in \mathrm{M}_{n,m}(\mathbb{R})$ is obtained by flipping A about its northwest–southeast diagonal; that is, show that the (i, j)th entry of A^T is a_{ji}. It follows that the rows of A^T are the columns of A, and the columns of A^T are the rows of A.

(Similarly, let $B \in \mathrm{M}_{n,p}(\mathbb{R})$ be the matrix of $T \in \mathcal{L}(\mathbb{R}^p, \mathbb{R}^n)$, so that B^T is the matrix of T^T. Because matrix multiplication is compatible with linear mapping composition, we know immediately from Exercise 3.1.14(b), with no reference to the concrete description of the matrix transposes A^T and B^T in terms of the original matrices A and B, that the transpose of the product is the product of the transposes in reverse order,

$$(AB)^\mathsf{T} = B^\mathsf{T} A^\mathsf{T} \quad \text{for all } A \in \mathrm{M}_{m,n}(\mathbb{R}) \text{ and } B \in \mathrm{M}_{n,p}(\mathbb{R}).$$

That is, by characterizing the transpose mapping in Exercise 3.1.14, we easily derived the construction of the transpose matrix here and obtained the formula for the product of transpose matrices with no reference to their construction.)

3.2.5. The **trace** of a square matrix $A \in \mathrm{M}_n(\mathbb{R})$ is the sum of its diagonal elements,

$$\mathrm{tr}(A) = \sum_{i=1}^{n} a_{ii}.$$

Show that

$$\mathrm{tr}(AB) = \mathrm{tr}(BA), \quad A, B \in \mathrm{M}_n(\mathbb{R}).$$

(This exercise may entail double subscripts.)

3.2.6. For every matrix $A \in \mathrm{M}_{m,n}(\mathbb{R})$ and column vector $a \in \mathbb{R}^m$, define the affine mapping (cf. Exercise 3.1.15)

$$\mathrm{Aff}_{A,a} : \mathbb{R}^n \longrightarrow \mathbb{R}^m$$

by the rule $\mathrm{Aff}_{A,a}(x) = Ax + a$ for all $x \in \mathbb{R}^n$, viewing x as a column vector.

(a) Explain why every affine mapping from $\mathbb{R}^n$ to $\mathbb{R}^m$ takes this form.

(b) Given such A and a, define the matrix $A' \in \mathrm{M}_{m+1,n+1}(\mathbb{R})$ to be

$$A' = \begin{bmatrix} A & a \\ \mathbf{0}_n & 1 \end{bmatrix}.$$

Show that for all $x \in \mathbb{R}^n$,

$$A' \begin{bmatrix} x \\ 1 \end{bmatrix} = \begin{bmatrix} \mathrm{Aff}_{A,a}(x) \\ 1 \end{bmatrix}.$$

Thus, affine mappings, like linear mappings, behave as matrix-by-vector multiplications but where the vectors are the usual input and output vectors augmented with an extra "1" at the bottom.

(c) The affine mapping $\mathrm{Aff}_{B,b} : \mathbb{R}^p \longrightarrow \mathbb{R}^n$ determined by $B \in \mathrm{M}_{n,p}(\mathbb{R})$ and $b \in \mathbb{R}^n$ has matrix

$$B' = \begin{bmatrix} B & b \\ 0_p & 1 \end{bmatrix}.$$

Show that $\mathrm{Aff}_{A,a} \circ \mathrm{Aff}_{B,b} : \mathbb{R}^p \longrightarrow \mathbb{R}^m$ has matrix $A'B'$. That is, matrix multiplication is compatible with composition of affine mappings.

3.2.7. The *exponential* of a square matrix A is the infinite matrix sum

$$e^A = I + A + \frac{1}{2!}A^2 + \frac{1}{3!}A^3 + \cdots.$$

Compute the exponentials of the following matrices:

$$A = [\lambda], \quad A = \begin{bmatrix} \lambda & 1 \\ 0 & \lambda \end{bmatrix}, \quad A = \begin{bmatrix} \lambda & 1 & 0 \\ 0 & \lambda & 1 \\ 0 & 0 & \lambda \end{bmatrix}, \quad A = \begin{bmatrix} \lambda & 1 & 0 & 0 \\ 0 & \lambda & 1 & 0 \\ 0 & 0 & \lambda & 1 \\ 0 & 0 & 0 & \lambda \end{bmatrix}.$$

What is the general pattern?

3.2.8. Let a, b, d be real numbers with $ad = 1$. Show that

$$\begin{bmatrix} a & b \\ 0 & d \end{bmatrix} = \begin{bmatrix} 1 & ab \\ 0 & 1 \end{bmatrix} \begin{bmatrix} a & 0 \\ 0 & d \end{bmatrix}.$$

Let a, b, c, d be real numbers with $c \neq 0$ and $ad - bc = 1$. Show that

$$\begin{bmatrix} a & b \\ c & d \end{bmatrix} = \begin{bmatrix} 1 & ac^{-1} \\ 0 & 1 \end{bmatrix} \begin{bmatrix} c^{-1} & 0 \\ 0 & c \end{bmatrix} \begin{bmatrix} 0 & -1 \\ 1 & 0 \end{bmatrix} \begin{bmatrix} 1 & c^{-1}d \\ 0 & 1 \end{bmatrix}.$$

Thus this exercise has shown that all matrices $\begin{bmatrix} a & b \\ c & d \end{bmatrix}$ with $ad - bc = 1$ can be expressed in terms of matrices $\begin{bmatrix} 1 & \beta \\ 0 & 1 \end{bmatrix}$ and matrices $\begin{bmatrix} \alpha & 0 \\ 0 & \alpha^{-1} \end{bmatrix}$ and the matrix $\begin{bmatrix} 0 & -1 \\ 1 & 0 \end{bmatrix}$.

3.3 The Inverse of a Linear Mapping

Given a linear mapping $S : \mathbb{R}^n \longrightarrow \mathbb{R}^m$, does it have an inverse? That is, is there a mapping $T : \mathbb{R}^m \longrightarrow \mathbb{R}^n$ such that

$$S \circ T = id_m \quad \text{and} \quad T \circ S = id_n?$$

If so, what is T?

The symmetry of the previous display shows that if T is an inverse of S then S is an inverse of T in turn. Also, the inverse T, if it exists, must be unique, for if $T' : \mathbb{R}^m \longrightarrow \mathbb{R}^n$ also inverts S then

$$T' = T' \circ \text{id}_m = T' \circ (S \circ T) = (T' \circ S) \circ T = \text{id}_n \circ T = T.$$

Thus T can unambiguously be denoted S^{-1}. In fact, this argument has shown a little bit more than claimed: if T' inverts S from the left and T inverts S from the right then $T' = T$. On the other hand, the argument does *not* show that if T inverts S from the left then T also inverts S from the right—this is not true.

If the inverse T exists then it too is linear. To see this, note that the elementwise description of S and T being inverses of one another is that every $y \in \mathbb{R}^m$ takes the form $y = S(x)$ for some $x \in \mathbb{R}^n$, every $x \in \mathbb{R}^n$ takes the form $x = T(y)$ for some $y \in \mathbb{R}^m$, and

$$\text{for all } x \in \mathbb{R}^n \text{ and } y \in \mathbb{R}^m, \qquad y = S(x) \iff x = T(y).$$

Now compute that for every $y_1, y_2 \in \mathbb{R}^m$,

$$
\begin{aligned}
T(y_1 + y_2) &= T(S(x_1) + S(x_2)) && \text{for some } x_1, x_2 \in \mathbb{R}^n \\
&= T(S(x_1 + x_2)) && \text{since } S \text{ is linear} \\
&= x_1 + x_2 && \text{since } T \text{ inverts } S \\
&= T(y_1) + T(y_2) && \text{since } y_1 = S(x_1) \text{ and } y_2 = S(x_2).
\end{aligned}
$$

Thus T satisfies (3.1). The argument that T satisfies (3.2) is similar.

Since matrices are more explicit than linear mappings, we replace the question at the beginning of this section with its matrix counterpart: given a matrix $A \in \mathrm{M}_{m,n}(\mathbb{R})$, does it have an inverse matrix, a matrix $B \in \mathrm{M}_{n,m}(\mathbb{R})$ such that

$$AB = I_m \quad \text{and} \quad BA = I_n?$$

As above, if the inverse exists then it is unique, and so it can be denoted A^{-1}.

The first observation to make is that if the equation $Ax = \mathbf{0}_m$ has a nonzero solution $x \in \mathbb{R}^n$ then A has no inverse. Indeed, also $A\mathbf{0}_n = \mathbf{0}_m$, so an inverse A^{-1} would have to take $\mathbf{0}_m$ both to x and to $\mathbf{0}_n$, which is impossible. And so we are led to a subordinate question: when does the matrix equation

$$Ax = \mathbf{0}_m$$

have nonzero solutions $x \in \mathbb{R}^n$?

For example, let A be the 5×6 matrix

$$A = \begin{bmatrix} 5 & 1 & 17 & 26 & 1 & 55 \\ -3 & -1 & -13 & -20 & 0 & -28 \\ -2 & 1 & 3 & 5 & 0 & 3 \\ -2 & 0 & -4 & -6 & 0 & -10 \\ 5 & 0 & 10 & 15 & 1 & 42 \end{bmatrix}.$$

If there is a nonzero $x \in \mathbb{R}^6$ such that $Ax = \mathbf{0}_5$ then A is not invertible.

Left multiplication by certain special matrices will simplify the matrix A.

Definition 3.3.1 (Elementary matrices). *There are three kinds of elementary matrices. For every $i, j \in \{1, \ldots, m\}$ $(i \neq j)$ and every $a \in \mathbb{R}$, the $m \times m$ $(i; j, a)$* **recombine matrix** *is*

$$R_{i;j,a} = \begin{bmatrix} 1 & & & & & & \\ & \ddots & & & & & \\ & & 1 & a & & & \\ & & & \ddots & & & \\ & & & & 1 & & \\ & & & & & \ddots & \\ & & & & & & 1 \end{bmatrix}.$$

(*Here the a sits in the (i, j)th position, the diagonal entries are 1 and all other entries are 0. The a is above the diagonal as shown only when $i < j$; otherwise it is below.*)

For every $i \in \{1, \ldots, m\}$ and every nonzero $a \in \mathbb{R}$, the $m \times m$ (i, a) **scale matrix** is

$$S_{i,a} = \begin{bmatrix} 1 & & & & & \\ & \ddots & & & & \\ & & 1 & & & \\ & & a & & & \\ & & & 1 & & \\ & & & & \ddots & \\ & & & & & 1 \end{bmatrix}.$$

(*Here the a sits in the ith diagonal position, all other diagonal entries are 1, and all other entries are 0.*)

For every $i, j \in \{1, \ldots, m\}$ $(i \neq j)$, the $m \times m$ $(i; j)$ **transposition matrix** is

$$T_{i;j} = \begin{bmatrix} 1 & & & & & & & & \\ & \ddots & & & & & & & \\ & & 1 & & & & & & \\ & & & 0 & & 1 & & & \\ & & & & 1 & & & & \\ & & & & & \ddots & & & \\ & & & & & & 1 & & \\ & & & 1 & & & 0 & & \\ & & & & & & & 1 & \\ & & & & & & & & \ddots \\ & & & & & & & & & 1 \end{bmatrix}.$$

(*Here the diagonal entries are 1 except the ith and jth, the (i, j)th and (j, i)th entries are 1, and all other entries are 0.*)

The plan is to study the equation $Ax = \mathbf{0}_m$ by using these elementary matrices to reduce A to a nicer matrix E and then solve the equation $Ex = \mathbf{0}_m$ instead. Thus we are developing an algorithm rather than a formula. The next proposition describes the effect that the elementary matrices produce by left multiplication.

Proposition 3.3.2 (Effects of the elementary matrices). *Let M be an $m \times n$ matrix; call its rows r_k. Then:*

(1) *The $m \times n$ matrix $R_{i;j,a}M$ has the same rows as M except that its ith row is $r_i + ar_j$.*

(2) *The $m \times n$ matrix $S_{i,a}M$ has the same rows as M except that its ith row is ar_i.*

(3) *The $m \times n$ matrix $T_{i;j}M$ has the same rows as M except that its ith row is r_j and its jth row is r_i.*

Proof. (1) As observed immediately after Definition 3.2.4, each row of $R_{i;j,a}M$ equals the corresponding row of $R_{i;j,a}$ times M. For every row index $k \neq i$, the only nonzero entry of the row is a 1 in the kth position, so the product of the row and M simply picks out the kth row of M. Similarly, the ith row of $R_{i;j,a}$ has a 1 in the ith position and an a in the jth, so the row times M equals the ith row of M plus a times the jth row of M.

The proofs of statements (2) and (3) are similar, left as Exercise 3.3.2. $\square$

To get a better sense of why the statements in the proposition are true, it may be helpful to do the calculations explicitly with some moderately sized matrices. But then, the point of the proposition is that once one believes it, left multiplication by elementary matrices no longer requires actual calculation. Instead, one simply carries out the appropriate row operations. For example,

$$R_{1;2,3} \cdot \begin{bmatrix} 1 & 2 & 3 \\ 4 & 5 & 6 \end{bmatrix} = \begin{bmatrix} 13 & 17 & 21 \\ 4 & 5 & 6 \end{bmatrix},$$

because $R_{1;2,3}$ adds 3 times the second row to the first. The slogan here is:

Elementary matrix TIMES is row operation ON.

Thus we use the elementary matrices to reason about this material, but for hand calculation we simply carry out the row operations.

The next result is that performing row operations on A doesn't change the set of solutions x to the equation $Ax = \mathbf{0}_m$.

Lemma 3.3.3 (Invertibility of products of the elementary matrices). *Products of elementary matrices are invertible. More specifically:*

(1) *The elementary matrices are invertible by other elementary matrices,*

$$(R_{i;j,a})^{-1} = R_{i;j,-a}, \qquad\qquad (S_{i,a})^{-1} = S_{i,a^{-1}}, \qquad\qquad (T_{i;j})^{-1} = T_{i;j}.$$

(2) *If the $m \times m$ matrices M and N are invertible by M^{-1} and N^{-1}, then the product matrix MN is invertible by $N^{-1}M^{-1}$. (Note the order reversal.)*

(3) *Every product of elementary matrices is invertible by another such product, the product of the inverses of the original matrices but taken in reverse order.*

Proof. (1) To prove that $R_{i;j,-a}R_{i;j,a} = I_m$, note that $R_{i;j,a}$ is the identity matrix I_m with a times its jth row added to its ith row, and multiplying this from the left by $R_{i;j,-a}$ subtracts off a times the jth row from its ith row, restoring I_m. The proof that $R_{i;j,a}R_{i;j,-a} = I_m$ is either done similarly or by citing the proof just given with a replaced by $-a$. The rest of (1) is similar.

(2) Compute

$$(MN)(N^{-1}M^{-1}) = M(NN^{-1})M^{-1} = MI_mM^{-1} = MM^{-1} = I_m,$$

and similarly for $(N^{-1}M^{-1})(MN) = I_m$.

(3) This is immediate from (1) and (2). □

Proposition 3.3.4 (Persistence of solution). *Let A be an $m \times n$ matrix and let P be a product of $m \times m$ elementary matrices. Then the equations*

$$Ax = 0_m \quad and \quad (PA)x = 0_m$$

are satisfied by the same vectors x in $\mathbb{R}^n$.

Proof. Suppose that the vector $x \in \mathbb{R}^n$ satisfies the left equation, $Ax = 0_m$. Then

$$(PA)x = P(Ax) = P0_m = 0_m.$$

Conversely, suppose that x satisfies $(PA)x = 0_m$. Lemma 3.3.3 says that P has an inverse P^{-1}, so

$$Ax = I_mAx = (P^{-1}P)Ax = P^{-1}(PA)x = P^{-1}0_m = 0_m.$$

□

The machinery is in place to solve the equation $Ax = 0_5$, where as before,

$$A = \begin{bmatrix} 5 & 1 & 17 & 26 & 1 & 55 \\ -3 & -1 & -13 & -20 & 0 & -28 \\ -2 & 1 & 3 & 5 & 0 & 3 \\ -2 & 0 & -4 & -6 & 0 & -10 \\ 5 & 0 & 10 & 15 & 1 & 42 \end{bmatrix}.$$

Scale A's fourth row by $-1/2$ and transpose A's first and fourth rows; call the result B:

$$T_{1;4}S_{4,-1/2}A = \begin{bmatrix} 1 & 0 & 2 & 3 & 0 & 5 \\ -3 & -1 & -13 & -20 & 0 & -28 \\ -2 & 1 & 3 & 5 & 0 & 3 \\ 5 & 1 & 17 & 26 & 1 & 55 \\ 5 & 0 & 10 & 15 & 1 & 42 \end{bmatrix} = B.$$

Note that B has a 1 as the leftmost entry of its first row. Recombine various multiples of the first row with the other rows to put 0's beneath the leading 1 of the first row; call the result C:

$$R_{5;1,-5}R_{4;1,-5}R_{3;1,2}R_{2;1,3}B = \begin{bmatrix} 1 & 0 & 2 & 3 & 0 & 5 \\ 0 & -1 & -7 & -11 & 0 & -13 \\ 0 & 1 & 7 & 11 & 0 & 13 \\ 0 & 1 & 7 & 11 & 1 & 30 \\ 0 & 0 & 0 & 0 & 1 & 17 \end{bmatrix} = C.$$

Recombine various multiples of the second row with the others to put 0's above and below its leftmost nonzero entry; scale the second row to make its leading nonzero entry a 1; call the result D:

$$S_{2,-1}R_{4;2,1}R_{3;2,1}C = \begin{bmatrix} 1 & 0 & 2 & 3 & 0 & 5 \\ 0 & 1 & 7 & 11 & 0 & 13 \\ 0 & 0 & 0 & 0 & 0 & 0 \\ 0 & 0 & 0 & 0 & 1 & 17 \\ 0 & 0 & 0 & 0 & 1 & 17 \end{bmatrix} = D.$$

Transpose the third and fifth rows; put 0's above and below the leading 1 in the third row; call the result E:

$$R_{4;3,-1}T_{3;5}D = \begin{bmatrix} 1 & 0 & 2 & 3 & 0 & 5 \\ 0 & 1 & 7 & 11 & 0 & 13 \\ 0 & 0 & 0 & 0 & 1 & 17 \\ 0 & 0 & 0 & 0 & 0 & 0 \\ 0 & 0 & 0 & 0 & 0 & 0 \end{bmatrix} = E.$$

Matrix E is a prime example of a so-called *echelon matrix*. (The term will be defined precisely in a moment.) Its virtue is that the equation $Ex = \mathbf{0}_5$ is now easy to solve. This equation expands out to

$$Ex = \begin{bmatrix} 1 & 0 & 2 & 3 & 0 & 5 \\ 0 & 1 & 7 & 11 & 0 & 13 \\ 0 & 0 & 0 & 0 & 1 & 17 \\ 0 & 0 & 0 & 0 & 0 & 0 \\ 0 & 0 & 0 & 0 & 0 & 0 \end{bmatrix} \begin{bmatrix} x_1 \\ x_2 \\ x_3 \\ x_4 \\ x_5 \\ x_6 \end{bmatrix} = \begin{bmatrix} x_1 + 2x_3 + 3x_4 + 5x_6 \\ x_2 + 7x_3 + 11x_4 + 13x_6 \\ x_5 + 17x_6 \\ 0 \\ 0 \end{bmatrix} = \begin{bmatrix} 0 \\ 0 \\ 0 \\ 0 \\ 0 \end{bmatrix}.$$

Matching the components in the last equality gives

$$x_1 = -2x_3 - 3x_4 - 5x_6$$
$$x_2 = -7x_3 - 11x_4 - 13x_6$$
$$x_5 = \qquad\qquad - 17x_6.$$

Thus, x_3, x_4, and x_6 are free variables that can take any values we wish, but then x_1, x_2, and x_5 are determined from these equations. For example, setting $x_3 = -5$, $x_4 = 3$, $x_6 = 2$ gives the solution $x = (-9, -24, -5, 3, -34, 2)$.

Definition 3.3.5 (Echelon matrix). *A matrix E is called* **echelon** *if it has the form*

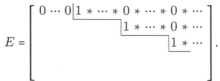

$$E = \left[\begin{array}{c} \end{array}\right].$$

Here the $*$'s are arbitrary entries, and all entries below the stairway are 0. Thus each row's first nonzero entry is a 1, each row's leading 1 is farther right than that of the row above it, each leading 1 has a column of 0's above it, and any rows of 0's are at the bottom.

Note that the identity matrix I is a special case of an echelon matrix.

The algorithm for reducing a matrix A to echelon form by row operations should be fairly clear from the previous example. The interested reader may want to codify it more formally, perhaps in the form of a computer program. Although different sequences of row operations may reduce A to echelon form, the resulting echelon matrix E will always be the same. This result can be proved by induction on the number of columns of A, and its proof is in many linear algebra books.

Theorem 3.3.6 (Matrices reduce to echelon form). *Every matrix A row reduces to a unique echelon matrix E.*

In an echelon matrix E, the columns with leading 1's are called **new columns**, and all others are **old columns**. The recipe for solving the equation $Ex = \mathbf{0}_m$ is then as follows.

1. Freely choose the entries in x that correspond to the old columns of E.
2. Then each nonzero row of E will determine the entry of x corresponding to its leading 1 (which sits in a new column). This entry will be a linear combination of the free entries to its right.

Let's return to the problem of determining whether $A \in \mathrm{M}_{m,n}(\mathbb{R})$ is invertible. The idea was to see whether the equation $Ax = \mathbf{0}_m$ has any nonzero solutions x, in which case A is not invertible. Equivalently, we may check whether $Ex = \mathbf{0}_m$ has nonzero solutions, where E is the echelon matrix to which A row reduces. The recipe for solving $Ex = \mathbf{0}_m$ shows that there are nonzero solutions unless all of the columns are new.

If $A \in \mathrm{M}_{m,n}(\mathbb{R})$ has more columns than rows then its echelon matrix E must have old columns. Indeed, each new column comes from the leading 1 in a distinct row, so

$$\text{new columns of } E \ \leq \text{rows of } E \ < \text{columns of } E,$$

showing that not all the columns are new. Thus A is not invertible when $m < n$. On the other hand, if $A \in \mathrm{M}_{m,n}(\mathbb{R})$ has more rows than columns and it has an inverse matrix $A^{-1} \in M_{n,m}(\mathbb{R})$, then A^{-1} in turn has inverse A, but this is impossible, because A^{-1} has more columns than rows. Thus A is also not invertible when $m > n$.

The remaining case is that A is square. The only square echelon matrix with all new columns is I, the identity matrix (Exercise 3.3.10). Thus, unless A's echelon matrix is I, A is not invertible. On the other hand, if A's echelon matrix is I, then $PA = I$ for some product P of elementary matrices. Multiply from the left by P^{-1} to get $A = P^{-1}$; this is invertible by P, giving $A^{-1} = P$. This discussion is summarized in the following theorem.

Theorem 3.3.7 (Invertibility and echelon form for matrices). *A non-square matrix A is never invertible. A square matrix A is invertible if and only if its echelon form is the identity matrix.*

When A is square, the discussion above gives an algorithm that simultaneously checks whether it is invertible and finds its inverse when it is.

Proposition 3.3.8 (Matrix inversion algorithm). *Given $A \in M_n(\mathbb{R})$, set up the matrix*

$$B = \begin{bmatrix} A \mid I_n \end{bmatrix}$$

in $M_{n,2n}(\mathbb{R})$. Carry out row operations on this matrix to reduce the left side to echelon form. If the left side reduces to I_n then A is invertible and the right side is A^{-1}. If the left side doesn't reduce to I_n then A is not invertible.

The algorithm works because if B is left multiplied by a product P of elementary matrices, the result is

$$PB = \begin{bmatrix} PA \mid P \end{bmatrix}.$$

As discussed, $PA = I_n$ exactly when $P = A^{-1}$.

For example, the calculation

$$R_{1;2,1} R_{2;3,1} \begin{bmatrix} 1 & -1 & 0 & 1 & 0 & 0 \\ 0 & 1 & -1 & 0 & 1 & 0 \\ 0 & 0 & 1 & 0 & 0 & 1 \end{bmatrix} = \begin{bmatrix} 1 & 0 & 0 & 1 & 1 & 1 \\ 0 & 1 & 0 & 0 & 1 & 1 \\ 0 & 0 & 1 & 0 & 0 & 1 \end{bmatrix}$$

shows that

$$\begin{bmatrix} 1 & -1 & 0 \\ 0 & 1 & -1 \\ 0 & 0 & 1 \end{bmatrix}^{-1} = \begin{bmatrix} 1 & 1 & 1 \\ 0 & 1 & 1 \\ 0 & 0 & 1 \end{bmatrix},$$

and one readily checks that the claimed inverse really works. Since arithmetic by hand is so error-prone a process, one always should confirm one's answer from the matrix inversion algorithm.

We now have an algorithmic answer to the question at the beginning of the section.

Theorem 3.3.9 (Echelon criterion for invertibility). *The linear mapping $S : \mathbb{R}^n \longrightarrow \mathbb{R}^m$ is invertible only when $m = n$ and its matrix A has echelon matrix I_n, in which case its inverse S^{-1} is the linear mapping with matrix A^{-1}.*

Exercises

3.3.1. Write down the following 3×3 elementary matrices and their inverses: $R_{3;2,\pi}$, $S_{3,3}$, $T_{3;2}$, $T_{2;3}$.

3.3.2. Finish the proof of Proposition 3.3.2.

3.3.3. Let $A = \begin{bmatrix} 1 & 2 \\ 3 & 4 \\ 5 & 6 \end{bmatrix}$. Evaluate the following products without actually multiplying matrices: $R_{3;2,\pi}A$, $S_{3,3}A$, $T_{3;2}A$, $T_{2;3}A$.

3.3.4. Finish the proof of Lemma 3.3.3, part (1).

3.3.5. What is the effect of right multiplying the $m \times n$ matrix M by an $n \times n$ matrix $R_{i;j,a}$? By $S_{i,a}$? By $Ti;j$?

3.3.6. Recall the transpose of a matrix M (cf. Exercise 3.2.4), denoted M^T. Prove: $R_{i;j,a}^\mathsf{T} = R_{j;i,a}$; $S_{i,a}^\mathsf{T} = S_{i,a}$; $T_{i;j}^\mathsf{T} = T_{i;j}$. Use these results and the formula $(AB)^\mathsf{T} = B^\mathsf{T}A^\mathsf{T}$ to redo the previous problem.

3.3.7. Are the following matrices echelon? For each matrix M, solve the equation $Mx = \mathbf{0}$.

$$\begin{bmatrix} 1 & 0 & 3 \\ 0 & 1 & 1 \\ 0 & 0 & 1 \end{bmatrix}, \quad \begin{bmatrix} 0 & 0 & 0 & 1 \\ 0 & 0 & 0 & 0 \end{bmatrix}, \quad \begin{bmatrix} 1 & 1 & 0 & 0 \\ 0 & 0 & 1 & 1 \end{bmatrix}, \quad \begin{bmatrix} 0 & 0 \\ 1 & 0 \\ 0 & 1 \\ 0 & 0 \end{bmatrix}, \quad \begin{bmatrix} 1 & 0 & 0 & 0 \\ 0 & 1 & 1 & 0 \\ 0 & 0 & 1 & 0 \end{bmatrix}, \quad \begin{bmatrix} 0 & 1 & 1 \\ 1 & 0 & 3 \\ 0 & 0 & 0 \end{bmatrix}.$$

3.3.8. For each matrix A solve the equation $Ax = \mathbf{0}$.

$$\begin{bmatrix} -1 & 1 & 4 \\ 1 & 3 & 8 \\ 1 & 2 & 5 \end{bmatrix}, \quad \begin{bmatrix} 2 & -1 & 3 & 2 \\ 1 & 4 & 0 & 1 \\ 2 & 6 & -1 & 5 \end{bmatrix}, \quad \begin{bmatrix} 3 & -1 & 2 \\ 2 & 1 & 1 \\ 1 & -3 & 0 \end{bmatrix}.$$

3.3.9. Balance the chemical equation

$$\mathrm{Ca} + \mathrm{H_3PO_4} \longrightarrow \mathrm{Ca_3P_2O_8} + \mathrm{H_2}.$$

3.3.10. Prove by induction that the only square echelon matrix with all new columns is the identity matrix.

3.3.11. Are the following matrices invertible? Find the inverse when possible, and then check your answer.

$$\begin{bmatrix} 1 & -1 & 1 \\ 2 & 0 & 1 \\ 3 & 0 & 1 \end{bmatrix}, \quad \begin{bmatrix} 2 & 5 & -1 \\ 4 & -1 & 2 \\ 6 & 4 & 1 \end{bmatrix}, \quad \begin{bmatrix} 1 & \frac{1}{2} & \frac{1}{3} \\ \frac{1}{2} & \frac{1}{3} & \frac{1}{4} \\ \frac{1}{3} & \frac{1}{4} & \frac{1}{5} \end{bmatrix}.$$

3.3.12. The matrix A is called **lower triangular** if $a_{ij} = 0$ whenever $i < j$. If A is a lower triangular square matrix with all diagonal entries equal to 1, show that A is invertible and A^{-1} takes the same form.

3.3.13. This exercise refers back to the Gram–Schmidt exercise in Chapter 2. That exercise expresses the relation between the vectors $\{x'_j\}$ and the vectors $\{x_j\}$ formally as $x' = Ax$, where x' is a column vector whose entries are the vectors $x'_1, \ldots, x'_n$, x is the corresponding column vector of x_j's, and A is an $n \times n$ lower triangular matrix.

Show that each x_j has the form

$$x_j = a'_{j1}x'_1 + a'_{j2}x'_2 + \cdots + a'_{j,j-1}x'_{j-1} + x'_j,$$

and thus every linear combination of the original $\{x_j\}$ is also a linear combination of the new $\{x'_j\}$.

3.4 Inhomogeneous Linear Equations

The question whether a linear mapping T is invertible led to solving the linear equation $Ax = 0$, where A was the matrix of T. Such a linear equation, with right side 0, is called **homogeneous**. An **inhomogeneous** linear equation has nonzero right side,

$$Ax = b, \qquad A \in \mathrm{M}_{m,n}(\mathbb{R}), \ x \in \mathbb{R}^n, \ b \in \mathbb{R}^m, \ b \neq 0.$$

The methods of the homogeneous case apply here too. If P is a product of $m \times m$ elementary matrices such that PA is echelon (call it E), then multiplying the inhomogeneous equation from the left by P gives

$$Ex = Pb,$$

and since Pb is just a vector, the solutions to this can be read off as in the homogeneous case. There may not always be solutions, however.

Exercises

3.4.1. Solve the inhomogeneous equations

$$\begin{bmatrix} 1 & -1 & 2 \\ 2 & 0 & 2 \\ 1 & -3 & 4 \end{bmatrix} x = \begin{bmatrix} 1 \\ 1 \\ 2 \end{bmatrix}, \qquad \begin{bmatrix} 1 & -2 & 1 & 2 \\ 1 & 1 & -1 & 1 \\ 1 & 7 & -5 & -1 \end{bmatrix} x = \begin{bmatrix} 1 \\ 2 \\ 3 \end{bmatrix}.$$

3.4.2. For what values b_1, b_2, b_3 does the equation

$$\begin{bmatrix} 3 & -1 & 2 \\ 2 & 1 & 1 \\ 1 & -3 & 0 \end{bmatrix} x = \begin{bmatrix} b_1 \\ b_2 \\ b_3 \end{bmatrix}$$

have a solution?

3.4.3. A parent has a son and a daughter. The parent is four times as old as the daughter, and the daughter is four years older than the son. In three years, the parent will be five times as old as the son. How old are the parent, daughter, and son?

3.4.4. Show that to solve an inhomogeneous linear equation, one may solve a homogeneous system in one more variable and then restrict to solutions for which the last variable is equal to -1.

3.5 The Determinant: Characterizing Properties and Their Consequences

In this section all matrices are square, $n \times n$. The goal is to define a function that takes such a matrix, with its n^2 entries, and returns a single number. The putative function is called the **determinant**,

$$\det : \mathrm{M}_n(\mathbb{R}) \longrightarrow \mathbb{R}.$$

For every square matrix $A \in \mathrm{M}_n(\mathbb{R})$, the scalar $\det(A)$ should contain as much algebraic and geometric information about the matrix as possible. Not surprisingly, so informative a function is complicated to encode.

This context nicely demonstrates a pedagogical principle already mentioned in Section 3.1: characterizing a mathematical object illuminates its construction and its use. Rather than beginning with a definition of the determinant, we will stipulate a few natural behaviors for it, and then we will eventually see that

- there is a function with these behaviors (*existence*),
- there is only one such function (*uniqueness*), and, most importantly,
- these behaviors, rather than the definition, further show how the function works (*consequences*).

We could start at the first bullet (existence) and proceed from the construction of the determinant to its properties, but when a construction is complicated (as the determinant's construction is), it fails to communicate intent, and pulling it out of thin air as the starting point of a long discussion is an obstacle to understanding. A few naturally gifted readers will see what the unexplained idea really is, enabling them to skim the ensuing technicalities and go on to start using the determinant effectively; some other tough-minded readers can work through the machinery and then see its operational consequences; but it is all too easy for the rest of us to be defeated by disorienting detail-fatigue before the presentation gets to the consequential points and provides any energizing clarity.

Another option would be to start at the second bullet (uniqueness), letting the desired properties of the determinant guide our construction of it. This process wouldn't be as alienating as starting with existence, but deriving the determinant's necessary construction has only limited benefit, because we intend to use the construction as little as possible. Working through the derivation would still squander our energy on the internal mechanisms of the determinant before getting to its behavior, when its behavior is what truly lets us understand it. We first want to learn to use the determinant easily and artfully. Doing so will make its internals feel of secondary importance, as they should.

The upshot is that in this section we will pursue the third bullet (consequences), and then the next section will proceed to the second bullet (uniqueness) and finally the first one (existence).

Instead of viewing the determinant only as a function of a matrix $A \in M_n(\mathbb{R})$ with n^2 scalar entries, view it also as a function of A's n rows, each of which is an n-vector. If A has rows $r_1, \ldots, r_n$, write $\det(r_1, \ldots, r_n)$ for $\det(A)$. Thus, det is now being interpreted as a function of n vectors, i.e., the domain of det is n copies of $\mathbb{R}^n$,

$$\det : \mathbb{R}^n \times \cdots \times \mathbb{R}^n \longrightarrow \mathbb{R}.$$

The advantage of this viewpoint is that now we can impose conditions on the determinant, using language already at our disposal in a natural way. Specifically, we make three requirements:

(1) The determinant is **multilinear**, meaning that it is linear as a function of each of its vector variables when the rest are held fixed. That is, for all vectors $r_1, \ldots, r_k, r'_k, \ldots, r_n$ and every scalar α,

$$\det(r_1, \ldots, \alpha r_k + r'_k, \ldots, r_n) = \alpha \det(r_1, \ldots, r_k, \ldots, r_n)$$
$$+ \det(r_1, \ldots, r'_k, \ldots, r_n).$$

(2) The determinant is **skew-symmetric** as a function of its vector variables, meaning that exchanging any two inputs changes the sign of the determinant,

$$\det(r_1, \ldots, r_j, \ldots, r_i, \ldots, r_n) = -\det(r_1, \ldots, r_i, \ldots, r_j, \ldots, r_n).$$

(Here $i \neq j$.) Consequently, the determinant is also **alternating**, meaning that if two inputs r_i and r_j are equal then $\det(r_1, \ldots, r_n) = 0$.

(3) The determinant is **normalized**, meaning that the standard basis has determinant 1,

$$\det(e_1, \ldots, e_n) = 1.$$

Condition (1) does not say that $\det(\alpha A + A') = \alpha \det(A) + \det(A')$ for scalars α and square matrices A, A'. Especially, the determinant is not additive,

$$\det(A + B) \text{ is in general not } \det(A) + \det(B). \tag{3.5}$$

What the condition does say is that if all rows but one of a square matrix are held fixed, then the determinant of the matrix varies linearly as a function of the one row. By induction, an equivalent statement of multilinearity is the more cluttered

$$\det(r_1, \ldots, \sum_i \alpha_i r_{k,i}, \ldots, r_n) = \sum_i \alpha_i \det(r_1, \ldots, r_{k,i}, \ldots, r_n),$$

but to keep the notation manageable, we work with the simpler version.

We will prove the following theorem in the next section.

Theorem 3.5.1 (Existence and uniqueness of the determinant). *One, and only one, multilinear skew-symmetric normalized function from the n-fold product of $\mathbb{R}^n$ to $\mathbb{R}$ exists. This function is the determinant,*

$$\det : \mathbb{R}^n \times \cdots \times \mathbb{R}^n \longrightarrow \mathbb{R}.$$

Furthermore, all multilinear skew-symmetric functions from the n-fold product of $\mathbb{R}^n$ to $\mathbb{R}$ are scalar multiples of of the determinant. That is, every multilinear skew-symmetric function $\delta : \mathbb{R}^n \times \cdots \times \mathbb{R}^n \longrightarrow \mathbb{R}$ is

$$\delta = c \cdot \det \quad where \quad c = \delta(e_1, \ldots, e_n).$$

In more structural language, Theorem 3.5.1 says that the multilinear skew-symmetric functions from the n-fold product of $\mathbb{R}^n$ to $\mathbb{R}$ form a 1-dimensional vector space over $\mathbb{R}$, and $\{\det\}$ is a basis.

The reader may object that even if the conditions of multilinearity, skew-symmetry, and normalization are grammatically natural, they are conceptually opaque. Indeed, they reflect considerable hindsight, since the idea of a determinant originally emerged from explicit calculations. But again, the payoff is that characterizing the determinant rather than constructing it illuminates its many useful properties. The rest of the section can be viewed as an amplification of this idea.

For one consequence of the determinant's existence, with no reference to its uniqueness, consider the standard basis of $\mathbb{R}^n$ taken in order,

$$(e_1, \ldots, e_n).$$

Suppose that some succession of m pair-exchanges of the vectors in this ordered n-tuple has no net effect, i.e., after the m pair-exchanges, the vectors are back in their original order. By skew-symmetry each pair-exchange changes the sign of the determinant, and so after all m pair-exchanges the net result is

$$(-1)^m \det(e_1, \ldots, e_n) = \det(e_1, \ldots, e_n).$$

Since the determinant is normalized, this says that $(-1)^m = 1$, i.e., m is even. That is, no odd number of pair-exchanges can leave an ordered n-tuple in its initial order. Consequently, if two different sequences of pair-exchanges have the same net effect then their lengths are both odd or both even—this is because running one sequence forward and then the other backward has no net effect and hence comes to an even number of moves. In other words, although a net rearrangement of an n-tuple does not determine a unique succession of pair-exchanges to bring it about, or even a unique number of such exchanges, it does determine the parity of any such number: the net rearrangement requires an odd number of pair-exchanges, or it requires an even number. (For reasons related to this, an old puzzle involving fifteen squares that slide in a 4×4 grid can be made unsolvable by popping two pieces out and exchanging them.)

The fact that the parity of a rearrangement is well defined may be easy to believe, perhaps so easy that the need for a proof is hard to see, but a proof really is required. The determinant's skew-symmetry and normalization are so powerful that they give the result essentially as an afterthought. Alternatively, see Exercise 3.5.2 for an elementary proof that does not invoke the existence of the determinant. To summarize:

> *The existence of a determinant with no reference to its uniqueness, or an argument that makes no reference to the determinant at all, shows that every rearrangement of n objects has a well-defined parity, meaning that either all sequences of pair-exchanges that put the objects back in order have even length or all such sequences have odd length.*

In the next section we will show that there are as many candidate determinants (multilinear skew-symmetric normalized functions) as there are ways to assign a parity to each rearrangement of n objects, with no assumption that any determinant exists. So there could be as many as $2^{n!}$ candidate determinants, in the extreme case that each rearrangement can be put back in order by an odd number of pair-exchanges and by an even number. And in the next section we will use one particular assignment of a parity to each rearrangement to show that a determinant exists. As in the previous displayed text, once a determinant exists, only one parity-assignment function exists, and so the determinant is unique. The logic here is subtle, and so the reader may prefer to rely on Exercise 3.5.2 to defray any concern about arguing in a circle. If the uniqueness of parity is established first then the ideas lay themselves out more clearly: a unique candidate determinant presents itself, and we show that it works.

The next result is the crucial property of the determinant, in consequence of its characterizing properties.

Theorem 3.5.2 (The determinant is multiplicative). *For all matrices $A, B \in M_n(\mathbb{R})$, the determinant of the matrix product is the product of the scalar determinants,*

$$\det(AB) = \det(A)\det(B).$$

Further, if A is invertible then the determinant of the matrix inverse is the scalar inverse of the determinant,

$$\det(A^{-1}) = (\det(A))^{-1}.$$

Multilinearity says that the determinant behaves well additively and scalar-multiplicatively as a function of each of n vectors, while (3.5) says that the determinant does not behave well additively as a function of one matrix. Theorem 3.5.2 says that the determinant behaves perfectly well multiplicatively as a function of one matrix. Also, the theorem tacitly says that if A is invertible then $\det(A)$ is nonzero. Soon we will establish the converse as well.

Proof. Let $B \in M_n(\mathbb{R})$ be fixed. Consider the function

$$\delta : M_n(\mathbb{R}) \longrightarrow \mathbb{R}, \qquad \delta(A) = \det(AB).$$

As a function of the rows of A, δ is the determinant of the rows of AB,

$$\delta : \mathbb{R}^n \times \cdots \times \mathbb{R}^n \longrightarrow \mathbb{R}, \qquad \delta(r_1, \ldots, r_n) = \det(r_1 B, \ldots, r_n B).$$

The function δ is multilinear and skew-symmetric. To show multilinearity, compute (using the definition of δ in terms of det, properties of vector–matrix algebra, the multilinearity of det, and the definition of δ again),

$$
\begin{aligned}
\delta(r_1, \ldots, \alpha r_k + r_k', \ldots, r_n) &= \det(r_1 B, \ldots, (\alpha r_k + r_k')B, \ldots, r_n B) \\
&= \det(r_1 B, \ldots, \alpha r_k B + r_k' B, \ldots, r_n B) \\
&= \alpha \det(r_1 B, \ldots, r_k B, \ldots, r_n B) \\
&\quad + \det(r_1 B, \ldots, r_k' B, \ldots, r_n B) \\
&= \alpha \, \delta(r_1, \ldots, r_k, \ldots, r_n) \\
&\quad + \delta(r_1, \ldots, r_k', \ldots, r_n).
\end{aligned}
$$

To show skew-symmetry, take two distinct indices $i, j \in \{1, \ldots, n\}$ and compute similarly,

$$
\begin{aligned}
\delta(r_1, \ldots, r_j, \ldots, r_i, \ldots, r_n) &= \det(r_1 B, \ldots, r_j B, \ldots, r_i B, \ldots, r_n B) \\
&= -\det(r_1 B, \ldots, r_i B, \ldots, r_j B, \ldots, r_n B) \\
&= -\delta(r_1, \ldots, r_i, \ldots, r_j, \ldots, r_n).
\end{aligned}
$$

Also compute that

$$\delta(e_1, \ldots, e_n) = \det(e_1 B, \ldots, e_n B) = \det(B).$$

It follows from Theorem 3.5.1 that $\delta(A) = \det(B) \det(A)$, and this is the desired main result $\det(AB) = \det(A) \det(B)$ of the theorem. Finally, if A is invertible then

$$\det(A) \det(A^{-1}) = \det(AA^{-1}) = \det(I) = 1.$$

That is, $\det(A^{-1}) = (\det(A))^{-1}$. The proof is complete. $\square$

One consequence of the theorem is

$$\det(A^{-1}BA) = \det(B), \quad A, B \in M_n(\mathbb{R}), \ A \text{ invertible.}$$

And we note that the same result holds for the trace, introduced in Exercise 3.2.5, in consequence of that exercise,

$$\operatorname{tr}(A^{-1}BA) = \operatorname{tr}(B), \quad A, B \in M_n(\mathbb{R}), \ A \text{ invertible.}$$

More facts about the determinant are immediate consequences of its characterizing properties.

Proposition 3.5.3 (Determinants of elementary and echelon matrices).

(1) $\det(R_{i;j,a}) = 1$ for all $i, j \in \{1, \dots, n\}$ $(i \neq j)$ and $a \in \mathbb{R}$.
(2) $\det(S_{i,a}) = a$ for all $i \in \{1, \dots, n\}$ and nonzero $a \in \mathbb{R}$.
(3) $\det(T_{i;j}) = -1$ for all $i, j \in \{1, \dots, n\}$ $(i \neq j)$.
(4) If E is $n \times n$ echelon then

$$\det(E) = \begin{cases} 1 & \text{if } E = I, \\ 0 & \text{otherwise.} \end{cases}$$

Proof. (1) Compute

$$
\begin{aligned}
\det(R_{i;j,a}) &= \det(e_1, \dots, e_i + ae_j, \dots, e_j, \dots, e_n) \\
&= \det(e_1, \dots, e_i, \dots, e_j, \dots, e_n) + a \det(e_1, \dots, e_j, \dots, e_j, \dots, e_n) \\
&= 1 + a \cdot 0 = 1.
\end{aligned}
$$

The proofs of statements (2) and (3) are similar. For (4), if $E = I$ then $\det(E) = 1$, because the determinant is normalized. Otherwise the bottom row of E is $\mathbf{0}$, and because a linear function takes $\mathbf{0}$ to 0 it follows that $\det(E) = 0$.   □

For one consequence of Theorem 3.5.2 and Proposition 3.5.3, recall that every matrix $A \in M_n(\mathbb{R})$ has a transpose matrix A^{T}, obtained by flipping A about its northwest–southeast diagonal. The next theorem (whose proof is Exercise 3.5.4) says that all statements about the determinant as a function of the rows of A also apply to the columns. This fact will be used without comment from now on. In particular, $\det(A)$ is the unique multilinear skew-symmetric normalized function of the columns of A.

Theorem 3.5.4 (Determinant and transpose). *For all* $A \in M_n(\mathbb{R})$, $\det(A^{\mathsf{T}}) = \det(A)$.

We also give another useful consequence of the determinant's characterizing properties. A type of matrix that has an easily calculable determinant is a **triangular** matrix, meaning a matrix all of whose subdiagonal entries are 0 or all of whose superdiagonal entries are 0. (Lower triangular matrices have already been introduced in Exercise 3.3.12.) For example, the matrices

$$\begin{bmatrix} a_{11} & a_{12} & a_{13} \\ 0 & a_{22} & a_{23} \\ 0 & 0 & a_{33} \end{bmatrix} \quad \text{and} \quad \begin{bmatrix} a_{11} & 0 & 0 \\ a_{21} & a_{22} & 0 \\ a_{31} & a_{32} & a_{33} \end{bmatrix}$$

are triangular.

Proposition 3.5.5 (Determinant of a triangular matrix). *The determinant of a triangular matrix is the product of its diagonal entries.*

Proof. We may consider only upper triangular matrices, because a lower triangular matrix has an upper triangular matrix for its transpose. The 3×3 case makes the general argument clear. The determinant of a 3×3 upper triangular matrix A is

$$\det A = \det\Big(\sum_{i_1=1}^{3} a_{1i_1} e_{i_1}, \sum_{i_2=2}^{3} a_{2i_2} e_{i_2}, \sum_{i_3=3}^{3} a_{3i_3} e_{i_3} \Big),$$

which, since the determinant is multilinear, is

$$\det A = \sum_{i_1=1}^{3} \sum_{i_2=2}^{3} \sum_{i_3=3}^{3} a_{1i_1} a_{2i_2} a_{3i_3} \det(e_{i_1}, e_{i_2}, e_{i_3}).$$

Because the summation-index i_3 takes only the value 3, this is

$$\det A = \sum_{i_1=1}^{3} \sum_{i_2=2}^{3} a_{1i_1} a_{2i_2} a_{33} \det(e_{i_1}, e_{i_2}, e_3),$$

and the terms with $i_1 = 3$ or $i_2 = 3$ vanish because the determinant is alternating, so the determinant further simplifies to

$$\det A = \sum_{i_1=1}^{2} a_{1i_1} a_{22} a_{33} \det(e_{i_1}, e_2, e_3).$$

Now the term with $i_1 = 2$ vanishes similarly, leaving

$$\det A = a_{11} a_{22} a_{33} \det(e_1, e_2, e_3).$$

Finally, because the determinant is normalized, we have

$$\det A = a_{11} a_{22} a_{33}.$$

□

A far more important consequence of Theorem 3.5.2 and Proposition 3.5.3 is one of the main results of this chapter. Recall that every matrix A row reduces as

$$R_1 \cdots R_N A = E$$

where the R_k are elementary, E is echelon, and A is invertible if and only if $E = I$. Because the determinant is multiplicative,

$$\det(R_1) \cdots \det(R_N) \det(A) = \det(E). \tag{3.6}$$

But each $\det(R_k)$ is nonzero, and $\det(E)$ is 1 if $E = I$ and 0 otherwise, so this gives the algebraic significance of the determinant:

Theorem 3.5.6 (Linear invertibility theorem). *The matrix $A \in \mathrm{M}_n(\mathbb{R})$ is invertible if and only if $\det(A) \neq 0$.*

That is, the zeroness or nonzeroness of the determinant says whether the matrix is invertible. Once the existence and uniqueness of the determinant are established in the next section, we will continue to use the determinant properties to interpret the magnitude and the sign of the determinant as well.

Not only does equation (3.6) prove the linear invertibility theorem, but furthermore it describes an algorithm for computing the determinant of any square matrix A: reduce A to echelon form by recombining, scaling, and transposition; if the echelon form is I then $\det(A)$ is the reciprocal product of the scaling factors times -1 raised to the number of transpositions, and if the echelon form is not I then $\det(A) = 0$. We will give a more efficient determinant algorithm in the next section.

Exercises

3.5.1. Consider a scalar-valued function of pairs of vectors,

$$\mathrm{ip} : \mathbb{R}^n \times \mathbb{R}^n \longrightarrow \mathbb{R},$$

satisfying the following three properties.

(1) The function is bilinear,

$$\mathrm{ip}(\alpha x + \alpha' x', y) = \alpha \, \mathrm{ip}(x, y) + \alpha' \, \mathrm{ip}(x', y),$$
$$\mathrm{ip}(x, \beta y + \beta' y') = \beta \, \mathrm{ip}(x, y) + \beta' \, \mathrm{ip}(x, y')$$

for all $\alpha, \alpha', \beta, \beta' \in \mathbb{R}$ and $x, x', y, y' \in \mathbb{R}^n$.

(2) The function is symmetric,

$$\mathrm{ip}(x, y) = \mathrm{ip}(y, x) \quad \text{for all } x, y \in \mathbb{R}^n.$$

(3) The function is normalized,

$$\mathrm{ip}(e_i, e_j) = \delta_{ij} \quad \text{for all } i, j \in \{1, \ldots, n\}.$$

(The Kronecker delta δ_{ij} was defined in Section 2.2.)

Compute that this function, if it exists at all, must be the inner product. On the other hand, we already know that the inner product has these three properties, so this exercise has shown that it is characterized by them.

3.5.2. Let $n \geq 2$. This exercise proves, without invoking the determinant, that every succession of pair-exchanges of the ordered set

$$(1, 2, \ldots, n)$$

that has no net effect consists of an even number of exchanges.

To see this, consider a shortest-possible succession of an odd number of pair-exchanges having in total no net effect. Certainly it must involve at least three exchanges. We want to show that it can't exist at all.

Let the notation

$$(i\,j) \quad (\text{where } i \neq j)$$

stand for exchanging the elements in positions i and j. Then in particular, the first two exchanges in the succession take the form

$$(i\,j)(*\,*),$$

meaning to exchange the elements in positions i and j and then to exchange the elements in another pair of positions. There are four cases,

$$(i\,j)(i\,j),$$
$$(i\,j)(i\,k), \quad k \notin \{i, j\},$$
$$(i\,j)(j\,k), \quad k \notin \{i, j\},$$
$$(i\,j)(k\,\ell), \quad k, \ell \notin \{i, j\}, \ k \neq \ell.$$

The first case gives a shorter succession of an odd number of pair-exchanges having in total no net effect, and this is a contradiction. Show that the other three cases can be rewritten in the form

$$(*\,*)(i\,*)$$

where the first exchange does not involve the ith slot. Next we may apply the same argument to the second and third exchanges, then to the third and fourth, and so on. Eventually, either a contradiction arises from the first of the four cases, or only the last pair-exchange involves the ith slot. Explain why the second possibility is untenable, completing the argument.

3.5.3. Let $f : \mathbb{R}^n \times \cdots \times \mathbb{R}^n \longrightarrow \mathbb{R}$ be a multilinear skew-symmetric function, and let c be a real number. Show that the function cf is again multilinear and skew-symmetric.

3.5.4. This exercise shows that $\det(A^{\mathsf{T}}) = \det(A)$ for every square matrix A.

(a) Show that $\det(R^{\mathsf{T}}) = \det(R)$ for every elementary matrix R. (That is, R can be a recombine matrix, a scale matrix, or a transposition matrix.)

(b) If E is a square echelon matrix then either $E = I$ or the bottom row of E is $\mathbf{0}$. In either case, show that $\det(E^\mathsf{T}) = \det(E)$. (For the case $E \neq I$, we know that E is not invertible. What is $E^\mathsf{T} e_n$, and what does this say about the invertibility of E^T?)

(c) Use the formula $(MN)^\mathsf{T} = N^\mathsf{T} M^\mathsf{T}$, Theorem 3.5.2, and Proposition 3.5.3 to show that $\det(A^\mathsf{T}) = \det(A)$ for all $A \in \mathrm{M}_n(\mathbb{R})$.

3.5.5. The square matrix A is **orthogonal** if $A^\mathsf{T} A = I$. Show that if A is orthogonal then $\det(A) = \pm 1$. Give an example with determinant -1.

3.5.6. The matrix A is **skew-symmetric** if $A^\mathsf{T} = -A$. Show that if A is $n \times n$ skew-symmetric with n odd then $\det(A) = 0$.

3.6 The Determinant: Uniqueness and Existence

Recall that Theorem 3.5.1 asserts that exactly one multilinear skew-symmetric normalized function from the n-fold product of $\mathbb{R}^n$ to $\mathbb{R}$ exists. That is, a unique determinant exists.

We warm up for the proof of the theorem by using the three defining conditions of the determinant to show that only one formula is possible for the determinant of a general 2×2 matrix,

$$A = \begin{bmatrix} a & b \\ c & d \end{bmatrix}.$$

The first row of this matrix is

$$r_1 = (a, b) = a(1, 0) + b(0, 1) = a e_1 + b e_2,$$

and similarly its second row is $r_2 = c e_1 + d e_2$. Thus, since we view the determinant as a function of rows, its determinant must be

$$\det(A) = \det(r_1, r_2) = \det(a e_1 + b e_2, c e_1 + d e_2).$$

Since the determinant is linear in its first vector variable, this expands to

$$\det(a e_1 + b e_2, c e_1 + d e_2) = a \det(e_1, c e_1 + d e_2) + b \det(e_2, c e_1 + d e_2),$$

and since the determinant is also linear in its second vector variable, this expands further,

$$a \det(e_1, c e_1 + d e_2) + b \det(e_2, c e_1 + d e_2)$$
$$= ac \det(e_1, e_1) + ad \det(e_1, e_2)$$
$$+ bc \det(e_2, e_1) + bd \det(e_2, e_2).$$

But since the determinant is skew-symmetric and alternating, this expanded expression simplifies considerably,

$$ac\det(e_1, e_1) + ad\det(e_1, e_2) + bc\det(e_2, e_1) + bd\det(e_2, e_2)$$
$$= (ad - bc)\det(e_1, e_2).$$

And finally, since the determinant is normalized, we have found the only possible formula for the 2×2 case,

$$\det(A) = ad - bc.$$

All three characterizing properties of the determinant were required to derive this formula. More subtly (though in this context trivially), the fact that this is the only possible formula tacitly relies on the fact that every sequence of exchanges of e_1 and e_2 that leaves them in order has even length, and every such sequence that exchanges their order has odd length.

As a brief digression, the reader can use the matrix inversion algorithm from Section 3.3 to verify that the 2×2 matrix A is invertible if and only if $ad-bc$ is nonzero, showing that the formula for the 2×2 determinant arises from considerations of invertibility as well as from our three conditions. However, the argument requires cases, e.g., $a \neq 0$ and $a = 0$, making this approach uninviting for larger matrices.

Returning to the main line of exposition, nothing here has yet shown that a determinant function exists at all for 2×2 matrices. What it has shown is that there is only one possibility,

$$\det((a,b),(c,d)) = ad - bc.$$

But now that we have the only possible formula, checking that indeed it satisfies the desired properties is purely mechanical. For example, to verify linearity in the first vector variable, compute

$$\det(\alpha(a,b) + (a',b'),(c,d)) = \det((\alpha a + a', \alpha b + b'),(c,d))$$
$$= (\alpha a + a')d - (\alpha b + b')c$$
$$= \alpha(ad - bc) + (a'd - b'c)$$
$$= \alpha\det((a,b),(c,d)) + \det((a',b'),(c,d)).$$

For skew-symmetry,

$$\det((c,d),(a,b)) = cb - da = -(ad - bc) = -\det((a,b),(c,d)).$$

And for normalization,

$$\det(1,0),(0,1)) = 1 \cdot 1 - 0 \cdot 0 = 1.$$

We should also verify linearity in the second vector variable, but this no longer requires the defining formula. Instead, since the formula is skew-symmetric and is linear in the first variable,

$$\det(r_1, \alpha r_2 + r_2') = -\det(\alpha r_2 + r_2', r_1)$$
$$= -\big(\alpha \det(r_2, r_1) + \det(r_2', r_1)\big)$$
$$= -\big(-\alpha \det(r_1, r_2) - \det(r_1, r_2')\big)$$
$$= \alpha \det(r_1, r_2) + \det(r_1, r_2').$$

This little trick illustrates the value of thinking in general terms: a slight modification, inserting a few occurrences of "..." and replacing the subscripts 1 and 2 by i and j, shows that for every n, the three required conditions for the determinant are redundant—linearity in one vector variable combines with skew-symmetry to ensure linearity in each vector variable.

One can similarly show that for a 1×1 matrix,

$$A = [a],$$

the only possible formula for its determinant is

$$\det(A) = a,$$

and that indeed this works. The result is perhaps silly, but the exercise of working through a piece of language and logic in the simplest instance can help one to understand its more elaborate cases. As another exercise, the same techniques show, granting that each permutation of three elements has only one parity, that the only possible formula for a 3×3 determinant is

$$\det \begin{bmatrix} a & b & c \\ d & e & f \\ g & h & k \end{bmatrix} = aek + bfg + cdh - afh - bdk - ceg.$$

This formula is complicated enough that we should rethink it in a more systematic way before verifying that it has the desired properties. And we may as well generalize it to arbitrary n in the process. Here are some observations about the 3×3 formula:

- It is a sum of 3-fold products of matrix entries.
- Every 3-fold product contains one element from each row of the matrix.
- Every 3-fold product also contains one element from each column of the matrix. So every 3-fold product arises from the positions of three rooks that don't threaten each other on a 3×3 chessboard.
- Every 3-fold product comes weighted by a "+" or a "−".

Similar observations apply to the 1×1 and 2×2 formulas. Our general formula should encode them. Making it do so is partly a matter of notation, but also an idea is needed to describe the appropriate distribution of plus signs and minus signs among the terms. The following language provides all of this.

Definition 3.6.1 (Permutation). *A* **permutation** *of* $\{1, 2, \ldots, n\}$ *is a vector*

$$\pi = (\pi(1), \pi(2), \ldots, \pi(n))$$

whose entries are $\{1, 2, \ldots, n\}$, *each appearing once, in any order. An* **inversion** *in the permutation* π *is a pair of entries with the larger one to the left. The* **sign** *of the permutation* π, *written* $(-1)^\pi$, *is* -1 *raised to the number of inversions in* π. *The set of permutations of* $\{1, \ldots, n\}$ *is denoted* S_n.

Examples are the permutations $\pi = (1, 2, 3, \ldots, n)$, $\sigma = (2, 1, 3, \ldots, n)$, and $\tau = (5, 4, 3, 2, 1)$ (here $n = 5$). In these examples π has no inversions, σ has one, and τ has ten. Thus $(-1)^\pi = 1$, $(-1)^\sigma = -1$, and $(-1)^\tau = 1$. In general, the sign of a permutation with an even number of inversions is 1 and the sign of a permutation with an odd number of inversions is -1. There are $n!$ permutations of $\{1, 2, \ldots, n\}$; that is, the set S_n contains $n!$ elements.

As advertised, permutations and their signs provide the notation for the only possible $n \times n$ determinant formulas. Consider any n vectors

$$r_1 = \sum_{i=1}^{n} a_{1i} e_i, \quad r_2 = \sum_{j=1}^{n} a_{2j} e_j, \quad \ldots, \quad r_n = \sum_{p=1}^{n} a_{np} e_p.$$

Every multilinear function δ (if it exists at all) must satisfy

$$\delta(r_1, r_2, \ldots, r_n) = \delta\left(\sum_{i=1}^{n} a_{1i} e_i, \sum_{j=1}^{n} a_{2j} e_j, \ldots, \sum_{p=1}^{n} a_{np} e_p\right)$$

$$= \sum_{i=1}^{n} \sum_{j=1}^{n} \cdots \sum_{p=1}^{n} a_{1i} a_{2j} \cdots a_{np} \delta(e_i, e_j, \ldots, e_p).$$

If δ is also alternating then for every $i, j, \ldots, p \in \{1, \ldots, n\}$,

$$\delta(e_i, e_j, \ldots, e_p) = 0 \quad \text{if any two subscripts agree.}$$

Thus we may sum only over permutations,

$$\delta(r_1, r_2, \ldots, r_n) = \sum_{(i,j,\ldots,p) \in S_n} a_{1i} a_{2j} \cdots a_{np} \det(e_i, e_j, \ldots, e_p).$$

Consider any permutation $\pi = (i, j, \ldots, p)$. Suppose that π contains an inversion, i.e., two elements are out of order. Then necessarily two elements in adjacent slots are out of order. (For example, if $i > p$ then either $i > j$, giving adjacent elements out of order as desired; or $j > i > p$, so that j and p are an out of order pair in closer slots than i and p, and so on.) If a permutation contains any inversions, then exchanging a suitable adjacent pair decreases the number of inversions by one, changing the sign of the permutation, while exchanging the corresponding two input vectors changes the sign of the determinant. Repeating this process until the permutation has no remaining inversions shows that

$$\delta(e_i, e_j, \ldots, e_p) = (-1)^\pi \delta(e_1, e_2, \ldots, e_n).$$

That is, a possible formula for a multilinear skew-symmetric function δ is

$$\delta(r_1, r_2, \ldots, r_n) = \sum_{\pi=(i,j,\ldots,p)} (-1)^{\pi} a_{1i} a_{2j} \cdots a_{np} \cdot c$$

where

$$c = \delta(e_1, \ldots, e_n).$$

Especially, a possible formula for a multilinear skew-symmetric normalized function is

$$\det(r_1, r_2, \ldots, r_n) = \sum_{\pi=(i,j,\ldots,p)} (-1)^{\pi} a_{1i} a_{2j} \cdots a_{np}.$$

Because $(-1)^{\pi}$ arises from a specific method of undoing any permutation—exchange out-of-order neighboring pairs until none remain—it conceivably need not be the only parity function of permutations. Further, the argument here has shown that for any parity function sgn of permutations, the function

$$\det_{\text{sgn}}(r_1, r_2, \ldots, r_n) = \sum_{\pi=(i,j,\ldots,p)} \text{sgn}(\pi) a_{1i} a_{2j} \cdots a_{np}$$

is a possible formula for a multilinear skew-symmetric normalized function, and these are the only candidates. As discussed in the previous section, either we already know that $(-1)^{\pi}$ is the unique parity of each permutation π by Exercise 3.5.2, or we will know it as soon as the function constructed with it in the penultimate display is shown to be multilinear, skew-symmetric, and normalized.

Definition 3.6.2 (Determinant). *The* **determinant** *function,*

$$\det : M_n(\mathbb{R}) \longrightarrow \mathbb{R},$$

is defined as follows. For every $A \in M_n(\mathbb{R})$ with entries (a_{ij}),

$$\det(A) = \sum_{\pi \in S_n} (-1)^{\pi} a_{1\pi(1)} a_{2\pi(2)} \cdots a_{n\pi(n)}.$$

The formula in the definition is indeed the formula computed a moment ago, because for every permutation $\pi = (i, j, \ldots, p) \in S_n$ we have $\pi(1) = i$, $\pi(2) = j, \ldots, \pi(n) = p$.

As an exercise to clarify the formula, we use it to reproduce the 3×3 determinant. Each permutation in S_3 determines a rook placement, and the sign of the permutation is the parity of the number of northeast–southwest segments joining any two of its rooks. For example, the permutation $(2, 3, 1)$ specifies that the rooks in the top, middle, and bottom rows are respectively in columns 2, 3, and 1, and the sign is positive because there are two northeast–southwest segments. (See Figure 3.9.) The following table lists each permutation in S_3 followed by the corresponding term in the determinant formula. For each permutation, the term is its sign times the product of the three matrix entries where its rooks are placed.

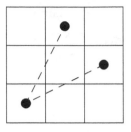

Figure 3.9. The rook placement for $(2,3,1)$, showing the two inversions

π	$(-1)^\pi a_{1\pi(1)}a_{2\pi(2)}a_{3\pi(3)}$
$(1,2,3)$	aek
$(1,3,2)$	$-afh$
$(2,1,3)$	$-bdk$
$(2,3,1)$	bfg
$(3,1,2)$	cdh
$(3,2,1)$	$-ceg$

The sum of the right column entries is the anticipated formula from before,

$$\det \begin{bmatrix} a & b & c \\ d & e & f \\ g & h & k \end{bmatrix} = aek + bfg + cdh - afh - bdk - ceg.$$

The same procedure reproduces the 2×2 determinant as well,

$$\det \begin{bmatrix} a & b \\ c & d \end{bmatrix} = ad - bc,$$

and even the silly 1×1 formula $\det[a] = a$. The 2×2 and 3×3 cases are worth memorizing. They can be visualized as adding the products along northwest–southeast diagonals of the matrix and then subtracting the products along southwest–northeast diagonals, where the word *diagonal* connotes wraparound in the 3×3 case. (See Figure 3.10.) But be aware that this pattern of the determinant as the northwest–southeast diagonals minus the southwest–northeast diagonals is valid only for $n = 2$ and $n = 3$.

We have completed the program of the second bullet at the beginning of the previous section, finding the only possible formula (the one in Definition 3.6.2) that could satisfy the three desired determinant properties, its uniqueness dependent on its doing so if we haven't already shown that each permutation has a unique sign. That is, we have now proved the uniqueness but not yet the existence of the determinant in Theorem 3.5.1, the uniqueness possibly provisional on the existence.

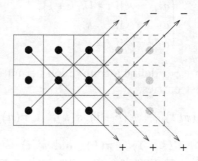

Figure 3.10. The 3×3 determinant

The first bullet tells us to prove the existence by verifying that the computed determinant formula indeed satisfies the three stipulated determinant properties. Similarly to the 2×2 case, this is a mechanical exercise. The impediments are purely notational, but the notation is admittedly cumbersome, and so the reader is encouraged to skim the next proof.

Proposition 3.6.3 (Properties of the determinant).

(1) *The determinant is linear as a function of each row of A.*
(2) *The determinant is skew-symmetric as a function of the rows of A.*
(3) *The determinant is normalized.*

Proof. (1) If A has rows $r_i = (a_{i1}, \ldots, a_{in})$ except that its kth row is the linear combination $\alpha r_k + r'_k$ where $r_k = (a_{k1}, \ldots, a_{kn})$ and $r'_k = (a'_{k1}, \ldots, a'_{kn})$, then its (i,j)th entry is

$$\begin{cases} a_{ij} & \text{if } i \neq k, \\ \alpha a_{kj} + a'_{kj} & \text{if } i = k. \end{cases}$$

Thus

$$\det(r_1, \ldots, \alpha r_k + r'_k, \ldots, r_n)$$
$$= \sum_{\pi \in S_n} (-1)^\pi a_{1\pi(1)} \cdots (\alpha a_{k\pi(k)} + a'_{k\pi(k)}) \cdots a_{n\pi(n)}$$
$$= \alpha \sum_{\pi \in S_n} (-1)^\pi a_{1\pi(1)} \cdots a_{k\pi(k)} \cdots a_{n\pi(n)}$$
$$+ \sum_{\pi \in S_n} (-1)^\pi a_{1\pi(1)} \cdots a'_{k\pi(k)} \cdots a_{n\pi(n)}$$
$$= \alpha \det(r_1, \ldots, r_k, \ldots, r_n) + \det(r_1, \ldots, r'_k, \ldots, r_n),$$

as desired.

(2) Let A have rows $r_1, \ldots, r_n$ where $r_i = (a_{i1}, \ldots, a_{in})$. Suppose that rows k and $k+1$ are exchanged. The resulting matrix has (i,j)th entry

$$\begin{cases} a_{ij} & \text{if } i \notin \{k, k+1\}, \\ a_{k+1,j} & \text{if } i = k, \\ a_{kj} & \text{if } i = k+1. \end{cases}$$

For each permutation $\pi \in S_n$, define a companion permutation π' by exchanging the kth and $(k+1)$st entries,

$$\pi' = (\pi(1), \ldots, \pi(k+1), \pi(k), \ldots, \pi(n)).$$

Thus $\pi'(k) = \pi(k+1)$, $\pi'(k+1) = \pi(k)$, and $\pi'(i) = \pi(i)$ for all other i. As π varies through S_n, so does π', and for each π we have the relation $(-1)^{\pi'} = -(-1)^{\pi}$ (Exercise 3.6.6). The defining formula of the determinant gives

$$\begin{aligned}
\det(r_1, &\ldots, r_{k+1}, r_k, \ldots, r_n) \\
&= \sum_{\pi} (-1)^{\pi} a_{1\pi(1)} \cdots a_{k+1,\pi(k)} a_{k\pi(k+1)} \cdots a_{n\pi(n)} \\
&= -\sum_{\pi'} (-1)^{\pi'} a_{1\pi'(1)} \cdots a_{k+1,\pi'(k+1)} a_{k\pi'(k)} \cdots a_{n\pi'(n)} \\
&= -\det(r_1, \ldots, r_k, r_{k+1}, \ldots, r_n).
\end{aligned}$$

The previous calculation establishes the result when adjacent rows of A are exchanged. To exchange rows k and ℓ in A where $\ell > k$, carry out the following adjacent row exchanges to trickle the kth row down to the ℓth and then bubble the ℓth row back up to the kth, bobbing each row in between them up one position and then back down:

rows k and $k+1$,	k and $k+1$.
$k+1$ and $k+2$,	$k+1$ and $k+2$,
$\ldots$,	$\ldots$,
$\ell-2$ and $\ell-1$,	$\ell-2$ and $\ell-1$,
$\ell-1$ and ℓ,	

The display shows that the process carries out an odd number of exchanges (all but the bottom one come in pairs), each of which changes the sign of the determinant.

(3) This is left to the reader (Exercise 3.6.7).   □

So a determinant function with the stipulated behavior exists, making our $(-1)^{\pi}$ the only possible sign of each permutation π if we don't know this already, and thus showing that the determinant is unique. Another construction of a determinant function, with no reference to permutations at all but proceeding instead by induction on the dimension n of the matrices, is given in Exercise 3.6.12. And we have seen that every multilinear skew-symmetric function must be a scalar multiple of the determinant. The last comment necessary to complete the proof of Theorem 3.5.1 is that since the determinant is multilinear and skew-symmetric, so are its scalar multiples. This fact was shown in Exercise 3.5.3.

The reader is invited to contemplate how unpleasant it would have been to prove the various theorems about the determinant in the previous section using the unwieldy determinant formula, with its $n!$ terms, each an n-fold product. That said, the theorems really can be shown directly from the formula. For example, to prove that $\det(A^{\mathsf{T}}) = \det(A)$, one can write

$$\det(A^{\mathsf{T}}) = \sum_{\pi \in S_n} (-1)^{\pi} a_{\pi(1)1} a_{\pi(2)2} \cdots a_{\pi(n)n},$$

and then persuade oneself that this is also the sum over the permutations π' that undo the permutations π, and the undo-permutations have the same signs as the originals,

$$\det(A^{\mathsf{T}}) = \sum_{\pi' \in S_n} (-1)^{\pi'} a_{1\pi'(1)} a_{2\pi'(2)} \cdots a_{n\pi'(n)},$$

and this is $\det(A)$. Here we are adumbrating basic ideas from *group theory*.

The previous section has already established that the determinant of a triangular matrix is the product of the diagonal entries, but the result also follows immediately from the determinant formula (Exercise 3.6.8). This fact should be cited freely to save time.

An algorithm for computing $\det(A)$ for every $A \in M_n(\mathbb{R})$ is now at hand. Algebraically, the idea is that if

$$P_1 A P_2 = \Delta,$$

where P_1 and P_2 are products of elementary matrices and Δ is a triangular matrix, then since the determinant is multiplicative,

$$\det(A) = \det(P_1)^{-1} \det(\Delta) \det(P_2)^{-1}.$$

Multiplying A by P_2 on the right carries out a sequence of column operations on A, just as multiplying A by P_1 on the left carries out row operations. Recall that the determinants of the elementary matrices are

$$\det(R_{i;j,a}) = 1,$$
$$\det(S_{i,a}) = a,$$
$$\det(T_{i;j}) = -1.$$

Procedurally, this all plays out as follows.

Proposition 3.6.4 (Determinant algorithm). *Given $A \in M_n(\mathbb{R})$, use row and column operations—recombines, scales, transpositions—to reduce A to a triangular matrix Δ. Then $\det(A)$ is $\det(\Delta)$ times the reciprocal of each scale factor and times -1 for each transposition.*

The only role that the determinant formula (as compared to the determinant properties) played in obtaining this algorithm is that it gave the determinant of a triangular matrix easily.

For example, the matrix

$$A = \begin{bmatrix} 1/0! & 1/1! & 1/2! & 1/3! \\ 1/1! & 1/2! & 1/3! & 1/4! \\ 1/2! & 1/3! & 1/4! & 1/5! \\ 1/3! & 1/4! & 1/5! & 1/6! \end{bmatrix}$$

becomes, after scaling the first row by 3!, the second row by 4!, the third row by 5!, and the fourth row by 6!,

$$B = \begin{bmatrix} 6 & 6 & 3 & 1 \\ 24 & 12 & 4 & 1 \\ 60 & 20 & 5 & 1 \\ 120 & 30 & 6 & 1 \end{bmatrix}.$$

Subtract the first row from each of the others to get

$$C = \begin{bmatrix} 6 & 6 & 3 & 1 \\ 18 & 6 & 1 & 0 \\ 54 & 14 & 2 & 0 \\ 114 & 24 & 3 & 0 \end{bmatrix},$$

and then scale the third row by 1/2 and the fourth row by 1/3, yielding

$$D = \begin{bmatrix} 6 & 6 & 3 & 1 \\ 18 & 6 & 1 & 0 \\ 27 & 7 & 1 & 0 \\ 38 & 8 & 1 & 0 \end{bmatrix}.$$

Next subtract the second row from the third row and the fourth rows, and scale the fourth row by 1/2 to get

$$E = \begin{bmatrix} 6 & 6 & 3 & 1 \\ 18 & 6 & 1 & 0 \\ 9 & 1 & 0 & 0 \\ 10 & 1 & 0 & 0 \end{bmatrix}.$$

Subtract the third row from the fourth, transpose the first and fourth columns, and transpose the second and third columns, leading to

$$\Delta = \begin{bmatrix} 1 & 3 & 6 & 6 \\ 0 & 1 & 6 & 18 \\ 0 & 0 & 1 & 9 \\ 0 & 0 & 0 & 1 \end{bmatrix}.$$

This triangular matrix has determinant 1, and so according to the algorithm,

$$\det(A) = \frac{2 \cdot 3 \cdot 2}{6! \, 5! \, 4! \, 3!} = \frac{1}{1036800}.$$

In the following exercises, feel free to use the determinant properties and the determinant formula in whatever combined way gives you the least work.

Exercises

3.6.1. For this exercise, let n and m be positive integers, not necessarily equal, and let $\mathbb{R}^n \times \cdots \times \mathbb{R}^n$ denote m copies of $\mathbb{R}^n$. Consider any multilinear function

$$f : \mathbb{R}^n \times \cdots \times \mathbb{R}^n \longrightarrow \mathbb{R}.$$

For any m vectors in $\mathbb{R}^n$,

$$a_1 = (a_{11}, \dots, a_{1n}),$$
$$a_2 = (a_{21}, \dots, a_{2n}),$$
$$\vdots$$
$$a_m = (a_{m1}, \dots, a_{mn}),$$

explain why

$$f(a_1, a_2, \dots, a_m) = \sum_{i=1}^{n} \sum_{j=1}^{n} \cdots \sum_{p=1}^{n} a_{1i} a_{2j} \cdots a_{mp} f(e_i, e_j, \dots, e_p).$$

Since each $f(e_i, e_j, \dots, e_p)$ is a constant (it depends on f, but not on the vectors $a_1, \dots, a_m$), the multilinear function f is a polynomial in the entries of its vector-variables. Therefore, this exercise has shown that every multilinear function is continuous.

3.6.2. Use the three desired determinant properties to derive the formulas in this section for 1×1 and 3×3 determinants. Verify that the 1×1 formula satisfies the properties.

3.6.3. For each permutation, count the inversions and compute the sign: $(2, 3, 4, 1)$, $(3, 4, 1, 2)$, $(5, 1, 4, 2, 3)$.

3.6.4. Explain why there are $n!$ permutations of $\{1, \dots, n\}$.

3.6.5. Define the permutation $\mu = (n, n-1, n-2, \dots, 1) \in S_n$. Show that μ has $(n-1)n/2$ inversions and that

$$(-1)^\mu = \begin{cases} 1 & \text{if } n \text{ has the form } 4k \text{ or } 4k+1 \ (k \in \mathbb{Z}), \\ -1 & \text{otherwise.} \end{cases}$$

3.6.6. Explain why $(-1)^{\pi'} = -(-1)^\pi$ in the proof of part (2) of Proposition 3.6.3.

3.6.7. Use the defining formula of the determinant to reproduce the result that $\det(I_n) = 1$.

3.6.8. Explain why in every term $(-1)^\pi a_{1\pi(1)} a_{2\pi(2)} \cdots a_{n\pi(n)}$ from the determinant formula, $\sum_{i=1}^n \pi(i) = \sum_{i=1}^n i$. Use this to reexplain why the determinant of a triangular matrix is the product of its diagonal entries.

3.6.9. Calculate the determinants of the following matrices:

$$\begin{bmatrix} 4 & 3 & -1 & 2 \\ 0 & 1 & 2 & 3 \\ 1 & 0 & 4 & 1 \\ 2 & 0 & 3 & 0 \end{bmatrix}, \quad \begin{bmatrix} 1 & -1 & 2 & 3 \\ 2 & 2 & 0 & 2 \\ 4 & 1 & -1 & -1 \\ 1 & 2 & 3 & 0 \end{bmatrix}.$$

3.6.10. Show that the **Vandermonde matrix**,

$$\begin{bmatrix} 1 & a & a^2 \\ 1 & b & b^2 \\ 1 & c & c^2 \end{bmatrix},$$

has determinant $(b-a)(c-a)(c-b)$. For what values of a, b, c is the Vandermonde matrix invertible? (The idea is to do the problem conceptually rather than writing out the determinant and then factoring it, so that the same ideas would work for larger matrices. The determinant formula shows that the determinant in the problem is a polynomial in a, b, and c. What is its degree in each variable? Why must it vanish if any two variables are equal? Once you have argued that that the determinant is as claimed, don't forget to finish the problem.)

3.6.11. Consider the following $n \times n$ matrix based on Pascal's triangle:

$$A = \begin{bmatrix} 1 & 1 & 1 & 1 & \cdots & 1 \\ 1 & 2 & 3 & 4 & \cdots & n \\ 1 & 3 & 6 & 10 & \cdots & \frac{n(n+1)}{2} \\ 1 & 4 & 10 & 20 & \cdots & \cdot \\ \vdots & \vdots & \vdots & \vdots & & \vdots \\ 1 & n & \frac{n(n+1)}{2} & \cdot & \cdots & \cdot \end{bmatrix}.$$

Find $\det(A)$. (Hint: Row and column reduce.)

3.6.12. This exercise constructs a determinant with no reference to permutations or their signs, inductively on the dimension n of the matrix. Define $\det_1([a]) = a$, and then

$$\det_n(A) = \sum_{j=1}^n (-1)^{1+j} a_{1j} \det_{n-1}(A^{1j}), \quad n \geq 2,$$

where A^{1j} is the $(n-1) \times (n-1)$ matrix obtained by removing the first row and jth column of A. One can start instead with $\det_0([\,]) = 1$ and then the displayed formula for $n \geq 1$. Show by induction on n that $\det_n$ is multilinear, alternating (hence skew-symmetric), and normalized as a function of the rows of A.

3.7 An Explicit Formula for the Inverse

Consider an invertible linear mapping

$$T : \mathbb{R}^n \longrightarrow \mathbb{R}^n$$

having matrix

$$A \in M_n(\mathbb{R}).$$

In Section 3.3 we discussed a process to invert A and thereby invert T. Now, with the determinant in hand, we can also write the inverse of A explicitly in closed form. Because the formula giving the inverse involves many determinants, it is hopelessly inefficient for computation. Nonetheless, it is of interest to us for a theoretical reason (the pending Corollary 3.7.3) that we will need in Chapter 5.

Definition 3.7.1 (Classical adjoint). *Let $n \geq 2$ be an integer, and let $A \in M_n(\mathbb{R})$ be an $n \times n$ matrix. For every $i, j \in \{1, \ldots, n\}$, let*

$$A^{i,j} \in M_{n-1}(\mathbb{R})$$

*be the $(n - 1) \times (n - 1)$ matrix obtained by deleting the ith row and the jth column of A. The **classical adjoint** of A is the $n \times n$ matrix whose (i, j)th entry is $(-1)^{i+j}$ times the determinant of $A^{j,i}$,*

$$A^{\mathrm{adj}} = [(-1)^{i+j} \det(A^{j,i})] \in M_n(\mathbb{R}).$$

The factor $(-1)^{i+j}$ in the formula produces an alternating checkerboard pattern of plus and minus signs, starting with a plus sign in the upper left corner of A^{adj}. Note that the (i, j)th entry of A^{adj} involves $A^{j,i}$ rather than $A^{i,j}$. For instance, in the 2×2 case,

$$\begin{bmatrix} a & b \\ c & d \end{bmatrix}^{\mathrm{adj}} = \begin{bmatrix} d & -b \\ -c & a \end{bmatrix}.$$

Already for a 3×3 matrix, the formula for the classical adjoint is daunting,

$$\begin{bmatrix} a & b & c \\ d & e & f \\ g & h & k \end{bmatrix}^{\mathrm{adj}} = \begin{bmatrix} \det\begin{bmatrix} e & f \\ h & k \end{bmatrix} & -\det\begin{bmatrix} b & c \\ h & k \end{bmatrix} & \det\begin{bmatrix} b & c \\ e & f \end{bmatrix} \\ -\det\begin{bmatrix} d & f \\ g & k \end{bmatrix} & \det\begin{bmatrix} a & c \\ g & k \end{bmatrix} & -\det\begin{bmatrix} a & c \\ d & f \end{bmatrix} \\ \det\begin{bmatrix} d & e \\ g & h \end{bmatrix} & -\det\begin{bmatrix} a & b \\ g & h \end{bmatrix} & \det\begin{bmatrix} a & b \\ d & e \end{bmatrix} \end{bmatrix}$$

$$= \begin{bmatrix} ek - fh & ch - bk & bf - ce \\ fg - dk & ak - cg & cd - af \\ dh - eg & bg - ah & ae - bd \end{bmatrix}.$$

Returning to the 2×2 case, where

$$A = \begin{bmatrix} a & b \\ c & d \end{bmatrix} \quad \text{and} \quad A^{\text{adj}} = \begin{bmatrix} d & -b \\ -c & a \end{bmatrix},$$

compute that

$$A A^{\text{adj}} = \begin{bmatrix} ad - bc & 0 \\ 0 & ad - bc \end{bmatrix} = (ad - bc) \begin{bmatrix} 1 & 0 \\ 0 & 1 \end{bmatrix} = \det(A) I_2.$$

The same result holds in general:

Proposition 3.7.2 (Classical adjoint identity). *Let $n \geq 2$ be an integer, let $A \in M_n(\mathbb{R})$ be an $n \times n$ matrix, and let A^{adj} be its classical adjoint. Then*

$$A A^{\text{adj}} = \det(A) I_n.$$

Especially, if A is invertible then

$$A^{-1} = \frac{1}{\det(A)} A^{\text{adj}}.$$

The idea of the proof is that the inner product of the ith row of A and the ith column of A^{adj} gives precisely the formula for $\det(A)$, while for $i \neq j$ the inner product of the ith row of A and the jth column of A^{adj} gives the formula for the determinant of a matrix having the ith row of A as two of its rows. The argument is purely formal but notationally tedious, and so we omit it.

In the 2×2 case the proposition gives us a slogan:

To invert a 2×2 matrix, exchange the diagonal elements, change the signs of the off-diagonal elements, and divide by the determinant.

Again, for $n > 2$ the explicit formula for the inverse is rarely of calculational use. We care about it for the following reason.

Corollary 3.7.3. *Let $A \in M_n(\mathbb{R})$ be an invertible $n \times n$ matrix. Then each entry of the inverse matrix A^{-1} is a continuous function of the entries of A.*

Proof. Specifically, the (i, j)th entry of A^{-1} is

$$(A^{-1})_{i,j} = (-1)^{i+j} \det(A^{j,i}) / \det(A),$$

a rational function (ratio of polynomials) of the entries of A. As such it varies continuously in the entries of A as long as A remains invertible.   □

Exercise

3.7.1. Verify at least one diagonal entry and at least one off-diagonal entry in the formula $A A^{\text{adj}} = \det(A) I_n$ for $n = 3$.

3.8 Geometry of the Determinant: Volume

Consider a linear mapping from n-space to n-space,

$$T : \mathbb{R}^n \longrightarrow \mathbb{R}^n.$$

This section discusses two ideas:

- The mapping T magnifies volume by a constant factor. (Here *volume* is a pandimensional term that in particular means *length* when $n = 1$, *area* when $n = 2$, and the usual notion of volume when $n = 3$.) That is, there is some number $t \geq 0$ such that if one takes a set,

$$\mathcal{E} \subset \mathbb{R}^n,$$

and passes it through the mapping to get another set,

$$T\mathcal{E} \subset \mathbb{R}^n,$$

then the set's volume is multiplied by t,

$$\mathrm{vol}\, T\mathcal{E} = t \cdot \mathrm{vol}\, \mathcal{E}.$$

The magnification factor t depends on T but is independent of the set $\mathcal{E}$.
- Furthermore, if the matrix of T is A then the magnification factor associated to T is

$$t = |\det A|.$$

That is, the absolute value of $\det A$ has a geometric interpretation as the factor by which T magnifies volume.

(The geometric interpretation of the sign of $\det A$ will be discussed in the next section.)

An obstacle to pursuing these ideas is that we don't have a theory of volume in $\mathbb{R}^n$ readily at hand. In fact, volume presents real difficulties. For instance, no notion of volume that has sensible properties can apply to all sets; so either volume behaves unreasonably or some sets don't have well-defined volumes at all. Here we have been tacitly assuming that volume does behave well and that the sets $\mathcal{E}$ under consideration do have volumes. This section will investigate volume informally by considering how it ought to behave, stating assumptions as they arise and arriving only at a partial description. The resulting arguments will be heuristic, and the skeptical reader will see gaps in the reasoning. Volume will be discussed further in Chapter 6, but a full treatment of the subject (properly called *measure*) is beyond the range of this text.

The standard basis vectors $e_1, \ldots, e_n$ in $\mathbb{R}^n$ span the **unit box**,

$$\mathcal{B} = \{\alpha_1 e_1 + \cdots + \alpha_n e_n : 0 \leq \alpha_1 \leq 1, \ldots, 0 \leq \alpha_n \leq 1\}.$$

Thus *box* means *interval* when $n = 1$, *rectangle* when $n = 2$, and the usual notion of box when $n = 3$. Let p be a point in $\mathbb{R}^n$, let $a_1, \ldots, a_n$ be positive real numbers, and let $\mathcal{B}'$ denote the box spanned by the vectors $a_1 e_1, \ldots, a_n e_n$ and translated by p,

$$\mathcal{B}' = \{\alpha_1 a_1 e_1 + \cdots + \alpha_n a_n e_n + p : 0 \leq \alpha_1 \leq 1, \ldots, 0 \leq \alpha_n \leq 1\}.$$

(See Figure 3.11. The figures of this section are set in two dimensions, but the ideas are general and hence so are the figure captions.) A **face** of a box is the set of its points such that some particular α_i is held fixed at 0 or at 1 while the others vary. A box in $\mathbb{R}^n$ has $2n$ faces.

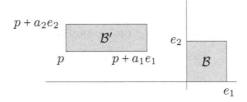

Figure 3.11. Scaling and translating the unit box

A natural definition is that the unit box has unit volume,

$$\text{vol } \mathcal{B} = 1.$$

We assume that volume is unchanged by translation. Also, we assume that box volume is *finitely additive*, meaning that given finitely many boxes $\mathcal{B}_1, \ldots, \mathcal{B}_M$ that are disjoint except possibly for shared faces or shared subsets of faces, the volume of their union is the sum of their volumes,

$$\text{vol } \bigcup_{i=1}^{M} \mathcal{B}_i = \sum_{i=1}^{M} \text{vol } \mathcal{B}_i. \tag{3.7}$$

And we assume that scaling any spanning vector of a box affects the box's volume continuously in the scaling factor. It follows that scaling any spanning vector of a box by a real number a magnifies the volume by $|a|$. To see this, first note that scaling a spanning vector by an integer ℓ creates $|\ell|$ abutting translated copies of the original box, and so the desired result follows in this case from finite additivity. A similar argument applies to scaling a spanning vector by a reciprocal integer $1/m$ ($m \neq 0$), since the original box is now $|m|$ copies of the scaled one. These two special cases show that the result holds for scaling a spanning vector by any rational number $r = \ell/m$. Finally, the continuity assumption extends the result from the rational numbers to the real numbers, since every real number is approached by a sequence of rational numbers. Since the volume of the unit box is normalized to 1, since volume

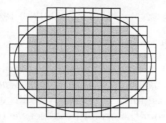

Figure 3.12. Inner and outer approximation of $\mathcal{E}$ by boxes

is unchanged by translation, and since scaling any spanning vector of a box by a magnifies its volume by $|a|$, the volume of the general box is (recalling that $a_1, \ldots, a_n$ are assumed to be positive)

$$\text{vol } \mathcal{B}' = a_1 \cdots a_n.$$

A subset of $\mathbb{R}^n$ that is well approximated by boxes plausibly has a volume. To be more specific, a subset $\mathcal{E}$ of $\mathbb{R}^n$ is well approximated by boxes if for every $\varepsilon > 0$ there exist boxes $\mathcal{B}_1, \ldots, \mathcal{B}_N, \mathcal{B}_{N+1}, \ldots, \mathcal{B}_M$, disjoint except possibly for shared faces, such that $\mathcal{E}$ is contained between a partial union of the boxes and the full union,

$$\bigcup_{i=1}^{N} \mathcal{B}_i \subset \mathcal{E} \subset \bigcup_{i=1}^{M} \mathcal{B}_i, \tag{3.8}$$

and such that the boxes that complete the partial union to the full union have a small sum of volumes,

$$\sum_{i=N+1}^{M} \text{vol } \mathcal{B}_i < \varepsilon. \tag{3.9}$$

(See Figure 3.12, where $\mathcal{E}$ is an elliptical region, the boxes $\mathcal{B}_1$ through $\mathcal{B}_N$ that it contains are dark, and the remaining boxes $\mathcal{B}_{N+1}$ through $\mathcal{B}_M$ are light.) To see that $\mathcal{E}$ should have a volume, note that the first containment of (3.8) says that a number at most big enough to serve as vol $\mathcal{E}$ (a lower bound) is $L = \text{vol } \bigcup_{i=1}^{N} \mathcal{B}_i$, and the second containment says that a number at least big enough (an upper bound) is $U = \text{vol } \bigcup_{i=1}^{M} \mathcal{B}_i$. By the finite additivity condition (3.7), the lower and upper bounds are $L = \sum_{i=1}^{N} \text{vol } \mathcal{B}_i$ and $U = \sum_{i=1}^{M} \text{vol } \mathcal{B}_i$. Thus they are close to each other by (3.9),

$$U - L = \sum_{i=N+1}^{M} \text{vol } \mathcal{B}_i < \varepsilon.$$

Since ε is arbitrarily small, the bounds should be squeezing down on a unique value that is the actual volume of $\mathcal{E}$, and so indeed $\mathcal{E}$ should have a volume. For now this is only a plausibility argument, but it is essentially the idea of integration, and it will be quantified in Chapter 6.

Every set of n vectors $v_1, \ldots, v_n$ in $\mathbb{R}^n$ spans a **parallelepiped**

$$\mathcal{P}(v_1, \ldots, v_n) = \{\alpha_1 v_1 + \cdots + \alpha_n v_n : 0 \le \alpha_1 \le 1, \ldots, 0 \le \alpha_n \le 1\},$$

abbreviated to $\mathcal{P}$ when the vectors are firmly fixed. Again the terminology is pandimensional, meaning in particular *interval, parallelogram,* and parallelepiped in the usual sense for $n = 1, 2, 3$. We will also consider translations of parallelepipeds away from the origin by offset vectors p,

$$\mathcal{P}' = \mathcal{P} + p = \{v + p : v \in \mathcal{P}\}.$$

(See Figure 3.13.) A face of a parallelepiped is the set of its points such that some particular α_i is held fixed at 0 or at 1 while the others vary. A parallelepiped in $\mathbb{R}^n$ has $2n$ faces. Boxes are special cases of parallelepipeds. The methods of Chapter 6 will show that parallelepipeds are well approximated by boxes, and so they have well-defined volumes. We assume that parallelepiped volume is finitely additive, and we assume that every finite union of parallelepipeds each having volume zero again has volume zero.

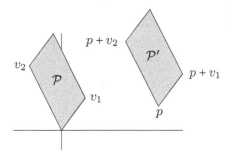

Figure 3.13. Parallelepipeds

To begin the argument that the linear mapping $T : \mathbb{R}^n \longrightarrow \mathbb{R}^n$ magnifies volume by a constant factor, we pass the unit box $\mathcal{B}$ and the scaled translated

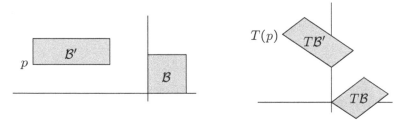

Figure 3.14. Linear image of the unit box and of a scaled translated box

box $\mathcal{B}'$ from earlier in the section through T. The image of $\mathcal{B}$ under T is a parallelepiped $T\mathcal{B}$ spanned by $T(e_1),\ldots,T(e_n)$, and the image of $\mathcal{B}'$ is a parallelepiped $T\mathcal{B}'$ spanned by $T(a_1e_1),\ldots,T(a_ne_n)$ and translated by $T(p)$. (See Figure 3.14.) Since $T(a_1e_1) = a_1T(e_1),\ldots,T(a_ne_n) = a_nT(e_n)$, it follows that scaling the sides of $T\mathcal{B}$ by $a_1,\ldots,a_n$ and then translating the scaled parallelepiped by $T(p)$ gives $T\mathcal{B}'$. As for boxes, scaling any spanning vector of a parallelepiped by a real number a magnifies the volume by $|a|$, and so we have

$$\text{vol } T\mathcal{B}' = \text{vol } T\mathcal{B} \cdot a_1 \cdots a_n.$$

But also,

$$a_1 \cdots a_n = \text{vol } \mathcal{B}'.$$

That is, the volume of the T-image of any box is a constant multiple of the volume of the box, regardless of the box's location or side lengths, the constant being the volume of $T\mathcal{B}$, the T-image of the unit box $\mathcal{B}$. Call this constant magnification factor t. Thus,

$$\text{vol } T\mathcal{B}' = t \cdot \text{vol } \mathcal{B}' \quad \text{for all boxes } \mathcal{B}'. \tag{3.10}$$

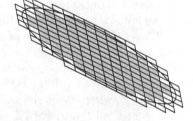

Figure 3.15. Inner and outer approximation of $T\mathcal{E}$ by parallelepipeds

We need one last preliminary result about volume. Again let $\mathcal{E}$ be a subset of $\mathbb{R}^n$ that is well approximated by boxes. Fix a linear mapping $T : \mathbb{R}^n \longrightarrow \mathbb{R}^n$. Very similarly to the argument for $\mathcal{E}$, the set $T\mathcal{E}$ also should have a volume, because it is well approximated by parallelepipeds. Indeed, the set containments (3.8) are preserved under the linear mapping T,

$$T \bigcup_{i=1}^{N} \mathcal{B}_i \subset T\mathcal{E} \subset T \bigcup_{i=1}^{M} \mathcal{B}_i.$$

In general, the image of a union is the union of the images, so this can be rewritten as

$$\bigcup_{i=1}^{N} T\mathcal{B}_i \subset T\mathcal{E} \subset \bigcup_{i=1}^{M} T\mathcal{B}_i.$$

(See Figure 3.15.) As before, numbers at most big enough and at least big enough for the volume of $T\mathcal{E}$ are

$$L = \text{vol} \bigcup_{i=1}^{N} T\mathcal{B}_i = \sum_{i=1}^{N} \text{vol } T\mathcal{B}_i, \qquad U = \text{vol} \bigcup_{i=1}^{M} T\mathcal{B}_i = \sum_{i=1}^{M} \text{vol } T\mathcal{B}_i.$$

The only new wrinkle is that citing the finite additivity of parallelepiped volume here assumes that the parallelepipeds $T\mathcal{B}_i$ either inherit from the original boxes $\mathcal{B}_i$ the property of being disjoint except possibly for shared faces, or they all have volume zero. The assumption is valid because if T is invertible then the inheritance holds, while if T is not invertible then we will see later in this section that the $T\mathcal{B}_i$ have volume zero, as desired. With this point established, let t be the factor by which T magnifies box-volume. The previous display and (3.10) combine to show that the difference of the bounds is

$$U - L = \sum_{i=N+1}^{M} \text{vol } T\mathcal{B}_i = \sum_{i=N+1}^{M} t \cdot \text{vol } \mathcal{B}_i = t \cdot \sum_{i=N+1}^{M} \text{vol } \mathcal{B}_i \le t\varepsilon.$$

The inequality is strict if $t > 0$, and it collapses to $U - L = 0$ if $t = 0$. In either case, since ε is arbitrarily small, the argument that $T\mathcal{E}$ should have a volume is the same as for $\mathcal{E}$.

To complete the argument that the linear mapping $T : \mathbb{R}^n \longrightarrow \mathbb{R}^n$ magnifies volume by a constant factor, we argue that for every subset $\mathcal{E}$ of $\mathbb{R}^n$ that is well approximated by boxes, vol $T\mathcal{E}$ is t times the volume of $\mathcal{E}$. Let $V = \text{vol} \bigcup_{i=1}^{N} \mathcal{B}_i$. Then $\mathcal{E}$ is contained between a set of volume V and a set of volume less than $V + \varepsilon$ (again see Figure 3.12, where V is the shaded area and $V + \varepsilon$ is the total area), and $T\mathcal{E}$ is contained between a set of volume tV and a set of volume at most $t(V + \varepsilon)$ (again see Figure 3.15, where tV is the shaded area and $t(V + \varepsilon)$ is the total area). Thus the volumes vol $\mathcal{E}$ and vol $T\mathcal{E}$ satisfy the condition

$$\frac{tV}{V + \varepsilon} \le \frac{\text{vol } T\mathcal{E}}{\text{vol } \mathcal{E}} \le \frac{t(V + \varepsilon)}{V}.$$

Since ε can be arbitrarily small, the left and right quantities in the display can be arbitrarily close to t, and so the only possible value for the quantity in the middle (which is independent of ε) is t. Thus we have the desired equality announced at the beginning of this section,

$$\text{vol } T\mathcal{E} = t \cdot \text{vol } \mathcal{E}.$$

In sum, subject to various assumptions about volume, T magnifies the volumes of all boxes and of all figures that are well approximated by boxes by the same factor, which we have denoted t.

Now we investigate the magnification factor t associated with the linear mapping T, with the goal of showing that it is $|\det A|$, where A is the matrix of T. As a first observation, if the linear mappings $S, T : \mathbb{R}^n \longrightarrow \mathbb{R}^n$ magnify volume by s and t respectively, then their composition $S \circ T$ magnifies volume by st. In other words, the magnification of linear mappings is multiplicative. Also, recall that the mapping T is simply multiplication by the matrix A. Since every matrix is a product of elementary matrices times an echelon matrix, we only need to study the magnification of multiplying by such matrices. Temporarily let $n = 2$.

The 2×2 recombine matrices take the form $R = \left[\begin{smallmatrix} 1 & a \\ 0 & 1 \end{smallmatrix}\right]$ and $R' = \left[\begin{smallmatrix} 1 & 0 \\ a & 1 \end{smallmatrix}\right]$ with $a \in \mathbb{R}$. The standard basis vectors e_1 and e_2 are taken by R to its columns, e_1 and $ae_1 + e_2$. Thus R acts geometrically as a shear by a in the e_1-direction, magnifying volume by 1. (See Figure 3.16.) Note that $1 = |\det R|$ as desired. The geometry of R' is left as an exercise.

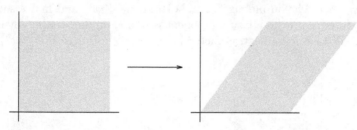

Figure 3.16. Shear

The scale matrices are $S = \left[\begin{smallmatrix} a & 0 \\ 0 & 1 \end{smallmatrix}\right]$ and $S' = \left[\begin{smallmatrix} 1 & 0 \\ 0 & a \end{smallmatrix}\right]$. The standard basis gets taken by S to ae_1 and e_2, so S acts geometrically as a scale in the e_1-direction, magnifying volume by $|a|$; this is $|\det S|$, again as desired. (See Figure 3.17.) The situation for S' is similar.

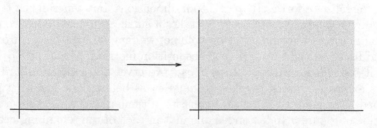

Figure 3.17. Scale

The transposition matrix is $T = \left[\begin{smallmatrix} 0 & 1 \\ 1 & 0 \end{smallmatrix}\right]$. It exchanges e_1 and e_2, acting as a reflection through the diagonal, magnifying volume by 1. (See Figure 3.18.) Since $\det T = -1$, the magnification factor is the absolute value of the determinant.

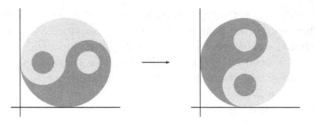

Figure 3.18. Reflection

Finally, the identity matrix $E = I$ has no effect, magnifying volume by 1, and every other echelon matrix E has bottom row $(0,0)$ and hence squashes e_1 and e_2 to vectors whose last component is 0, magnifying volume by 0. (See Figure 3.19.) The magnification factor is $|\det E|$ in both cases.

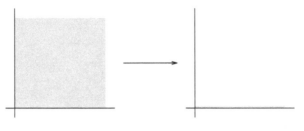

Figure 3.19. Squash

The discussion for scale matrices, transposition matrices, and echelon matrices generalizes effortlessly from 2 to n dimensions, but generalizing the discussion for recombine matrices $R_{i;j,a}$ takes a small argument. Because transposition matrices have no effect on volume, we may multiply $R_{i;j,a}$ from the left and from the right by various transposition matrices to obtain $R_{1;2,a}$ and study it instead. Multiplication by $R_{1;2,a}$ preserves all of the standard basis vectors except e_2, which is taken to $ae_1 + e_2$ as before. The resulting parallelepiped $\mathcal{P}(e_1, ae_1 + e_2, e_3, \ldots, e_n)$ consists of the parallelogram shown in the right side of Figure 3.16, extended one unit in each of the remaining orthogonal $n-2$ directions of $\mathbb{R}^n$. The n-dimensional volume of the parallelepiped is its base (the area of the parallelogram, 1) times its height (the $(n-2)$-dimensional volume of the unit box over each point of the parallelogram, again 1). That is, the $n \times n$ recombine matrix still magnifies volume by 1, the absolute value of its determinant, as desired. The base times height property of volume is yet another invocation here, but it is a consequence of a theorem to be proved in Chapter 6, Fubini's theorem. Summarizing, we have the following result.

Theorem 3.8.1 (Geometry of linear mappings). *Every linear mapping* $T : \mathbb{R}^n \longrightarrow \mathbb{R}^n$ *is the composition of a possible squash followed by shears, scales, and reflections. If the matrix of T is A then T magnifies volume by* $|\det A|$.

Proof. The matrix A of T is a product of elementary matrices and an echelon matrix. The elementary matrices act as shears, scales, and reflections, and if the echelon matrix is not the identity then it acts as a squash. This proves the first statement. Each elementary or echelon matrix magnifies volume by the absolute value of its determinant. The second statement follows since magnification and $|\det|$ are both multiplicative. $\square$

The work of this section has given a geometric interpretation of the magnitude of $\det A$: it is the magnification factor of multiplication by A. If the columns of A are denoted $c_1, \ldots, c_n$ then $Ae_j = c_j$ for $j = 1, \ldots, n$, so that even more explicitly $|\det A|$ is the volume of the parallelepiped spanned by the columns of A. For instance, to find the volume of the 3-dimensional parallelepiped spanned by the vectors $(1, 2, 3)$, $(2, 3, 4)$, and $(3, 5, 8)$, compute that

$$\left| \det \begin{bmatrix} 1 & 2 & 3 \\ 2 & 3 & 5 \\ 3 & 4 & 8 \end{bmatrix} \right| = 1.$$

Exercises

3.8.1. (a) This section states that the image of a union is the union of the images. More specifically, let A and B be any sets, let $f : A \longrightarrow B$ be any mapping, and let $A_1, \ldots, A_N$ be any subsets of A. Show that

$$f \left(\bigcup_{i=1}^N A_i \right) = \bigcup_{i=1}^N f(A_i).$$

(This exercise is purely set-theoretic, making no reference to our working environment of $\mathbb{R}^n$.)

(b) Consider a two-point set $A = \{a_1, a_2\}$ where $a_1 \ne a_2$, a one-point set $B = \{b\}$, and the only possible mapping $f : A \longrightarrow B$, given by $f(a_1) = f(a_2) = b$. Let $A_1 = \{a_1\}$ and $A_2 = \{a_2\}$, subsets of A. What is the intersection $A_1 \cap A_2$? What is the image of the intersection, $f(A_1 \cap A_2)$? What are the images $f(A_1)$ and $f(A_2)$? What is the intersection of the images, $f(A_1) \cap f(A_2)$? Is the image of an intersection in general the intersection of the images?

3.8.2. Describe the geometric effect of multiplying by the matrices R' and S' in this section. Describe the effect of multiplying by R and S if $a < 0$.

3.8.3. Describe the geometric effect of multiplying by the 3×3 elementary matrices $R_{2;3,1}$, $R_{3;1,2}$, and $S_{2,-3}$.

3.8.4. (a) Express the matrix $\left[\begin{smallmatrix} 0 & -1 \\ 1 & 0 \end{smallmatrix}\right]$ as a product of recombine and scale matrices (you may not need both types).

(b) Use part (a) to describe counterclockwise rotation of the plane through the angle $\pi/2$ as a composition of shears and scales.

3.8.5. Describe counterclockwise rotation of the plane through the angle θ (where $\cos\theta \neq 0$ and $\sin\theta \neq 0$) as a composition of shears and scales.

3.8.6. In $\mathbb{R}^3$, describe the linear mapping that takes e_1 to e_2, e_2 to e_3, and e_3 to e_1 as a composition of shears, scales, and transpositions.

3.8.7. Let $\mathcal{P}$ be the parallelogram in $\mathbb{R}^2$ spanned by (a, c) and (b, d). Calculate directly that $\left|\det\left[\begin{smallmatrix} a & b \\ c & d \end{smallmatrix}\right]\right| = $ area $\mathcal{P}$. (Hint: area = base $\times$ height = $|(a, c)|\,|(b, d)|\,|\sin\theta_{(a,c),(b,d)}|$. It may be cleaner to find the square of the area.)

3.8.8. This exercise shows directly that $|\det| = $ volume in $\mathbb{R}^3$. Let $\mathcal{P}$ be the parallelepiped in $\mathbb{R}^3$ spanned by v_1, v_2, v_3, let $\mathcal{P}'$ be spanned by the vectors v_1', v_2', v_3' obtained from performing the Gram–Schmidt process on the v_j's, let $A \in M_3(\mathbb{R})$ have rows v_1, v_2, v_3, and let $A' \in M_3(\mathbb{R})$ have rows v_1', v_2', v_3'.
(a) Explain why $\det A' = \det A$.
(b) Give a plausible geometric argument that vol $\mathcal{P}' = $ vol $\mathcal{P}$.
(c) Show that

$$A'A'^t = \begin{bmatrix} |v_1'|^2 & 0 & 0 \\ 0 & |v_2'|^2 & 0 \\ 0 & 0 & |v_3'|^2 \end{bmatrix}.$$

Explain why therefore $|\det A'| = $ vol $\mathcal{P}'$. It follows from parts (a) and (b) that $|\det A| = $ vol $\mathcal{P}$.

3.9 Geometry of the Determinant: Orientation

Recall from Section 2.1 that a basis of $\mathbb{R}^n$ is a set of vectors $\{f_1, \ldots, f_p\}$ such that every vector in $\mathbb{R}^n$ is a unique linear combination of the $\{f_j\}$. Though strictly speaking, a basis is only a set, we adopt here the convention that the basis vectors are given in the specified order indicated. Given such a basis, view the vectors as columns and let F denote the matrix in $M_{n,p}(\mathbb{R})$ with columns $f_1, \ldots, f_p$. Thus the order of the basis vectors is now relevant. For a standard basis vector e_j of $\mathbb{R}^p$, the matrix-by-vector product Fe_j gives the jth column f_j of F. Therefore, for every vector $x = (x_1, \ldots, x_p) \in \mathbb{R}^p$ (viewed as a column),

$$Fx = F \cdot \left(\sum_{j=1}^{p} x_j e_j\right) = \sum_{j=1}^{p} x_j F e_j = \sum_{j=1}^{p} x_j f_j.$$

Thus, multiplying all column vectors $x \in \mathbb{R}^p$ by the matrix F gives precisely the linear combinations of $f_1, \ldots, f_p$, and so we have the equivalences

$\{f_1, \ldots, f_p\}$ is a basis of $\mathbb{R}^n$

$\Longleftrightarrow \begin{pmatrix} \text{each } y \in \mathbb{R}^n \text{ is uniquely expressible} \\ \text{as a linear combination of the } \{f_j\} \end{pmatrix}$

$\Longleftrightarrow \begin{pmatrix} \text{each } y \in \mathbb{R}^n \text{ takes the form} \\ y = Fx \text{ for a unique } x \in \mathbb{R}^p \end{pmatrix}$

$\Longleftrightarrow F$ is invertible

$\Longleftrightarrow F$ is square (i.e., $p = n$) and $\det F \neq 0$.

These considerations have proved the following result.

Theorem 3.9.1 (Characterization of bases). *Every basis of $\mathbb{R}^n$ has n elements. The vectors $\{f_1, \ldots, f_n\}$ form a basis exactly when the matrix F having them as its columns has nonzero determinant.*

Let $\{f_1, \ldots, f_n\}$ be a basis of $\mathbb{R}^n$, and let F be the matrix formed by their columns. Abuse terminology and call $\det F$ the **determinant of the basis**, written $\det\{f_1, \ldots, f_n\}$. Again, this depends on the order of the $\{f_j\}$. There are then two kinds of bases of $\mathbb{R}^n$, **positive** and **negative bases**, according to the sign of their determinants. The standard basis $\{e_1, \ldots, e_n\}$ forms the columns of the identity matrix I and is therefore positive.

The multilinear function $\det F$ is continuous in the n^2 entries of $f_1, \ldots, f_n$ (see Exercise 3.6.1). If a basis $\{f_1, \cdots, f_n\}$ can be smoothly deformed via other bases to the standard basis then the corresponding determinants must change continuously to 1 without passing through 0. Such a basis must therefore be positive. Similarly, a negative basis cannot be smoothly deformed via other bases to the standard basis. It is also true but less clear (and not proved here) that every positive basis deforms smoothly to the standard basis.

The plane $\mathbb{R}^2$ is by convention drawn with $\{e_1, e_2\}$ forming a counterclockwise angle of $\pi/2$. Two vectors $\{f_1, f_2\}$ form a basis if they are not collinear. Therefore the basis $\{f_1, f_2\}$ can be deformed via bases to $\{e_1, e_2\}$ exactly when the angle θ_{f_1, f_2} goes counterclockwise from f_1 to f_2. (Recall from equation (2.2) that the angle between two nonzero vectors is between 0 and π.) That is, in $\mathbb{R}^2$, the basis $\{f_1, f_2\}$ is positive exactly when the angle from f_1 to f_2 is counterclockwise. (See Figure 3.20.)

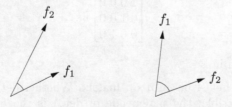

Figure 3.20. Positive and negative bases of $\mathbb{R}^2$

Three-space $\mathbb{R}^3$ is by convention drawn with $\{e_1, e_2, e_3\}$ forming a right-handed triple, meaning that when the fingers of your right hand curl from e_1 to e_2, your thumb forms an acute angle with e_3. Three vectors $\{f_1, f_2, f_3\}$ form a basis if they are not coplanar. In other words, they must form a right- or left-handed triple. Only right-handed triples deform via other nonplanar triples to $\{e_1, e_2, e_3\}$. Therefore in $\mathbb{R}^3$, the basis $\{f_1, f_2, f_3\}$ is positive exactly when it forms a right-handed triple. (See Figure 3.21.)

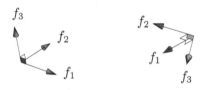

Figure 3.21. Positive and negative bases of $\mathbb{R}^3$

The geometric generalization to $\mathbb{R}^n$ of a counterclockwise angle in the plane and a right-handed triple in space is not so clear, but the algebraic notion of positive basis is the same for all n.

Consider any invertible mapping $T : \mathbb{R}^n \longrightarrow \mathbb{R}^n$ with matrix $A \in M_n(\mathbb{R})$, and any basis $\{f_1, \ldots, f_n\}$ of $\mathbb{R}^n$. If F again denotes the matrix with columns $f_1, \ldots, f_n$ then AF has columns $\{Af_1, \ldots, Af_n\} = \{T(f_1), \ldots, T(f_n)\}$. These form a new basis of $\mathbb{R}^n$ with determinant

$$\det\{T(f_1), \ldots, T(f_n)\} = \det AF = \det A \det F = \det A \det\{f_1, \ldots, f_n\}.$$

The calculation lets us interpret the sign of $\det A$ geometrically: if $\det A > 0$ then T preserves the orientation of bases, and if $\det A < 0$ then T reverses orientation. For example, the mapping with matrix

$$\begin{bmatrix} 0 & 0 & 0 & 1 \\ 1 & 0 & 0 & 0 \\ 0 & 1 & 0 & 0 \\ 0 & 0 & 1 & 0 \end{bmatrix}$$

reverses orientation in $\mathbb{R}^4$.

To summarize: Let A be an $n \times n$ matrix. Whether $\det A$ is nonzero says whether A is invertible; the magnitude of $\det A$ is the factor by which A magnifies volume; and (assuming that $\det A \neq 0$) the sign of $\det A$ determines how A affects orientation. The determinant is astonishing.

Exercises

3.9.1. Every invertible mapping $T : \mathbb{R}^n \longrightarrow \mathbb{R}^n$ is a composition of scales, shears, and transpositions. Give conditions on such a composition to make the mapping orientation-preserving, orientation-reversing.

3.9.2. Does the linear mapping $T : \mathbb{R}^n \longrightarrow \mathbb{R}^n$ that takes e_1 to e_2, e_2 to e_3, ..., e_n to e_1 preserve or reverse orientation? (The answer depends on n.) More generally, if π is a permutation in S_n, does the linear mapping taking e_1 to $e_{\pi(1)}, \ldots, e_n$ to $e_{\pi(n)}$ preserve or reverse orientation? (This depends on π.)

3.9.3. Argue geometrically in $\mathbb{R}^2$ that every basis can be smoothly deformed via other bases to the standard basis or to $\{e_1, -e_2\}$. Do the same for $\mathbb{R}^3$ and $\{e_1, e_2, -e_3\}$.

3.10 The Cross Product, Lines, and Planes in $\mathbb{R}^3$

Generally in $\mathbb{R}^n$ there is no natural way to associate to a pair of vectors u and v a third vector. In $\mathbb{R}^3$, however, the plane specified by u and v has only one orthogonal direction, i.e., dimension 3 is special because $3 - 2 = 1$. In $\mathbb{R}^3$ a normal vector to u and v can be specified by making suitable conventions on its orientation vis-à-vis the other two vectors, and on its length. This will give a vector-valued product of two vectors that is special to 3-dimensional space, called the *cross product*. The first part of this section develops these ideas.

Given any two vectors $u, v \in \mathbb{R}^3$, we want their cross product $u \times v \in \mathbb{R}^3$ to be orthogonal to u and v,

$$u \times v \perp u \quad \text{and} \quad u \times v \perp v. \tag{3.11}$$

There is the question of which way $u \times v$ should point along the line orthogonal to the plane spanned by u and v. The natural answer is that the direction should be chosen to make the ordered triple of vectors $\{u, v, u \times v\}$ positive unless it is degenerate,

$$\det(u, v, u \times v) \geq 0. \tag{3.12}$$

Also there is the question of how long $u \times v$ should be. With hindsight, we assert that specifying the length to be the area of the parallelogram spanned by u and v will work well. That is,

$$|u \times v| = \operatorname{area} \mathcal{P}(u, v). \tag{3.13}$$

The three desired geometric properties (3.11) through (3.13) seem to describe the cross product completely. (See Figure 3.22.)

The three geometric properties also seem disparate. However, they combine into a uniform algebraic property, as follows. Since the determinant in (3.12) is nonnegative, it is the volume of the parallelepiped spanned by u, v, and $u \times v$.

Figure 3.22. The cross product of u and v

The volume is the base times the height, and because $u \times v$ is normal to u and v, the base is the area of $\mathcal{P}(u, v)$ and the height is $|u \times v|$. Thus

$$\det(u, v, u \times v) = \operatorname{area} \mathcal{P}(u, v) \, |u \times v|.$$

It follows from the previous display and (3.13) that

$$|u \times v|^2 = \det(u, v, u \times v).$$

Since orthogonal vectors have inner product 0, since the determinant is 0 when two rows agree, and since the square of the absolute value is the vector's inner product with itself, we can rewrite (3.11) and this last display (obtained from (3.12) and (3.13)) uniformly as equalities of the form $\langle u \times v, w \rangle = \det(u, v, w)$ for various w,

$$\langle u \times v, u \rangle = \det(u, v, u),$$
$$\langle u \times v, v \rangle = \det(u, v, v), \tag{3.14}$$
$$\langle u \times v, u \times v \rangle = \det(u, v, u \times v).$$

Instead of saying what the cross product *is*, as an equality of the form $u \times v = f(u, v)$ would, the three equalities of (3.14) say how the cross product *interacts* with certain vectors—including itself—via the inner product. Again, the idea is to characterize rather than construct.

(The reader may object to the argument just given that $\det(u, v, u \times v) = \operatorname{area} \mathcal{P}(u, v) \, |u \times v|$, on the grounds that we don't really understand the area of a 2-dimensional parallelogram in 3-dimensional space to start with, that in $\mathbb{R}^3$ we measure volume rather than area, and the parallelogram surely has volume zero. In fact, the argument can be viewed as motivating the formula as the *definition* of the area. This idea will be discussed more generally in Section 9.1.)

Based on (3.14), we leap boldly to an intrinsic algebraic characterization of the cross product.

Definition 3.10.1 (Cross product). *Let u and v be any two vectors in $\mathbb{R}^3$. Their* **cross product** *$u \times v$ is defined by the property*

$$\langle u \times v, w \rangle = \det(u, v, w) \quad \textit{for all } w \in \mathbb{R}^3.$$

That is, $u \times v$ is the unique vector $x \in \mathbb{R}^3$ such that $\langle x, w \rangle = \det(u, v, w)$ for all $w \in \mathbb{R}^3$.

As with the determinant earlier, we do not yet know that the characterizing property determines the cross product uniquely, or even that a cross product that satisfies the characterizing property exists at all. But also as with the determinant, we defer those issues and first reap the consequences of the characterizing property with no reference to an unpleasant formula for the cross product. Of course the cross product will exist and be unique, but for now the point is that graceful arguments with its characterizing property show that it has all the further properties that we want it to have.

Proposition 3.10.2 (Properties of the cross product).

(CP1) *The cross product is skew-symmetric: $v \times u = -u \times v$ for all $u, v \in \mathbb{R}^3$.*

(CP2) *The cross product is bilinear: for all scalars $a, a', b, b' \in \mathbb{R}$ and all vectors $u, u', v, v' \in \mathbb{R}^3$,*

$$(au + a'u') \times v = a(u \times v) + a'(u' \times v),$$
$$u \times (bv + b'v') = b(u \times v) + b'(u \times v').$$

(CP3) *The cross product $u \times v$ is orthogonal to u and v.*

(CP4) *$u \times v = \mathbf{0}$ if and only if u and v are collinear (meaning that $u = av$ or $v = au$ for some $a \in \mathbb{R}$).*

(CP5) *If u and v are not collinear then the triple $\{u, v, u \times v\}$ is right-handed.*

(CP6) *The magnitude $|u \times v|$ is the area of the parallelogram spanned by u and v.*

Proof. (1) This follows from the skew-symmetry of the determinant. For every $w \in \mathbb{R}^3$,

$$\langle v \times u, w \rangle = \det(v, u, w) = -\det(u, v, w) = -\langle u \times v, w \rangle = \langle -u \times v, w \rangle.$$

Since w is arbitrary, $v \times u = -u \times v$.

(2) For the first variable, this follows from the linearity of the determinant in its first row-vector variable and the linearity of the inner product in its first vector variable. Fix $a, a' \in \mathbb{R}$, $u, u', v \in \mathbb{R}^3$. For every $w \in \mathbb{R}^3$,

$$
\begin{aligned}
\langle (au + a'u') \times v, w \rangle &= \det(au + a'u', v, w) \\
&= a\det(u, v, w) + a'\det(u', v, w) \\
&= a\langle u \times v, w \rangle + a'\langle u' \times v, w \rangle \\
&= \langle a(u \times v) + a'(u' \times v), w \rangle.
\end{aligned}
$$

Since w is arbitrary, $(au + a'u') \times v = a(u \times v) + a'(u' \times v)$. The proof for the second variable follows from the result for the first variable and from (1).

(3) $\langle u \times v, u \rangle = \det(u, v, u) = 0$ because the determinant of a matrix with two equal rows vanishes. Similarly, $\langle u \times v, v \rangle = 0$.

(4) If $u = av$ then for every $w \in \mathbb{R}^3$,

$$\langle u \times v, w \rangle = \langle av \times v, w \rangle = \det(av, v, w) = a \det(v, v, w) = 0.$$

Since w is arbitrary, $u \times v = \mathbf{0}$. And similarly if $v = au$.

Conversely, suppose that u and v are not collinear. Then they are linearly independent, and so no element of $\mathbb{R}^3$ can be written as a linear combination of u and v in more than one way. The set $\{u, v\}$ is not a basis of $\mathbb{R}^3$, because every basis consists of three elements. Since no elements of $\mathbb{R}^3$ can be written as a linear combination of u and v in more than one way, and since $\{u, v\}$ is not a basis, the only possibility is that some $w \in \mathbb{R}^3$ cannot be written as a linear combination of u and v at all. Thus the set $\{u, v, w\}$ is a linearly independent set of three elements, making it a basis of $\mathbb{R}^3$. Compute that since $\{u, v, w\}$ is a basis,

$$\langle u \times v, w \rangle = \det(u, v, w) \neq 0.$$

Therefore $u \times v \neq \mathbf{0}$.

(5) By (4), $u \times v \neq \mathbf{0}$, so $0 < \langle u \times v, u \times v \rangle = \det(u, v, u \times v)$. By the results on determinants and orientation, $\{u, v, u \times v\}$ is right-handed.

(6) By definition, $|u \times v|^2 = \langle u \times v, u \times v \rangle = \det(u, v, u \times v)$. As discussed earlier in this section, $\det(u, v, u \times v) = \operatorname{area} \mathcal{P}(u, v) |u \times v|$. The result follows from dividing by $|u \times v|$ if it is nonzero, and from (4) otherwise. $\qquad\square$

Now we show that the characterizing property determines the cross product uniquely. The idea is that a vector's inner products with all other vectors completely describe the vector itself. The observation to make is that for every vector $x \in \mathbb{R}^n$ (n need not be 3 in this paragraph),

$$\text{if } \langle x, w \rangle = 0 \text{ for all } w \in \mathbb{R}^n \text{ then } x = \mathbf{0}_n.$$

To justify this observation, specialize w to x to show that $\langle x, x \rangle = 0$, giving the result because $\mathbf{0}_n$ is the only vector whose inner product with itself is 0. (Here we use the nontrivial direction of the degeneracy condition in the positive definiteness property of the inner product.) In consequence of the observation, for any two vectors $x, x' \in \mathbb{R}^n$,

$$\text{if } \langle x, w \rangle = \langle x', w \rangle \text{ for all } w \in \mathbb{R}^n \text{ then } x = x'.$$

That is, the inner product values $\langle x, w \rangle$ for all $w \in \mathbb{R}^n$ specify x, as anticipated.

To prove that the cross product exists, it suffices to write a formula for it that satisfies the characterizing property in Definition 3.10.1. Since we need the cross product to have components

$$\langle u \times v, e_1 \rangle = \det(u, v, e_1),$$
$$\langle u \times v, e_2 \rangle = \det(u, v, e_2),$$
$$\langle u \times v, e_3 \rangle = \det(u, v, e_3),$$

the only possible formula is to construct the cross product from these components,

$$u \times v = (\det(u, v, e_1), \det(u, v, e_2), \det(u, v, e_3)).$$

This formula indeed satisfies the definition, because by definition of the inner product and then by the linearity of the determinant in its third argument, we have for every $w = (w_1, w_2, w_3) \in \mathbb{R}^3$,

$$\langle u \times v, w \rangle = \det(u, v, e_1) \cdot w_1 + \det(u, v, e_2) \cdot w_2 + \det(u, v, e_3) \cdot w_3$$
$$= \det(u, v, w_1 e_1 + w_2 e_2 + w_3 e_3)$$
$$= \det(u, v, w).$$

In coordinates, the formula for the cross product is

$$u \times v = (\det \begin{bmatrix} u_1 & u_2 & u_3 \\ v_1 & v_2 & v_3 \\ 1 & 0 & 0 \end{bmatrix}, \det \begin{bmatrix} u_1 & u_2 & u_3 \\ v_1 & v_2 & v_3 \\ 0 & 1 & 0 \end{bmatrix}, \det \begin{bmatrix} u_1 & u_2 & u_3 \\ v_1 & v_2 & v_3 \\ 0 & 0 & 1 \end{bmatrix})$$
$$= (u_2 v_3 - u_3 v_2, u_3 v_1 - u_1 v_3, u_1 v_2 - u_2 v_1).$$

A bit more conceptually, the cross product formula in coordinates is

$$u \times v = \det \begin{bmatrix} u_1 & u_2 & u_3 \\ v_1 & v_2 & v_3 \\ e_1 & e_2 & e_3 \end{bmatrix}.$$

The previous display is only a mnemonic device: strictly speaking, it doesn't lie within our grammar, because the entries of the bottom row are vectors rather than scalars. But even so, its two terms $u_1 v_2 e_3 - u_2 v_1 e_3$ do give the third entry of the cross product, and similarly for the others. In Chapter 9, where we will have to compromise our philosophy of working intrinsically rather than in coordinates, this formula will be cited and generalized. In the meantime, its details are not important except for mechanical calculations, and we want to use it as little as possible, as with the determinant earlier. Indeed, the display shows that the cross product is essentially a special case of the determinant.

It is worth knowing the cross products of the standard basis pairs,

$$e_1 \times e_1 = \mathbf{0}_3, \quad e_1 \times e_2 = e_3, \quad e_1 \times e_3 = -e_2,$$
$$e_2 \times e_1 = -e_3, \quad e_2 \times e_2 = \mathbf{0}_3, \quad e_2 \times e_3 = e_1,$$
$$e_3 \times e_1 = e_2, \quad e_3 \times e_2 = -e_1, \quad e_3 \times e_3 = \mathbf{0}_3.$$

Here $e_i \times e_j$ is $\mathbf{0}_3$ if $i = j$, and $e_i \times e_j$ is the remaining standard basis vector if $i \neq j$ and i and j are in order in the diagram

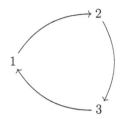

and $e_i \times e_j$ is minus the remaining standard basis vector if $i \neq j$ and i and j are out of order in the diagram.

The remainder of this section describes lines and planes in $\mathbb{R}^3$.

A line ℓ in $\mathbb{R}^3$ is determined by a point p and a direction vector d. (See Figure 3.23.) A point q lies in the line exactly when it is a translation from p by some multiple of d. Therefore the line ℓ is given by

$$\ell(p, d) = \{p + td : t \in \mathbb{R}\}.$$

In coordinates, a point (x, y, z) lies in $\ell((x_p, y_p, z_p), (x_d, y_d, z_d))$ exactly when

$$x = x_p + tx_d, \quad y = y_p + ty_d, \quad z = z_p + tz_d \quad \text{for some } t \in \mathbb{R}.$$

If the components of d are all nonzero then the relation between the coordinates can be expressed without the parameter t,

$$\frac{x - x_p}{x_d} = \frac{y - y_p}{y_d} = \frac{z - z_p}{z_d}.$$

For example, the line through $(1, 1, 1)$ in the direction $(1, 2, 3)$ consists of all points (x, y, z) satisfying $x = 1 + t$, $y = 1 + 2t$, $z = 1 + 3t$ for $t \in \mathbb{R}$, or equivalently, satisfying $x - 1 = (y - 1)/2 = (z - 1)/3$.

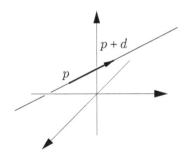

Figure 3.23. Line in $\mathbb{R}^3$

A plane P in $\mathbb{R}^3$ is determined by a point p and a normal (orthogonal) vector n. (See Figure 3.24.) A point q lies in the plane exactly when the vector from p to q is orthogonal to n. Therefore the plane P is given by

$$P(p,n) = \{q \in \mathbb{R}^3 : \langle q - p, n \rangle = 0\}.$$

In coordinates, a point (x, y, z) lies in $P((x_p, y_p, z_p), (x_n, y_n, z_n))$ exactly when

$$(x - x_p)x_n + (y - y_p)y_n + (z - z_p)z_n = 0.$$

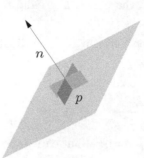

Figure 3.24. Plane in $\mathbb{R}^3$

Exercises

3.10.1. Evaluate $(2, 0, -1) \times (1, -3, 2)$.

3.10.2. Suppose that a vector $v \in \mathbb{R}^3$ takes the form $v = u_1 \times e_1 = u_2 \times e_2$ for some u_1 and u_2. Describe v.

3.10.3. True or false: For all u, v, w in $\mathbb{R}^3$, $(u \times v) \times w = u \times (v \times w)$.

3.10.4. Express $(u + v) \times (u - v)$ as a scalar multiple of $u \times v$.

3.10.5. (a) Let $U, V \in M_n(\mathbb{R})$ be skew-symmetric, meaning that $U^\mathsf{T} = -U$ and similarly for V, where U^T is the transpose of U (Exercise 3.2.4). Show that aU is skew-symmetric for every $a \in \mathbb{R}$, and that $U + V$ is skew-symmetric. Thus the skew-symmetric matrices form a vector space. Show furthermore that the *Lie bracket* $[U, V] = UV - VU$ is skew-symmetric. One can optionally check that although the Lie bracket product is not in general associative, it instead satisfies the *Jacobi identity*,

$$[[U, [V, W]] + [V, [W, U]] + [W, [U, V]] = 0.$$

(b) Encode the vectors $u = (u_1, u_2, u_3)$ and $v = (v_1, v_2, v_3)$ as 3×3 skew-symmetric matrices,

$$U = \begin{bmatrix} 0 & -u_1 & -u_2 \\ u_1 & 0 & -u_3 \\ u_2 & u_3 & 0 \end{bmatrix}, \qquad V = \begin{bmatrix} 0 & -v_1 & -v_2 \\ v_1 & 0 & -v_3 \\ v_2 & v_3 & 0 \end{bmatrix}.$$

Show that the Lie bracket product $[U, V]$ encodes the cross product $u \times v$.

3.10.6. Investigate the extent to which a cancellation law holds for the cross product, as follows: for fixed u, v in $\mathbb{R}^3$ with $u \neq 0$, describe the vectors w satisfying the condition $u \times v = u \times w$.

3.10.7. What is the line specified by two points p and p'?

3.10.8. Give conditions on the points p, p' and the directions d, d' so that $\ell(p, d) = \ell(p', d')$.

3.10.9. Express the relation between the coordinates of a point on $\ell(p, d)$ if the x-component of d is 0.

3.10.10. What can you conclude about the lines

$$\frac{x - x_p}{x_d} = \frac{y - y_p}{y_d} = \frac{z - z_p}{z_d} \quad \text{and} \quad \frac{x - x_p}{x_D} = \frac{y - y_p}{y_D} = \frac{z - z_p}{z_D}$$

given that $x_d x_D + y_d y_D + z_d z_D = 0$? What can you conclude if instead $x_d/x_D = y_d/y_D = z_d/z_D$?

3.10.11. Show that $\ell(p, d)$ and $\ell(p', d')$ intersect if and only if the linear equation $Dt = \Delta p$ is solvable, where $D \in M_{3,2}(\mathbb{R})$ has columns d and d', t is the column vector $\left[\begin{smallmatrix} t_1 \\ t_2 \end{smallmatrix}\right]$, and $\Delta p = p' - p$. For what points p and p' do $\ell(p, (1, 2, 2))$ and $\ell(p', (2, -1, 4))$ intersect?

3.10.12. Use vector geometry to show that the distance from the point q to the line $\ell(p, d)$ is

$$\frac{|(q - p) \times d|}{|d|}.$$

(Hint: what is the area of the parallelogram spanned by $q - p$ and d?) Find the distance from the point $(3, 4, 5)$ to the line $\ell((1, 1, 1), (1, 2, 3))$.

3.10.13. Show that the time of nearest approach of two particles whose positions are $s(t) = p + tv$, $\tilde{s}(t) = \tilde{p} + t\tilde{v}$ is $t = -\langle \Delta p, \Delta v\rangle/|\Delta v|^2$. (You may assume that the particles are at their nearest approach when the difference of their velocities is orthogonal to the difference of their positions.)

3.10.14. Write the equation of the plane through $(1, 2, 3)$ with normal direction $(1, 1, 1)$.

3.10.15. Where does the plane $x/a + y/b + z/c = 1$ intersect each axis?

3.10.16. Specify the plane containing the point p and spanned by directions d and d'. Specify the plane containing the three points p, q, and r.

3.10.17. Use vector geometry to show that the distance from the point q to the plane $P(p, n)$ is

$$\frac{|\langle q - p, n\rangle|}{|n|}.$$

(Hint: Resolve $q - p$ into components parallel and normal to n.) Find the distance from the point $(3, 4, 5)$ to the plane $P((1, 1, 1), (1, 2, 3))$.

4

The Derivative

In one-variable calculus the derivative is a limit of difference quotients, but this idea does not generalize to many variables. The multivariable definition of the derivative to be given in this chapter has three noteworthy features:

- The derivative is defined as a linear mapping.
- The derivative is characterized intrinsically rather than constructed in co-ordinates.
- The derivative is characterized by the property of closely approximating the original mapping near the point of approximation.

Section 4.1 shows that the familiar definition of the one-variable derivative cannot scale up to many variables. Section 4.2 introduces a pandimensional notation scheme that describes various closenesses of approximation. The notation packages a range of ideas that arise in calculus, handling them uniformly. Section 4.3 revisits the one-variable derivative, rephrasing it in the new scheme, and then scales it up to many variables. Handy basic properties of the derivative follow immediately. Section 4.4 obtains some basic results about the derivative intrinsically, notably the chain rule. Section 4.5 computes with coordinates to calculate the derivative by considering one variable at a time and using the techniques of one-variable calculus. This section also obtains a coordinate-based version of the chain rule. Section 4.6 studies the multivariable counterparts of higher-order derivatives from one-variable calculus. Section 4.7 discusses optimization of functions of many variables. Finally, Section 4.8 discusses the rate of change of a function of many variables as its input moves in any fixed direction, not necessarily parallel to a coordinate axis.

© Springer International Publishing AG 2016
J. Shurman, *Calculus and Analysis in Euclidean Space*,
Undergraduate Texts in Mathematics, DOI 10.1007/978-3-319-49314-5_4

4.1 Trying to Extend the Symbol-Pattern: Immediate, Irreparable Catastrophe

In one-variable calculus, the derivative of a function $f : \mathbb{R} \longrightarrow \mathbb{R}$ at a point $a \in \mathbb{R}$ is defined as a limit,

$$f'(a) = \lim_{h \to 0} \frac{f(a+h) - f(a)}{h}.$$

But for every integer $n > 1$, the corresponding expression makes no sense for a mapping $f : \mathbb{R}^n \longrightarrow \mathbb{R}^m$ and for a point a of $\mathbb{R}^n$. Indeed, the expression is

$$\lim_{h \to \mathbf{0}_n} \frac{f(a+h) - f(a)}{h},$$

but this is not even grammatically admissible—there is no notion of division by the vector h. That is, the standard definition of derivative does not generalize to more than one input variable.

The breakdown here cannot be repaired by any easy patch. We must re-think the derivative altogether in order to extend it to many variables.

Fortunately, the reconceptualization is richly rewarding.

Exercise

4.1.1. For a mapping $f : \mathbb{R}^n \longrightarrow \mathbb{R}^m$ and a point a of $\mathbb{R}^n$, the repair-attempt of defining $f'(a)$ as

$$\lim_{h \to \mathbf{0}_n} \frac{f(a+h) - f(a)}{|h|}$$

is grammatically sensible. Does it reproduce the usual derivative if $n = m = 1$?

4.2 New Environment: The Bachmann–Landau Notation

The notation to be introduced in this section, originally due to Bachmann late in the nineteenth century, was also employed by Landau. It was significantly repopularized in the 1960s by Knuth in his famous computer science books, and it is now integral to mathematics, computer science, and mathematical statistics.

Definition 4.2.1 ($o(1)$-mapping, $\mathcal{O}(h)$-mapping, $o(h)$-mapping). *Consider a mapping from some ball about the origin in one Euclidean space to a second Euclidean space,*

$$\varphi : B(\mathbf{0}_n, \varepsilon) \longrightarrow \mathbb{R}^m$$

where n and m are positive integers and $\varepsilon > 0$ is a positive real number. The mapping φ is **smaller than order 1** *if* *for every $c > 0$, $|\varphi(h)| \le c$ for all small enough h.*

The mapping φ is **of order** h *if*

for some $c > 0$, $|\varphi(h)| \le c|h|$ for all small enough h.

The mapping φ is **smaller than order** h *if*

for every $c > 0$, $|\varphi(h)| \le c|h|$ for all small enough h.

A mapping smaller than order 1 is denoted $o(1)$, a mapping of order h is denoted $\mathcal{O}(h)$, and a mapping smaller than order h is denoted $o(h)$. Also $o(1)$ can denote the collection of $o(1)$-mappings, and similarly for $\mathcal{O}(h)$ and $o(h)$.

The definition says that in terms of magnitudes, an $o(1)$-mapping is smaller than every constant as h gets small, and an $\mathcal{O}(h)$-mapping is at most some constant multiple of h as h gets small, and an $o(h)$-mapping is smaller than every constant multiple of h as h gets small. That is,

$$\left\{\begin{array}{l} |o(1)| \to 0 \\[4pt] \dfrac{|\mathcal{O}(h)|}{|h|} \text{ is bounded} \\[4pt] \dfrac{|o(h)|}{|h|} \to 0 \end{array}\right\} \quad \text{as } h \to \mathbf{0},$$

but the definitions of $\mathcal{O}(h)$ and $o(h)$ avoid the divisions in the previous display, and the definitions further stipulate that every $o(1)$-mapping or $\mathcal{O}(h)$-mapping or $o(h)$-mapping takes the value $\mathbf{0}$ at $h = \mathbf{0}$. That is, beyond avoiding division, the definitions are strictly speaking slightly stronger than the previous display. Also, the definitions quickly give the containments

$$o(h) \subset \mathcal{O}(h) \subset o(1),$$

meaning that every $o(h)$-mapping is an $\mathcal{O}(h)$-mapping, and every $\mathcal{O}(h)$-mapping is an $o(1)$-mapping.

Visually, the idea is that:

- For every $c > 0$, however small, close enough to the origin the graph of an $o(1)$-mapping lies between the horizontal lines at height $\pm c$, although the requisite closeness of h to $\mathbf{0}$ can change as c gets smaller.
- For some particular $c > 0$, close enough to the origin the graph of an $\mathcal{O}(h)$-mapping lies inside the bow-tie-shaped envelope determined by the lines $y = \pm cx$.
- For every $c > 0$, however small, close enough to the origin the graph of an $o(h)$-mapping lies inside the $y = \pm cx$ bow-tie, although the requisite closeness of h to $\mathbf{0}$ can change as c gets smaller.

These images are oversimplified, representing a mapping's n-dimensional domain-ball and m-dimensional codomain-space as axes, but still the images correctly suggest that the $o(1)$ condition describes continuity in local coordinates, and the $\mathcal{O}(h)$ condition describes at-most-linear growth in local coordinates, and the $o(h)$ condition describes smaller-than-linear growth in local coordinates. (A *local* coordinate system has its origin placed at some particular point of interest, allowing us to assume that the point is simply the origin.)

The next proposition gives the important basic example to have at hand.

Proposition 4.2.2 (Basic family of Landau functions). *Consider the function*

$$\varphi_e : \mathbb{R}^n \longrightarrow \mathbb{R}, \quad \varphi_e(x) = |x|^e \quad (where\ e \geq 0\ is\ a\ real\ number).$$

Then

- *φ_e is $o(1)$ if $e > 0$,*
- *φ_e is $\mathcal{O}(h)$ if $e \geq 1$,*
- *φ_e is $o(h)$ if $e > 1$.*

The proof is Exercise 4.2.2. Examples are shown in Figure 4.1.

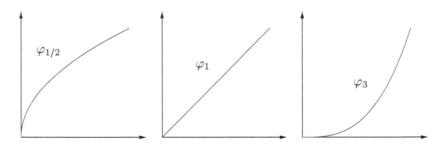

Figure 4.1. Basic $o(1)$, $\mathcal{O}(h)$, and $o(h)$ functions

Since Definition 4.2.1 stipulates growth-bounds, the following result is immediate.

Proposition 4.2.3 (Dominance principle for the Landau spaces). *Let φ be $o(1)$, and suppose that $|\psi(h)| \leq |\varphi(h)|$ for all small enough h. Then also ψ is $o(1)$. And similarly for $\mathcal{O}(h)$ and for $o(h)$.*

For example, the function

$$\psi : \mathbb{R} \longrightarrow \mathbb{R}, \quad \psi(h) = \begin{cases} h^2 \sin(1/h) & \text{if } h \neq 0, \\ 0 & \text{if } h = 0 \end{cases}$$

is $o(h)$ despite oscillating ever faster as h approaches 0, because $|\psi| \le |\varphi_2|$ where $\varphi_2(h) = h^2$ is $o(h)$ by Proposition 4.2.2. The reader should draw a sketch of this situation.

Similarly, the functions $\psi, \phi : \mathbb{R}^2 \longrightarrow \mathbb{R}$ given by

$$\psi(h,k) = h, \qquad \phi(h,k) = k$$

are $\mathcal{O}((h,k))$ because the size bounds say that they are bounded absolutely by the $\mathcal{O}(h)$-mapping $\varphi_1(h,k) = |(h,k)|$, i.e., $|\psi(h,k)| = |h| \le |(h,k)|$ and similarly for ϕ. For general n and for every $i \in \{1, \ldots, n\}$, now letting h denote a vector again as usual rather than the first component of a vector as it did a moment ago, the ith component function

$$\psi : \mathbb{R}^n \longrightarrow \mathbb{R}, \quad \psi(h) = h_i$$

is $\mathcal{O}(h)$ by the same argument. We will use this observation freely in the sequel.

The $o(1)$ and $\mathcal{O}(h)$ and $o(h)$ conditions give rise to predictable closure properties.

Proposition 4.2.4 (Vector space properties of the Landau spaces).
For every fixed domain-ball $B(\mathbf{0}_n, \varepsilon)$ and codomain-space $\mathbb{R}^m$, the $o(1)$-mappings form a vector space, and $\mathcal{O}(h)$ forms a subspace, of which $o(h)$ forms a subspace in turn. Symbolically,

$$o(1) + o(1) = o(1), \qquad \mathbb{R}\, o(1) = o(1),$$
$$\mathcal{O}(h) + \mathcal{O}(h) = \mathcal{O}(h), \qquad \mathbb{R}\, \mathcal{O}(h) = \mathcal{O}(h),$$
$$o(h) + o(h) = o(h), \qquad \mathbb{R}\, o(h) = o(h),$$

i.e., $o(1)$ and $\mathcal{O}(h)$ and $o(h)$ absorb addition and scalar multiplication.

The fact that $o(1)$ forms a vector space encodes the rules that sums and constant multiples of continuous mappings are again continuous.

Proof (Sketch). Consider any $\varphi, \psi \in o(1)$. For every $c > 0$,

$$|\varphi(h)| \le c/2 \text{ and } |\psi(h)| \le c/2 \quad \text{for all small enough } h,$$

and so by the triangle inequality,

$$|(\varphi + \psi)(h)| \le c \quad \text{for all small enough } h.$$

(A fully quantified version of the argument is as follows. Let $c > 0$ be given. There exists $\delta_\varphi > 0$ such that $|\varphi(h)| \le c/2$ if $|h| \le \delta_\varphi$, and there exists $\delta_\psi > 0$ such that $|\psi(h)| \le c/2$ if $|h| \le \delta_\psi$. Let $\delta = \min\{\delta_\varphi, \delta_\psi\}$. Then $|(\varphi + \psi)(h)| \le c$ if $|h| \le \delta$.) Similarly, for every nonzero $\alpha \in \mathbb{R}$,

$$|\varphi(h)| \le c/|\alpha| \quad \text{for all small enough } h,$$

so that since the modulus is absolute-homogeneous,

$$|(\alpha\varphi)(h)| \le c \quad \text{for all small enough } h.$$

If instead $\varphi, \psi \in \mathcal{O}(h)$ then for all small enough h,

$$|\varphi(h)| \le c|h| \text{ and } |\psi(h)| \le c'|h| \quad \text{for some } c, c' > 0,$$

so that for all small enough h,

$$|(\varphi + \psi)(h)| \le (c + c')|h|.$$

Similarly, for every nonzero $\alpha \in \mathbb{R}$, for all small enough h,

$$|(\alpha\varphi)(h)| \le (|\alpha|c)|h|.$$

The argument for $o(h)$ is similar to the argument for $o(1)$ (Exercise 4.2.3). $\quad\square$

For example, the function

$$\varphi : \mathbb{R}^n \longrightarrow \mathbb{R}, \quad \varphi(x) = 12|x|^{1/2} - 7|x| + 5|x|^{3/2}$$

is an $o(1)$-function because all three of its terms are. It is not an $\mathcal{O}(h)$-function even though its second and third terms are, and it is not an $o(h)$-function even though its third term is.

Another handy fact is the componentwise nature of the conditions $o(1)$ and $\mathcal{O}(h)$ and $o(h)$. To see this, first note that every $\varphi : B(\mathbf{0}_n, \varepsilon) \longrightarrow \mathbb{R}^m$ is $o(1)$ if and only if the corresponding absolute value $|\varphi| : B(\mathbf{0}_n, \varepsilon) \longrightarrow \mathbb{R}$ is. Now let φ have component functions $\varphi_1, \ldots, \varphi_m$. For every $h \in B(\mathbf{0}_n, \varepsilon)$ and for each $j \in \{1, \ldots, m\}$, the size bounds give

$$|\varphi_j(h)| \le |\varphi(h)| \le \sum_{i=1}^{m} |\varphi_i(h)|.$$

Using the left side of the size bounds and then the vector space properties of $o(1)$ and then the right side of the size bounds, we get

$$|\varphi| \text{ is } o(1) \implies \text{each } |\varphi_j| \text{ is } o(1) \implies \sum_{i=1}^{m} |\varphi_i| \text{ is } o(1) \implies |\varphi| \text{ is } o(1).$$

Thus $|\varphi|$ is $o(1)$ if and only if each $|\varphi_i|$ is. As explained just above, we may drop the absolute values, and so in fact φ is $o(1)$ if and only if each φ_i is, as desired. The arguments for the $\mathcal{O}(h)$ and $o(h)$ conditions are the same (Exercise 4.2.4). The componentwise nature of the $o(1)$ condition encodes the componentwise nature of continuity.

The role of linear mappings in the Landau notation scheme is straightforward, affirming the previously mentioned intuition that the $\mathcal{O}(h)$ condition describes at-most-linear growth and the $o(h)$ condition describes smaller-than-linear growth.

Proposition 4.2.5. *Every linear mapping is $\mathcal{O}(h)$. The only $o(h)$ linear mapping is the zero mapping.*

Proof. Let $T : \mathbb{R}^n \longrightarrow \mathbb{R}^m$ be a linear mapping. The unit sphere in $\mathbb{R}^n$ is compact and T is continuous, so the image of the unit sphere under T is again compact, hence bounded. That is, some positive $c \in \mathbb{R}$ exists such that $|T(h_o)| \leq c$ whenever $|h_o| = 1$. The homogeneity of T shows that $|T(h)| \leq c|h|$ for all nonzero h: letting $h_o = h/|h|$,

$$|T(h)| = |T(|h|h_o)| = ||h|T(h_o)| = |h||T(h_o)| \leq c|h|.$$

And the inequality holds for $h = \mathbf{0}$ as well. Thus T is $\mathcal{O}(h)$.

Now assume that T is not the zero mapping. Thus $T(h_o)$ is nonzero for some nonzero h_o, and we may take $|h_o| = 1$. Let $c = |T(h_o)|/2$, a positive real number. For every scalar multiple $h = \alpha h_o$ of h_o, however small, compute (noting for the last step that $|h| = |\alpha|$)

$$|T(h)| = |T(\alpha h_o)| = |\alpha T(h_o)| = |\alpha||T(h_o)| = 2c|\alpha| = 2c|h|.$$

That is, $|T(h)| > c|h|$ for some arbitrarily small h-values, i.e., it is not the case that $|T(h)| \leq c|h|$ for all small enough h. Thus T fails the $o(h)$ definition for the particular constant $c = |T(h_o)|/2$. □

For scalar-valued functions, a product property is useful to have at hand.

Proposition 4.2.6 (Product property for Landau functions). *Consider two scalar-valued functions and their product function,*

$$\varphi, \psi, \varphi\psi : B(\mathbf{0}_n, \varepsilon) \longrightarrow \mathbb{R}.$$

If φ is $o(1)$ and ψ is $\mathcal{O}(h)$ then $\varphi\psi$ is $o(h)$. Especially, the product of two linear functions is $o(h)$.

Proof. Let $c > 0$ be given. For some $d > 0$, for all h close enough to $\mathbf{0}_n$,

$$|\varphi(h)| \leq c/d \quad \text{and} \quad |\psi(h)| \leq d|h|,$$

and so

$$|(\varphi\psi)(h)| \leq c|h|.$$

The second statement of the proposition follows from its first statement and the previous proposition. □

For two particular examples, consider the linear functions

$$\pi_1, \pi_2 : \mathbb{R}^2 \longrightarrow \overset{\text{not } \mathbb{R}^m}{\mathbb{R}}, \qquad \pi_1(h, k) = h, \quad \pi_2(h, k) = k.$$

The proposition combines with the vector space properties of $o(h, k)$ to say that the functions

$$\alpha, \beta : \mathbb{R}^2 \longrightarrow \mathbb{R}, \qquad \alpha(h, k) = h^2 - k^2, \qquad \beta(h, k) = hk$$

are both $o(h, k)$.

Beyond their vector space properties, the Landau spaces carry composition properties. If $\varphi : B(\mathbf{0}_n, \varepsilon) \longrightarrow \mathbb{R}^m$ and $\psi : B(\mathbf{0}_m, \rho) \longrightarrow \mathbb{R}^\ell$ are both $o(1)$, then after shrinking ε if necessary, the composition $\psi \circ \varphi : B(\mathbf{0}_n, \varepsilon) \longrightarrow \mathbb{R}^\ell$ is also defined. That is, composition of $o(1)$-mappings is defined after suitably shrinking a domain-ball. From now on, we shrink domain-balls as necessary without further comment.

Proposition 4.2.7 (Composition properties of the Landau spaces). *The composition of $o(1)$-mappings is again an $o(1)$-mapping. Also, the composition of $\mathcal{O}(h)$-mappings is again an $\mathcal{O}(h)$-mapping. Furthermore, the composition of an $\mathcal{O}(h)$-mapping and an $o(h)$-mapping, in either order, is again an $o(h)$-mapping. Symbolically,*

$$o(o(1)) = o(1),$$
$$\mathcal{O}(\mathcal{O}(h)) = \mathcal{O}(h),$$
$$o(\mathcal{O}(h)) = o(h),$$
$$\mathcal{O}(o(h)) = o(h).$$

That is, $o(1)$ and $\mathcal{O}(h)$ absorb themselves, and $o(h)$ absorbs $\mathcal{O}(h)$ from either side.

The rule $o(o(1)) = o(1)$ encodes the persistence of continuity under composition.

Proof. For example, to verify the third rule, suppose that $\varphi : B(\mathbf{0}_n, \varepsilon) \longrightarrow \mathbb{R}^m$ is $\mathcal{O}(h)$ and that $\psi : B(\mathbf{0}_m, \rho) \longrightarrow \mathbb{R}^\ell$ is $o(k)$. Then

for some $c > 0$, $|\varphi(h)| \leq c|h|$ for all small enough h.

Thus if h is small then so is $\varphi(h)$, so that

for any $d > 0$, $|\psi(\varphi(h))| \leq d|\varphi(h)|$ for all small enough h.

Since c is some particular positive number and d can be any positive number, cd again can be any positive number. That is, letting $e = cd$ and combining the previous two displays, we have

for every $e > 0$, $|(\psi \circ \varphi)(h)| \leq e|h|$ for all small enough h.

Hence $\psi \circ \varphi$ is $o(h)$, as desired.

A fully quantified version of the argument is as follows. The hypotheses are that

there exist $c > 0$ and $\delta > 0$ such that $|\varphi(h)| \leq c|h|$ if $|h| \leq \delta$

and that

for every $d > 0$ there exists $\varepsilon_d > 0$ such that $|\psi(k)| \le d|k|$ if $|k| \le \varepsilon_d$.

Now let $e > 0$ be given. Define $d = e/c$ and $\rho_e = \min\{\delta, \varepsilon_d/c\}$. Suppose that $|h| \le \rho_e$. Then

$$|\varphi(h)| \le c|h| \le \varepsilon_d \quad \text{since } |h| \le \delta \text{ and } |h| \le \varepsilon_d/c,$$

and so

$$|\psi(\varphi(h))| \le d|\varphi(h)| \le cd|h| \quad \text{since } |\varphi(h)| \le \varepsilon_d \text{ and } |\varphi(h)| \le c|h|.$$

That is,

$$|\psi(\varphi(h))| \le e|h| \quad \text{since } cd = e.$$

This shows that $\psi \circ \varphi$ is $o(h)$, since for every $e > 0$ there exists $\rho_e > 0$ such that $|(\psi \circ \phi)(h)| \le e|h|$ if $|h| \le \rho_e$.

The other rules are proved similarly (Exercise 4.2.5). $\qquad\qquad\square$

Exercises

4.2.1. By analogy to Definition 4.2.1, give the appropriate definition of an $\mathcal{O}(1)$-mapping. What is the geometric interpretation of the definition? Need an $\mathcal{O}(1)$-mapping take $\mathbf{0}$ to 0?

4.2.2. Let e be a nonnegative real number. Consider the function

$$\varphi_e : \mathbb{R}^n \longrightarrow \mathbb{R}, \quad \varphi(x) = |x|^e.$$

(a) Suppose that $e > 0$. Let $c > 0$ be given. If $|h| \le c^{1/e}$ then what do we know about $|\varphi_e(h)|$ in comparison to c? What does this tell us about φ_e?

(b) Prove that φ_1 is $\mathcal{O}(h)$.

(c) Suppose that $e > 1$. Combine parts (a) and (b) with the product property for Landau functions (Proposition 4.2.6) to show that φ_e is $o(h)$.

(d) Explain how parts (a), (b), and (c) have proved Proposition 4.2.2.

4.2.3. Complete the proof of Proposition 4.2.4.

4.2.4. Establish the componentwise nature of the $\mathcal{O}(h)$ condition, and establish the componentwise nature of the $o(h)$ condition.

4.2.5. Complete the proof of Proposition 4.2.7.

4.3 One-Variable Revisionism: The Derivative Redefined

The one-variable derivative as recalled at the beginning of the chapter,

$$f'(a) = \lim_{h \to 0} \frac{f(a + h) - f(a)}{h},$$

is a construction. To rethink the derivative, we should characterize it instead.

To think clearly about what it means for the graph of a function to have a tangent of slope t at a point $(a, f(a))$, we should work in local coordinates and normalize to the case of a horizontal tangent. That is, given a function f of x-values near some point a, and given a candidate tangent-slope t at $(a, f(a))$, define a related function g of h-values near 0,

$$g(h) = f(a + h) - f(a) - th.$$

Thus g takes 0 to 0, and the graph of g near the origin is like the graph of f near $(a, f(a))$ but with the line of slope t subtracted. To reiterate, the idea that f has a tangent of slope t at $(a, f(a))$ has been normalized to the tidier idea that g has slope 0 at the origin:

> *To say that the graph of g is horizontal at the origin is to say that for every positive real number c, however small, the region between the lines of slope $\pm c$ contains the graph of g close enough to the origin.*

That is:

> *The intuitive condition for the graph of g to be horizontal at the origin is precisely that g is $o(h)$. The horizontal nature of the graph of g at the origin connotes that the graph of f has a tangent of slope t at $(a, f(a))$.*

The symbolic connection between this characterization of the derivative and the constructive definition is immediate. As always, the definition of f having derivative $f'(a)$ at a is

$$\lim_{h \to 0} \frac{f(a + h) - f(a)}{h} = f'(a),$$

which is to say,

$$\lim_{h \to 0} \frac{f(a + h) - f(a) - f'(a)h}{h} = 0,$$

and indeed, this is precisely the $o(h)$ condition on g. Figure 4.2 illustrates the idea that when h is small, not only is the vertical distance $f(a + h) - f(a) - f'(a)h$ from the tangent line to the curve small as well, but it is small even relative to the horizontal distance h.

We need to scale these ideas up to many dimensions. Instead of viewing the one-variable derivative as the scalar $f'(a)$, think of it as the corresponding

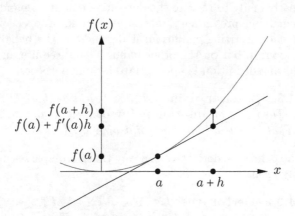

Figure 4.2. Vertical distance from tangent line to curve

linear mapping $T_a : \mathbb{R} \longrightarrow \mathbb{R}$, multiplication by $f'(a)$. That is, think of it as the mapping

$$T_a(h) = f'(a)h \qquad \text{for all } h \in \mathbb{R}.$$

Figure 4.3 incorporates this idea. The figure is similar to Figure 4.2, but it shows the close approximation in the local coordinate system centered at the point of tangency, and in the local coordinate system the tangent line is indeed the graph of the linear mapping T_a. The shaded axis-portions in the figure are h horizontally and $g(h) = f(a + h) - f(a) - f'(a)h$ vertically, and the fact that the vertical portion is so much smaller illustrates that $g(h)$ is $o(h)$.

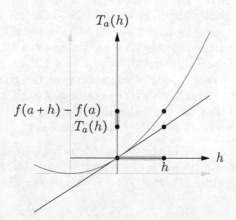

Figure 4.3. Vertical distance in local coordinates

We are nearly ready to rewrite the derivative definition pandimensionally. The small remaining preliminary matter is to take into account the local nature of the characterizing condition: it depends on the behavior of f only on an ε-ball about a, but on the other hand, it does require an entire ε-ball. Thus the following definition is appropriate for our purposes.

Definition 4.3.1 (Interior point). *Let A be a subset of $\mathbb{R}^n$, and let a be a point of A. Then a is an* **interior point** *of A if some ε-ball about a is a subset of A. That is, a is an interior point of A if $B(a, \varepsilon) \subset A$ for some $\varepsilon > 0$.*

Now we can define the derivative in a way that encompasses many variables and is suitably local.

Definition 4.3.2 (Derivative). *Let A be a subset of $\mathbb{R}^n$, let $f : A \longrightarrow \mathbb{R}^m$ be a mapping, and let a be an interior point of A. Then f is* **differentiable at** *a if there exists a linear mapping $T_a : \mathbb{R}^n \longrightarrow \mathbb{R}^m$ satisfying the condition*

$$f(a + h) - f(a) - T_a(h) \quad is \quad o(h). \tag{4.1}$$

This T_a is called **the derivative of** *f at a, written Df_a or $(Df)_a$. When f is differentiable at a, the matrix of the linear mapping Df_a is written $f'(a)$ and is called the* **Jacobian matrix** *of f at a.*

Here are two points to note about Definition 4.3.2:

- Again, an assertion that a mapping is differentiable at a point has the connotation that the point is an interior point of the mapping's domain. That is, if f is differentiable at a then $B(a, \varepsilon) \subset A$ for some $\varepsilon > 0$. In the special case $n = 1$, we are disallowing the derivative at an endpoint of the domain.
- The domain of the linear mapping T_a is unrestricted even if f itself is defined only locally about a. Indeed, the definition of linearity requires that the linear mapping have all of $\mathbb{R}^n$ as its domain. Every linear mapping is so uniform that in any case its behavior on all of $\mathbb{R}^n$ is determined by its behavior on any ε-ball about $\mathbf{0}_n$ (Exercise 4.3.1). In geometric terms, the graph of T, the tangent object approximating the graph of f at $(a, f(a))$, extends without bound, even if the graph of f itself is restricted to points near $(a, f(a))$. But the approximation of the graph by the tangent object needs to be close only near the point of tangency.

Returning to the idea of the derivative as a linear mapping, when $n = 2$ and $m = 1$ a function $f : A \longrightarrow \mathbb{R}$ is differentiable at an interior point (a, b) of A if for small scalar values h and k, $f(a + h, b + k) - f(a, b)$ is well approximated by a linear function

$$T(h, k) = \alpha h + \beta k$$

where α and β are scalars. Since the equation $z = f(a, b) + \alpha h + \beta k$ describes a plane in (x, y, z)-space (where $h = x - a$ and $k = y - b$), f is differentiable at (a,b) if its graph has a well-fitting tangent plane through $(a,b,f(a,b))$. (See Figure 4.4.) Here the derivative of f at (a,b) is the linear mapping taking (h,k) to $\alpha h + \beta k$, and the Jacobian matrix of f at a is therefore $[\alpha, \beta]$. The tangent plane in the figure is not the graph of the derivative $Df_{(a,b)}$, but rather a translation of the graph. Another way to say this is that the $(h,k,Df_{(a,b)}(h,k))$-coordinate system has its origin at the point $(a,b,f(a,b))$ in the figure.

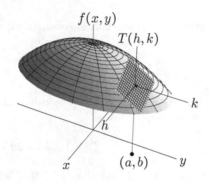

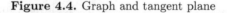

Figure 4.4. Graph and tangent plane

When $n=1$ and $m=3$, a mapping $f : A \longrightarrow \mathbb{R}^3$ is differentiable at an interior point a of A if $f(a+h)-f(a)$ is closely approximated for small real h by a linear mapping

$$T(h) = \begin{bmatrix} \alpha \\ \beta \\ \gamma \end{bmatrix} h$$

for some scalars α, β, and γ. As h varies through $\mathbb{R}$, $f(a)+T(h)$ traverses the line $\ell = \ell(f(a),(\alpha,\beta,\gamma))$ in $\mathbb{R}^3$ that is tangent at $f(a)$ to the output curve of f. (See Figure 4.5.) Here $Df_a(h) = \begin{bmatrix} \alpha \\ \beta \\ \gamma \end{bmatrix} h$, and the corresponding Jacobian matrix is $\begin{bmatrix} \alpha \\ \beta \\ \gamma \end{bmatrix}$. Note that the figure does not show the domain of f, so it may help to think of f as a time-dependent traversal of the curve rather than as the curve itself. The figure does not have room for the $(h,Df_a(h))$-coordinate system (which is 4-dimensional), but the $Df_a(h)$-coordinate system has its origin at the point $f(a)$.

For an example, let $A = B((0,0),1)$ be the unit disk in $\mathbb{R}^2$, and consider the function

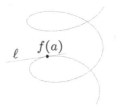

Figure 4.5. Tangent to a parametrized curve

$$f : A \longrightarrow \mathbb{R}, \qquad f(x,y) = x^2 - y^2.$$

We show that for every point $(a,b) \in A$, f is differentiable at (a,b), and its derivative is the linear mapping

$$T_{(a,b)} : \mathbb{R}^2 \longrightarrow \mathbb{R}, \qquad T_{(a,b)}(h,k) = 2ah - 2bk.$$

To verify this, we need to check Definition 4.3.2. The point that is written in the definition intrinsically as a (where a is a vector) is written here in coordinates as (a,b) (where a and b are scalars), and similarly the vector h in the definition is written (h,k) here, because the definition is intrinsic, whereas here we are going to compute. To check the definition, first note that every point (a,b) of A is an interior point; the fact that every point of A is interior doesn't deserve a detailed proof right now, only a quick comment. Second, confirm the derivative's characterizing property (4.1) by calculating that

$$
\begin{aligned}
f(a+h,b+k) &- f(a,b) - T_{(a,b)}(h,k) \\
&= (a+h)^2 - (b+k)^2 - a^2 + b^2 - 2ah + 2bk \\
&= h^2 - k^2.
\end{aligned}
$$

We saw immediately after the product property for Landau functions (Proposition 4.2.6) that $h^2 - k^2$ is $o(h,k)$. This is the desired result. Also, the calculation tacitly shows how the derivative was found for us to verify: the difference $f(a+h,b+k) - f(a,b)$ is $2ah - 2bk + h^2 - k^2$, which as a function of h and k has a linear part $2ah - 2bk$ and a quadratic part $h^2 - k^2$ that is much smaller when h and k are small. The linear approximation of the difference is the derivative.

Before continuing, we need to settle a grammatical issue. Definition 4.3.2 refers to *any* linear mapping that satisfies condition (4.1) as *the* derivative of f at a. Fortunately, the derivative, if it exists, is unique, justifying the definite article. The uniqueness is geometrically plausible: if two straight objects (e.g., lines or planes) approximate the graph of f well near $(a, f(a))$, then they should also approximate each other well enough that straightness forces them to coincide. The quantitative argument amounts to recalling that the only linear $o(h)$-mapping is zero.

Proposition 4.3.3 (Uniqueness of the derivative). *Let* $f : A \longrightarrow \mathbb{R}^m$ *(where* $A \subset \mathbb{R}^n$*) be differentiable at* a*. Then there is only one linear mapping satisfying the definition of* Df_a*.*

Proof. Suppose that the linear mappings $T_a, \tilde{T}_a : \mathbb{R}^n \longrightarrow \mathbb{R}^m$ are both derivatives of f at a. Then the two mappings

$$f(a+h) - f(a) - T_a(h) \quad \text{and} \quad f(a+h) - f(a) - \tilde{T}_a(h)$$

are both $o(h)$. By the vector space properties of $o(h)$, so is their difference $(\tilde{T}_a - T_a)(h)$. Since the linear mappings from $\mathbb{R}^n$ to $\mathbb{R}^m$ form a vector space as well, the difference $\tilde{T}_a - T_a$ is linear. But the only $o(h)$ linear mapping is the zero mapping, so $\tilde{T}_a = T_a$ as desired.   □

Finally, another result is immediate in our setup.

Proposition 4.3.4 (Differentiability implies continuity). *If* f *is differentiable at* a *then* f *is continuous at* a*.*

Proof. Compute, using the differentiability of f at a and the fact that linear mappings are $\mathcal{O}(h)$, then the containment $o(h) \subset \mathcal{O}(h)$ and the closure of $\mathcal{O}(h)$ under addition, and finally the containment $\mathcal{O}(h) \subset o(1)$, that

$$f(a+h) - f(a) = f(a+h) - f(a) - T_a(h) + T_a(h) = o(h) + \mathcal{O}(h) = \mathcal{O}(h) = o(1).$$

Since the $o(1)$ condition describes continuity, the argument is complete.   □

We will study the derivative via two routes. On the one hand, the linear mapping $Df_a : \mathbb{R}^n \longrightarrow \mathbb{R}^m$ is specified by mn scalar entries of its matrix $f'(a)$, and so calculating the derivative is tantamount to determining these scalars by using coordinates. On the other hand, developing conceptual theorems without getting lost in coefficients and indices requires the intrinsic idea of the derivative as a well-approximating linear mapping.

Exercises

4.3.1. Let $T : \mathbb{R}^n \longrightarrow \mathbb{R}^m$ be a linear mapping. Show that for every $\varepsilon > 0$, the behavior of T on $B(\mathbf{0}_n, \varepsilon)$ determines the behavior of T everywhere.

4.3.2. Give a geometric interpretation of the derivative when $n = m = 2$. Give a geometric interpretation of the derivative when $n = 1$ and $m = 2$.

4.3.3. Let $f : A \longrightarrow \mathbb{R}^m$ (where $A \subset \mathbb{R}^n$) have component functions $f_1, \ldots, f_m$, and let a be an interior point of A. Let $T : \mathbb{R}^n \longrightarrow \mathbb{R}^m$ be a linear mapping with component functions $T_1, \ldots, T_m$. Using the componentwise nature of the $o(h)$ condition, established in Section 4.2, prove the **componentwise nature of differentiability**: f is differentiable at a with derivative T if and only if each component f_i is differentiable at a with derivative T_i.

4.3.4. Let $f(x, y) = (x^2 - y^2, 2xy)$. Show that $Df_{(a,b)}(h, k) = (2ah - 2bk, 2bh + 2ak)$ for all $(a, b) \in \mathbb{R}^2$. (By the previous problem, you may work componentwise.)

4.3.5. Let $g(x, y) = xe^y$. Show that $Dg_{(a,b)}(h, k) = he^b + kae^b$ for all $(a, b) \in \mathbb{R}^2$. (Note that because $e^0 = 1$ and because the derivative of the exponential function at 0 is 1, the one-variable characterizing property says that $e^k - 1 = k + o(k)$.)

4.3.6. Show that if $f : \mathbb{R}^n \longrightarrow \mathbb{R}^m$ satisfies $|f(x)| \le |x|^2$ for all $x \in \mathbb{R}^n$ then f is differentiable at $\mathbf{0}_n$.

4.3.7. Show that the function $f(x, y) = \sqrt{|xy|}$ for all $(x, y) \in \mathbb{R}^2$ is not differentiable at $(0, 0)$. (First see what $Df_{(0,0)}(h, 0)$ and $Df_{(0,0)}(0, k)$ need to be.)

4.4 Basic Results and the Chain Rule

Before constructing the derivative coordinatewise via the Jacobian matrix, we derive some results intrinsically from its characterizing property. We begin by computing two explicit derivatives.

Proposition 4.4.1 (Derivatives of constant and linear mappings).

(1) *Let $C : A \longrightarrow \mathbb{R}^m$ (where $A \subset \mathbb{R}^n$) be the constant mapping $C(x) = c$ for all $x \in A$, where c is some fixed value in $\mathbb{R}^m$. Then the derivative of C at every interior point a of A is the zero mapping.*

(2) *The derivative of a linear mapping $T : \mathbb{R}^n \longrightarrow \mathbb{R}^m$ at every point $a \in \mathbb{R}^n$ is again T.*

Proof. Both of these results hold essentially by grammar. In general, the derivative of a mapping f at a is the linear mapping that well approximates $f(a + h) - f(a)$ for h near $\mathbf{0}_n$. But $C(a + h) - C(a)$ is the zero mapping for all $h \in A$, so it is well approximated near $\mathbf{0}_n$ by the zero mapping on $\mathbb{R}^n$. Similarly, $T(a + h) - T(a)$ is $T(h)$ for all $h \in \mathbb{R}^n$, and this linear mapping is well approximated by itself near $\mathbf{0}_n$.

To prove (1) more symbolically, let $Z : \mathbb{R}^n \longrightarrow \mathbb{R}^m$ denote the zero mapping, $Z(h) = \mathbf{0}_m$ for all $h \in \mathbb{R}^n$. Then

$$C(a + h) - C(a) - Z(h) = c - c - 0 = 0 \quad \text{for all } h \in \mathbb{R}^n.$$

Being the zero mapping, $C(a+h) - C(a) - Z(h)$ is crushingly $o(h)$, showing that Z meets the condition to be DC_a. And (2) is similar (Exercise 4.4.1). $\square$

Of course, differentiation passes through addition and scalar multiplication of mappings.

Proposition 4.4.2 (Linearity of differentiation). *Let $f : A \longrightarrow \mathbb{R}^m$ (where $A \subset \mathbb{R}^n$) and $g : B \longrightarrow \mathbb{R}^m$ (where $B \subset \mathbb{R}^n$) be mappings, and let a be a point of $A \cap B$. Suppose that f and g are differentiable at a with derivatives Df_a and Dg_a. Then:*

(1) *The sum $f + g : A \cap B \longrightarrow \mathbb{R}^m$ is differentiable at a with derivative $D(f + g)_a = Df_a + Dg_a$.*

(2) *For every $\alpha \in \mathbb{R}$, the scalar multiple $\alpha f : A \longrightarrow \mathbb{R}^m$ is differentiable at a with derivative $D(\alpha f)_a = \alpha Df_a$.*

The proof is a matter of seeing that the vector space properties of $o(h)$ encode the sum rule and constant multiple rule for derivatives.

Proof. Since f and g are differentiable at a, some ball about a lies in A and some ball about a lies in B. The smaller of these two balls lies in $A \cap B$. That is, a is an interior point of the domain of $f + g$. With this topological issue settled, proving the proposition reduces to direct calculation. For (1),

$$(f+g)(a+h) - (f+g)(a) - (Df_a + Dg_a)(h)$$
$$= f(a+h) - f(a) - Df_a(h) + g(a+h) - g(a) - Dg_a(h)$$
$$= o(h) + o(h) = o(h).$$

And (2) is similar (Exercise 4.4.2). $\square$

Elaborate mappings are built by composing simpler ones. The next theorem is the important result that the derivative of a composition is the composition of the derivatives. That is, the best linear approximation of a composition is the composition of the best linear approximations.

Theorem 4.4.3 (Chain rule). *Let $f : A \longrightarrow \mathbb{R}^m$ (where $A \subset \mathbb{R}^n$) be a mapping, let $B \subset \mathbb{R}^m$ be a set containing $f(A)$, and let $g : B \longrightarrow \mathbb{R}^\ell$ be a mapping. Thus the composition $g \circ f : A \longrightarrow \mathbb{R}^\ell$ is defined. If f is differentiable at the point $a \in A$, and g is differentiable at the point $f(a) \in B$, then the composition $g \circ f$ is differentiable at the point a, and its derivative there is*

$$D(g \circ f)_a = Dg_{f(a)} \circ Df_a.$$

In terms of Jacobian matrices, since the matrix of a composition is the product of the matrices, the chain rule is

$$(g \circ f)'(a) = g'(f(a)) \, f'(a).$$

The fact that we can prove that the derivative of a composition is the composition of the derivatives without an explicit formula for the derivative is akin to the fact in the previous chapter that we could prove that the determinant of the product is the product of the determinants without an explicit formula for the determinant.

Proof. To showcase the true issues of the argument clearly, we reduce the problem to a normalized situation. For simplicity, we first take $a = \mathbf{0}_n$ and $f(a) = \mathbf{0}_m$. So we are given that

$$f(h) = S(h) + o(h),$$
$$g(k) = T(k) + o(k),$$

and we need to show that

$$(g \circ f)(h) = (T \circ S)(h) + o(h).$$

Compute that

$$g(f(h)) = g(Sh + o(h)) \qquad\qquad \text{by the first given}$$
$$= TSh + T(o(h)) + o(Sh + o(h)) \quad \text{by the second.}$$

We know that $Tk = \mathcal{O}(k)$ and $Sh = \mathcal{O}(h)$, so the previous display gives

$$(g \circ f)(h) = (T \circ S)(h) + \mathcal{O}(o(h)) + o\big(\mathcal{O}(h) + o(h)\big).$$

Since $o(h) \subset \mathcal{O}(h)$ and $\mathcal{O}(h)$ is closed under addition, since $o(h)$ absorbs $\mathcal{O}(h)$ from either side, and since $o(h)$ is closed under addition, the error (the last two terms on the right side of the previous display) is

$$\mathcal{O}(o(h)) + o\big(\mathcal{O}(h) + o(h)\big) = \mathcal{O}(o(h)) + o(\mathcal{O}(h)) = o(h) + o(h) = o(h).$$

Therefore we have shown that

$$(g \circ f)(h) = (T \circ S)(h) + o(h),$$

exactly as desired. The crux of the matter is that $o(h)$ absorbs $\mathcal{O}(h)$ from either side.

For the general case, no longer assuming that $a = \mathbf{0}_n$ and $f(a) = \mathbf{0}_m$, we are given that

$$f(a + h) = f(a) + S(h) + o(h),$$
$$g(f(a) + k) = g(f(a)) + T(k) + o(k),$$

and we need to show that

$$(g \circ f)(a + h) = (g \circ f)(a) + (T \circ S)(h) + o(h).$$

Compute that

$$g(f(a+h)) = g(f(a) + Sh + o(h)) \qquad\qquad \text{by the first given}$$
$$= g(f(a)) + TSh + T(o(h)) + o(Sh + o(h)) \quad \text{by the second,}$$

and from here the proof that the remainder term is $o(h)$ is precisely as it is in the normalized case. $\qquad\square$

Two quick applications of the chain rule arise naturally for scalar-valued functions. Given two such functions, not only is their sum defined, but because $\mathbb{R}$ is a field (unlike $\mathbb{R}^m$ for $m > 1$), so is their product and so is their quotient at points where g is nonzero. With some help from the chain rule, the derivative laws for product and quotient follow easily from elementary calculations.

Lemma 4.4.4 (Derivatives of the product and reciprocal functions).
Define the product function,

$$p : \mathbb{R}^2 \longrightarrow \mathbb{R}, \qquad p(x,y) = xy,$$

and define the reciprocal function

$$r : \mathbb{R} - \{0\} \longrightarrow \mathbb{R}, \qquad r(x) = 1/x.$$

Then:

(1) *The derivative of p at every point $(a,b) \in \mathbb{R}^2$ exists and is*

$$Dp_{(a,b)}(h,k) = bh + ak.$$

(2) *The derivative of r at every nonzero real number a exists and is*

$$Dr_a(h) = -h/a^2.$$

Proof. (1) Compute

$$p(a+h, b+k) - p(a,b) - bh - ak = (a+h)(b+k) - ab - bh - ak = hk.$$

By the size bounds, $|h| \le |(h,k)|$ and $|k| \le |(h,k)|$, so $|hk| = |h|\,|k| \le |(h,k)|^2$. Since $|(h,k)|^2$ is $\varphi_2(h,k)$ (where φ_e is the example from Proposition 4.2.2), it is $o(h,k)$.

Statement (2) is left as Exercise 4.4.3. $\qquad\square$

Proposition 4.4.5 (Multivariable product and quotient rules). *Let $f : A \longrightarrow \mathbb{R}$ (where $A \subset \mathbb{R}^n$) and $g : B \longrightarrow \mathbb{R}$ (where $B \subset \mathbb{R}^n$) be functions, and let f and g differentiable at a. Then:*

(1) *fg is differentiable at a with derivative*

$$D(fg)_a(h) = g(a)Df_a(h) + f(a)Dg_a(h).$$

(2) *If $g(a) \neq 0$ then f/g is differentiable at a with derivative*

$$D\left(\frac{f}{g}\right)_a(h) = \frac{g(a)Df_a(h) - f(a)Dg_a(h)}{g(a)^2}.$$

Proof. (1) As explained in the proof of Proposition 4.4.2, a is an interior point of the domain $A \cap B$ of fg, so we have only to compute. The product function fg is the composition $p \circ (f, g)$, where $(f, g) : A \cap B \longrightarrow \mathbb{R}^2$ is the mapping with component functions f and g. For every $h \in \mathbb{R}^n$, the chain rule and the componentwise nature of differentiation (this was Exercise 4.3.3) give

$$D(fg)_a(h) = D(p \circ (f,g))_a(h) = \left(Dp_{(f,g)(a)} \circ D(f,g)_a\right)(h)$$
$$= Dp_{(f(a),g(a))}(Df_a(h), Dg_a(h)),$$

and by the previous lemma,

$$Dp_{(f(a),g(a))}(Df_a(h), Dg_a(h)) = g(a)Df_a(h) + f(a)Dg_a(h).$$

This proves (1). Statement (2) is similar (Exercise 4.4.4) but with the wrinkle that one needs to show that since $g(a) \neq 0$ and since Dg_a exists, it follows that a is an interior point of the domain of f/g. Here it is relevant that g must be continuous at a, and so by the persistence of inequality principle (Proposition 2.3.10), g is nonzero on some ε-ball at a, as desired.   □

With the results accumulated so far, we can compute the derivative of every mapping whose component functions are given by rational expressions in its component input scalars. By the componentwise nature of differentiability, it suffices to find the derivatives of the component functions. Since these are compositions of sums, products, and reciprocals of constants and linear functions, their derivatives are calculable with the existing machinery.

Suppose, for instance, that $f(x, y) = (x^2 - y)/(y + 1)$ for all $(x, y) \in \mathbb{R}^2$ such that $y \neq -1$. Note that every point of the domain of f is an interior point. Rewrite f as

$$f = \frac{X^2 - Y}{Y + 1}$$

where X is the linear function $X(x, y) = x$ on $\mathbb{R}^2$ and similarly $Y(x, y) = y$. Applications of the chain rule and virtually every other result on derivatives so far shows that at every point (a, b) in the domain of f, the derivative $Df_{(a,b)}$ is given by (justify the steps)

$Df_{(a,b)}(h,k)$

$$= \frac{(Y+1)(a,b)D(X^2 - Y)_{(a,b)} - (X^2 - Y)(a,b)D(Y+1)_{(a,b)}}{((Y+1)(a,b))^2}(h,k)$$

$$= \frac{(b+1)(D(X^2)_{(a,b)} - DY_{(a,b)}) - (a^2 - b)(DY_{(a,b)} + D1_{(a,b)})}{(b+1)^2}(h,k)$$

$$= \frac{(b+1)(2X(a,b)DX_{(a,b)} - Y) - (a^2 - b)Y}{(b+1)^2}(h,k)$$

$$= \frac{(b+1)(2aX - Y) - (a^2 - b)Y}{(b+1)^2}(h,k)$$

$$= \frac{(b+1)(2ah - k) - (a^2 - b)k}{(b+1)^2}$$

$$= \frac{2a}{b+1}h - \frac{a^2 + 1}{(b+1)^2}k.$$

In practice, this method is too unwieldy for any functions beyond the simplest, and in any case, it applies only to mappings with rational component functions. But on the other hand, there is no reason to expect much in the way of computational results from our methods so far, since we have been studying the derivative based on its intrinsic characterization. In the next section we will construct the derivative in coordinates, enabling us to compute easily by drawing on the results of one-variable calculus.

For another application of the chain rule, let A and B be subsets of $\mathbb{R}^n$, and suppose that $f : A \longrightarrow B$ is invertible with inverse $g : B \longrightarrow A$. Suppose further that f is differentiable at $a \in A$ and that g is differentiable at $f(a)$. The composition $g \circ f$ is the identity mapping $\mathrm{id}_A : A \longrightarrow A$, which, being the restriction of a linear mapping, has that linear mapping $\mathrm{id} : \mathbb{R}^n \longrightarrow \mathbb{R}^n$ as its derivative at a. Therefore,

$$\mathrm{id} = D(\mathrm{id}_A)_a = D(g \circ f)_a = Dg_{f(a)} \circ Df_a.$$

This argument partly shows that for invertible f as described, the linear mapping Df_a is also invertible. A symmetric argument completes the proof by showing that also $\mathrm{id} = Df_a \circ Dg_{f(a)}$. Because we have methods available to check the invertibility of a linear map, we can apply this criterion once we know how to compute derivatives.

Not too much should be made of this result, however; its hypotheses are too strong. Even in the one-variable case, the function $f(x) = x^3$ from $\mathbb{R}$ to $\mathbb{R}$ is invertible and yet has the noninvertible derivative 0 at $x = 0$. (The inverse, $g(x) = \sqrt[3]{x}$, is not differentiable at 0, so the conditions above are not met.) Besides, we would prefer a converse statement, that if the derivative is invertible then so is the mapping. The converse statement is not true, but we will see in Chapter 5 that it is *locally* true, i.e., it is true in the small.

Exercises

4.4.1. Prove part (2) of Proposition 4.4.1.

4.4.2. Prove part (2) of Proposition 4.4.2.

4.4.3. Prove part (2) of Lemma 4.4.4.

4.4.4. Prove the quotient rule.

4.4.5. Let $f(x, y, z) = xyz$. Find $Df_{(a,b,c)}$ for arbitrary $(a, b, c) \in \mathbb{R}^3$. (Hint: f is the product XYZ, where X is the linear function $X(x, y, z) = x$ and similarly for Y and Z.)

4.4.6. Define $f(x, y) = xy^2/(y-1)$ on $\{(x, y) \in \mathbb{R}^2 : y \neq 1\}$. Find $Df_{(a,b)}$ where (a, b) is a point in the domain of f.

4.4.7. (A generalization of the product rule.) Recall that a function

$$f : \mathbb{R}^n \times \mathbb{R}^n \longrightarrow \mathbb{R}$$

is called bilinear if for all $x, x', y, y' \in \mathbb{R}^n$ and all $\alpha \in \mathbb{R}$,

$$f(x + x', y) = f(x, y) + f(x', y),$$
$$f(x, y + y') = f(x, y) + f(x, y'),$$
$$f(\alpha x, y) = \alpha f(x, y) = f(x, \alpha y).$$

(a) Show that if f is bilinear then $f(h, k)$ is $o(h, k)$.

(b) Show that if f is bilinear then f is differentiable with $Df_{(a,b)}(h, k) = f(a, k) + f(h, b)$.

(c) What does this exercise say about the inner product?

4.4.8. (A bigger generalization of the product rule.) A function

$$f : \mathbb{R}^n \times \cdots \times \mathbb{R}^n \longrightarrow \mathbb{R}$$

(there are k copies of $\mathbb{R}^n$) is called **multilinear** if for each $j \in \{1, \ldots, k\}$, for all $x_1, \ldots, x_j, x_j', \ldots, x_k \in \mathbb{R}^n$ and all $\alpha \in \mathbb{R}$,

$$f(x_1, \ldots, x_j + x_j', \ldots, x_k) = f(x_1, \ldots, x_j, \ldots, x_k) + f(x_1, \ldots, x_j', \ldots, x_k)$$
$$f(x_1, \ldots, \alpha x_j, \ldots, x_k) = \alpha f(x_1, \ldots, x_j, \ldots, x_k).$$

(a) Show that if f is multilinear and $a_1, \ldots, a_k, h_1, \ldots, h_k \in \mathbb{R}^n$ then for any $j \in \{2, \ldots, k\}$, $f(h_1, \ldots, h_j, a_{j+1} \ldots, a_k)$ is $o(h_1, \ldots, h_k)$. The same result holds if any j inputs to f are h's, rather than the first j inputs, because permuting the inputs of a multilinear function creates another multilinear function. Flesh this argument out as much as feels necessary for your understanding.

(b) Show that if f is multilinear then f is differentiable with

$$Df_{(a_1,\ldots,a_k)}(h_1, \ldots, h_k) = \sum_{j=1}^{k} f(a_1, \ldots, a_{j-1}, h_j, a_{j+1}, \ldots, a_k).$$

(c) When $k = n$, what does this exercise say about the determinant?

4.5 Calculating the Derivative

Working directly from Definition 4.3.2 of the multivariable derivative without using coordinates has yielded some easy results and one harder one—the chain rule—but no explicit description of the derivative except in the simplest cases. We don't even know that any multivariable derivatives exist except for mappings with rational coefficient functions.

Following the general principle that necessary conditions are more easily obtained than sufficient ones, we assume that the derivative exists and determine what it then must be. Geometry provides the insight. By the usual componentwise argument, there is no loss in studying a function f with scalar output, i.e., we may take $m = 1$. Setting $n = 2$ fits the graph of f in $\mathbb{R}^3$ where we can see it. Thus take $f : A \longrightarrow \mathbb{R}$ where $A \subset \mathbb{R}^2$.

Suppose that f is differentiable at the point (a, b). Then the graph of f has a well-fitting tangent plane $\mathcal{P}$ at the point $(a, b, f(a, b))$, as shown earlier, in Figure 4.4. To determine this plane, we need two of its lines through $(a, b, f(a, b))$. The natural lines to consider are those whose (x, y)-shadows run in the x and y directions. Call them ℓ_x and ℓ_y. (See Figure 4.6.)

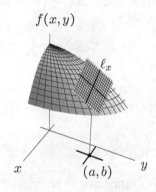

Figure 4.6. Cross-sectional lines

The line ℓ_x is tangent to a cross section of the graph of f. To see this cross section, freeze the variable y at the value b and look at the resulting function of one variable, $\varphi(x) = f(x, b)$. The slope of ℓ_x in the vertical (x, b, z)-plane is precisely $\varphi'(a)$. A small technicality here is that since (a, b) is an interior point of A, also a is an interior point of the domain of φ.

Similarly, ℓ_y has slope $\psi'(b)$ where $\psi(y) = f(a, y)$. The linear function approximating $f(a + h, b + k) - f(a, b)$ for small (h, k) is now specified as $T(h, k) = \varphi'(a)h + \psi'(b)k$. Thus $Df_{(a,b)}$ has matrix $[\varphi'(a) \quad \psi'(b)]$. Since the entries of this matrix are simply one-variable derivatives, this is something that we can compute.

Definition 4.5.1 (Partial derivative). *Let A be a subset of $\mathbb{R}^n$, let $f : A \longrightarrow \mathbb{R}$ be a function, and let $a = (a_1, \ldots, a_n)$ be an interior point of A. Fix $j \in \{1, \ldots, n\}$. Define*

$$\varphi(t) = f(a_1, \ldots, a_{j-1}, t, a_{j+1}, \ldots, a_n) \quad \text{for } t \text{ near } a_j.$$

Then the jth **partial derivative of** f **at** a *is defined as*

$$D_j f(a) = \varphi'(a_j)$$

if $\varphi'(a_j)$ exists. Here the prime signifies ordinary one-variable differentiation. Equivalently,

$$D_j f(a) = \lim_{t \to 0} \frac{f(a + te_j) - f(a)}{t}$$

if the limit exists and it is not being taken at an endpoint of the domain of the difference quotient.

Partial derivatives are easy to compute: fix all but one of the variables, and then take the one-variable derivative with respect to the variable that remains. For example, if

$$f(x, y, z) = e^y \cos x + z$$

then

$$
\begin{bmatrix}
D_1 f(a, b, c) = \dfrac{d}{dx}(e^b \cos x + c)\Big|_{x=a} = -e^b \sin a, \\
D_2 f(a, b, c) = e^b \cos a, \\
D_3 f(a, b, c) = 1.
\end{bmatrix}
$$

Theorem 4.5.2 (The derivative in coordinates: necessity). *Let the mapping $f : A \longrightarrow \mathbb{R}^m$ (where $A \subset \mathbb{R}^n$) be differentiable at the point $a \in A$. Then for each $i \in \{1, \ldots, m\}$ and $j \in \{1, \ldots, n\}$, the partial derivative $D_j f_i(a)$ exists. Furthermore, each $D_j f_i(a)$ is the (i, j)th entry of the Jacobian matrix of f at a. Thus the Jacobian matrix is*

$$f'(a) = \begin{bmatrix} D_1 f_1(a) & \cdots & D_n f_1(a) \\ D_1 f_2(a) & \cdots & D_n f_2(a) \\ \vdots & \ddots & \vdots \\ D_1 f_m(a) & \cdots & D_n f_m(a) \end{bmatrix} = [D_j f_i(a)]_{\substack{i=1,\ldots,m \\ j=1,\ldots,n}}.$$

Proof. The idea is to read off the (i, j)th entry of $f'(a)$ by studying the ith component function of f and letting $h \to 0_n$ along the jth coordinate direction in the defining property (4.1) of the derivative. The ensuing calculation will repeat the quick argument in Section 4.3 that the characterization of the derivative subsumes the construction in the one-variable case.

The derivative of the component function f_i at a is described by the ith row of $f'(a)$. Call the row entries $d_{i1}, d_{i2}, \ldots, d_{in}$. Since *linear of* is *matrix times*, it follows that

$$(Df_i)_a(te_j) = d_{ij}t \quad \text{for all } t \in \mathbb{R}.$$

Let $h = te_j$ with t a variable real number, so that $h \to \mathbf{0}_n$ as $t \to 0_\mathbb{R}$. Since $(Df_i)_a$ exists, we have as a particular instance of the characterizing property that $f_i(a+h) - f_i a) - (Df_i)_a(h)$ is $o(h)$,

$$0 = \lim_{t \to 0} \frac{|f_i(a + te_j) - f_i(a) - (Df_i)_a(te_j)|}{|te_j|}$$

$$= \lim_{t \to 0} \left| \frac{f_i(a + te_j) - f_i(a) - d_{ij}t}{t} \right|$$

$$= \lim_{t \to 0} \left| \frac{f_i(a + te_j) - f_i(a)}{t} - d_{ij} \right|.$$

That is,

$$\lim_{t \to 0} \frac{f_i(a + te_j) - f_i(a)}{t} = d_{ij}.$$

The previous display says precisely that $D_j f_i(a)$ exists and equals d_{ij}.   □

So the existence of the derivative Df_a makes *necessary* the existence of all partial derivatives of all component functions of f at a. The natural question is whether their existence is also *sufficient* for the existence of Df_a. It is not. The proof of Theorem 4.5.2 was akin to the straight line test from Section 2.3: the general condition $h \to \mathbf{0}_n$ was specialized to $h = te_j$, i.e., to letting h approach $\mathbf{0}_n$ only along the axes. The specialization let us show that the derivative matrix entries are the partial derivatives of the component functions of f. But the price for this specific information was loss of generality, enough loss that the derived necessary conditions are not sufficient.

For example, the function

$$f : \mathbb{R}^2 \longrightarrow \mathbb{R}, \quad f(x,y) = \begin{cases} \frac{2xy}{x^2+y^2} & \text{if } (x,y) \neq (0,0), \\ 0 & \text{if } (x,y) = (0,0) \end{cases}$$

has for its first partial derivative at the origin

$$D_1 f(0,0) = \lim_{t \to 0} \frac{f(t,0) - f(0,0)}{t} = \lim_{t \to 0} \frac{0-0}{t} = 0,$$

and similarly $D_2 f(0,0) = 0$; but as discussed in Chapter 2, f is not continuous at the origin, much less differentiable there. However, this example is contrived, the sort of function that one sees only in a mathematics class, and in fact a result in the spirit of the converse to Theorem 4.5.2 does hold, though with stronger hypotheses.

Theorem 4.5.3 (The derivative in coordinates: sufficiency). *Let* f :
$A \longrightarrow \mathbb{R}^m$ *(where* $A \subset \mathbb{R}^n$*) be a mapping, and let* a *be an interior point of* A.
Suppose that for each $i \in \{1,\dots,m\}$ *and* $j \in \{1,\dots,n\}$*, the partial derivative*
$D_j f_i$ *exists not only at* a *but at all points in some* ε*-ball about* a*, and the*
partial derivative $D_j f_i$ *is continuous at* a*. Then* f *is differentiable at* a.

Note that if f meets the conditions of Theorem 4.5.3 (all partial derivatives
of all component functions of f exist at and about a, and they are continuous
at a) then the theorem's conclusion (f is differentiable at a) is the condition
of Theorem 4.5.2, so that the latter theorem tells us the derivative of f (the
entries of its matrix are the partial derivatives). But the example given just
before Theorem 4.5.3 shows that the converse fails: even if all partial derivatives of all component functions of f exist at a, the function f need not be
differentiable at a.

The difference between the necessary conditions in Theorem 4.5.2 and the
sufficient conditions in Theorem 4.5.3 has a geometric interpretation when
$n = 2$ and $m = 1$. The necessary conditions in Theorem 4.5.2 are:

> *If a graph has a well-fitting plane at some point, then at that point*
> *we see well-fitting lines in the cross sections parallel to the coordinate*
> *axes.*

The sufficient conditions in Theorem 4.5.3 are:

> *If a graph has well-fitting lines in the cross sections at and near the*
> *point, and if those lines don't change much as we move among cross*
> *sections at and near the point, then the graph has a well-fitting plane.*

But well-fitting cross-sectional lines at the point are not enough to guarantee a well-fitting plane at the point. The multivariable derivative is truly a
pandimensional construct, not just an amalgamation of cross-sectional data.

Proof. It suffices to prove the differentiability of each component function f_i,
so we may assume that $m = 1$, i.e., that f is scalar-valued. To thin out the
notation, the proof will be done for $n = 3$ (so for example, $a = (a_1, a_2, a_3)$),
but its generality should be clear.

Theorem 4.5.2 says that if the derivative Df_a exists then it is defined by
the matrix of partial derivatives $D_j f(a)$. The goal therefore is to show that
the linear mapping

$$T_a(h_1, h_2, h_3) = D_1 f(a)h_1 + D_2 f(a)h_2 + D_3 f(a)h_3$$

satisfies the defining property of the derivative. That is, we need to show that

$$f(a + h) - f(a) = D_1 f(a)h_1 + D_2 f(a)h_2 + D_3 f(a)h_3 + o(h).$$

We may take h small enough that the partial derivatives $D_j f$ exist at all
points within distance $|h|$ of a. Here we use the hypothesis that the partial
derivatives exist everywhere near a.

The idea is to move from a to $a + h$ in steps, changing one coordinate at a time,

$$
\begin{aligned}
f(a + h) - f(a) &= f(a_1 + h_1, a_2 + h_2, a_3 + h_3) - f(a_1, a_2 + h_2, a_3 + h_3) \\
&+ f(a_1, a_2 + h_2, a_3 + h_3) - f(a_1, a_2, a_3 + h_3) \\
&+ f(a_1, a_2, a_3 + h_3) - f(a_1, a_2, a_3).
\end{aligned}
$$

Because the partial derivatives exist, we may apply the mean value theorem in two directions and the one-variable derivative's characterizing property in the third,

$$
\begin{aligned}
f(a + h) - f(a) &= D_1 f(a_1 + c_1, a_2 + h_2, a_3 + h_3) h_1 \\
&+ D_2 f(a_1, a_2 + c_2, a_3 + h_3) h_2 \\
&+ D_3 f(a_1, a_2, a_3) h_3 + o(h_3),
\end{aligned}
$$

where $|c_i| \le |h_i|$ for $i = 1, 2$. Since $D_1 f$ and $D_2 f$ are continuous at the point $a = (a_1, a_2, a_3)$, and since the condition $h \to 0_3$ squeezes each h_i and c_i to 0,

$$
\begin{aligned}
D_1 f(a_1 + c_1, a_2 + h_2, a_3 + h_3) &= D_1 f(a) + o(1), \\
D_2 f(a_1, a_2 + c_2, a_3 + h_3) &= D_2 f(a) + o(1).
\end{aligned}
$$

Also, $o(1)h_i = o(h)$ for $i = 1, 2$ and $o(h_3) = o(h)$, and so altogether we have

$$
f(a + h) - f(a) = D_1 f(a) h_1 + D_2 f(a) h_2 + D_3 f(a) h_3 + o(h).
$$

This is the desired result. $\qquad\qquad\qquad\qquad\qquad\qquad\qquad\qquad\qquad\qquad\qquad$ $\square$

Thus, to reiterate some earlier discussion and to amplify slightly:

- The differentiability of f at a implies the existence of all the partial derivatives at a, and the partial derivatives are the entries of the derivative matrix,
- while the existence of all the partial derivatives *at and about* a, and their *continuity* at a, combine to imply the differentiability of f at a,
- but the existence of all partial derivatives at a need not imply the differentiability of f at a.
- And in fact, the previous proof shows that we need to check the scope and continuity only of *all but one* of the partial derivatives. The proof used the existence of $D_3 f$ at a but not its existence near a or its continuity at a, and a variant argument or a reindexing shows that nothing is special about the last variable. This observation is a bit of a relief, telling us that in the case of one input variable, our methods do not need to assume that the derivative exists at and about a point and is continuous at the point in order to confirm merely that it exists at the point. We codify this bullet as a variant sufficiency theorem:

Theorem 4.5.4 (The derivative in coordinates: sufficiency). *Let* $f :$
$A \longrightarrow \mathbb{R}^m$ *(where* $A \subset \mathbb{R}^n$*) be a mapping, and let* a *be an interior point of* A.
Suppose that for each $i \in \{1, \ldots, m\}$,

* *for each* $j \in \{1, \ldots, n\}$, *the partial derivative* $D_j f_i(a)$ *exists,*
* *and for each but at most one* $j \in \{1, \ldots, m\}$, *the partial derivative* $D_j f_i$
  exists in some ε-*ball about* a *and is continuous at* a.

Then f *is differentiable at* a.

Note how all this compares to the discussion of the determinant in the previous chapter. There we wanted the determinant to satisfy characterizing properties. We found the only function that could possibly satisfy them, and then we verified that it did. Here we wanted the derivative to satisfy a characterizing property, and we found the only possibility for the derivative—the linear mapping whose matrix consists of the partial derivatives, which must exist if the derivative does. But analysis is more subtle than algebra: this linear mapping need not satisfy the characterizing property of the derivative unless we add further assumptions. The derivative-existence theorem, Theorem 4.5.3 or the slightly stronger Theorem 4.5.4, is the most substantial result so far in this chapter. We have already seen a counterexample to the converse of Theorem 4.5.3, in which the function had partial derivatives but wasn't differentiable because it wasn't even continuous (page 155). For a one-dimensional counterexample to the converse of Theorem 4.5.3, in which the derivative exists but is not continuous, see Exercise 4.5.3. The example in the exercise does not contradict the weaker converse of the stronger Theorem 4.5.4.

To demonstrate the ideas of this section so far, consider the function

$$f(x,y) = \begin{cases} \frac{x^2 y}{x^2 + y^2} & \text{if } (x,y) \neq (0,0), \\ 0 & \text{if } (x,y) = (0,0). \end{cases}$$

The top formula in the definition describes a rational function of x and y on the punctured plane $\mathbb{R}^2 - \{(0,0)\}$. Every rational function and all of its partial derivatives are continuous on its domain (feel free to invoke this result), and furthermore every point (a,b) away from $(0,0)$ lies in some ε-ball that is also away from $(0,0)$. That is, for every point $(a,b) \neq (0,0)$, the partial derivatives of f exist at and about (a,b) and they are continuous at (a,b). Thus the conditions for Theorem 4.5.3 are met, and so its conclusion follows: f is differentiable at (a,b). Now Theorem 4.5.2 says that the derivative matrix at (a,b) is the matrix of partial derivatives,

$$f'(a,b) = \left[D_1 f(a,b) \; D_2 f(a,b) \right] = \left[\frac{2ab^3}{(a^2 + b^2)^2} \quad \frac{a^2(a^2 - b^2)}{(a^2 + b^2)^2} \right].$$

Consequently, the derivative of f at every nonzero (a,b) is the corresponding linear map

$$Df_{(a,b)}(h,k) = \frac{2ab^3}{(a^2+b^2)^2}h + \frac{a^2(a^2-b^2)}{(a^2+b^2)^2}k.$$

However, this analysis breaks down at the point $(a,b) = (0,0)$. Here our only recourse is to figure out whether a candidate derivative exists and then test whether it works. The first partial derivative of f at $(0,0)$ is

$$D_1 f(0,0) = \lim_{t\to 0}\frac{f(t,0)-f(0,0)}{t} = \lim_{t\to 0}\frac{0-0}{t} = 0,$$

and similarly $D_2 f(0,0) = 0$. So by Theorem 4.5.2, the only possibility for the derivative of f at $(0,0)$ is the zero mapping. Now the question is,

$$\text{is}\quad f(h,k) - f(0,0) - 0 \quad o(h,k)?$$

Because the denominator $h^2 + k^2$ of f away from the origin is $|(h,k)|^2$,

$$|f(h,k) - f(0,0) - 0| = |f(h,k)| = \frac{|h|^2|k|}{|(h,k)|^2}.$$

Let (h,k) approach $\mathbf{0}_2$ along the line $h = k$. Because $|h| = |(h,h)|/\sqrt{2}$,

$$|f(h,h) - f(0,0) - 0| = \frac{|h|^3}{|(h,h)|^2} = \frac{|(h,h)|}{2\sqrt{2}}.$$

Thus along this line, the condition $|f(h,k)-f(0,0)-0| \le c|(h,k)|$ fails for (say) $c = 1/4$, and so $f(h,k)-f(0,0)-0$ is not $o(h,k)$. That is, the function f is not differentiable at $(0,0)$. And indeed, the graph of f near $(0,0)$ shows a surface that isn't well approximated by any plane through its center, no matter how closely we zoom in. (See Figure 4.7. The figure shows that the cross-sectional slopes over the axes are 0, while the cross-sectional slopes over the diagonals are not, confirming our symbolic calculations.) Here we have used the straight line test to get a negative answer; but recall that the straight line test alone cannot give a positive answer, so the method here would need modification to show that a function is differentiable.

For another example, Exercise 4.3.4 used the characterizing property to confirm the derivative of the function $f(x,y) = (x^2 - y^2, 2xy)$. Now we can use the theorems of this section to obtain the derivative and know that it works. The function f has domain $\mathbb{R}^2$, so every domain point is interior. Since each component of f is a polynomial, so are all partial derivatives of the components, making them continuous everywhere. Thus f is differentiable at every point $(a,b) \in \mathbb{R}^2$. The matrix of partial derivatives at (a,b) is

$$\begin{bmatrix} D_1 f_1(a,b) & D_2 f_1(a,b) \\ D_1 f_2(a,b) & D_2 f_2(a,b) \end{bmatrix} = \begin{bmatrix} 2a & -2b \\ 2b & 2a \end{bmatrix},$$

and so the derivative of f at (a,b) is, as before,

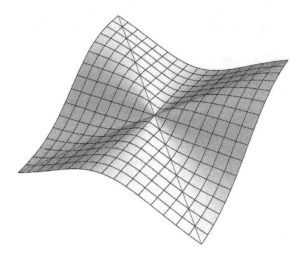

Figure 4.7. The crimped sheet is differentiable everywhere except at the origin

$$Df_{(a,b)}(h,k) = (2ah - 2bk, 2bh + 2ak).$$

Similarly, the function $g(x,y) = xe^y$ from Exercise 4.3.5 has domain $\mathbb{R}^2$, all of whose points are interior, and its partial derivatives $D_1g(x,y) = e^y$ and $D_2g(x,y) = xe^y$ are continuous everywhere. Thus it is differentiable everywhere. Its matrix of partial derivatives at every point (a,b) is

$$[D_1g(a,b) \quad D_2g(a,b)] = [e^b \quad ae^b],$$

and so its derivative at (a,b) is

$$Dg_{(a,b)}(h,k) = e^bh + ae^bk.$$

The reader is encouraged to reproduce the derivative of the product function (Lemma 4.4.4, part (1)) similarly.

Returning to the discussion (at the end of the previous section) of invertibility of a mapping and invertibility of its derivative, consider the mapping

$$f : \mathbb{R}^2 - \{(0,0)\} \longrightarrow \mathbb{R}^2 - \{(0,0)\}, \qquad f(x,y) = (x^2 - y^2, 2xy).$$

At every (x,y) where f is defined, the partial derivatives are $D_1f_1(x,y) = 2x$, $D_2f_1(x,y) = -2y$, $D_1f_2(x,y) = 2y$, and $D_2f_2(x,y) = 2x$. These are continuous functions of (x,y), so for every $(a,b) \neq (0,0)$, $Df_{(a,b)}$ exists and its matrix is

$$f'(a,b) = \begin{bmatrix} D_1f_1(a,b) & D_2f_1(a,b) \\ D_1f_2(a,b) & D_2f_2(a,b) \end{bmatrix} = \begin{bmatrix} 2a & -2b \\ 2b & 2a \end{bmatrix}.$$

The matrix has determinant $4(a^2 + b^2) > 0$, and hence it is always invertible. On the other hand, the mapping f takes the same value at points (x, y) and $-(x, y)$, so it is definitely not invertible.

With the Jacobian matrix described explicitly, a more calculational version of the chain rule is available.

Theorem 4.5.5 (Chain rule in coordinates). *Let $f : A \longrightarrow \mathbb{R}^m$ (where $A \subset \mathbb{R}^n$) be differentiable at the point a of A, and let $g : f(A) \longrightarrow \mathbb{R}^\ell$ be differentiable at the point $b = f(a)$. Then the composition $g \circ f : A \longrightarrow \mathbb{R}^\ell$ is differentiable at a, and its partial derivatives are*

$$D_j(g \circ f)_i(a) = \sum_{k=1}^{m} D_k g_i(b) D_j f_k(a) \quad \text{for } i = 1, \ldots, \ell, \ j = 1, \ldots, n.$$

Proof. The composition is differentiable by the intrinsic chain rule. The Jacobian matrix of g at b is

$$g'(b) = [D_k g_i(b)]_{\ell \times m} \quad \text{(row index } i\text{, column index } k\text{)},$$

the Jacobian matrix of f at a is

$$f'(a) = [D_j f_k(a)]_{m \times n} \quad \text{(row index } k\text{, column index } j\text{)},$$

and the Jacobian matrix of $g \circ f$ at a is

$$(g \circ f)'(a) = [D_j(g \circ f)_i(a)]_{\ell \times n} \quad \text{(row index } i\text{, column index } j\text{)}.$$

By the intrinsic chain rule,

$$(g \circ f)'(a) = g'(b) f'(a).$$

Equate the (i, j)th entries to obtain the result. $\qquad\qquad\square$

Notations for the partial derivative vary. A function is often described by a formula such as $w = f(x, y, z)$. Other notations for $D_1 f$ are

$$f_1, \qquad f_x, \qquad \frac{\partial f}{\partial x}, \qquad w_x, \qquad \frac{\partial w}{\partial x}.$$

If x, y, z are in turn functions of s and t then a classical formulation of the chain rule would be

$$\frac{\partial w}{\partial t} = \frac{\partial w}{\partial x} \frac{\partial x}{\partial t} + \frac{\partial w}{\partial y} \frac{\partial y}{\partial t} + \frac{\partial w}{\partial z} \frac{\partial z}{\partial t}. \tag{4.2}$$

The formula is easily visualized as chasing back along all *dependency chains* from t to w in a diagram where an arrow means *contributes to:*

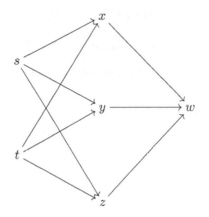

Unfortunately, for all its mnemonic advantages, the classical notation is a veritable minefield of misinterpretation. Formula (4.2) doesn't indicate where the various partial derivatives are to be evaluated, for one thing. Specifying the variable of differentiation by name rather than by position also becomes confusing when different symbols are substituted for the same variable, especially since the symbols themselves may denote specific values or other variables. For example, one can construe many different meanings for the expression

$$\frac{\partial f}{\partial x}(y, x, z).$$

Blurring the distinction between functions and the variables denoting their outputs is even more problematic. If one has, say, $z = f(x, t, u)$, $x = g(t, u)$,

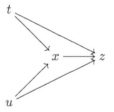

then chasing all paths from z back to t gives

$$\frac{\partial z}{\partial t} = \frac{\partial z}{\partial x}\frac{\partial x}{\partial t} + \frac{\partial z}{\partial t}$$

with "$\partial z / \partial t$" meaning something different on each side of the equality. While the classical formulas are useful and perhaps simpler to apply in elementary situations, they are not particularly robust until one has a solid understanding of the chain rule. On the other hand, the classical formulas work fine in straightforward applications, so several exercises are phrased in the older language to give you practice with it.

For example, let

$$(x, y) = f(r, \theta) = (r \cos \theta, r \sin \theta),$$
$$(z, w) = g(x, y) = (x^2 - y^2, 2xy).$$

We compute $(\partial z/\partial r)(2, \pi/3)$. The chain rule in coordinates gives

$$\begin{bmatrix} \partial z/\partial r & \partial z/\partial \theta \\ \partial w/\partial r & \partial w/\partial \theta \end{bmatrix} = \begin{bmatrix} \partial z/\partial x & \partial z/\partial y \\ \partial w/\partial x & \partial w/\partial y \end{bmatrix} \cdot \begin{bmatrix} \partial x/\partial r & \partial x/\partial \theta \\ \partial y/\partial r & \partial y/\partial \theta \end{bmatrix},$$

and the upper left entry is

$$\frac{\partial z}{\partial r} = \frac{\partial z}{\partial x} \frac{\partial x}{\partial r} + \frac{\partial z}{\partial y} \frac{\partial y}{\partial r} = 2x \cos \theta - 2y \sin \theta.$$

We are given $(r, \theta) = (2, \pi/3)$, and it follows that $(x, y) = (1, \sqrt{3})$. So the answer is

$$\frac{\partial z}{\partial r}(2, \pi/3) = 2 \cdot 1 \cdot \frac{1}{2} - 2 \cdot \sqrt{3} \cdot \frac{\sqrt{3}}{2} = -2.$$

To confirm the result without using the chain rule, note that f is the polar-to-Cartesian change of coordinates, and g is the complex squaring function in Cartesian coordinates, so that the composition $g \circ f$ is the squaring function in polar coordinates. That is, the composition is

$$(z, w) = (g \circ f)(r, \theta) = (r^2 \cos 2\theta, r^2 \sin 2\theta).$$

Consequently $\partial z/\partial r = 2r \cos 2\theta$, and substituting $(r, \theta) = (2, \pi/3)$ gives in particular $(\partial z/\partial r)(2, \pi/3) = 2 \cdot 2 \cos 2\pi/3 = 2 \cdot 2 \cdot (-1/2) = -2$, as we know it must.

For another example, the function $f(x) = x^x$ is usually differentiated as follows in one-variable calculus: Consider the related function $\ln(f(x)) = \ln(x^x) = x \ln(x)$, and take derivatives of both sides to get $f'(x)/f(x) = 1 + \ln(x)$; thus $f'(x) = x^x(1 + \ln(x))$. On the other hand, if we differentiate x^x treating the first x as variable and the second x as constant then we get $xx^{x-1} = x^x$, and if we differentiate x^x treating the first x as constant and the second x as variable then we get $x^x \ln(x)$; the sum of these two sort-of-derivatives is $x^x(1 + \ln(x))$, the derivative of x^x as computed a moment ago. The method of treating the two x's as independent has produced the right answer, despite its illegality. This can't be a coincidence, and it isn't. In general, if $F(x_1, \ldots, x_n)$ is a differentiable function of many variables then the derivative of the one-variable function $f(x) = F(x, x, \ldots, x)$ is $f'(x) = \sum_{i=1}^{n} D_i F(x, x, \ldots, x)$. Exercise 4.5.10 is to prove this formula as an immediate consequence of the chain rule, and then to use it to establish a result known as Leibniz's Rule. Exercise 4.5.11(a) is to use this formula to differentiate the function $f(x) = x^{x^x}$, and more generally Exercise 4.5.11(b) is to differentiate the function $f(x) = x^{x^{\cdot^{\cdot^{\cdot^x}}}}$.

Exercises

4.5.1. Explain why in the discussion beginning this section the tangent plane $\mathcal{P}$ consists of all points $(a, b, f(a, b)) + (h, k, T(h, k))$ where $T(h, k) = \varphi'(a)h + \psi'(b)k$.

4.5.2. This exercise shows that all partial derivatives of a function can exist at and about a point without being continuous at the point. Define $f : \mathbb{R}^2 \longrightarrow \mathbb{R}$ by

$$f(x, y) = \begin{cases} \frac{2xy}{x^2 + y^2} & \text{if } (x, y) \neq (0, 0), \\ 0 & \text{if } (x, y) = (0, 0). \end{cases}$$

(a) Show that $D_1 f(0, 0) = D_2 f(0, 0) = 0$.

(b) Show that $D_1 f(a, b)$ and $D_2 f(a, b)$ exist and are continuous at all other $(a, b) \in \mathbb{R}^2$.

(c) Show that $D_1 f$ and $D_2 f$ are discontinuous at $(0, 0)$.

4.5.3. Define $f : \mathbb{R} \longrightarrow \mathbb{R}$ by

$$f(x) = \begin{cases} x^2 \sin \frac{1}{x} & \text{if } x \neq 0, \\ 0 & \text{if } x = 0. \end{cases}$$

Show that $f'(x)$ exists for all x but that f' is discontinuous at 0. Explain how this disproves the converse of Theorem 4.5.3.

4.5.4. Discuss the derivatives of the following mappings at the following points.

(a) $f(x, y) = \frac{x^2 - y}{y + 1}$ on $\{(x, y) \in \mathbb{R}^2 : y \neq -1\}$ at generic (a, b) with $b \neq -1$. (After you are done, compare the effort of doing the problem now to the effort of doing it as we did at the end of Section 4.4.)

(b) $f(x, y) = \frac{xy^2}{y - 1}$ on $\{(x, y) \in \mathbb{R}^2 : y \neq 1\}$ at generic (a, b) with $b \neq 1$.

(c) $f(x, y) = \begin{cases} \frac{xy}{\sqrt{x^2 + y^2}} & \text{if } (x, y) \neq (0, 0) \\ 0 & \text{if } (x, y) = (0, 0) \end{cases}$ at generic $(a, b) \neq (0, 0)$ and at $(0, 0)$.

For the rest of these exercises, assume as much differentiability as necessary.

4.5.5. For what differentiable mappings $f : A \longrightarrow \mathbb{R}^m$ is $f'(a)$ a diagonal matrix for all $a \in A$? (A diagonal matrix is a matrix whose (i, j)th entries for all $i \neq j$ are 0.)

4.5.6. Show that if $z = f(xy)$ then x, y, and z satisfy the differential equation $x \cdot z_x - y \cdot z_y = 0$.

4.5.7. Let $w = F(xz, yz)$. Show that $x \cdot w_x + y \cdot w_y = z \cdot w_z$.

4.5.8. If $z = f(ax + by)$, show that $bz_x = az_y$.

4.5.9. The function $f : \mathbb{R}^2 \longrightarrow \mathbb{R}$ is called **homogeneous of degree** k if $f(tx, ty) = t^k f(x, y)$ for all scalars t and vectors (x, y). Letting f_1 and f_2 denote the first and second partial derivatives of f, show that such f satisfies the differential equation

$$x f_1(x, y) + y f_2(x, y) = k f(x, y).$$

(Hint: First differentiate the homogeneity condition with respect to t, viewing x and y as fixed but generic; the derivative of one side will require the chain rule. Second, since the resulting condition holds for all scalars t, it holds for any particular t of your choosing.)

4.5.10. (a) Consider a function $f(x) = F(x, x, \ldots, x)$ where $F(x_1, x_2, \ldots, x_n)$ is a differentiable function of n variables. Note that $f = F \circ \gamma$ where $\gamma(x) = (x, x, \ldots, x)$, and use this to show that $f'(x) = \sum_{i=1}^{n} D_i F(x, x, \ldots, x)$.

(b) (Leibniz's Rule.) Let

$$f : \mathbb{R}^2 \longrightarrow \mathbb{R}$$

be a function such that for all $a, b \in \mathbb{R}$, the integral

$$F : \mathbb{R} \longrightarrow \mathbb{R}, \qquad F(x) = \int_{y=a}^{b} f(x, y) \, dy$$

exists and is differentiable with respect to x, its derivative obtained by passing the x-derivative through the y-integral,

$$\begin{aligned}
\frac{dF(x, y)}{dx} &= \frac{d}{dx} \int_{y=a}^{b} f(x, y) \, dy \\
&= \lim_{h \to 0} \frac{\int_{y=a}^{b} f(x+h, y) \, dy - \int_{y=a}^{b} f(x, y) \, dy}{h} \\
&= \lim_{h \to 0} \int_{y=a}^{b} \frac{f(x+h, y) - f(x, y)}{h} \, dy \\
&\overset{!}{=} \int_{y=a}^{b} \lim_{h \to 0} \frac{f(x+h, y) - f(x, y)}{h} \, dy \\
&= \int_{y=a}^{b} \frac{\partial f}{\partial x}(x, y) \, dy.
\end{aligned}$$

(The "!" step requires justification, but under reasonable circumstances it can be carried out.) Let $\alpha, \beta : \mathbb{R} \longrightarrow \mathbb{R}$ be differentiable functions. Define a function

$$G : \mathbb{R} \longrightarrow \mathbb{R}, \qquad G(x) = \int_{y=\alpha(x)}^{\beta(x)} f(x, y) \, dy.$$

Thus x affects G in three ways: as a contributor the lower and upper limits of integration, and as a parameter for the integrand. What is $dG(x)/dx$? (Hint: $G(x) = H(x, x, x)$ where $H(x_1, x_2, x_3) = \int_{y=\alpha(x_1)}^{\beta(x_2)} f(x_3, y) \, dy$.)

4.5.11. (a) Use the ideas at the end of the section to differentiate the function $f(x) = x^{x^{x^x}}$.

(b) For $x > 0$, define $f_{-1}(x) = 0$ and then $f_n(x) = x^{f_{n-1}(x)}$ for $n \geq 0$. Thus $f_0(x) = x^0 = 1$, $f_1(x) = x^1 = x$, $f_2(x) = x^x$, $f_3(x) = x^{x^x}$, and so on. Show that

$$x f_n'(x) = f_n(x)\big(f_{n-1}(x) + \ln x \cdot x f_{n-1}'(x)\big), \quad n \geq 0.$$

Use this result and induction to establish the closed form

$$x f_n'(x) = f_n(x) f_{n-1}(x) \sum_{i=0}^{n-1} (\ln x)^i \prod_{j=1}^{i} f_{n-1-j}(x), \quad n \geq 0.$$

4.6 Higher-Order Derivatives

Partial differentiation can be carried out more than once on nice enough functions. For example, if

$$f(x, y) = e^{x \sin y}$$

then

$$D_1 f(x, y) = \sin y\, e^{x \sin y}, \quad D_2 f(x, y) = x \cos y\, e^{x \sin y}.$$

Taking partial derivatives again yields

$$D_1 D_1 f(x, y) = \sin^2 y\, e^{x \sin y},$$
$$D_1 D_2 f(x, y) = \cos y\, e^{x \sin y} + x \sin y \cos y\, e^{x \sin y},$$
$$D_2 D_1 f(x, y) = \cos y\, e^{x \sin y} + x \sin y \cos y\, e^{x \sin y} = D_1 D_2 f(x, y),$$
$$D_2 D_2 f(x, y) = -x \sin y\, e^{x \sin y} + x^2 \cos^2 y\, e^{x \sin y},$$

and some partial derivatives of these in turn are

$$D_1 D_1 D_2 f(x, y) = 2 \sin y \cos y\, e^{x \sin y} + x \sin^2 y \cos y\, e^{x \sin y},$$
$$D_1 D_2 D_1 f(x, y) = D_1 D_1 D_2 f(x, y),$$
$$D_2 D_1 D_2 f(x, y) = -\sin y\, e^{x \sin y} + 2x \cos^2 y\, e^{x \sin y} - x \sin^2 y\, e^{x \sin y}$$
$$\qquad\qquad + x^2 \sin y \cos^2 y\, e^{x \sin y},$$
$$D_2 D_2 D_1 f(x, y) = D_2 D_1 D_2 f(x, y),$$
$$D_1 D_2 D_2 f(x, y) = -\sin y\, e^{x \sin y} + 2x \cos^2 y\, e^{x \sin y} - x \sin^2 y\, e^{x \sin y}$$
$$\qquad\qquad + x^2 \sin y \cos^2 y\, e^{x \sin y}$$
$$\qquad\qquad = D_2 D_1 D_2 f(x, y),$$
$$D_2 D_1 D_1 f(x, y) = 2 \sin y \cos y\, e^{x \sin y} + x \sin^2 y \cos y\, e^{x \sin y}$$
$$\qquad\qquad = D_1 D_1 D_2 f(x, y).$$

Suspiciously many of these match. The result of two or three partial differentiations seems to depend only on how many were taken with respect to x and how many with respect to y, not on the order in which they were taken.

To analyze the situation, it suffices to consider only two differentiations. Streamline the notation by writing $D_2 D_1 f$ as $D_{12} f$. (The subscripts may look reversed, but reading D_{12} from left to right as D-*one-two* suggests the appropriate order of differentiating.) The definitions for $D_{11} f$, $D_{21} f$, and $D_{22} f$ are similar. These four functions are called the **second-order** partial derivatives of f, and in particular $D_{12} f$ and $D_{21} f$ are the second-order **mixed** partial derivatives. More generally, the kth-order partial derivatives of a function f are those that come from k partial differentiations. A $\mathcal{C}^k$-**function** is a function for which all the kth-order partial derivatives exist and are continuous. The theorem is that with enough continuity, the order of differentiation doesn't matter. That is, the mixed partial derivatives agree.

Theorem 4.6.1 (Equality of mixed partial derivatives). *Suppose that* $f : A \longrightarrow \mathbb{R}$ *(where* $A \subset \mathbb{R}^2$*) is a* $\mathcal{C}^2$*-function. Then at every point* (a, b) *of* A,

$$D_{12} f(a, b) = D_{21} f(a, b).$$

We might try to prove the theorem as follows:

$$
\begin{aligned}
D_{12} f(a, b) &= \lim_{k \to 0} \frac{D_1 f(a, b+k) - D_1 f(a, b)}{k} \\
&= \lim_{k \to 0} \frac{\lim_{h \to 0} \frac{f(a+h, b+k) - f(a, b+k)}{h} - \lim_{h \to 0} \frac{f(a+h, b) - f(a, b)}{h}}{k} \\
&= \lim_{k \to 0} \lim_{h \to 0} \frac{f(a+h, b+k) - f(a, b+k) - f(a+h, b) + f(a, b)}{hk},
\end{aligned}
$$

and similarly

$$D_{21} f(a, b) = \lim_{h \to 0} \lim_{k \to 0} \frac{f(a+h, b+k) - f(a+h, b) - f(a, b+k) + f(a, b)}{hk}.$$

So, letting $\Delta(h, k) = f(a+h, b+k) - f(a, b+k) - f(a+h, b) + f(a, b)$, we want to show that

$$\lim_{h \to 0} \lim_{k \to 0} \frac{\Delta(h, k)}{hk} = \lim_{k \to 0} \lim_{h \to 0} \frac{\Delta(h, k)}{hk}.$$

If the order of taking the limits doesn't matter then we have the desired result. However, if f is not a $\mathcal{C}^2$-function then the order of taking the limits can in fact matter, i.e., the two mixed partial derivatives can both exist but not be equal (see Exercise 4.6.1 for an example). Thus a correct proof of Theorem 4.6.1 requires a little care. The theorem is similar to Taylor's theorem from Section 1.3 in that both are stated entirely in terms of derivatives, but they are most easily proved using integrals. The following proof uses integration to show that $\Delta(h, k)/(hk)$ is an average value of both $D_{12} f$ and $D_{21} f$

near (a, b), and then letting h and k shrink to 0 forces $D_{12}f$ and $D_{21}f$ to agree at (a, b), as desired. That is, the proof shows that the two quantities in the previous display are equal by showing that each of them equals a common third quantity.

Proof. Since f is a $\mathcal{C}^2$-function on A, every point of A is interior. Take any point $(a, b) \in A$. Then some box $B = [a, a + h] \times [b, b + k]$ lies in A. Compute the nested integral

$$\int_a^{a+h} \int_b^{b+k} dy\, dx = \int_a^{a+h} k\, dx = hk.$$

Also, by the fundamental theorem of integral calculus twice,

$$\int_a^{a+h} \int_b^{b+k} D_{12}f(x, y)\, dy\, dx = \int_a^{a+h} (D_1 f(x, b + k) - D_1 f(x, b))\, dx$$
$$= f(a + h, b + k) - f(a, b + k) - f(a + h, b) + f(a, b) = \Delta(h, k).$$

(Thus the integral has reproduced the quantity that arose in the discussion leading into this proof.) Let $m_{h,k}$ be the minimum value of $D_{12}f$ on the box B, and let $M_{h,k}$ be the maximum value. These exist by Theorem 2.4.15, because B is nonempty and compact, and $D_{12}f : B \longrightarrow \mathbb{R}$ is continuous. Thus

$$m_{h,k} \le D_{12}f(x, y) \le M_{h,k} \quad \text{for all } (x, y) \in B.$$

Integrate this inequality, using the two previous calculations, to get

$$m_{h,k}hk \le \Delta(h, k) \le M_{h,k}hk,$$

or

$$m_{h,k} \le \frac{\Delta(h, k)}{hk} \le M_{h,k}.$$

As $(h, k) \to (0^+, 0^+)$, the continuity of $D_{12}f$ at (a, b) forces $m_{h,k}$ and $M_{h,k}$ to $D_{12}f(a, b)$, and hence

$$\frac{\Delta(h, k)}{hk} \to D_{12}f(a, b) \quad \text{as } (h, k) \to (0^+, 0^+).$$

But also, reversing the order of the integrations and of the partial derivatives gives the symmetric calculations

$$\int_b^{b+k} \int_a^{a+h} dx\, dy = hk$$

and

$$\int_b^{b+k} \int_a^{a+h} D_{21}f(x, y)\, dx\, dy = \Delta(h, k),$$

and so the same argument shows that

$$\frac{\Delta(h, k)}{hk} \to D_{21}f(a, b) \quad \text{as } (h, k) \to (0^+, 0^+).$$

Because both $D_{12}f(a, b)$ and $D_{21}f(a, b)$ are the limit of $\Delta(h, k)/(hk)$, they are equal. $\qquad\square$

Extending Theorem 4.6.1 to more variables and to higher derivatives is straightforward, provided that one supplies enough continuity. The hypotheses of the theorem can be weakened a bit, in which case a subtler proof is required, but such technicalities are more distracting than useful.

Higher-order derivatives are written in many ways. If a function is described by the equation $w = f(x, y, z)$ then $D_{233}f$ is also denoted

$$f_{233}, \qquad f_{yzz}, \qquad \frac{\partial}{\partial z}\left(\frac{\partial}{\partial z}\left(\frac{\partial f}{\partial y}\right)\right), \qquad \frac{\partial^3 f}{\partial z^2 \partial y},$$

$$w_{yzz}, \qquad \frac{\partial}{\partial z}\left(\frac{\partial}{\partial z}\left(\frac{\partial w}{\partial y}\right)\right), \qquad \frac{\partial^3 w}{\partial z^2 \partial y}.$$

As with one derivative, these combine mnemonic advantages with conceptual dangers.

A calculation using higher-order derivatives and the chain rule transforms the heat equation of Laplace from Cartesian to polar coordinates. The C^2 quantity $u = f(x, y)$ depending on the Cartesian variables x and y satisfies **Laplace's equation** if (blurring the distinction between u and f)

$$\frac{\partial^2 u}{\partial x^2} + \frac{\partial^2 u}{\partial y^2} = 0.$$

If instead u is viewed as a function $g(r, \theta)$ of the polar variables r and θ then how is Laplace's equation expressed?

The Cartesian coordinates in terms of the polar coordinates are

$$x = r\cos\theta, \quad y = r\sin\theta.$$

Thus $u = f(x, y) = f(r\cos\theta, r\sin\theta) = g(r, \theta)$, showing that u depends on r and θ via x and y:

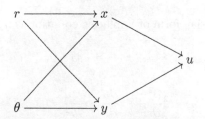

The chain rule begins a hieroglyphic calculation,

$$u_r = u_x x_r + u_y y_r,$$

so that by the product rule,

$$u_{rr} = (u_x x_r + u_y y_r)_r$$
$$= u_{xr} x_r + u_x x_{rr} + u_{yr} y_r + u_y y_{rr}.$$

Since u_x and u_y depend on r and θ via x and y just as u does, each of them can take the place of u in the diagram above, and the chain rule gives expansions of u_{xr} and u_{yr} as it did for u_r,

$$
\begin{aligned}
u_{rr} &= u_{xr}x_r + u_x x_{rr} + u_{yr}y_r + u_y y_{rr} \\
&= (u_{xx}x_r + u_{xy}y_r)\,x_r + u_x x_{rr} + (u_{yx}x_r + u_{yy}y_r)\,y_r + u_y y_{rr} \\
&= u_{xx}x_r^2 + u_{xy}y_r x_r + u_x x_{rr} + u_{yx}x_r y_r + u_{yy}y_r^2 + u_y y_{rr} \\
&= u_{xx}x_r^2 + 2u_{xy}x_r y_r + u_{yy}y_r^2 + u_x x_{rr} + u_y y_{rr}.
\end{aligned}
$$

Note the use of equality of mixed partial derivatives. The same calculation with θ instead of r gives

$$
u_{\theta\theta} = u_{xx}x_\theta^2 + 2u_{xy}x_\theta y_\theta + u_{yy}y_\theta^2 + u_x x_{\theta\theta} + u_y y_{\theta\theta}.
$$

Because $x = r\cos\theta$ and $y = r\sin\theta$, we have the relations

$$
\begin{aligned}
x_r &= x/r, & y_r &= y/r, & x_\theta &= -y, & y_\theta &= x, \\
x_{rr} &= 0, & y_{rr} &= 0, & x_{\theta\theta} &= -x, & y_{\theta\theta} &= -y.
\end{aligned}
$$

It follows that

$$
\begin{aligned}
r^2 u_{rr} &= u_{xx}x^2 + 2u_{xy}xy + u_{yy}y^2, \\
r u_r &= u_x x + u_y y, \\
u_{\theta\theta} &= u_{xx}y^2 - 2u_{xy}xy + u_{yy}x^2 - u_x x - u_y y,
\end{aligned}
$$

and so

$$
\begin{aligned}
r^2 u_{rr} + r u_r + u_{\theta\theta} &= u_{xx}x^2 + u_{yy}y^2 + u_{xx}y^2 + u_{yy}x^2 \\
&= (u_{xx} + u_{yy})(x^2 + y^2).
\end{aligned}
$$

Recall that the Cartesian form of Laplace's equation is $u_{xx} + u_{yy} = 0$. Now the polar form follows:

$$
r^2 u_{rr} + r u_r + u_{\theta\theta} = 0.
$$

That is,

$$
r^2 \frac{\partial^2 u}{\partial r^2} + r \frac{\partial u}{\partial r} + \frac{\partial^2 u}{\partial \theta^2} = 0.
$$

The point of this involved calculation is that having done it once, and only once, we now can check directly whether any given function g of the polar variables r and θ satisfies Laplace's equation. We no longer need to transform each $u = g(r, \theta)$ into Cartesian terms $u = f(x, y)$ before checking.

An $n \times n$ matrix A is **orthogonal** if $A^{\mathsf{T}}A = I$. (This concept was introduced in Exercise 3.5.5.) Let A be orthogonal and consider its associated linear map,

$$
T_A : \mathbb{R}^n \longrightarrow \mathbb{R}^n, \quad T_A(x) = Ax.
$$

We show that prepending T_A to a twice-differentiable function on $\mathbb{R}^n$ is independent of applying the Laplacian operator to the function. That is, letting Δ denote the Laplacian operator on $\mathbb{R}^n$,

$$\Delta = D_{11} + D_{22} + \cdots + D_{nn},$$

and taking any twice-differentiable function on $\mathbb{R}^n$,

$$f : \mathbb{R}^n \longrightarrow \mathbb{R},$$

we show that

$$\Delta(f \circ T_A) = \Delta f \circ T_A.$$

To see this, start by noting that for every $x \in \mathbb{R}^n$, the chain rule and then the fact that the derivative of every linear map is itself give two equalities of linear mappings,

$$D(f \circ T_A)_x = Df_{T_A(x)} \circ D(T_A)_x = Df_{T_A(x)} \circ T_A.$$

In terms of matrices, the equality of the first and last quantities in the previous display is an equality of row-vector-valued functions of x,

$$\left[D_1(f \circ T_A) \quad \cdots \quad D_n(f \circ T_A) \right](x) = (\left[D_1 f \quad \cdots \quad D_n f \right] \circ T_A)(x) \cdot A.$$

Because we view vectors as columns, transpose the quantities in the previous display, using the fact that A is orthogonal to write A^{-1} for A^{T}, and universalize over x to get an equality of column-valued functions,

$$\begin{bmatrix} D_1(f \circ T_A) \\ \vdots \\ D_n(f \circ T_A) \end{bmatrix} = T_{A^{-1}} \circ \begin{bmatrix} D_1 f \\ \vdots \\ D_n f \end{bmatrix} \circ T_A.$$

The derivative matrix of the left side has as its rows the row vector derivative matrices of its entries, while the derivative matrix of the right side is computed by the chain rule and the fact that the derivative of every linear map is itself,

$$\left[D_{ij}(f \circ T_A) \right]_{n \times n} = A^{-1} \cdot \left[D_{ij} f \circ T_A \right]_{n \times n} \cdot A.$$

The trace of a square matrix was introduced in Exercise 3.2.5 as the sum of its diagonal entries, and the fact that $\operatorname{tr}(A^{-1}BA) = \operatorname{tr}(B)$ if A is invertible was noted just after the proof of Theorem 3.5.2. Equate the traces of the matrices in the previous display to get the desired result,

$$\Delta(f \circ T_A) = \Delta f \circ T_A.$$

To complement the proof just given in functional notation, here is a more elementary second proof. Let the matrix A have entries a_{ij}. For every $x \in \mathbb{R}^n$, compute that for $i = 1, \ldots, n$,

$$D_i(f \circ T_A)(x) = \sum_{j=1}^{n} D_j f(Ax) D_i(Ax)_j = \sum_{j=1}^{n} a_{ji} D_j f(Ax),$$

and thus

$$D_{ii}(f \circ T_A)(x) = \sum_{j=1}^{n} a_{ji} \sum_{k=1}^{n} D_{jk} f(Ax) D_i(Ax)_k = \sum_{j,k=1}^{n} a_{ji} a_{ki} D_{jk} f(Ax),$$

and thus, because A is orthogonal, so that $(AA^\mathsf{T})_{jk}$ is 1 when $j = k$ and 0 otherwise,

$$\Delta(f \circ T_A)(x) = \sum_{j,k=1}^{n} \sum_{i=1}^{n} a_{ji} a_{ki} D_{jk} f(Ax)$$

$$= \sum_{j,k=1}^{n} (AA^\mathsf{T})_{jk} D_{jk} f(Ax)$$

$$= \sum_{i=1}^{n} D_{ii} f(Ax) = (\Delta f \circ T_A)(x),$$

as desired.

Exercises

4.6.1. This exercise shows that continuity is necessary for the equality of mixed partial derivatives. Let

$$f(x,y) = \begin{cases} \frac{xy(y^2-x^2)}{x^2+y^2} & \text{if } (x,y) \neq (0,0), \\ 0 & \text{if } (x,y) = (0,0). \end{cases}$$

Away from $(0,0)$, f is rational, and so it is continuous and all its partial derivatives of all orders exist and are continuous. Show: (a) f is continuous at $(0,0)$, (b) $D_1 f$ and $D_2 f$ exist and are continuous at $(0,0)$, (c) $D_{12} f(0,0) = 1 \neq -1 = D_{21} f(0,0)$.

For the rest of these exercises, assume that the relevant functions are C^2.

4.6.2. Suppose u, as a function of x and y, satisfies the differential equation $u_{xx} - u_{yy} = 0$. Make the change of variables $x = s + t$, $y = s - t$. What corresponding differential equation does u satisfy when viewed as a function of s and t? (That is, find a nontrivial relation involving at least one of u, u_s, u_t, u_{ss}, u_{tt}, and u_{st}.)

4.6.3. (The wave equation) (a) Let c be a constant, tacitly understood to denote the speed of light. Let x and t denote a space variable and a time variable, and introduce variables

$$p = x + ct, \quad q = x - ct.$$

Show that a quantity w, viewed as a function of x and t, satisfies the wave equation,

$$c^2 w_{xx} = w_{tt},$$

if and only if it satisfies the equation

$$w_{pq} = 0.$$

(b) Using part (a), show that in particular if $w = F(x + ct) + G(x - ct)$ (where F and G are arbitrary C^2-functions of one variable) then w satisfies the wave equation. Here F and G are traveling waves, F traveling backward and G forward.

(c) Now let $0 < v < c$ (both v and c are constant), and define new space and time variables in terms of the original ones by a Lorentz transformation,

$$y = \gamma(x - vt), \quad u = \gamma(t - (v/c^2)x) \quad \text{where } \gamma = (1 - v^2/c^2)^{-1/2}.$$

Show that

$$y + cu = \gamma(1 - v/c)(x + ct), \quad y - cu = \gamma(1 + v/c)(x - ct),$$

so that consequently (y, u) has the same spacetime norm as (x, t),

$$y^2 - c^2 u^2 = x^2 - c^2 t^2.$$

(d) Recall the variables $p = x + ct$ and $q = x - ct$ from part (a). Similarly, let $r = y + cu$ and $s = y - cu$. Suppose that a quantity w, viewed as a function of p and q, satisfies the wave equation $w_{pq} = 0$. Use the results $r = \gamma(1 - v/c)p$, $s = \gamma(1 + v/c)q$ from part (c) to show that it also satisfies the wave equation in the (r, s)-coordinate system, $w_{rs} = 0$. Consequently, if w satisfies the wave equation $c^2 w_{xx} = w_{tt}$ in the original space and time variables then it also satisfies the wave equation $c^2 w_{yy} = w_{uu}$ in the new space and time variables.

4.6.4. Show that the substitution $x = e^s$, $y = e^t$ converts the equation

$$x^2 u_{xx} + y^2 u_{yy} + x u_x + y u_y = 0$$

into Laplace's equation $u_{ss} + u_{tt} = 0$.

4.6.5. (a) Show that the substitution $x = s^2 - t^2$, $y = 2st$ converts Laplace's equation $u_{xx} + u_{yy} = 0$ back into Laplace's equation $u_{ss} + u_{tt} = 0$.

(b) Let k be a nonzero real number. Show that the substitution $r = \rho^k$, $\theta = k\phi$ converts the polar Laplace's equation $r^2 u_{rr} + r u_r + u_{\theta\theta} = 0$ back into the polar Laplace's equation $\rho^2 u_{\rho\rho} + \rho u_\rho + u_{\phi\phi} = 0$. (When $k = 2$ this subsumes part (a), because the substitution here encodes the complex kth-power function in polar coordinates while the substitution in part (a) encodes the complex squaring function in Cartesian coordinates.)

4.6.6. Let u be a function of x and y, and suppose that x and y in turn depend linearly on s and t,

$$\begin{bmatrix} x \\ y \end{bmatrix} = \begin{bmatrix} a & b \\ c & d \end{bmatrix} \begin{bmatrix} s \\ t \end{bmatrix}, \quad ad - bc = 1.$$

What is the relation between $u_{ss}u_{tt} - u_{st}^2$ and $u_{xx}u_{yy} - u_{xy}^2$?

4.6.7. (a) Let $\mathcal{H}$ denote the set of points $(x, y) \in \mathbb{R}^2$ such that $y > 0$. Associate to each point $(x, y) \in \mathcal{H}$ another point,

$$(z, w) = \left(\frac{-x}{x^2 + y^2}, \frac{y}{x^2 + y^2} \right).$$

You may take for granted or verify that

$$z_x = z^2 - w^2, \quad z_y = -2zw, \quad z_{xx} = 2z(z^2 - 3w^2), \quad z_{yy} = -2z(z^2 - 3w^2)$$

and

$$w_x = 2zw, \quad w_y = z^2 - w^2, \quad w_{xx} = 2w(3z^2 - w^2), \quad w_{yy} = -2w(3z^2 - w^2).$$

Consider a quantity $u = f(z, w)$, so that also $u = \tilde{f}(x, y)$ for a different function $\tilde{f}$. As usual, we have

$$u_{xx} = u_{zz}z_x^2 + 2u_{zw}z_xw_x + u_{ww}w_x^2 + u_zz_{xx} + u_ww_{xx},$$
$$u_{yy} = u_{zz}z_y^2 + 2u_{zw}z_yw_y + u_{ww}w_y^2 + u_zz_{yy} + u_ww_{yy}.$$

Show that

$$y^2(u_{xx} + u_{yy}) = w^2(u_{zz} + u_{ww}).$$

The operator $y^2(\partial^2/\partial x^2 + \partial^2/\partial y^2)$ on $\mathcal{H}$ is the *hyperbolic Laplacian*, denoted $\Delta^{\mathcal{H}}$. We have just established the invariance of $\Delta^{\mathcal{H}}$ under the hyperbolic transformation that takes (x, y) to $(z, w) = (-x/(x^2 + y^2), y/(x^2 + y^2))$.

(b) Show that the invariance relation $y^2(u_{xx} + u_{yy}) = w^2(u_{zz} + u_{ww})$ also holds when $(z, w) = (x + b, y)$ for every fixed real number b, and that the relation also holds when $(z, w) = (rx, ry)$ for every fixed positive real number r. It is known that every hyperbolic transformation of $\mathcal{H}$ takes the form $(z, w) = \phi(x, y)$ where ϕ is a finite succession of transformations of the type in part (a) or of the two types just addressed here. Note that consequently this exercise has shown that the invariance relation holds for every hyperbolic transformation of $\mathcal{H}$. That is, for every hyperbolic transformation ϕ and for every twice-differential function $f : \mathcal{H} \longrightarrow \mathbb{R}$ we have, analogously to the result at the very end of this section,

$$\Delta^{\mathcal{H}}(f \circ \phi) = \Delta^{\mathcal{H}} f \circ \phi.$$

4.6.8. Consider three matrices,

$$X = \begin{bmatrix} 0 & 1 \\ 0 & 0 \end{bmatrix}, \qquad Y = \begin{bmatrix} 0 & 0 \\ 1 & 0 \end{bmatrix}, \qquad H = \begin{bmatrix} 1 & 0 \\ 0 & -1 \end{bmatrix}.$$

Establish the relations

$$XY - YX = H, \qquad HX - XH = 2X, \qquad HY - YH = -2Y.$$

Now consider three operators on smooth functions from $\mathbb{R}^n$ to $\mathbb{R}$, reusing the names X, Y, and H, and letting $\Delta = D_{11} + D_{22} + \cdots + D_{nn}$ denote the Laplacian operator,

$$(Xf)(x) = \tfrac{1}{2}|x|^2 f(x),$$
$$(Yf)(x) = -\tfrac{1}{2}\Delta f(x),$$
$$(Hf)(x) = \tfrac{n}{2}f(x) + \sum_{i=1}^{n} x_i D_i f(x).$$

Establish the same relations as a moment ago,

$$XY - YX = H, \qquad HX - XH = 2X, \qquad HY - YH = -2Y.$$

The three matrices generate a small instance of a *Lie algebra*, and this exercise shows that the space of smooth functions on $\mathbb{R}^n$ can be made a *representation* of the Lie algebra. Further show, partly by citing the work at the end of this section, that the action of every orthogonal matrix A on smooth functions commutes with the representation,

$$X(f \circ T_A) = (Xf) \circ T_A,$$
$$Y(f \circ T_A) = (Yf) \circ T_A,$$
$$H(f \circ T_A) = (Hf) \circ T_A.$$

4.7 Extreme Values

In one-variable calculus the derivative is used to find maximum and minimum values (extrema) of differentiable functions. Recall the following useful facts.

- (Extreme value theorem.) If $f : [\alpha, \beta] \longrightarrow \mathbb{R}$ is continuous then it assumes a maximum and a minimum on the interval $[\alpha, \beta]$.
- (Critical point theorem.) Suppose that $f : [\alpha, \beta] \longrightarrow \mathbb{R}$ is differentiable on (α, β) and that f assumes a maximum or minimum at an interior point a of $[\alpha, \beta]$. Then $f'(a) = 0$.
- (Second derivative test.) Suppose that $f : [\alpha, \beta] \longrightarrow \mathbb{R}$ is C^2 on (α, β) and that $f'(a) = 0$ at an interior point a of $[\alpha, \beta]$. If $f''(a) > 0$ then $f(a)$ is a local minimum of f, and if $f''(a) < 0$ then $f(a)$ is a local maximum.

Geometrically the idea is that just as the affine function

$$A(a + h) = f(a) + f'(a)h$$

specifies the tangent line to the graph of f at $(a, f(a))$, the quadratic function

$$P(a + h) = f(a) + f'(a)h + \frac{1}{2}f''(a)h^2$$

determines the best-fitting parabola. When $f'(a) = 0$, the tangent line is horizontal and the sign of $f''(a)$ specifies whether the parabola opens upward or downward. When $f'(a) = 0$ and $f''(a) = 0$, the parabola degenerates to the horizontal tangent line, and the second derivative provides no information. (See Figure 4.8.)

Figure 4.8. Approximating parabolas

This section generalizes these facts to functions f of n variables. The extreme value theorem has already generalized as Theorem 2.4.15: a continuous function f on a compact subset of $\mathbb{R}^n$ takes maximum and minimum values. The critical point theorem also generalizes easily to say that each extreme value of the function $f : A \longrightarrow \mathbb{R}$ that occurs at a point where f is differentiable occurs at a **critical point** of f, meaning a point a where Df_a is the zero function.

Theorem 4.7.1 (Multivariable critical point theorem). *Suppose that the function $f : A \longrightarrow \mathbb{R}$ (where $A \subset \mathbb{R}^n$) takes an extreme value at the point a of A, and suppose that f is differentiable at a. Then all partial derivatives of f at a are zero.*

Proof. For each $j \in \{1, \ldots, n\}$, the value $f(a)$ is an extreme value for the one-variable function φ from Definition 4.5.1 of the partial derivative $D_j f(a)$. By the one-variable critical point theorem, $\varphi'(a_j) = 0$. That is, $D_j f(a) = 0$. □

The generalization of the second derivative test is more elaborate. From now on, all functions are assumed to be of type $\mathcal{C}^2$ on the interiors of their domains, meaning that all their second-order partial derivatives exist and are continuous.

Definition 4.7.2 (Second derivative matrix). *Let $f : A \longrightarrow \mathbb{R}$ (where $A \subset \mathbb{R}^n$) be a function and let a be an interior point of A. The **second derivative matrix** of f at a is the $n \times n$ matrix whose (i,j)th entry is the second-order partial derivative $D_{ij}f(a)$. Thus*

$$f''(a) = \begin{bmatrix} D_{11}f(a) & \cdots & D_{1n}f(a) \\ \vdots & \ddots & \vdots \\ D_{n1}f(a) & \cdots & D_{nn}f(a) \end{bmatrix}.$$

By the equality of mixed partial derivatives, the second derivative matrix is symmetric, i.e., $f''(a)^\mathsf{T} = f''(a)$. Beware of confusing the second derivative matrix and the Jacobian matrix: the second derivative matrix is a square matrix defined only for scalar-valued functions and its entries are second-order partial derivatives, while for scalar-valued functions the Jacobian matrix is the row vector of first partial derivatives.

The eminently plausible formula $f'' = (f')'$ indeed holds, provided that we view f' as a mapping to $\mathbb{R}^n$, each of whose outputs is an ordered list with no shape rather than a row vector. Thus

$$(f')'(a) = f''(a) \quad \text{for interior points } a \text{ of } A.$$

As an example, if
$$f(x,y) = \sin^2 x + x^2 y + y^2,$$
then for every $(a,b) \in \mathbb{R}^2$,

$$f'(a,b) = [\sin 2a + 2ab \ \ a^2 + 2b]$$

and

$$f''(a,b) = \begin{bmatrix} 2\cos 2a + 2b & 2a \\ 2a & 2 \end{bmatrix}.$$

Every $n \times n$ matrix M determines a quadratic function

$$Q_M : \mathbb{R}^n \longrightarrow \mathbb{R}, \quad Q_M(h) = h^\mathsf{T} M h.$$

Here h is viewed as a column vector. If M has entries m_{ij} and $h = (h_1, \ldots, h_n)$ then the rules of matrix multiplication show that

$$Q_M(h) = \begin{bmatrix} h_1 & \cdots & h_n \end{bmatrix} \begin{bmatrix} m_{11} & \cdots & m_{1n} \\ \vdots & \ddots & \vdots \\ m_{n1} & \cdots & m_{nn} \end{bmatrix} \begin{bmatrix} h_1 \\ \vdots \\ h_n \end{bmatrix} = \sum_{i=1}^{n} \sum_{j=1}^{n} m_{ij} h_i h_j.$$

The function Q_M is homogeneous of degree 2, meaning that each of its terms has degree 2 in the entries of h and therefore $Q_M(th) = t^2 Q_M(h)$ for all $t \in \mathbb{R}$ and $h \in \mathbb{R}^n$.

When M is the second derivative matrix of a function f at a point a, the corresponding quadratic function is denoted Qf_a rather than $Q_{f''(a)}$. Just as

$f(a) + Df_a(h)$ gives the best affine approximation of $f(a + h)$ for small h, $f(a) + Df_a(h) + \frac{1}{2}Qf_a(h)$ gives the best quadratic approximation.

In the example $f(x, y) = \sin^2 x + x^2 y + y^2$, the second derivative matrix at a point (a, b) defines the quadratic function

$$Qf_{(a,b)}(h, k) = \begin{bmatrix} h & k \end{bmatrix} \begin{bmatrix} 2\cos 2a + 2b & 2a \\ 2a & 2 \end{bmatrix} \begin{bmatrix} h \\ k \end{bmatrix}$$

$$= 2((\cos 2a + b) h^2 + 2a\, hk + k^2) \quad \text{for } (h, k) \in \mathbb{R}^2,$$

and so the best quadratic approximation of f near, for instance, the point $(\pi/2, 1)$ is

$$f(\pi/2 + h, 1 + k) \approx f(\pi/2, 1) + Df_{(\pi/2,1)}(h, k) + \frac{1}{2}Qf_{(\pi/2,1)}(h, k)$$

$$= \pi^2/4 + 2 + \pi h + (\pi^2/4 + 2)k + \pi hk + k^2.$$

Suppose that $f : A \longrightarrow \mathbb{R}$ (where $A \subset \mathbb{R}^2$) has a critical point at (a, b), i.e., $f'(a, b) = [0 \quad 0]$. Working in local coordinates, we will approximate f by a quadratic function on $\mathbb{R}^2$ having a critical point at $(0, 0)$. The graphs of nine such quadratic functions are shown in Figure 4.9. If the best quadratic approximation of f at (a, b) is a bowl then f should have a minimum at (a, b). Similarly for an inverted bowl and a maximum. If the best quadratic approximation is a saddle then there should be points (x, y) near (a, b) where $f(x, y) > f(a, b)$ and points (x', y') near (a, b) where $f(x', y') < f(a, b)$. In this case, (a, b) is called for obvious reasons a **saddle point** of f.

Returning to the example $f(x, y) = \sin^2 x + x^2 y + y^2$, note that $(0, 0)$ is a critical point of f because $f'(0, 0) = [0 \quad 0]$. The second derivative matrix $f''(0, 0)$ is $\begin{bmatrix} 2 & 0 \\ 0 & 2 \end{bmatrix}$, and so the quadratic function $\frac{1}{2}Qf_{(0,0)}$ is given by

$$\frac{1}{2}Qf_{(0,0)}(h, k) = \frac{1}{2}\begin{bmatrix} h & k \end{bmatrix} \begin{bmatrix} 2 & 0 \\ 0 & 2 \end{bmatrix} \begin{bmatrix} h \\ k \end{bmatrix} = h^2 + k^2.$$

Thus the graph of f looks like a bowl near $(0, 0)$, and $f(0, 0)$ should be a local minimum.

This discussion is not yet rigorous. Justifying the ideas and proving the appropriate theorems will occupy the rest of this section. The first task is to study quadratic approximation of C^2-functions.

Proposition 4.7.3 (Special case of Taylor's theorem). *Let I be an open interval in $\mathbb{R}$ containing $[0, 1]$. Let $\varphi : I \longrightarrow \mathbb{R}$ be a C^2-function. Then*

$$\varphi(1) = \varphi(0) + \varphi'(0) + \frac{1}{2}\varphi''(c) \quad \text{for some } c \in [0, 1].$$

The proposition follows from the general Taylor's theorem in Section 1.3 because the first-degree Taylor polynomial of φ at 0 is $T_1(t) = \varphi(0) + \varphi'(0)t$, so that in particular $T_1(1) = \varphi(0) + \varphi'(0)$.

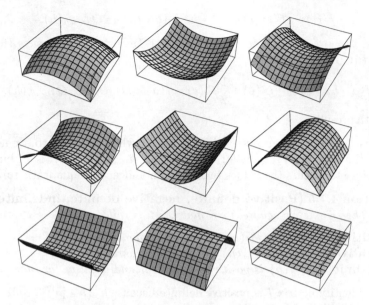

Figure 4.9. Two bowls, two saddles, four half-pipes, and a plane

Theorem 4.7.4 (Quadratic Taylor approximation). *Let $f : A \longrightarrow \mathbb{R}$ (where $A \subset \mathbb{R}^n$) be a C^2-function on the interior points of A. Let a be an interior point of A. Then for all small enough $h \in \mathbb{R}^n$,*

$$f(a + h) = f(a) + Df_a(h) + \frac{1}{2}Qf_{a+ch}(h) \quad \text{for some } c \in [0,1],$$

or, in matrices, viewing h as a column vector,

$$f(a + h) = f(a) + f'(a)h + \frac{1}{2}h^{\mathsf{T}}f''(a + ch)h \quad \text{for some } c \in [0,1].$$

Proof. Let $I = (-\varepsilon, 1 + \varepsilon)$ be a small superinterval of $[0,1]$ in $\mathbb{R}$. Define

$$\gamma : I \longrightarrow A, \quad \gamma(t) = a + th.$$

Thus $\gamma(0) = a$, $\gamma(1) = a + h$, and $\gamma'(t) = h$ for all $t \in I$. Further define

$$\varphi = f \circ \gamma : I \longrightarrow \mathbb{R}.$$

That is, $\varphi(t) = f(a + th)$ is the restriction of f to the line segment from a to $a + h$. By the chain rule and the fact that $\gamma' = h$,

$$\varphi'(t) = (f \circ \gamma)'(t) = f'(\gamma(t))h = Df_{a+th}(h).$$

The previous display can be rephrased as $\varphi'(t) = \langle f'(\gamma(t)), h \rangle$, and so the chain rule and the symmetry of f'' give

$$\varphi''(t) = \langle f''(\gamma(t))h, h \rangle = h^{\mathsf{T}} f''(a + th)h = Q f_{a+th}(h).$$

Because $f(a + h) = \varphi(1)$, the special case of Taylor's theorem says that for some $c \in [0, 1]$,

$$f(a + h) = \varphi(0) + \varphi'(0) + \frac{1}{2}\varphi''(c) = f(a) + Df_a(h) + \frac{1}{2}Q f_{a+ch}(h),$$

giving the result. □

Thus, to study f near a critical point $a \in \mathbb{R}^n$ where Df_a is zero, we need to look at the sign of $Q f_{a+ch}(h)$ for small vectors h. The next order of business is therefore to discuss the values taken by a homogeneous quadratic function.

Definition 4.7.5 (Positive definite, negative definite, indefinite matrix). *The symmetric square $n \times n$ matrix M is called*

- **positive definite** *if $Q_M(h) > 0$ for every nonzero $h \in \mathbb{R}^n$,*
- **negative definite** *if $Q_M(h) < 0$ for every nonzero $h \in \mathbb{R}^n$,*
- **indefinite** *if $Q_M(h)$ is positive for some h and negative for others.*

The identity matrix I is positive definite because $h^{\mathsf{T}} I h = |h|^2$ for all h. The matrix $\begin{bmatrix} 1 & 0 \\ 0 & -1 \end{bmatrix}$ is indefinite. The general question whether a symmetric $n \times n$ matrix is positive definite leads to an excursion into linear algebra too lengthy for this course. (See Exercise 4.7.10 for the result without proof.) However, in the special case of $n = 2$, basic methods give the answer. Recall that the quadratic polynomial $\alpha h^2 + 2\beta h + \delta$ takes positive and negative values if and only if it has distinct real roots, i.e., $\alpha\delta - \beta^2 < 0$.

Proposition 4.7.6 (Two-by-two definiteness Test). *Consider a matrix $M = \begin{bmatrix} \alpha & \beta \\ \beta & \delta \end{bmatrix} \in M_2(\mathbb{R})$. Then*

(1) *M is positive definite if and only if $\alpha > 0$ and $\alpha\delta - \beta^2 > 0$.*
(2) *M is negative definite if and only if $\alpha < 0$ and $\alpha\delta - \beta^2 > 0$.*
(3) *M is indefinite if and only if $\alpha\delta - \beta^2 < 0$.*

Proof. Since $Q_M(t(h, k)) = t^2 Q_M(h, k)$ for all real t, scaling the input vector (h, k) by nonzero real numbers doesn't affect the sign of the output. The second entry k can therefore be scaled to 0 or 1, and if $k = 0$ then the first entry h can be scaled to 1. Therefore, to prove (1), reason that

$$M \text{ is positive definite} \iff Q_M(1, 0) > 0 \text{ and } Q_M(h, 1) > 0 \text{ for all } h \in \mathbb{R}$$
$$\iff \alpha > 0 \text{ and } \alpha h^2 + 2\beta h + \delta > 0 \text{ for all } h \in \mathbb{R}$$
$$\iff \alpha > 0 \text{ and } \alpha\delta - \beta^2 > 0.$$

Statement (2) is similar. As for (3),

$$M \text{ is indefinite} \iff \alpha h^2 + 2\beta h + \delta \text{ takes positive and negative values}$$
$$\iff \alpha\delta - \beta^2 < 0.$$

□

The proposition provides no information if $\alpha\delta - \beta^2 = 0$. Geometrically, the proposition gives conditions on M to determine that the graph of Q_M is a bowl, an inverted bowl, or a saddle. The condition $\alpha\delta - \beta^2 = 0$ indicates a degenerate graph: a half-pipe (see Figure 4.9), an inverted half-pipe, or a plane.

For nonzero α, the matrix calculation

$$\begin{bmatrix} \alpha & \beta \\ \beta & \delta \end{bmatrix} = \begin{bmatrix} 1 & 0 \\ \alpha^{-1}\beta & 1 \end{bmatrix} \begin{bmatrix} \alpha & 0 \\ 0 & \alpha^{-1}(\alpha\delta - \beta^2) \end{bmatrix} \begin{bmatrix} 1 & \alpha^{-1}\beta \\ 0 & 1 \end{bmatrix}$$

gives a corresponding equality of quadratic functions,

$$\alpha x^2 + 2\beta xy + \delta y^2 = \alpha\tilde{x}^2 + \alpha^{-1}(\alpha\delta - \beta^2)y^2, \quad \tilde{x} = x + \alpha^{-1}\beta y.$$

That is, a change of variables eliminates the cross term, and the variant quadratic function makes the results of the definiteness test clear.

The positive definite, negative definite, or indefinite character of a matrix is preserved if the matrix entries vary by small enough amounts. Again we restrict our discussion to the 2×2 case. Here the result is plausible geometrically, since it says that if the matrix $M(a,b)$ defines a function whose graph is (for example) a bowl, then matrices close to $M(a,b)$ should define functions with similar graphs, which thus should still be bowl-shaped. The same persistence holds for a saddle, but a half-pipe can deform immediately into either a bowl or a saddle, and so can a plane.

Proposition 4.7.7 (Persistence of definiteness). *Let A be a subset of $\mathbb{R}^2$, and let the matrix-valued mapping*

$$M : A \longrightarrow \mathrm{M}_2(\mathbb{R}), \quad M(x,y) = \begin{bmatrix} \alpha(x,y) & \beta(x,y) \\ \beta(x,y) & \delta(x,y) \end{bmatrix}$$

be continuous. Let (a,b) be an interior point of A. Suppose that the matrix $M(a,b)$ is positive definite. Then for all (x,y) in some ε-ball about (a,b), the matrix $M(x,y)$ is also positive definite. Similar statements hold for negative definite and indefinite matrices.

Proof. By the persistence of inequality principle (Proposition 2.3.10), the criteria $\alpha > 0$ and $\alpha\delta - \beta^2 > 0$ remain valid if x and y vary by a small enough amount. The other statements follow similarly. $\qquad\square$

When a function f has continuous second-order partial derivatives, the entries of the second derivative matrix $f''(a)$ vary continuously with a. The upshot of the last proposition is therefore that we may replace the nebulous notion of Qf_{a+ch} *for some c* with the explicit function Qf_a.

Proposition 4.7.8 (Two-variable max/min test). *Let $f : A \longrightarrow \mathbb{R}$ (where $A \subset \mathbb{R}^2$) be C^2 on its interior points. Let (a,b) be an interior point of A, and suppose that $f'(a,b) = [0 \quad 0]$. Let $f''(a,b) = \begin{bmatrix} \alpha & \beta \\ \beta & \delta \end{bmatrix}$. Then:*

(1) *If $\alpha > 0$ and $\alpha\delta - \beta^2 > 0$ then $f(a,b)$ is a local minimum.*
(2) *If $\alpha < 0$ and $\alpha\delta - \beta^2 > 0$ then $f(a,b)$ is a local maximum.*
(3) *If $\alpha\delta - \beta^2 < 0$ then $f(a,b)$ is a saddle point.*

Proof. This follows from Theorem 4.7.4, Proposition 4.7.6, and Proposition 4.7.7. □

Again, the test gives no information if $\alpha\delta - \beta^2 = 0$.

Returning once again to the example $f(x,y) = \sin^2 x + x^2 y + y^2$ with its critical point $(0,0)$ and second derivative matrix $f''(0,0) = \begin{bmatrix} 2 & 0 \\ 0 & 2 \end{bmatrix}$, the max/min test shows that f has a local minimum at $(0,0)$.

Another example is to find the extrema of the function

$$f(x,y) = xy(x + y - 3)$$

on the triangle

$$T = \{(x,y) \in \mathbb{R}^2 : x \geq 0, y \geq 0, x + y \leq 3\}.$$

To solve this, first note that T is compact. Therefore f is guaranteed to take a maximum and a minimum value on T. These are assumed either at interior points of T or along the edge. Examining the signs of x, y, and $x + y - 3$ shows that f is zero at all points on the edge of T and negative on the interior of T. Thus f assumes its maximum value—zero—along the boundary of T and must assume its minimum somewhere inside. (See Figure 4.10.) To find the extrema of f inside T, we first find the critical points. The partial derivatives of f (now viewed as a function only on the interior of T) are

$$f_x(x,y) = y(2x + y - 3), \qquad f_y(x,y) = x(x + 2y - 3),$$

and since x and y are nonzero on the interior of T, these are both zero only at the unique solution $(x,y) = (1,1)$ of the simultaneous equations $2x + y = 3$, $x + 2y = 3$. Therefore $f(1,1) = -1$ must be the minimum value of f. A quick calculation shows that $f''(1,1) = \begin{bmatrix} 2 & 1 \\ 1 & 2 \end{bmatrix}$, and the max/min test confirms the minimum at $(1,1)$.

Another example is to find the extreme values of the function

$$f : \mathbb{R}^2 \longrightarrow \mathbb{R}, \quad f(x,y) = \frac{1}{2}x^2 + xy - 2x - \frac{1}{2}y^2.$$

Since $\mathbb{R}^2$ is not compact, there is no guarantee that f has any extrema. In fact, for large x, $f(x,0)$ gets arbitrarily large, and for large y, $f(0,y)$ gets arbitrarily large in the negative direction. So f has no global extrema. Nonetheless, there may be local ones. Every point of $\mathbb{R}^2$ is interior, so it suffices to examine the critical points of f. The partial derivatives are

$$f_x(x,y) = x + y - 2, \qquad f_y(x,y) = x - y,$$

and the only point where both of them vanish is $(x,y) = (1,1)$. The second derivative matrix is $f''(1,1) = \begin{bmatrix} 1 & 1 \\ 1 & -1 \end{bmatrix}$, so the critical point $(1,1)$ is a saddle point. The function f has no extrema, local or global.

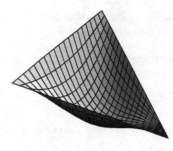

Figure 4.10. Zero on the boundary, negative on the interior

Exercises

4.7.1. Compute the best quadratic approximation of $f(x,y) = e^x \cos y$ at the point $(0,0)$, $f(h,k) \approx f(0,0) + Df_{(0,0)}(h,k) + \frac{1}{2}Qf_{(0,0)}(h,k)$.

4.7.2. Compute the best quadratic approximation of $f(x,y) = e^{x+2y}$ at the point $(0,0)$.

4.7.3. Explain, making whatever reasonable assumptions seem to be helpful, why the n-dimensional conceptual analogue of Figure 4.9 should have 3^n pictures. How does this relate to Figure 4.8?

4.7.4. Find the extreme values taken by $f(x,y) = xy(4x^2 + y^2 - 16)$ on the quarter-ellipse

$$E = \{(x,y) \in \mathbb{R}^2 : x \geq 0, y \geq 0, 4x^2 + y^2 \leq 16\}.$$

4.7.5. Find the local extrema of the function $f(x,y) = x^2 + xy - 4x + \frac{3}{2}y^2 - 7y$ on $\mathbb{R}^2$.

4.7.6. Determine the nature of $f(x,y) = \frac{1}{3}x^3 + \frac{1}{3}y^3 + (x-\frac{3}{2})^2 - (y+4)^2$ at each of its critical points. Are there global extrema?

4.7.7. Find the critical points. Are they maxima, minima, or saddle points? (The max/min test will not always help.)

$$f(x,y) = x^2 y + xy^2, \qquad g(x,y) = e^{x+y}, \qquad h(x,y) = x^5 y + xy^5 + xy.$$

4.7.8. Discuss local and global extrema of $f(x,y) = \frac{1}{x-1} - \frac{1}{y-1}$ on the open ball $B((0,0);1)$ in $\mathbb{R}^2$.

4.7.9. The graph of the function $m(x,y) = 6xy^2 - 2x^3 - 3y^4$ is called a **monkey saddle**. Find the three critical points of m and classify each as a maximum, minimum, or saddle. (The max/min test will work on two. Study $m(x,0)$ and $m(0,y)$ to classify the third.) Explain the name *monkey saddle*—a computer picture may help.

4.7.10. Linear algebra readily addresses the question whether an $n \times n$ matrix is positive definite, negative definite, or indefinite.

Definition 4.7.9 (Characteristic polynomial). *Let M be an $n \times n$ matrix. Its* **characteristic polynomial** *is*

$$p_M(\lambda) = \det(M - \lambda I).$$

The characteristic polynomial of M is a polynomial of degree n in the scalar variable λ.

While the roots of a polynomial with real coefficients are in general complex, the roots of the characteristic polynomial of a symmetric matrix in $M_n(\mathbb{R})$ are guaranteed to be real. The characterization we want is contained in the following theorem.

Theorem 4.7.10 (Description of definite/indefinite matrices). *Let M be a symmetric matrix in $M_n(\mathbb{R})$. Then:*

(1) *M is positive definite if and only if all the roots of $p_M(\lambda)$ are positive.*
(2) *M is negative definite if and only if all the roots of $p_M(\lambda)$ are negative.*
(3) *M is indefinite if and only if $p_M(\lambda)$ has positive roots and negative roots.*

With this result one can extend the methods in this section to functions of more than two variables.

(a) Let M be the symmetric matrix $\begin{bmatrix} \alpha & \beta \\ \beta & \delta \end{bmatrix} \in M_2(\mathbb{R})$. Show that

$$p_M(\lambda) = \lambda^2 - (\alpha + \delta)\lambda + (\alpha\delta - \beta^2).$$

(b) Show that Theorem 4.7.10 is equivalent to Proposition 4.7.6 when $n = 2$.

(c) Classify the 3×3 matrices

$$\begin{bmatrix} 1 & -1 & 0 \\ -1 & 2 & 0 \\ 0 & 0 & 1 \end{bmatrix}, \quad \begin{bmatrix} 0 & 1 & 0 \\ 1 & 0 & 1 \\ 0 & 1 & 0 \end{bmatrix}.$$

A generalization of Proposition 4.7.7 also holds, because the roots of a polynomial vary continuously with the polynomial's coefficients. The generalized proposition leads to the following result.

Proposition 4.7.11 (General max/min test). *Let $f : A \longrightarrow \mathbb{R}$ (where $A \subset \mathbb{R}^n$) be $\mathcal{C}^2$ on its interior points. Let a be an interior point of A, and suppose that $f'(a) = \mathbf{0}_n$. Let the second derivative matrix $f''(a)$ have characteristic polynomial $p(\lambda)$.*

(1) *If all roots of $p(\lambda)$ are positive then $f(a)$ is a local minimum.*
(2) *If all roots of $p(\lambda)$ are negative then $f(a)$ is a local maximum.*
(3) *If $p(\lambda)$ has positive and negative roots then $f(a)$ is a saddle point.*

4.7.11. This exercise eliminates the cross terms from a quadratic function of n variables, generalizing the calculation for $n = 2$ in this section. Throughout, we abbreviate *positive definite* to *positive*. Let M be a positive $n \times n$ symmetric matrix where $n > 1$. This exercise shows how to diagonalize M as a quadratic function. (This is different from diagonalizing M as a transformation, as is done in every linear algebra course.) Decompose M as

$$M = \left[\begin{array}{c|c} a & c^{\mathsf{T}} \\ \hline c & N \end{array}\right],$$

with $a > 0$ and $c \in \mathbb{R}^{n-1}$ a column vector and N positive $(n-1) \times (n-1)$ symmetric. Define

$$M_2 = N - a^{-1}cc^{\mathsf{T}},$$

again $(n-1) \times (n-1)$ symmetric, though we don't yet know whether it is positive. Check that

$$M = \left[\begin{array}{c|c} 1 & a^{-1}c^{\mathsf{T}} \\ \hline 0 & I_{n-1} \end{array}\right]^{\mathsf{T}} \left[\begin{array}{c|c} a & \mathbf{0}^{\mathsf{T}} \\ \hline 0 & M_2 \end{array}\right] \left[\begin{array}{c|c} 1 & a^{-1}c^{\mathsf{T}} \\ \hline 0 & I_{n-1} \end{array}\right].$$

Show that in terms of quadratic functions, this says (letting $v = (x_1, \ldots, x_n)$ and $v_2 = (x_2, \ldots, x_n)$ with these vectors viewed as columns, and letting $\tilde{x}_1 = x_1 + a^{-1}c^{\mathsf{T}}v_2$) that

$$v^{\mathsf{T}} M v = a\tilde{x}_1^2 + v_2^{\mathsf{T}} M_2 v_2.$$

Consequently M_2 is positive: indeed, if the last term of the previous display is nonpositive then setting $x_1 = -a^{-1}c^{\mathsf{T}}v_2$ makes $\tilde{x}_1$ zero and thus makes the entire right side nonpositive, so that $v = \mathbf{0}_n$ because M is positive, and consequently $v_2 = \mathbf{0}_{n-1}$. Repeating the process on M_2, and so on, eventually gives

$$v^{\mathsf{T}} M v = a_1 \tilde{x}_1^2 + \cdots + a_n \tilde{x}_n^2,$$

with all $a_i > 0$ and with the vector $\tilde{v} = (\tilde{x}_1, \ldots, \tilde{x}_n)$ of modified variables the image of the vector v of original variables by a linear transformation whose matrix is upper triangular with 1's on the diagonal.

4.8 Directional Derivatives and the Gradient

Let f be a scalar-valued function, $f : A \longrightarrow \mathbb{R}$ where $A \subset \mathbb{R}^n$, and assume that f is differentiable at a point a of A. While the derivative Df_a is a rather abstract object—the linear mapping that gives the best approximation of $f(a+h) - f(a)$ for small h—the partial derivatives $D_j f(a)$ are easy to understand. The jth partial derivative of f at a,

$$D_j f(a) = \lim_{t \to 0} \frac{f(a + te_j) - f(a)}{t},$$

measures the rate of change of f at a as its input varies in the jth direction. Visually, $D_j f(a)$ gives the slope of the jth cross section through a of the graph of f.

Analogous formulas measure the rate of change of f at a as its input varies in a direction that doesn't necessarily parallel a coordinate axis. A direction in $\mathbb{R}^n$ is specified by a *unit* vector d, i.e., a vector d such that $|d| = 1$. As the input to f moves a distance t in the d direction, f changes by $f(a+td) - f(a)$. Thus the following definition is natural.

Definition 4.8.1 (Directional derivative). *Let $f : A \longrightarrow \mathbb{R}$ (where $A \subset \mathbb{R}^n$) be a function, let a be an interior point of A, and let $d \in \mathbb{R}^n$ be a unit vector. The* **directional derivative of f at a in the d direction** *is*

$$D_d f(a) = \lim_{t \to 0} \frac{f(a + td) - f(a)}{t},$$

if this limit exists.

The directional derivatives of f in the standard basis vector directions are simply the partial derivatives.

When $n = 2$ and f is differentiable at $(a, b) \in \mathbb{R}^2$, its graph has a well-fitting tangent plane through $(a, b, f(a, b))$. The plane is determined by the two slopes $D_1 f(a, b)$ and $D_2 f(a, b)$, and it geometrically determines the rate of increase of f in all other directions. (See Figure 4.11.) The geometry suggests that if $f : A \longrightarrow \mathbb{R}$ (where $A \subset \mathbb{R}^n$) is differentiable at a then all directional derivatives are expressible in terms of the partial derivatives. This is true and easy to show. A special case of the differentiability property (4.1) is

$$f(a + td) - f(a) - Df_a(td) \quad \text{is} \quad o(td) = o(t),$$

or, since the constant t passes through the linear map Df_a,

$$\lim_{t \to 0} \frac{f(a + td) - f(a)}{t} = Df_a(d),$$

or, since the linear map Df_a has matrix $[D_1 f(a), \ldots, D_n f(a)]$,

$$D_d f(a) = \sum_{j=1}^{n} D_j f(a) d_j$$

as desired.

The derivative matrix $f'(a)$ of a scalar-valued function f at a is often called the **gradient** of f at a and written $\nabla f(a)$. That is,

$$\nabla f(a) = f'(a) = [D_1 f(a), \ldots, D_n f(a)].$$

The previous calculation and this definition lead to the following theorem.

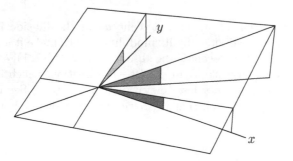

Figure 4.11. General directional slope determined by axis-directional slopes

Theorem 4.8.2 (Directional derivative and gradient). *Let the function* $f : A \longrightarrow \mathbb{R}$ *(where $A \subset \mathbb{R}^n$) be differentiable at a, and let $d \in \mathbb{R}^n$ be a unit vector. Then the directional derivative of f at a in the d direction exists, and it is equal to*

$$D_d f(a) = \sum_{j=1}^{n} D_j f(a) d_j = \langle \nabla f(a), d \rangle = |\nabla f(a)| \cos \theta_{\nabla f(a), d}.$$

Therefore:

- *The rate of increase of f at a in the d direction varies with d, from $-|\nabla f(a)|$ when d points in the direction opposite to $\nabla f(a)$, to $|\nabla f(a)|$ when d points in the same direction as $\nabla f(a)$.*
- *In particular, the vector $\nabla f(a)$ points in the direction of greatest increase of f at a, and its modulus $|\nabla f(a)|$ is precisely this greatest rate.*
- *Also, the directions orthogonal to $\nabla f(a)$ are the directions in which f neither increases nor decreases at a.*

This theorem gives necessary conditions that arise in consequence of the derivative of f existing at a point a. As in Section 4.5, the converse statement, that these conditions are sufficient to make the derivative of f exist at a, is false. Each directional derivative $D_d f(a)$ can exist without the derivative Df_a existing (Exercise 4.8.10). Furthermore, each directional derivative can exist at a and satisfy the formula $D_d f(a) = \langle \nabla f(a), d \rangle$ in the theorem, but still without the derivative Df_a existing (Exercise 4.8.11). The existence of the multivariable derivative Df_a is a stronger condition than any amount of one-variable cross-sectional derivative data at a.

For an example illustrating the theorem, if you are skiing on the quadratic mountain $f(x, y) = 9 - x^2 - 2y^2$ at the point $(a, f(a)) = (1, 1, 6)$, then your gradient meter shows

$$\nabla f(1,1) = (D_1 f(1,1), D_2 f(1,1)) = (-2x, -4y)\big|_{(x,y)=(1,1)} = (-2,-4).$$

Therefore the direction of steepest descent *down* the hillside is the $(2,4)$-direction (this could be divided by its modulus $\sqrt{20}$ to make it a unit vector), and the slope of steepest descent is the absolute value $|\nabla f(1,1)| = \sqrt{20}$. On the other hand, cross-country skiing in the $(2,-1)$-direction, which is orthogonal to $\nabla f(1,1)$, neither gains nor loses elevation immediately. (See Figure 4.12.) The cross-country skiing trail that neither climbs nor descends has a mathematical name.

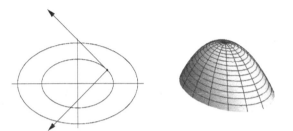

Figure 4.12. Gradient and its orthogonal vector for the parabolic mountain

Definition 4.8.3 (Level set). *Let* $f : A \longrightarrow \mathbb{R}$ *(where* $A \subset \mathbb{R}^n$*) be a function. A* **level set** *of* f *is the set of points in* A *that map under* f *to some fixed value* b *in* $\mathbb{R}$,

$$L = \{x \in A : f(x) = b\}.$$

The curves on a topographical map are level sets of the altitude function. The isotherms on a weather map are level sets of the temperature function, and the isobars on a weather map are level sets of the pressure function. Indifference curves in economics are level sets of the utility function, and isoquants are level sets of the production function. Surfaces of constant potential in physics are level sets of the potential function.

For example, on the mountain

$$f : \mathbb{R}^2 \longrightarrow \mathbb{R}, \qquad f(x,y) = 9 - x^2 - 2y^2,$$

the level set for $b = 5$ is an ellipse in the plane,

$$L = \{(x,y) \in \mathbb{R}^2 : x^2 + 2y^2 = 4\}.$$

And similarly, the level set is an ellipse for every real number b up to 9. As just mentioned, plotting the level sets of a function f of two variables gives a topographical map description of f. The geometry is different for a function

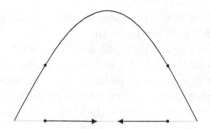

Figure 4.13. Level set and gradients for the sine function

of one variable: each level set is a subset of the line. For example, consider a restriction of the sine function,

$$f : (0, \pi) \longrightarrow \mathbb{R}, \qquad f(x) = \sin(x).$$

The level set taken by f to $1/2$ consists of two points,

$$L = \{\pi/6, 5\pi/6\}.$$

For a function of three variables, each level set is a subset of space. For example, if a, b, and c are positive numbers, and the function is

$$f : \mathbb{R}^3 \longrightarrow \mathbb{R}, \qquad f(x, y, z) = (x/a)^2 + (y/b)^2 + (z/c)^2,$$

then its level sets are ellipsoids. Specifically, for every positive r, the level set of points taken by f to r is the ellipsoid of x-radius $a\sqrt{r}$, y-radius $b\sqrt{r}$, and z-radius $c\sqrt{r}$,

$$L = \left\{ (x, y, z) \in \mathbb{R}^3 : \left(\frac{x}{a\sqrt{r}} \right)^2 + \left(\frac{y}{b\sqrt{r}} \right)^2 + \left(\frac{z}{c\sqrt{r}} \right)^2 = 1 \right\}.$$

The third bullet in Theorem 4.8.2 says that *the gradient is normal to the level set*. This fact may seem surprising, since the gradient is a version of the derivative, and we think of the derivative as describing a tangent object to a graph. The reason that the derivative has become a normal object is that

a level set is different from a graph.

A level set of f is a subset of the domain of f, whereas the graph of f, which simultaneously shows the domain and the range of f, is a subset of a space that is one dimension larger. For instance, if we think of f as measuring elevation, then the graph of f is terrain in three-dimensional space, while a level set of f is the set of points in the plane that lie beneath the terrain at some constant altitude; the level set is typically a curve. Figure 4.12 illustrates the difference in the case of the mountain function. Note that in the left part of the figure, the gradient is orthogonal to the ellipse on which it starts. Similarly, Figure 4.13 illustrates the difference in the case of the restricted sine function from the previous paragraph. In the figure, the x-axis shows the two-point level set from the previous paragraph and the gradient of f at each of the two points. The fact that one gradient points rightward indicates that to climb the graph of f over that point, one should move to the right, and the slope to be encountered on the graph will be the length of the gradient on the axis. Similarly, the other gradient points leftward, because to climb the graph over the other point, one should move to the left. Here each gradient is trivially orthogonal to the level set, because the level set consists of isolated points. For the three-variable function from the previous paragraph, we still can see the level sets—they are concentric ellipsoids—but not the graph, which would require four dimensions. Instead, we can conceive of the function as measuring temperature in space, and of the gradient as pointing in the direction to move for greatest rate of temperature-increase, with the length of the gradient being that rate. Figure 4.14 shows a level set for the temperature function and several gradients, visibly orthogonal to the level set.

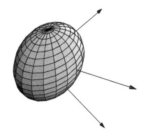

Figure 4.14. Level set and gradients for the temperature function

Although Theorem 4.8.2 has already stated that the gradient is orthogonal to the level set, we now amplify the argument. Let $f : A \longrightarrow \mathbb{R}$ (where $A \subset \mathbb{R}^n$) be given, and assume that it is differentiable. Let a be a point of A, and let $b = f(a)$. Consider the level set of f containing a,

$$L = \{x \in A : f(x) = b\} \subset \mathbb{R}^n,$$

and consider any smooth curve from some interval into the level set, passing through a,

$$\gamma : (-\varepsilon, \varepsilon) \longrightarrow L, \qquad \gamma(0) = a.$$

The composite function

$$f \circ \gamma : (-\varepsilon, \varepsilon) \longrightarrow \mathbb{R}$$

is the constant function b, so that its derivative at 0 is 0. By the chain rule this relation is

$$\nabla f(a) \cdot \gamma'(0) = 0.$$

Every tangent vector to L at a takes the form $\gamma'(0)$ for some γ of the sort that we are considering. Therefore, $\nabla f(a)$ is orthogonal to every tangent vector to L at a, i.e., $\nabla f(a)$ is normal to L at a.

Before continuing to work with the gradient, we pause to remark that level sets and graphs are related. For one thing:

The graph of a function is also the level set of a different function.

To see this, let $n > 1$, let A_0 be a subset of $\mathbb{R}^{n-1}$, and let $f : A_0 \longrightarrow \mathbb{R}$ be any function. Given this information, let $A = A_0 \times \mathbb{R}$ and define a second function $g : A \longrightarrow \mathbb{R}$,

$$g(x_1, \ldots, x_{n-1}, x_n) = f(x_1, \ldots, x_{n-1}) - x_n.$$

Then the graph of f is a level of g, specifically the set of inputs that g takes to 0,

$$\begin{aligned} \text{graph}(f) &= \{x \in A_0 \times \mathbb{R} : x_n = f(x_1, \ldots, x_{n-1})\} \\ &= \{x \in A : g(x) = 0\}. \end{aligned}$$

For example, the graph of the mountain function $f(x, y) = 9 - x^2 - 2y^2$ is also a level set of the function $g(x, y, z) = 9 - x^2 - 2y^2 - z$. But in contrast to this quick method of defining g explicitly in terms of f to show that every graph is a level set, the converse question is much more subtle:

To what extent is some given level set also a graph?

For example, the level sets of the mountain function f are ellipses (as shown in Figure 4.12), but an ellipse is not the graph of y as a function of x or vice versa. This converse question will be addressed by the implicit function theorem in the next chapter.

Returning to the gradient, the geometric fact that it is normal to the level set makes it easy to find the tangent plane to a two-dimensional surface in $\mathbb{R}^3$. For example, consider the surface

$$H = \{(x, y, z) \in \mathbb{R}^3 : x^2 + y^2 - z^2 = 1\}.$$

(This surface is a hyperboloid of one sheet.) The point $(2\sqrt{2}, 3, 4)$ belongs to H. Note that H is a level set of the function $f(x, y, z) = x^2 + y^2 - z^2$, and compute the gradient

$$\nabla f(2\sqrt{2}, 3, 4) = (4\sqrt{2}, 6, -8).$$

Since this is the normal vector to H at $(2\sqrt{2}, 3, 4)$, the tangent plane equation at the end of Section 3.10 shows that the equation of the tangent plane to H at $(2\sqrt{2}, 3, 4)$ is

$$4\sqrt{2}(x - 2\sqrt{2}) + 6(y - 3) - 8(z - 4) = 0.$$

If a function $f : \mathbb{R}^n \longrightarrow \mathbb{R}$ has a continuous gradient, then from every starting point $a \in \mathbb{R}^n$ where the gradient $\nabla f(a)$ is nonzero, there is a path of steepest ascent of f (called an **integral curve of** ∇f) starting at a. If $n = 2$ and the graph of f is seen as a surface in 3-space, then the integral curve from the point $(a, b) \in \mathbb{R}^2$ is the shadow of the path followed by a particle climbing the graph, starting at $(a, b, f(a, b))$. If $n = 2$ or $n = 3$ and f is viewed as temperature, then the integral curve is the path followed by a heat-seeking bug.

To find the integral curve, we set up an equation that describes it. The idea is to treat the gradient vector as a divining rod and follow it starting at a. Doing so produces a path in $\mathbb{R}^n$ that describes time-dependent motion, always in the direction of the gradient, and always with speed equal to the modulus of the gradient. Computing the path amounts to finding an interval $I \subset \mathbb{R}$ containing 0 and a mapping

$$\gamma : I \longrightarrow \mathbb{R}^n$$

that satisfies the differential equation with initial conditions

$$\gamma'(t) = \nabla f(\gamma(t)), \qquad \gamma(0) = a. \tag{4.3}$$

Whether (and how) one can solve this for γ depends on the data f and a.

In the case of the mountain function $f(x, y) = 9 - x^2 - 2y^2$, with gradient $\nabla f(x, y) = (-2x, -4y)$, the path γ has two components γ_1 and γ_2, and the differential equation and initial conditions (4.3) become

$$(\gamma_1'(t), \gamma_2'(t)) = (-2\gamma_1(t), -4\gamma_2(t)), \qquad (\gamma_1(0), \gamma_2(0)) = (a, b),$$

to which the unique solution is

$$(\gamma_1(t), \gamma_2(t)) = (ae^{-2t}, be^{-4t}).$$

Let $x = \gamma_1(t)$ and $y = \gamma_2(t)$. Then the previous display shows that

$$a^2 y = bx^2,$$

and so the integral curve lies on a parabola. The parabola is degenerate if the starting point (a, b) lies on either axis. Every parabola that forms an integral curve for the mountain function meets orthogonally with every ellipse that forms a level set. (See Figure 4.15.)

For another example, let $f(x, y) = x^2 - y^2$. The level sets for this function are hyperbolas having the 45 degree lines $x = y$ and $x = -y$ as asymptotes. The gradient of the function is $\nabla f(x, y) = (2x, -2y)$, so to find the integral curve starting at (a, b), we need to solve the equations

$$(\gamma_1'(t), \gamma_2'(t)) = (2\gamma_1(t), -2\gamma_2(t)), \qquad (\gamma_1(0), \gamma_2(0)) = (a, b).$$

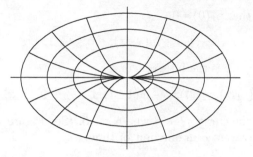

Figure 4.15. Level sets and integral curves for the parabolic mountain

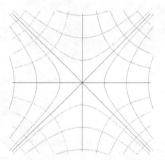

Figure 4.16. Hyperbolic level sets and integral curves

Thus $(\gamma_1(t), \gamma_2(t)) = (ae^{2t}, be^{-2t})$, so that the integral curve lies on the hyperbola $xy = ab$ having the axes $x = 0$ and $y = 0$ as asymptotes. The integral curve hyperbola is orthogonal to the level set hyperbolas. (See Figure 4.16.)

For another example, let $f(x, y) = e^x - y$. The level sets for this function are the familiar exponential curve $y = e^x$ and all of its vertical translates. The gradient of the function is $\nabla f(x, y) = (e^x, -1)$, so to find the integral curve starting at $(0, 1)$, we need to solve the equations

$$(\gamma_1'(t), \gamma_2'(t)) = (e^{\gamma_1(t)}, -1), \qquad (\gamma_1(0), \gamma_2(0)) = (0, 1).$$

To find γ_1, reason that

$$e^{-\gamma_1(t)} \gamma_1'(t) = 1 \quad \text{for all } t \geq 0 \text{ where the system is sensible,}$$

and so for all $t \geq 0$ where the system is sensible,

$$\int_{\tau=0}^{t} e^{-\gamma_1(\tau)} \gamma_1'(\tau) \, d\tau = t.$$

Integration gives

$$-e^{-\gamma_1(t)} + e^{-\gamma_1(0)} = t,$$

and so, recalling that $\gamma_1(0) = 0$,

$$\gamma_1(t) = -\ln(1-t), \quad 0 \le t < 1.$$

Also, $\gamma_2(t) = 1 - t$. Thus the integral curve,

$$(\gamma_1(t), \gamma_2(t)) = (-\ln(1-t), 1-t), \quad 0 \le t < 1$$

is the portion of the curve $y = e^{-x}$ where $x \ge 0$. (See Figure 4.17.) The entire integral curve is traversed in one unit of time.

Figure 4.17. Negative exponential integral curve for exponential level sets

For another example, let $f(x, y) = x^2 + xy + y^2$. The level sets for this function are tilted ellipses. The gradient of f is $\nabla f(x, y) = (2x + y, x + 2y)$, so to find the integral curve starting at (a, b), we need to solve the equations

$$\gamma_1'(t) = 2\gamma_1(t) + \gamma_2(t), \qquad \gamma_1(0) = a,$$
$$\gamma_2'(t) = \gamma_1(t) + 2\gamma_2(t), \qquad \gamma_2(0) = b.$$

Here the two differential equations are coupled, meaning that the derivative of γ_1 depends on both γ_1 and γ_2, and similarly for the derivative of γ_2. However, the system regroups conveniently,

$$(\gamma_1 + \gamma_2)'(t) = 3(\gamma_1 + \gamma_2)(t), \qquad (\gamma_1 + \gamma_2)(0) = a + b,$$
$$(\gamma_1 - \gamma_2)'(t) = (\gamma_1 - \gamma_2)(t), \qquad (\gamma_1 - \gamma_2)(0) = a - b.$$

Thus

$$(\gamma_1 + \gamma_2)(t) = (a + b)e^{3t},$$
$$(\gamma_1 - \gamma_2)(t) = (a - b)e^{t},$$

from which

$$\gamma_1(t) = \tfrac{1}{2}(a + b)e^{3t} + \tfrac{1}{2}(a - b)e^{t},$$
$$\gamma_2(t) = \tfrac{1}{2}(a + b)e^{3t} - \tfrac{1}{2}(a - b)e^{t}.$$

These call to be checked, and indeed,

$$\gamma_1'(t) = \tfrac{3}{2}(a+b)e^{3t} + \tfrac{1}{2}(a-b)e^t = 2\gamma_1(t) + \gamma_2(t),$$
$$\gamma_2'(t) = \tfrac{3}{2}(a+b)e^{3t} - \tfrac{1}{2}(a-b)e^t = \gamma_1(t) + 2\gamma_2(t).$$

The motion takes place along the cubic curve having equation

$$\frac{x+y}{a+b} = \frac{(x-y)^3}{(a-b)^3}.$$

(See Figure 4.18.) The integral curves in the first two examples were quadratic only by happenstance, in consequence of the functions $9 - x^2 - 2y^2$ and $x^2 - y^2$ having such simple coefficients. Changing the mountain function to $9 - x^2 - 3y^2$ would produce cubic integral curves, and changing $x^2 - y^2$ to $x^2 - 5y^2$ in the second example would produce integral curves $x^5 y = a^5 b$.

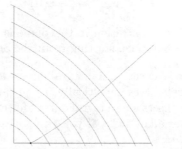

Figure 4.18. Cubic integral curve for elliptic level sets

For another example, suppose the temperature in space is given by $T(x, y, z) = 1/(x^2 + y^2 + z^2)$. (This function blows up at the origin, so we don't work there.) The level sets of this function are spheres, and the integral curves are rays going toward the origin. The level set passing through the point (a, b, c) in space is again orthogonal to the integral curve through the same point. In general, solving the vector differential equation (4.3) to find the integral curves γ of a function f can be difficult.

Exercises

4.8.1. Let $f(x, y, z) = xy^2 + yz$. Find $D_{(\frac{2}{3}, -\frac{1}{3}, \frac{2}{3})} f(1, 1, 2)$.

4.8.2. Let $g(x, y, z) = xyz$, and let d be the unit vector in the direction from $(1, 2, 3)$ to $(3, 1, 5)$. Find $D_d g(1, 2, 3)$.

4.8.3. Let f be differentiable at a point a, and let $d = -e_1$, a unit vector. Are the directional derivative $D_d f(a)$ and the partial derivative $D_1 f(a)$ equal? Explain.

4.8.4. Formulate and prove a version of Rolle's theorem for functions of n variables.

4.8.5. Show that if $f : \mathbb{R}^n \longrightarrow \mathbb{R}$ and $g : \mathbb{R}^n \longrightarrow \mathbb{R}$ are differentiable then so is their product $fg : \mathbb{R}^n \longrightarrow \mathbb{R}$, and $\nabla(fg) = f\nabla g + g\nabla f$.

4.8.6. Find the tangent plane to the surface $\{(x, y, z) : x^2 + 2y^2 + 3zx - 10 = 0\}$ in $\mathbb{R}^3$ at the point $(1, 2, \frac{1}{3})$.

4.8.7. (a) Consider the surface $S = \{(x, y, z) \in \mathbb{R}^3 : xy = z\}$. Let $p = (a, b, c)$ be a generic point of S. Find the tangent plane T_p to S at p.
    (b) Show that the intersection $S \cap T_p$ consists of two lines.

4.8.8. (a) Let A and α be nonzero constants. Similarly to an example in the section, solve the one-variable differential equation
$$z'(t) = A\alpha e^{\alpha z(t)}, \quad z(0) = 0.$$

    (b) The pheromone concentration in the plane is given by $f(x, y) = e^{2x} + 4e^y$. What path does a bug take, starting from the origin?

4.8.9. (a) Sketch some level sets and integral curves for the function $f(x, y) = x^2 + y$. Find the integral curves analytically if you can.
    (b) Sketch some level sets and integral curves for the function $f(x, y) = xy$. Find the integral curves analytically if you can.

4.8.10. Recall the function $f : \mathbb{R}^2 \longrightarrow \mathbb{R}$ whose graph is the crimped sheet,

$$f(x, y) = \begin{cases} \frac{x^2 y}{x^2 + y^2} & \text{if } (x, y) \neq (0, 0), \\ 0 & \text{if } (x, y) = (0, 0). \end{cases}$$

    (a) Show that f is continuous at $(0, 0)$.
    (b) Find the partial derivatives $D_1 f(0, 0)$ and $D_2 f(0, 0)$.
    (c) Let d be any unit vector in $\mathbb{R}^2$ (thus d takes the form $d = (\cos\theta, \sin\theta)$ for some $\theta \in \mathbb{R}$). Show that $D_d f(0, 0)$ exists by finding it.
    (d) Show that in spite of (c), f is not differentiable at $(0, 0)$. (Use your results from parts (b) and (c) to contradict Theorem 4.8.2.) Thus, the existence of every directional derivative at a point is not sufficient for differentiability at the point.

4.8.11. Define $f : \mathbb{R}^2 \longrightarrow \mathbb{R}$ by

$$f(x, y) = \begin{cases} 1 & \text{if } y = x^2 \text{ and } (x, y) \neq (0, 0), \\ 0 & \text{otherwise.} \end{cases}$$

    (a) Show that f is discontinuous at $(0, 0)$. It follows that f is not differentiable at $(0, 0)$.

(b) Let d be any unit vector in $\mathbb{R}^2$. Show that $D_d f(0,0) = 0$. Show that consequently the formula $D_d f(0,0) = \langle \nabla f(0,0), d \rangle$ holds for every unit vector d. Thus, the existence of every directional derivative at a point and the fact that each directional derivative satisfies the formula are still not sufficient for differentiability at the point.

4.8.12. Fix two real numbers a and b satisfying $0 < a < b$. Define a mapping $T = (T_1, T_2, T_3) : \mathbb{R}^2 \longrightarrow \mathbb{R}^3$ by

$$T(s,t) = ((b + a \cos s) \cos t, (b + a \cos s) \sin t, a \sin s).$$

(a) Describe the shape of the set in $\mathbb{R}^3$ mapped to by T. (The answer will explain the name T.)

(b) Find the points $(s,t) \in \mathbb{R}^2$ such that $\nabla T_1(s,t) = \mathbf{0}_2$. The points map to only four image points p under T. Show that one such p is a maximum of T_1, another is a minimum, and the remaining two are saddle points.

(c) Find the points $(s,t) \in \mathbb{R}^2$ such that $\nabla T_3(s,t) = \mathbf{0}_2$. To what points q do these (s,t) map under T? Which such q are maxima of T_3? Minima? Saddle points?

5

Inverse and Implicit Functions

The question whether a mapping $f : A \longrightarrow \mathbb{R}^n$ (where $A \subset \mathbb{R}^n$) is globally invertible is beyond the local techniques of differential calculus. However, a local theorem is finally in reach. The idea sounds plausible: if the derivative of f is invertible at the point a then f itself, being well approximated near a by its derivative, should also be invertible in the small. However, it is by no means a general principle that an approximated object must inherit the properties of the object approximating it. On the contrary, mathematics often approximates complicated objects by simpler ones. For instance, Taylor's theorem approximates any function that has many derivatives by a polynomial, but this does not make the function itself a polynomial as well.

To further illustrate the issue via an example, consider an argument in support of the one-variable critical point theorem. Let $f : A \longrightarrow \mathbb{R}$ (where $A \subset \mathbb{R}$) be differentiable, and let $f'(a)$ be positive at an interior point a of A. We might reason as follows:

> f cannot have a maximum at a, because the tangent line to the graph of f at $(a, f(a))$ has a positive slope, so that as we move our input rightward from a, we climb.

But this reasoning is vague. What do we climb, the tangent line or the graph? The argument *linearizes* the question by fitting the tangent line through the graph, and then it solves the linearized problem instead by checking whether we climb the tangent line rather than whether we climb the graph. The calculus is light and graceful. But strictly speaking, part of the argument is tacit:

> Since the tangent line closely approximates the graph near the point of tangency, the fact that we climb the tangent line means that we climb the graph as well for a while.

And the tacit part of the argument is not fully quantitative. How does the climbing property of the tangent line transfer to the graph? The mean value theorem, and a stronger hypothesis that f' is positive about a as well as at a, resolve the question, since for x slightly larger than a,

J. Shurman, *Calculus and Analysis in Euclidean Space*,
Undergraduate Texts in Mathematics, DOI 10.1007/978-3-319-49314-5_5

$$f(x) - f(a) = f'(c)(x - a) \quad \text{for some } c \in (a, x),$$

and the right side is the product of two positive numbers, hence positive. But the mean value theorem is an abstract existence theorem (*"for some c"*) whose proof relies on foundational properties of the real number system. Thus, moving from the linearized problem to the actual problem is far more sophisticated technically than linearizing the problem or solving the linearized problem. In sum, this one-variable example is meant to amplify the point of the preceding paragraph, that (now returning to n dimensions) if $f : A \longrightarrow \mathbb{R}^n$ has an invertible derivative at a then the inverse function theorem—that f itself is invertible in the small near a—is surely inevitable, but its proof will be technical and require strengthening our hypotheses.

Already in the one-variable case, the inverse function theorem relies on foundational theorems about the real number system, on a property of continuous functions, and on a foundational theorem of differential calculus. We quickly review the ideas. Let $f : A \longrightarrow \mathbb{R}$ (where $A \subset \mathbb{R}$) be a function, let a be an interior point of A, and let f be continuously differentiable on some interval about a, meaning that f' exists and is continuous on the interval. Suppose that $f'(a) > 0$. Since f' is continuous about a, the persistence of inequality principle (Proposition 2.3.10) says that f' is positive on some closed interval $[a - \delta, a + \delta]$ about a. By an application of the mean value theorem as in the previous paragraph, f is therefore strictly increasing on the interval, and so its restriction to the interval does not take any value twice. By the intermediate value theorem, f takes every value from $f(a - \delta)$ to $f(a + \delta)$ on the interval. Therefore f takes every such value exactly once, making it locally invertible. A slightly subtle point is that the inverse function f^{-1} is continuous at $f(a)$, but then a purely formal calculation with difference quotients will verify that the derivative of f^{-1} exists at $f(a)$ and is $1/f'(a)$. Note how heavily this proof relies on the fact that $\mathbb{R}$ is an ordered field. A proof of the multivariable inverse function theorem must use other methods.

Although the proof to be given in this chapter is technical, its core idea is simple common sense. Let a mapping f be given that takes x-values to y-values and in particular takes a to b. Then the local inverse function must take y-values near b to x-values near a, taking each such y back to the unique x that f took to y in the first place. We need to determine conditions on f that make us believe that a local inverse exists. As explained above, the basic condition is that the derivative of f at a—giving a good approximation of f near a, but easier to understand than f itself—should be invertible, and the derivative should be continuous as well. With these conditions in hand, an argument similar to that in the one-variable case (though more painstaking) shows that f is locally injective:

- Given y near b, there is *at most one* x near a that f takes to y.

So the remaining problem is to show that f is locally surjective:

- Given y near b, show that there is *some* x near a that f takes to y.

This problem decomposes into two subproblems. First:

- Given y near b, show that there is some x near a that f takes *closest* to y.

Then:

- Show that f takes this particular x *exactly* to y.

And once the appropriate environment is established, solving each subproblem is just a matter of applying the main theorems from the previous three chapters.

Not only does the inverse function theorem have a proof that uses so much previous work from this course so nicely, it also has useful consequences. It leads easily to the implicit function theorem, which answers a different question: when does a set of constraining relations among a set of variables make some of the variables dependent on the others? The implicit function theorem in turn fully justifies (rather than linearizing) the Lagrange multiplier method, a technique for solving optimization problems with constraints. As discussed in the preface to these notes, optimization with constraints has no one-variable counterpart, and it can be viewed as the beginning of calculus on curved spaces.

5.1 Preliminaries

The basic elements of topology in $\mathbb{R}^n$—ε-balls; limit points; closed, bounded, and compact sets—were introduced in Section 2.4 to provide the environment for the extreme value theorem. A little more topology is now needed before we proceed to the inverse function theorem. Recall that for every point $a \in \mathbb{R}^n$ and every radius $\varepsilon > 0$, the ε-ball at a is the set

$$B(a,\varepsilon) = \{x \in \mathbb{R}^n : |x - a| < \varepsilon\}.$$

Recall also that a subset of $\mathbb{R}^n$ is called closed if it contains all of its limit points. Not unnaturally, a subset S of $\mathbb{R}^n$ is called **open** if its **complement** $S^c = \mathbb{R}^n - S$ is closed. A set, however, is not a door: it can be neither open nor closed, and it can be both open and closed. (Examples?)

Proposition 5.1.1 (ε-balls are open). *For every $a \in \mathbb{R}^n$ and every $\varepsilon > 0$, the ball $B(a,\varepsilon)$ is open.*

Proof. Let x be any point in $B(a,\varepsilon)$, and set $\delta = \varepsilon - |x - a|$, a positive number. The triangle inequality shows that $B(x,\delta) \subset B(a,\varepsilon)$ (Exercise 5.1.1), and therefore x is not a limit point of the complement $B(a,\varepsilon)^c$. Consequently all limit points of $B(a,\varepsilon)^c$ are in fact elements of $B(a,\varepsilon)^c$, which is thus closed, making $B(a,\varepsilon)$ itself open. $\qquad\square$

This proof shows that every point $x \in B(a, \varepsilon)$ is an interior point. In fact, an equivalent definition of *open* is that a subset of $\mathbb{R}^n$ is open if each of its points is interior (Exercise 5.1.2).

The **closed** ε-**ball at** a, denoted $\overline{B(a, \varepsilon)}$, consists of the corresponding open ball with its edge added in,

$$\overline{B(a, \varepsilon)} = \{x \in \mathbb{R}^n : |x - a| \le \varepsilon\}.$$

The **boundary** of the closed ball $\overline{B(a, \varepsilon)}$, denoted $\partial \overline{B(a, \varepsilon)}$, is the set of points on the edge,

$$\partial \overline{B(a, \varepsilon)} = \{x \in \mathbb{R}^n : |x - a| = \varepsilon\}.$$

(See Figure 5.1.) Every closed ball $\overline{B}$ and its boundary $\partial \overline{B}$ are compact sets (Exercise 5.1.3).

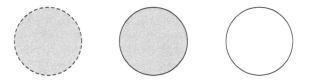

Figure 5.1. Open ball, closed ball, and boundary

Let $f : A \longrightarrow \mathbb{R}^m$ (where $A \subset \mathbb{R}^n$) be continuous, let W be an open subset of $\mathbb{R}^m$, and let V be the set of all points in A that f maps into W,

$$V = \{x \in A : f(x) \in W\}.$$

The set V is called the **inverse image of** W **under** f; it is often denoted $f^{-1}(W)$, but this is a little misleading because f need not actually have an inverse mapping f^{-1}. For example, if $f : \mathbb{R} \longrightarrow \mathbb{R}$ is the squaring function $f(x) = x^2$, then the inverse image of $[4, 9]$ is $[-3, -2] \cup [2, 3]$, and this set is denoted $f^{-1}([4, 9])$ even though f has no inverse. (See Figure 5.2, in which f is not the squaring function, but the inverse image $f^{-1}(W)$ also has two components.) The inverse image concept generalizes an idea that we saw in Section 4.8: the inverse image of a one-point set under a mapping f is a level set of f, as in Definition 4.8.3.

Although the forward image under a continuous function of an open set need not be open (Exercise 5.1.4), inverse images behave more nicely. The connection between continuous mappings and open sets is provided by the following theorem.

Theorem 5.1.2 (Inverse image characterization of continuity). *Let* $f : A \longrightarrow \mathbb{R}^m$ *(where A is an open subset of $\mathbb{R}^n$) be continuous. Let $W \subset \mathbb{R}^m$ be open. Then $f^{-1}(W)$, the inverse image of W under f, is open.*

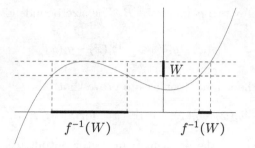

Figure 5.2. Inverse image with two components

Proof. Let a be a point of $f^{-1}(W)$. We want to show that it is an interior point. Let $w = f(a)$, a point of W. Since W is open, some ball $B(w, \rho)$ is contained in W. Consider the function

$$g : A \longrightarrow \mathbb{R}, \qquad g(x) = \rho - |f(x) - w|.$$

This function is continuous, and it satisfies $g(a) = \rho > 0$, and so by a slight variant of the persistence of inequality principle (Proposition 2.3.10) there exists a ball $B(a, \varepsilon) \subset A$ on which g remains positive. That is,

$$f(x) \in B(w, \rho) \quad \text{for all } x \in B(a, \varepsilon).$$

Since $B(w, \rho) \subset W$, this shows that $B(a, \varepsilon) \subset f^{-1}(W)$, making a an interior point of $f^{-1}(W)$ as desired. $\qquad\qquad\square$

The converse to Theorem 5.1.2 is also true and is Exercise 5.1.8. We need one last technical result for the proof of the inverse function theorem.

Lemma 5.1.3 (Difference magnification lemma). *Let $\overline{B}$ be a closed ball in $\mathbb{R}^n$ and let g be a differentiable mapping from an open superset of $\overline{B}$ in $\mathbb{R}^n$ to $\mathbb{R}^n$. Suppose that there is a number c such that $|D_j g_i(x)| \le c$ for all $i, j \in \{1, \ldots, n\}$ and all $x \in \overline{B}$. Then*

$$|g(\tilde{x}) - g(x)| \le n^2 c |\tilde{x} - x| \quad \text{for all } x, \tilde{x} \in \overline{B}.$$

A comment about the lemma's environment might be helpful before we go into the details of the proof. We know that continuous mappings behave well on compact sets. On the other hand, since differentiability is sensible only at interior points, differentiable mappings behave well on open sets. And so to work effectively with differentiability, we want a mapping on a domain that is open, allowing differentiability everywhere, but then we restrict our attention to a compact subset of the domain so that continuity (which follows from differentiability) will behave well too. The closed ball and its open superset in the lemma arise from these considerations.

Proof. Consider any two points $x, \tilde{x} \in \overline{B}$. The size bounds give

$$|g(x) - g(\tilde{x})| \le \sum_{i=1}^{n} |g_i(\tilde{x}) - g_i(x)|,$$

and so to prove the lemma it suffices to prove that

$$|g_i(\tilde{x}) - g_i(x)| \le nc|\tilde{x} - x| \quad \text{for } i = 1, \ldots, n.$$

Thus we have reduced the problem from vector output to scalar output. To create an environment of scalar input as well, make the line segment from x to $\tilde{x}$ the image of a function of one variable,

$$\gamma : [0, 1] \longrightarrow \mathbb{R}^n, \qquad \gamma(t) = x + t(\tilde{x} - x).$$

Note that $\gamma(0) = x$, $\gamma(1) = \tilde{x}$, and $\gamma'(t) = \tilde{x} - x$ for all $t \in (0, 1)$. Fix any $i \in \{1, \ldots, n\}$ and consider the restriction of g_i to the segment, a scalar-valued function of scalar input,

$$\varphi : [0, 1] \longrightarrow \mathbb{R}, \qquad \varphi(t) = (g_i \circ \gamma)(t).$$

Thus $\varphi(0) = g_i(x)$ and $\varphi(1) = g_i(\tilde{x})$. By the mean value theorem,

$$g_i(\tilde{x}) - g_i(x) = \varphi(1) - \varphi(0) = \varphi'(t) \quad \text{for some } t \in (0, 1),$$

and so since $\varphi = g_i \circ \gamma$, the chain rule gives

$$g_i(\tilde{x}) - g_i(x) = (g_i \circ \gamma)'(t) = g_i'(\gamma(t))\gamma'(t) = g_i'(\gamma(t))(\tilde{x} - x).$$

Because $g_i'(\gamma(t))$ is a row vector and $\tilde{x} - x$ is a column vector, the last quantity in the previous display is their inner product. Hence the display and the Cauchy–Schwarz inequality give

$$|g_i(\tilde{x}) - g_i(x)| \le |g_i'(\gamma(t))| \, |\tilde{x} - x|.$$

For each j, the jth entry of the vector $g_i'(\gamma(t))$ is the partial derivative $D_j g_i(\gamma(t))$. And we are given that $|D_j g_i(\gamma(t))| \le c$, so the size bounds show that $|g_i'(\gamma(t))| \le nc$ and therefore

$$|g_i(\tilde{x}) - g_i(x)| \le nc|\tilde{x} - x|.$$

As explained at the beginning of the proof, the result follows. $\square$

Exercises

5.1.1. Let $x \in B(a; \varepsilon)$ and let $\delta = \varepsilon - |x - a|$. Explain why $\delta > 0$ and why $B(x; \delta) \subset B(a; \varepsilon)$.

5.1.2. Show that a subset of $\mathbb{R}^n$ is open if and only if each of its points is interior.

5.1.3. Prove that every closed ball $\overline{B}$ is indeed a closed set, as is its boundary $\partial\overline{B}$. Show that every closed ball and its boundary are also bounded, hence compact.

5.1.4. Find a continuous function $f : \mathbb{R}^n \longrightarrow \mathbb{R}^m$ and an open set $A \subset \mathbb{R}^n$ such that the image $f(A) \subset \mathbb{R}^m$ of A under f is not open. Feel free to choose n and m.

5.1.5. Define $f : \mathbb{R} \longrightarrow \mathbb{R}$ by $f(x) = x^3 - 3x$. Compute $f(-1/2)$. Find $f^{-1}((0, 11/8))$, $f^{-1}((0, 2))$, $f^{-1}((-\infty, -11/8) \cup (11/8, \infty))$. Does f^{-1} exist?

5.1.6. Show that for $f : \mathbb{R}^n \longrightarrow \mathbb{R}^m$ and $B \subset \mathbb{R}^m$, the inverse image of the complement is the complement of the inverse image,

$$f^{-1}(B^c) = f^{-1}(B)^c.$$

Does the analogous formula hold for forward images?

5.1.7. If $f : \mathbb{R}^n \longrightarrow \mathbb{R}^m$ is continuous and $B \subset \mathbb{R}^m$ is closed, show that $f^{-1}(B)$ is closed. What does this say about the level sets of continuous functions?

5.1.8. Prove the converse to Theorem 5.1.2: if $f : A \longrightarrow \mathbb{R}^m$ (where $A \subset \mathbb{R}^n$ is open) is such that for every open $W \subset \mathbb{R}^m$ also $f^{-1}(W) \subset A$ is open, then f is continuous.

5.1.9. Let a and b be real numbers with $a < b$. Let $n > 1$, and suppose that the mapping $g : [a, b] \longrightarrow \mathbb{R}^n$ is continuous and that g is differentiable on the open interval (a, b). It is tempting to generalize the mean value theorem (Theorem 1.2.3) to the assertion

$$g(b) - g(a) = g'(c)(b - a) \quad \text{for some } c \in (a, b). \tag{5.1}$$

The assertion is grammatically meaningful, since it posits an equality between two n-vectors. The assertion would lead to a slight streamlining of the proof of Lemma 5.1.3, since there would be no need to reduce to scalar output. However, the assertion is false.

   (a) Let $g : [0, 2\pi] \longrightarrow \mathbb{R}^2$ be $g(t) = (\cos t, \sin t)$. Show that (5.1) fails for this g. Describe the situation geometrically.

   (b) Let $g : [0, 2\pi] \longrightarrow \mathbb{R}^3$ be $g(t) = (\cos t, \sin t, t)$. Show that (5.1) fails for this g. Describe the situation geometrically.

   (c) Here is an attempt to prove (5.1): *Let $g = (g_1, \ldots, g_n)$. Since each g_i is scalar-valued, we have for $i = 1, \ldots, n$ by the mean value theorem,*

$$g_i(b) - g_i(a) = g_i'(c)(b - a) \quad \text{for some } c \in (a, b).$$

Assembling the scalar results gives the desired vector result.
   What is the error here?

5.2 The Inverse Function Theorem

Theorem 5.2.1 (Inverse function theorem). *Let A be an open subset of $\mathbb{R}^n$, and let $f : A \longrightarrow \mathbb{R}^n$ have continuous partial derivatives at every point of A. Let a be a point of A. Suppose that $\det f'(a) \neq 0$. Then there exist an open set $V \subset A$ containing a and an open set $W \subset \mathbb{R}^n$ containing $f(a)$ such that $f : V \longrightarrow W$ has a continuously differentiable inverse $f^{-1} : W \longrightarrow V$. For each $y = f(x) \in W$, the derivative of the inverse is the inverse of the derivative,*

$$D(f^{-1})_y = (Df_x)^{-1}.$$

Before the proof, it is worth remarking that the formula for the derivative of the local inverse, and the fact that the derivative of the local inverse is continuous, are easy to establish once everything else is in place. If the local inverse f^{-1} of f is known to exist and to be differentiable, then for every $x \in V$ the fact that the identity mapping is its own derivative combines with the chain rule to say that

$$\mathrm{id}_n = D(\mathrm{id}_n)_x = D(f^{-1} \circ f)_x = D(f^{-1})_y \circ Df_x \quad \text{where } y = f(x),$$

and similarly $\mathrm{id}_n = Df_x \circ (Df^{-1})_y$, where this time id_n is the identity mapping on y-space. The last formula in the theorem follows. In terms of matrices, the formula is

$$(f^{-1})'(y) = f'(x)^{-1} \quad \text{where } y = f(x).$$

This formula combines with Proposition 4.3.4 (differentiability implies continuity) and Corollary 3.7.3 (the entries of the inverse matrix are continuous functions of the entries of the matrix) to show that since the mapping is continuously differentiable and the local inverse is differentiable, the local inverse is continuously differentiable: If y varies slightly, then so does x because f^{-1} is continuous, hence so does $f'(x)$ because f' is continuous, hence so does $f'(x)^{-1}$, which is $(f^{-1})'(y)$. Thus we need to show only that the local inverse exists and is differentiable.

Proof. The proof begins with a simplification. Let $T = Df_a$, a linear mapping from $\mathbb{R}^n$ to $\mathbb{R}^n$ that is invertible because its matrix $f'(a)$ has nonzero determinant. Let

$$\tilde{f} = T^{-1} \circ f.$$

By the chain rule, the derivative of $\tilde{f}$ at a is

$$D\tilde{f}_a = D(T^{-1} \circ f)_a = D(T^{-1})_{f(a)} \circ Df_a = T^{-1} \circ T = \mathrm{id}_n.$$

Also, suppose we have a local inverse $\tilde{g}$ of $\tilde{f}$, so that

$$\tilde{g} \circ \tilde{f} = \mathrm{id}_n \text{ near } a$$

and

$$\tilde{f} \circ \tilde{g} = \mathrm{id}_n \text{ near } \tilde{f}(a).$$

The situation is shown in the following diagram, in which V is an open set containing a, W is an open set containing $f(a)$, and $\widetilde{W}$ is an open set containing $T^{-1}(f(a)) = \tilde{f}(a)$.

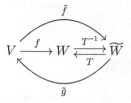

The diagram shows that the way to invert f locally, going from W back to V, is to proceed through $\widetilde{W}$: $g = \tilde{g} \circ T^{-1}$. Indeed, since $f = T \circ \tilde{f}$,

$$g \circ f = (\tilde{g} \circ T^{-1}) \circ (T \circ \tilde{f}) = \mathrm{id}_n \text{ near } a,$$

and, since $T^{-1}(f(a)) = \tilde{f}(a)$,

$$f \circ g = (T \circ \tilde{f}) \circ (\tilde{g} \circ T^{-1}) = \mathrm{id}_n \text{ near } f(a).$$

That is, to invert f, it suffices to invert $\tilde{f}$. And if $\tilde{g}$ is differentiable then so is $g = \tilde{g} \circ T^{-1}$. The upshot is that we may prove the theorem for $\tilde{f}$ rather than f. Equivalently, we may assume with no loss of generality that $Df_a = \mathrm{id}_n$ and therefore that $f'(a) = I_n$. This normalization will let us carry out a clean, explicit computation in the following paragraph. (Note: With the normalization complete, our use of the symbol g to denote a local inverse of f now ends. The mapping to be called g in the following paragraph is unrelated to the local inverse g in this paragraph.)

Next we find a closed ball $\overline{B}$ around a where the behavior of f is somewhat controlled by the fact that $f'(a) = I_n$. More specifically, we will quantify the idea that since $f'(x) \approx I_n$ for x near a, also $f(\tilde{x}) - f(x) \approx \tilde{x} - x$ for $x, \tilde{x}$ near a. Recall that the (i,j)th entry of I_n is δ_{ij} and that $\det(I_n) = 1$. As x varies continuously near a, the (i,j)th entry $D_j f_i(x)$ of $f'(x)$ varies continuously near δ_{ij}, and so the scalar $\det f'(x)$ varies continuously near 1. Since $D_j f_i(a) - \delta_{ij} = 0$ and since $\det f'(a) = 1$, applying the persistence of inequality principle (Proposition 2.3.10) $n^2 + 1$ times shows that there exists a closed ball $\overline{B}$ about a small enough that

$$|D_j f_i(x) - \delta_{ij}| < \frac{1}{2n^2} \quad \text{for all } i, j \in \{1, \dots, n\} \text{ and } x \in \overline{B} \qquad (5.2)$$

and

$$\det f'(x) \neq 0 \quad \text{for all } x \in \overline{B}. \qquad (5.3)$$

Let $g = f - \mathrm{id}_n$, a differentiable mapping near a, whose Jacobian matrix at x, $g'(x) = f'(x) - I_n$, has (i,j)th entry $D_j g_i(x) = D_j f_i(x) - \delta_{ij}$. Equation (5.2) and Lemma 5.1.3 (with $c = 1/(2n^2)$) show that for every two points x and $\tilde{x}$ in $\overline{B}$,

$$|g(\tilde{x}) - g(x)| \leq \tfrac{1}{2}|\tilde{x} - x|,$$

and therefore, since $f = \mathrm{id}_n + g$,

$$\begin{aligned}
|f(\tilde{x}) - f(x)| &= |(\tilde{x} - x) + (g(\tilde{x}) - g(x))| \\
&\geq |\tilde{x} - x| - |g(\tilde{x}) - g(x)| \\
&\geq |\tilde{x} - x| - \tfrac{1}{2}|\tilde{x} - x| \quad \text{(by the previous display)} \\
&= \tfrac{1}{2}|\tilde{x} - x|.
\end{aligned}$$

The previous display shows that f is injective on $\overline{B}$, i.e., every two distinct points of $\overline{B}$ are taken by f to distinct points of $\mathbb{R}^n$. For future reference, we note that the result of the previous calculation can be rearranged as

$$|\tilde{x} - x| \leq 2|f(\tilde{x}) - f(x)| \quad \text{for all } x, \tilde{x} \in \overline{B}. \tag{5.4}$$

The boundary $\partial\overline{B}$ of $\overline{B}$ is compact, and so is the image set $f(\partial\overline{B})$ because f is continuous. Also, $f(a) \notin f(\partial\overline{B})$ because f is injective on $\overline{B}$. And $f(a)$ is not a limit point of $f(\partial\overline{B})$ because $f(\partial\overline{B})$, being compact, is closed. Consequently, some open ball $B(f(a), 2\varepsilon)$ contains no point from $f(\partial\overline{B})$. (See Figure 5.3.)

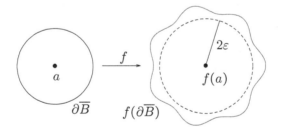

Figure 5.3. Ball about $f(a)$ away from $f(\partial\overline{B})$

Let $W = B(f(a), \varepsilon)$, the open ball with radius less than half the distance from $f(a)$ to $f(\partial\overline{B})$. Thus

$$|f(a) - y| < |f(x) - y| \quad \text{for all } y \in W \text{ and } x \in \partial\overline{B}. \tag{5.5}$$

That is, for every point y of W, $f(a)$ is closer to y than every point of $f(\partial\overline{B})$ is close to y. (See Figure 5.4.)

The goal now is to exhibit a mapping on W that inverts f near a. In other words, the goal is to show that for each $y \in W$, there exists a unique x interior to $\overline{B}$ such that $f(x) = y$. So fix an arbitrary $y \in W$. Define a function $\Delta : \overline{B} \longrightarrow \mathbb{R}$ that measures for each x the square of the distance between $f(x)$ and y,

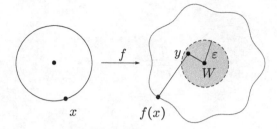

Figure 5.4. Ball closer to $f(a)$ than to $f(\partial \overline{B})$

$$\Delta(x) = |f(x) - y|^2 = \sum_{i=1}^{n} (f_i(x) - y_i)^2.$$

The idea is to show that for one and only one x near a, $\Delta(x) = 0$. Because the modulus is always nonnegative, the x we seek must minimize Δ. As mentioned at the beginning of the chapter, this simple idea inside all the technicalities is the heart of the proof: the x to be taken to y by f must be the x that is taken closest to y by f.

The function Δ is continuous and $\overline{B}$ is compact, so the extreme value theorem guarantees that Δ does indeed take a minimum on $\overline{B}$. Condition (5.5) guarantees that Δ takes no minimum on the boundary $\partial \overline{B}$. Therefore the minimum of Δ must occur at an interior point x of $\overline{B}$; this interior point x must be a critical point of Δ, so all partial derivatives of Δ vanish at x. Thus by the chain rule,

$$0 = D_j \Delta(x) = 2 \sum_{i=1}^{n} (f_i(x) - y_i) D_j f_i(x) \quad \text{for } j = 1, \dots, n.$$

This condition is equivalent to the matrix equation

$$\begin{bmatrix} D_1 f_1(x) & \cdots & D_1 f_n(x) \\ \vdots & \ddots & \vdots \\ D_n f_1(x) & \cdots & D_n f_n(x) \end{bmatrix} \begin{bmatrix} f_1(x) - y_1 \\ \vdots \\ f_n(x) - y_n \end{bmatrix} = \begin{bmatrix} 0 \\ \vdots \\ 0 \end{bmatrix},$$

or

$$f'(x)^{\mathsf{T}} (f(x) - y) = \mathbf{0}_n.$$

But $\det f'(x)^{\mathsf{T}} = \det f'(x) \neq 0$ by condition (5.3), so $f'(x)^{\mathsf{T}}$ is invertible, and the only solution of the equation is $f(x) - y = \mathbf{0}_n$. Thus our x is the desired x interior to $\overline{B}$ such that $f(x) = y$. And there is only one such x, because f is injective on $\overline{B}$. We no longer need the boundary $\partial \overline{B}$, whose role was to make a set compact. In sum, we now know that f is injective on B and that $f(B)$ contains W.

Let $V = f^{-1}(W) \cap B$, the set of all points $x \in B$ such that $f(x) \in W$. (See Figure 5.5.) By the inverse image characterization of continuity (Theorem 5.1.2), V is open. We have established that $f : V \longrightarrow W$ is inverted by $f^{-1} : W \longrightarrow V$.

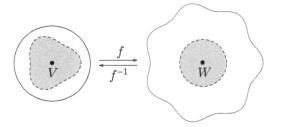

Figure 5.5. The sets V and W of the inverse function theorem

The last thing to prove is that f^{-1} is differentiable on W. Again, reducing the problem makes it easier. By (5.3), the condition $\det f'(x) \neq 0$ is in effect at each $x \in V$. Therefore a is no longer a distinguished point of V, and it suffices to prove that the local inverse f^{-1} is differentiable at $f(a)$. To reduce the problem to working at the origin, consider the mapping $\tilde{f}$ defined by the formula $\tilde{f}(x) = f(x + a) - b$. Because $f(a) = b$, it follows that $\tilde{f}(\mathbf{0}_n) = \mathbf{0}_n$, and since $\tilde{f}$ is f up to prepended and postpended translations, $\tilde{f}$ is locally invertible at $\mathbf{0}_n$ and its derivative there is $D\tilde{f}_0 = Df_a = \mathrm{id}_n$. The upshot is that in proving that f^{-1} is differentiable at $f(a)$, there is no loss of generality in normalizing to $a = \mathbf{0}_n$ and $f(a) = \mathbf{0}_n$ while also retaining the normalization that Df_a is the identity mapping.

So now we have that $f(\mathbf{0}_n) = \mathbf{0}_n = f^{-1}(\mathbf{0}_n)$ and

$$f(h) - h = o(h),$$

and we want to show that

$$f^{-1}(k) - k = o(k).$$

For every point $k \in W$, let $h = f^{-1}(k)$. Note that $|h| \leq 2|k|$ by condition (5.4) with $\tilde{x} = h$ and $x = \mathbf{0}_n$, so that $f(\tilde{x}) = k$ and $f(x) = \mathbf{0}_n$, and thus $h = \mathcal{O}(k)$. So now we have

$$f^{-1}(k) - k = -(f(h) - h) = -o(h) = o(h) = o(\mathcal{O}(k)) = o(k),$$

exactly as desired. That is, f^{-1} is indeed differentiable at $\mathbf{0}_n$ with the identity mapping for its derivative. For an unnormalized proof that f^{-1} is differentiable on W, see Exercise 5.2.9.   □

Note the range of mathematical skills that this proof of the inverse function theorem required. The ideas were motivated and guided by pictures, but the actual argument was symbolic. At the level of fine detail, we normalized the derivative to the identity in order to reduce clutter, we made an adroit choice of quantifier in choosing a small enough $\overline{B}$ to apply the difference magnification lemma with $c = 1/(2n^2)$, and we used the full triangle inequality to obtain (5.4). This technique sufficed to prove that f is locally injective. Since the proof of the difference magnification lemma used the mean value theorem many times, the role of the mean value theorem in the multivariable inverse function theorem is thus similar to its role in the one-variable proof reviewed at the beginning of this chapter. However, while the one-variable proof that f is locally surjective relied on the intermediate value theorem, the multivariable argument was far more elaborate. The idea was that the putative x taken by f to a given y must be the actual x taken by f closest to y. We exploited this idea by working in broad strokes:

- The extreme value theorem from Chapter 2 guaranteed that there is such an actual x.
- The critical point theorem and then the chain rule from Chapter 4 described necessary conditions associated to x.
- And finally, the linear invertibility theorem from Chapter 3 showed that $f(x) = y$ as desired. Very satisfyingly, the hypothesis that the derivative is invertible sealed the argument that the mapping itself is locally invertible.

Indeed, the proof of local surjectivity used nearly every significant result from Chapters 2 through 4 of these notes.

For an example, define $f : \mathbb{R}^2 \longrightarrow \mathbb{R}^2$ by $f(x,y) = (x^3 - 2xy^2, x + y)$. Is f locally invertible at $(1,-1)$? If so, what is the best affine approximation to the inverse near $f(1,-1)$? To answer the first question, calculate the Jacobian

$$f'(1,-1) = \begin{bmatrix} 3x^2 - 2y^2 & -4xy \\ 1 & 1 \end{bmatrix}\Bigg|_{(x,y)=(1,-1)} = \begin{bmatrix} 1 & 4 \\ 1 & 1 \end{bmatrix}.$$

This matrix is invertible with inverse $f'(1,-1)^{-1} = \frac{1}{3}\begin{bmatrix} -1 & 4 \\ 1 & -1 \end{bmatrix}$. Therefore f is locally invertible at $(1,-1)$, and the affine approximation to f^{-1} near $f(1,-1) = (-1,0)$ is

$$f^{-1}(-1+h,0+k) \approx \begin{bmatrix} 1 \\ -1 \end{bmatrix} + \frac{1}{3}\begin{bmatrix} -1 & 4 \\ 1 & -1 \end{bmatrix}\begin{bmatrix} h \\ k \end{bmatrix} = (1 - \frac{1}{3}h + \frac{4}{3}k, -1 + \frac{1}{3}h - \frac{1}{3}k).$$

The actual inverse function f^{-1} about $(-1,0)$ may not be clear, but the inverse function theorem guarantees its existence, and its affine approximation is easy to find.

Exercises

5.2.1. Define $f : \mathbb{R}^2 \longrightarrow \mathbb{R}^2$ by $f(x,y) = (x^3 + 2xy + y^2, x^2 + y)$. Is f locally invertible at $(1,1)$? If so, what is the best affine approximation to the inverse near $f(1,1)$?

5.2.2. Same question for $f(x,y) = (x^2 - y^2, 2xy)$ at $(2,1)$.

5.2.3. Same question for $C(r, \theta) = (r \cos \theta, r \sin \theta)$ at $(1, 0)$.

5.2.4. Same question for $C(\rho, \theta, \phi) = (\rho \cos \theta \sin \phi, \rho \sin \theta \sin \phi, \rho \cos \phi)$ at $(1, 0, \pi/2)$.

5.2.5. At what points $(a, b) \in \mathbb{R}^2$ is each of the following mappings guaranteed to be locally invertible by the inverse function theorem? In each case, find the best affine approximation to the inverse near $f(a, b)$.
   (a) $f(x, y) = (x + y, 2xy^2)$.
   (b) $f(x, y) = (\sin x \cos y + \cos x \sin y, \cos x \cos y - \sin x \sin y)$.

5.2.6. Define $f : \mathbb{R}^2 \longrightarrow \mathbb{R}^2$ by $f(x, y) = (e^x \cos y, e^x \sin y)$. Show that f is locally invertible at each point $(a, b) \in \mathbb{R}^2$, but that f is not globally invertible. Let $(a, b) = (0, \frac{\pi}{3})$; let $(c, d) = f(a, b)$; let g be the local inverse to f near (a, b). Find an explicit formula for g, compute $g'(c, d)$, and verify that it agrees with $f'(a, b)^{-1}$.

5.2.7. If f and g are functions from $\mathbb{R}^3$ to $\mathbb{R}$, show that the mapping $F = (f, g, f + g) : \mathbb{R}^3 \longrightarrow \mathbb{R}^3$ does not have a differentiable local inverse anywhere.

5.2.8. Define $f : \mathbb{R} \longrightarrow \mathbb{R}$ by

$$f(x) = \begin{cases} x + 2x^2 \sin \frac{1}{x} & \text{if } x \neq 0, \\ 0 & \text{if } x = 0. \end{cases}$$

   (a) Show that f is differentiable at $x = 0$ and that $f'(0) \neq 0$. (Because this is a one-dimensional problem, you may verify the old definition of derivative rather than the new one.)
   (b) Despite the result from (a), show that f is not locally invertible at $x = 0$. Why doesn't this contradict the inverse function theorem?

5.2.9. The proof of the inverse function theorem ended with a normalized argument that the inverse function on W is again differentiable. Supply explanation as necessary to the unnormalized version of the argument, as follows. Let y be a fixed point of W, and let $y + k$ lie in W as well. Take $x = f^{-1}(y)$ in V, and let $f^{-1}(y + k) = x + h$, thus defining $h = f^{-1}(y + k)) - f^{-1}(y)$. We know that $f'(x)$ is invertible and that

$$f(x + h) - f(x) - f'(x)h = o(h).$$

We want to show that

$$f^{-1}(y + k) - f^{-1}(y) - f'(x)^{-1}k = o(k).$$

Compute,

$$\begin{aligned} f^{-1}(y + k) - f^{-1}(y) - f'(x)^{-1}k &= h - f'(x)^{-1}(f(x + h) - f(x)) \\ &= h - f'(x)^{-1}(f'(x)h + o(h)) \\ &= -f'(x)^{-1} o(h). \end{aligned}$$

Using (5.4) yields $|h| = |x + h - x| \leq 2|f(x+h) - f(x)| = 2|k| = \mathcal{O}(k)$, so we have

$$f^{-1}(y+k) - f^{-1}(y) - f'(x)^{-1}k = -f'(x)^{-1}o(\mathcal{O}(k)) = -f'(x)^{-1}o(k).$$

Multiplication by the fixed matrix $-f'(x)^{-1}$ is a linear mapping, and every linear mapping is $\mathcal{O}$ of its input. Altogether,

$$f^{-1}(y+k) - f^{-1}(y) - f'(x)^{-1}k = -f'(x)^{-1}o(k) = \mathcal{O}(o(k)) = o(k),$$

as desired.

5.3 The Implicit Function Theorem

Let n and c be positive integers with $c \leq n$, and let $r = n - c$. This section addresses the following question:

> When do c conditions on n variables locally specify c of the variables in terms of the remaining r variables?

The symbols in this question will remain in play throughout this section. That is:

- $n = r + c$ is the total number of variables;
- c is the number of conditions, i.e., the number of constraints on the variables, and therefore the number of variables that might be dependent on the others;
- and r is the number of remaining variables and therefore the number of variables that might be free.

The word *conditions* (or *constraints*) provides a mnemonic for the symbol c, and similarly *remaining* (or *free*) provides a mnemonic for r.

The question can be rephrased:

> When is a level set locally a graph?

To understand the rephrasing, we begin by reviewing the idea of a level set, given here in a slightly more general form than in Definition 4.8.3.

Definition 5.3.1 (Level set). *Let $g : A \longrightarrow \mathbb{R}^m$ (where $A \subset \mathbb{R}^n$) be a mapping. A **level set** of g is the set of points in A that map under g to some fixed vector w in $\mathbb{R}^m$,*

$$L = \{v \in A : g(v) = w\}.$$

That is, L is the inverse image under g of the one-point set $\{w\}$.

Also, we review the argument in Section 4.8 that every graph is a level set. Let A_0 be a subset of $\mathbb{R}^r$, and let $f : A_0 \longrightarrow \mathbb{R}^c$ be any mapping. Let $A = A_0 \times \mathbb{R}^c$ (a subset of $\mathbb{R}^n$) and define a second mapping $g : A \longrightarrow \mathbb{R}^c$,

$$g(x,y) = f(x) - y, \qquad (x,y) \in A_0 \times \mathbb{R}^c.$$

Then the graph of f is

$$\begin{aligned}\mathrm{graph}(f) &= \{(x,y) \in A_0 \times \mathbb{R}^c : y = f(x)\} \\ &= \{(x,y) \in A : g(x,y) = \mathbf{0}_c\},\end{aligned}$$

and this is the set of inputs to g that g takes to $\mathbf{0}_c$, a level set of g as desired.

Now we return to rephrasing the question at the beginning of this section. Let A be an open subset of $\mathbb{R}^n$, and let a mapping $g : A \longrightarrow \mathbb{R}^c$ have continuous partial derivatives at every point of A. Points of A can be written

$$(x,y), \quad x \in \mathbb{R}^r, \ y \in \mathbb{R}^c.$$

(Throughout this section, we routinely will view an n-vector as the concatenation of an r-vector and c-vector in this fashion.) Consider the level set

$$L = \{(x,y) \in A : g(x,y) = \mathbf{0}_c\}.$$

The question was whether the c scalar conditions $g(x,y) = \mathbf{0}_c$ on the $n = c + r$ scalar entries of (x,y) define the c scalars of y in terms of the r scalars of x near (a,b). That is, the question is whether the vector relation $g(x,y) = \mathbf{0}_c$ for (x,y) near (a,b) is equivalent to a vector relation $y = \varphi(x)$ for some mapping φ that takes r-vectors near a to c-vectors near b. This is precisely the question whether the level set L is locally the graph of such a mapping φ. If the answer is yes, then we would like to understand φ as well as possible by using the techniques of differential calculus. In this context we view the mapping φ as *implicit* in the condition $g = \mathbf{0}_c$, explaining the name of the pending implicit function theorem.

The first phrasing of the question, whether c conditions on n variables specify c of the variables in terms of the remaining r variables, is easy to answer when the conditions are affine. Affine conditions take the matrix form $Pv = w$, where $P \in \mathrm{M}_{c,n}(\mathbb{R})$, $v \in \mathbb{R}^n$, and $w \in \mathbb{R}^c$, and P and w are fixed while v is the vector of variables. Partition the matrix P into a left $c \times r$ block M and a right square $c \times c$ block N, and partition the vector v into its first r entries x and its last c entries y. Then the relation $Pv = w$ is

$$\begin{bmatrix} M & N \end{bmatrix} \begin{bmatrix} x \\ y \end{bmatrix} = w,$$

that is,

$$Mx + Ny = w.$$

Assume that N is invertible. Then subtracting Mx from both sides and then left multiplying by N^{-1} shows that the relation is

$$y = N^{-1}(w - Mx).$$

Thus, when the right $c \times c$ submatrix of P is invertible, the relation $Pv = w$ explicitly specifies the last c variables of v in terms of the first r variables. A similar statement applies to every invertible $c \times c$ submatrix of P and the corresponding variables. A special case of this calculation, the linear case, will be used throughout this section: for every $M \in M_{c,r}(\mathbb{R})$, invertible $N \in M_c(\mathbb{R})$, $h \in \mathbb{R}^r$, and $k \in \mathbb{R}^c$,

$$\begin{bmatrix} M & N \end{bmatrix} \begin{bmatrix} h \\ k \end{bmatrix} = \mathbf{0}_c \qquad \Longleftrightarrow \qquad k = -N^{-1}Mh. \tag{5.6}$$

When the conditions are nonaffine, the situation is not so easy to analyze. However:

- The problem is easy to linearize. That is, given a point (a, b) (where $a \in \mathbb{R}^r$ and $b \in \mathbb{R}^c$) on the level set $\{(x, y) : g(x, y) = w\}$, differential calculus tells us how to describe the tangent object to the level set at the point. Depending on the value of r, the tangent object will be a line, or a plane, or higher-dimensional. But regardless of its dimension, it is described by the linear conditions $g'(a, b)v = \mathbf{0}_c$, and these conditions take the form that we have just considered,

$$\begin{bmatrix} M & N \end{bmatrix} \begin{bmatrix} h \\ k \end{bmatrix} = \mathbf{0}_c, \quad M \in M_{c,r}(\mathbb{R}), \ N \in M_c(\mathbb{R}), \ h \in \mathbb{R}^r, \ k \in \mathbb{R}^c.$$

  Thus if N is invertible then we can solve the linearized problem as in (5.6).
- The inverse function theorem says:

  If the linearized inversion problem is solvable then the actual inversion problem is locally solvable.

  With a little work, we can use the inverse function theorem to establish the implicit function theorem:

  If the linearized level set is a graph then the actual level set is locally a graph.

  And in fact, the implicit function theorem will imply the inverse function theorem as well.

For example, the unit circle C is described by one constraint on two variables ($n = 2$ and $c = 1$, so $r = 1$),

$$x^2 + y^2 = 1.$$

Globally (in the large), this relation specifies neither x as a function of y nor y as a function of x. It can't: the circle is visibly not the graph of a function of either sort—recall the vertical line test to check whether a curve is the graph of a function $y = \varphi(x)$, and analogously for the horizontal line test. The situation does give a function, however, if one works locally (in the small) by looking only at part of the circle at a time. Every arc in the bottom half of the circle is described by the function

$$y = \varphi(x) = -\sqrt{1 - x^2}.$$

Similarly, every arc in the right half is described by

$$x = \psi(y) = \sqrt{1 - y^2}.$$

Every arc in the bottom right quarter is described by both functions. (See Figure 5.6.) On the other hand, no arc of the circle about the point $(a, b) = (1, 0)$ is described by a function $y = \varphi(x)$, and no arc about $(a, b) = (0, 1)$ is described by a function $x = \psi(y)$. (See Figure 5.7.) Thus, about some points (a, b), the circle relation $x^2 + y^2 = 1$ contains the information to specify each variable as a function of the other. These functions are implicit in the relation. About other points, the relation implicitly defines one variable as a function of the other, but not the second as a function of the first.

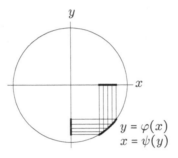

Figure 5.6. Arc of a circle

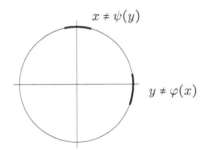

Figure 5.7. Trickier arcs of a circle

To bring differential calculus to bear on the situation, think of the circle as a level set. Specifically, it is a level set of the function $g(x, y) = x^2 + y^2$,

$$C = \{(x,y) : g(x,y) = 1\}.$$

Let (a,b) be a point on the circle. The derivative of g at the point is

$$g'(a,b) = \begin{bmatrix} 2a\ 2b \end{bmatrix}.$$

The tangent line to the circle at (a,b) consists of the points $(a+h, b+k)$ such that (h,k) is orthogonal to $g'(a,b)$,

$$\begin{bmatrix} 2a\ 2b \end{bmatrix} \begin{bmatrix} h \\ k \end{bmatrix} = 0.$$

That is,

$$2ah + 2bk = 0.$$

Thus, whenever $b \neq 0$ we have

$$k = -(a/b)h,$$

showing that on the tangent line, the second coordinate is a linear function of the first, and the function has derivative $-a/b$. And so on the circle itself near (a,b), plausibly the second coordinate is a function of the first as well, provided that $b \neq 0$. Note that indeed this argument excludes the two points $(1,0)$ and $(-1,0)$, about which y is not an implicit function of x. But about points $(a,b) \in C$ where $D_2g(a,b) \neq 0$, the circle relation should implicitly define y as a function of x. And at such points (say, on the lower half-circle), the function is explicitly

$$\varphi(x) = -\sqrt{1 - x^2},$$

so that $\varphi'(x) = x/\sqrt{1 - x^2} = -x/y$ (the last minus sign is present because the square root is positive but y is negative) and in particular,

$$\varphi'(a) = -a/b.$$

Thus $\varphi'(a)$ is exactly the slope that we found a moment earlier by solving the linear problem $g'(a,b)v = 0$ where $v = (h,k)$ is a column vector. That is, using the constraint $g(x,y) = 0$ to set up and solve the linear problem, making no reference in the process to the function φ implicitly defined by the constraint, we found the derivative $\varphi'(a)$ nonetheless. The procedure illustrates the general idea of the pending implicit function theorem:

> *Constraining conditions locally define some variables implicitly in terms of others, and the implicitly defined function can be differentiated without being found explicitly.*

(And returning to the circle example, yet another way to find the derivative is to differentiate the relation $x^2 + y^2 = 1$ at a point (a,b) about which we assume that $y = \varphi(x)$,

$$2a + 2b\varphi'(a) = 0,$$

so that again $\varphi'(a) = -a/b$. The reader may recall from elementary calculus that this technique is called *implicit differentiation.*)

It may help the reader to visualize the situation if we revisit the idea of the previous paragraph more geometrically. Since C is a level set of g, the gradient $g'(a,b)$ is orthogonal to C at the point (a,b). When $g'(a,b)$ has a nonzero y-component, C should locally have a big shadow on the x-axis, from which there is a function φ back to C. (See Figure 5.8, in which the arrow drawn is quite a bit shorter than the true gradient, for graphical reasons.)

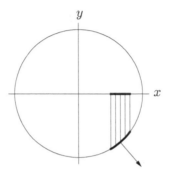

Figure 5.8. Nonhorizontal gradient and x-shadow

Another set defined by a constraining relation is the unit sphere, also specified as a level set. Let

$$g(x,y,z) = x^2 + y^2 + z^2.$$

Then the sphere is

$$S = \{(x,y,z) : g(x,y,z) = 1\}.$$

Imposing one condition on three variables should generally leave two of them free (say, the first two) and define the remaining one in terms of the free ones. That is, $n = 3$ and $c = 1$, so that $r = 2$. And indeed, the sphere implicitly describes z as a function $\varphi(x,y)$ about every point $p = (a,b,c) \in S$ off the equator, where $c = 0$. (So for this example we have just overridden the general use of c as the number of constraints; here c is the third coordinate of a point on the level set.) The equator is precisely the points where $D_3g(p) = 2c$ vanishes. Again geometry makes this plausible. The gradient $g'(p)$ is orthogonal to S at p. When $g'(p)$ has a nonzero z-component, S should locally have a big shadow in the (x,y)-plane from which there is a function back to S and then to the z-axis. (See Figure 5.9.)

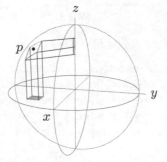

Figure 5.9. Function from the (x, y)-plane to the z-axis via the sphere

The argument based on calculus and linear algebra to suggest that near points $(a, b, c) \in S$ such that $D_3 g(a, b, c) \neq 0$, z is implicitly a function $\varphi(x, y)$ on S is similar to the case of the circle. The derivative of g at the point is

$$g'(a, b, c) = \begin{bmatrix} 2a & 2b & 2c \end{bmatrix}.$$

The tangent plane to the sphere at (a, b, c) consists of the points $(a + h, b + k, c + \ell)$ such that (h, k, ℓ) is orthogonal to $g'(a, b, c)$,

$$\begin{bmatrix} 2a & 2b & 2c \end{bmatrix} \begin{bmatrix} h \\ k \\ \ell \end{bmatrix} = 0.$$

That is,

$$2ah + 2bk + 2c\ell = 0.$$

Thus, whenever $c \neq 0$ we have

$$\ell = -(a/c)h - (b/c)k,$$

showing that on the tangent plane, the third coordinate is a linear function of the first two, and the function has partial derivatives $-a/c$ and $-b/c$. And so on the sphere itself near (a, b, c), plausibly the third coordinate is a function of the first two as well, provided that $c \neq 0$. This argument excludes points on the equator, about which z is not an implicit function of (x, y). But about points $(a, b, c) \in S$ where $D_3 g(a, b, c) \neq 0$, the sphere relation should implicitly define z as a function of (x, y). And at such points (say, on the upper hemisphere), the function is explicitly

$$\varphi(x, y) = \sqrt{1 - x^2 - y^2},$$

so that $\varphi'(x,y) = -[x/\sqrt{1-x^2-y^2} \ \ y/\sqrt{1-x^2-y^2}] = -[x/z \ \ y/z]$, and in particular,

$$\varphi'(a,b) = -[a/c \ \ b/c].$$

The partial derivatives are exactly as predicted by solving the linear problem $g'(a,b,c)v = 0$, where $v = (h,k,\ell)$ is a column vector, with no reference to φ. (As with the circle, a third way to find the derivative is to differentiate the sphere relation $x^2 + y^2 + z^2 = 1$ at a point (a,b,c) about which we assume that $z = \varphi(x,y)$, differentiating with respect to x and then with respect to y,

$$2a + 2cD_1\varphi(a,b) = 0, \quad 2b + 2cD_2\varphi(a,b) = 0.$$

Again we obtain $\varphi'(a,b) = -[a/c \ \ b/c]$.)

Next consider the intersection of the unit sphere and the 45-degree plane $z = -y$. The intersection is a great circle, again naturally described as a level set. That is, if we consider the mapping

$$g : \mathbb{R}^3 \longrightarrow \mathbb{R}^2, \qquad g(x,y,z) = (x^2 + y^2 + z^2, y + z),$$

then the great circle is a level set of g,

$$GC = \{(x,y,z) : g(x,y,z) = (1,0)\}.$$

The two conditions on the three variables should generally leave one variable (say, the first one) free and define the other two variables in terms of it. That is, $n = 3$ and $c = 2$, so that $r = 1$. Indeed, GC is a circle that is orthogonal to the plane of the page, and away from its two points $(\pm 1, 0, 0)$ that are farthest in and out of the page, it does define (y,z) locally as functions of x. (See Figure 5.10.) This time we first proceed by linearizing the problem to obtain the derivatives of the implicit function without finding the implicit function $\varphi = (\varphi_1, \varphi_2)$ itself. The derivative matrix of g at p is

$$g'(a,b,c) = \begin{bmatrix} 2a & 2b & 2c \\ 0 & 1 & 1 \end{bmatrix}.$$

The level set GC is defined by the condition that $g(x,y,z)$ remain constant at $(1,0)$ as (x,y,z) varies. Thus the tangent line to GC at a point (a,b,c) consists of points $(a+h, b+k, c+\ell)$ such that neither component function of g is instantaneously changing in the (h,k,ℓ)-direction,

$$\begin{bmatrix} 2a & 2b & 2c \\ 0 & 1 & 1 \end{bmatrix} \begin{bmatrix} h \\ k \\ \ell \end{bmatrix} = \begin{bmatrix} 0 \\ 0 \end{bmatrix}.$$

The right 2×2 submatrix of $g'(a,b,c)$ has nonzero determinant whenever $b \neq c$, that is, at all points of GC except the two aforementioned extreme points $(\pm 1, 0, 0)$. Assuming that $b \neq c$, let M denote the first column of $g'(a,b,c)$ and let N denote the right 2×2 submatrix. Then by (5.6), the linearized problem has solution

$$\begin{bmatrix} k \\ \ell \end{bmatrix} = -N^{-1}Mh = \frac{1}{2(c-b)} \begin{bmatrix} 1 & -2c \\ -1 & 2b \end{bmatrix} \begin{bmatrix} 2a \\ 0 \end{bmatrix} h = \begin{bmatrix} -\frac{a}{2b} \\ -\frac{a}{2c} \end{bmatrix} h$$

(the condition $c = -b$ was used in the last step), or

$$k = -\frac{a}{2b}h, \quad \ell = -\frac{a}{2c}h. \tag{5.7}$$

And so for all points $(a+h, b+k, c+\ell)$ on the tangent line to GC at (a,b,c), the last two coordinate-offsets k and ℓ are specified in terms of the first coordinate offset h via (5.7), and the component functions have partial derivatives $-a/(2b)$ and $-a/(2c)$. (And as with the circle and the sphere, the two partial derivatives can be obtained by implicit differentiation as well.)

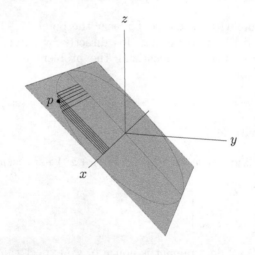

Figure 5.10. y and z locally as functions of x on a great circle

To make the implicit function in the great circle relations explicit, note that near the point $p = (a,b,c)$ in the figure,

$$(y,z) = (\varphi_1(x), \varphi_2(x)) = \left(-\sqrt{\frac{1-x^2}{2}}, \sqrt{\frac{1-x^2}{2}} \right).$$

At p the component functions have derivatives

$$\varphi_1'(a) = \frac{a}{2\sqrt{\frac{1-a^2}{2}}} \quad \text{and} \quad \varphi_2'(a) = \frac{-a}{2\sqrt{\frac{1-a^2}{2}}}.$$

But $1 - a^2 = 2b^2 = 2c^2$, and $\sqrt{b^2} = -b$ since $b < 0$, while $\sqrt{c^2} = c$ since $c > 0$, so the derivatives are

$$\varphi_1'(a) = -\frac{a}{2b} \qquad \text{and} \qquad \varphi_2'(a) = -\frac{a}{2c}.$$

Predictably enough, the implicitly calculated values displayed in (5.7) are matched by these component derivatives of the true mapping φ that defines y and z in terms of x for points near p on GC.

In the examples of the circle, the sphere, and the great circle, the functions implicit in the defining relations could in fact be found explicitly. But in general, relations may snarl the variables so badly that expressing some as functions of the others is beyond our algebraic capacity. For instance, do the simultaneous conditions

$$y^2 = e^z \cos(y + x^2) \qquad \text{and} \qquad y^2 + z^2 = x^2 \tag{5.8}$$

define y and z implicitly in terms of x near the point $(1, -1, 0)$? (This point meets both conditions.) Answering this directly by solving for y and z is manifestly unappealing. But linearizing the problem is easy. At our point $(1, -1, 0)$, the mapping

$$g(x, y, z) = (y^2 - e^z \cos(y + x^2), y^2 + z^2 - x^2)$$

has derivative matrix

$$g'(1, -1, 0) = \left[\begin{matrix} 2xe^z \sin(y + x^2) & 2y + e^z \sin(y + x^2) & -e^z \cos(y + x^2) \\ -2x & 2y & 2z \end{matrix} \right] \Bigg|_{(1,-1,0)}$$

$$= \left[\begin{matrix} 0 & -2 & -1 \\ -2 & -2 & 0 \end{matrix} \right].$$

Since the right 2×2 determinant is nonzero, we expect that indeed y and z are implicit functions $\varphi_1(x)$ and $\varphi_2(x)$ near $(1, -1, 0)$. Furthermore, solving the linearized problem as in the previous example with M and N similarly defined suggests that if $(y, z) = \varphi(x) = (\varphi_1(x), \varphi_2(x))$ then

$$\varphi'(1) = -N^{-1}M = -\left[\begin{matrix} -2 & -1 \\ -2 & 0 \end{matrix} \right]^{-1} \left[\begin{matrix} 0 \\ -2 \end{matrix} \right] = \frac{1}{2} \left[\begin{matrix} 0 & 1 \\ 2 & -2 \end{matrix} \right] \left[\begin{matrix} 0 \\ -2 \end{matrix} \right] = \left[\begin{matrix} -1 \\ 2 \end{matrix} \right].$$

Thus for a point $(x, y, z) = (1 + h, -1 + k, 0 + \ell)$ near $(1, -1, 0)$ satisfying conditions (5.8), we expect that $(k, \ell) \approx (-h, 2h)$, i.e.,

$$\text{for } x = 1 + h, \quad (y, z) \approx (-1, 0) + (-h, 2h).$$

The implicit function theorem fulfills these expectations.

Theorem 5.3.2 (Implicit function theorem). *Let c and n be positive integers with $n > c$, and let $r = n - c$. Let A be an open subset of $\mathbb{R}^n$, and let $g : A \longrightarrow \mathbb{R}^c$ have continuous partial derivatives at every point of A. Consider the level set*

$$L = \{v \in A : g(v) = \mathbf{0}_c\}.$$

Let p be a point of L, i.e., let $g(p) = \mathbf{0}_c$. Let $p = (a, b)$ where $a \in \mathbb{R}^r$ and $b \in \mathbb{R}^c$, and let $g'(p) = \begin{bmatrix} M & N \end{bmatrix}$ where M is the left $c \times r$ submatrix and N is the remaining right square $c \times c$ submatrix.

If $\det N \neq 0$ then the level set L is locally a graph near p. That is, the condition $g(x, y) = \mathbf{0}_c$ for (x, y) near (a, b) implicitly defines y as a function $y = \varphi(x)$ where φ takes r-vectors near a to c-vectors near b, and in particular $\varphi(a) = b$. The function φ is differentiable at a with derivative matrix

$$\varphi'(a) = -N^{-1}M.$$

Hence φ is well approximated near a by its affine approximation,

$$\varphi(a + h) \approx b - N^{-1}Mh.$$

We make three remarks before the proof.

- The condition $g(x, y) = \mathbf{0}_c$ could just as easily be $g(x, y) = w$ for every fixed point $w \in \mathbb{R}^c$, as in our earlier examples. Normalizing to $w = \mathbf{0}_c$ amounts to replacing g by $g - w$ (with no effect on g'), which we do to tidy up the statement of the theorem.
- The implicit function theorem gives no information when $\det N = 0$. In this case, the condition $g(x, y) = \mathbf{0}_c$ may or may not define y in terms of x.
- While the theorem strictly addresses only whether the last c of n variables subject to c conditions depend on the first r variables, it can be suitably modified to address whether any c variables depend on the remaining ones by checking the determinant of a suitable $c \times c$ submatrix of $g'(p)$. The modification is merely a matter of reindexing or permuting the variables, not worth writing down formally in cumbersome notation, but the reader should feel free to use the modified version.

Proof. Examining the derivative has already shown the theorem's plausibility in specific instances. Shoring up these considerations into a proof is easy with a well-chosen change of variables and the inverse function theorem. For the change of variables, define

$$G : A \longrightarrow \mathbb{R}^n$$

as follows: for all $x \in \mathbb{R}^r$ and $y \in \mathbb{R}^c$ such that $(x, y) \in A$,

$$G(x, y) = (x, g(x, y)).$$

Note that G incorporates g, but unlike g it is a map between spaces of the same dimension n. Note also that the augmentation that changes g into G is highly reversible, being the identity mapping on the x-coordinates. That is, it is easy to recover g from G. The mapping G affects only y-coordinates, and it is designed to take the level set $L = \{(x, y) \in A : g(x, y) = \mathbf{0}_c\}$ to the x-axis. (See Figure 5.11, in which the inputs and the outputs of G are shown in the same copy of $\mathbb{R}^n$.)

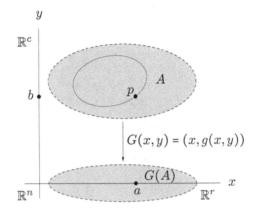

Figure 5.11. Mapping A to $\mathbb{R}^n$ and the constrained set to x-space

The mapping G is differentiable at the point $p = (a, b)$ with derivative matrix

$$G'(a, b) = \begin{bmatrix} I_r & \mathbf{0}_{r \times c} \\ M & N \end{bmatrix} \in M_n(\mathbb{R}).$$

This matrix has determinant $\det G'(a, b) = \det N \neq 0$, and so by the inverse function theorem, G has a local inverse mapping Φ defined near the point $G(a, b) = (a, \mathbf{0}_c)$. (See Figure 5.12.) Since the first r components of G are the identity mapping, the same holds for the inverse. That is, the inverse takes the form

$$\Phi(x, y) = (x, \phi(x, y)),$$

where ϕ maps n-vectors near $(a, \mathbf{0}_c)$ to c-vectors near b. The inversion criterion is that for all (x, y) near (a, b) and all $(x, \tilde{y})$ near $(a, \mathbf{0}_c)$,

$$G(x, y) = (x, \tilde{y}) \quad \Longleftrightarrow \quad (x, y) = \Phi(x, \tilde{y}).$$

Equivalently, since neither G nor Φ affects x-coordinates, for all x near a, y near b, and $\tilde{y}$ near $\mathbf{0}_c$,

$$g(x, y) = \tilde{y} \quad \Longleftrightarrow \quad y = \phi(x, \tilde{y}). \tag{5.9}$$

Also by the inverse function theorem and a short calculation,

$$\Phi'(a, \mathbf{0}_c) = G'(a, b)^{-1} = \begin{bmatrix} I_r & \mathbf{0}_{r \times c} \\ -N^{-1}M & N^{-1} \end{bmatrix}.$$

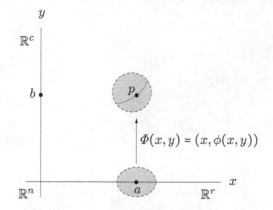

Figure 5.12. Local inverse of G

Now we can exhibit the desired mapping implicit in the original g. Define a mapping

$$\varphi(x) = \phi(x, \mathbf{0}_c) \quad \text{for } x \text{ near } a. \tag{5.10}$$

The idea is that locally this lifts the x-axis to the level set L where $g(x,y) = \mathbf{0}_c$ and then projects horizontally to the y-axis. (See Figure 5.13.) For every (x,y) near (a,b), a specialization of condition (5.9) combines with the definition (5.10) of φ to give

$$g(x,y) = \mathbf{0}_c \quad \Longleftrightarrow \quad y = \varphi(x).$$

This equivalence exhibits y as a local function of x on the level set of g, as desired. And since by definition (5.10), φ is the last c component functions of Φ restricted to the first r inputs to Φ, the derivative $\varphi'(a)$ is exactly the lower left $c \times r$ block of $\Phi'(a, \mathbf{0}_c)$, which is $-N^{-1}M$. This completes the proof. $\square$

Thus the implicit function theorem follows easily from the inverse function theorem. The converse implication is even easier. Imagine a scenario in which somehow we know the implicit function theorem but not the inverse function theorem. Let $f : A \longrightarrow \mathbb{R}^n$ (where $A \subset \mathbb{R}^n$) be a mapping that satisfies the hypotheses for the inverse function theorem at a point $a \in A$. That is, f is continuously differentiable in an open set containing a, and $\det f'(a) \neq 0$. Define a mapping

$$g : A \times \mathbb{R}^n \longrightarrow \mathbb{R}^n, \qquad g(x,y) = f(x) - y.$$

(This mapping should look familiar from the beginning of this section.) Let $b = f(a)$. Then $g(a,b) = 0$, and the derivative matrix of g at (a,b) is

$$g'(a,b) = \big[f'(a) \; -I_n \big].$$

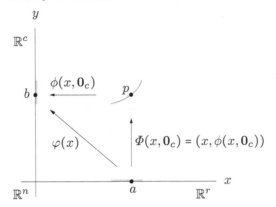

Figure 5.13. The implicit mapping from x-space to y-space via the level set

Since $f'(a)$ is invertible, we may apply the implicit function theorem, with the roles of c, r, and n in the theorem taken by the values n, n, and $2n$ here, and with the theorem modified as in the third remark before its proof so that we are checking whether the first n variables depend on the last n values. The theorem supplies us with a differentiable mapping φ defined for values of y near b such that for all (x, y) near (a, b),

$$g(x, y) = 0 \quad \Longleftrightarrow \quad x = \varphi(y).$$

But by the definition of g, this equivalence is

$$y = f(x) \quad \Longleftrightarrow \quad x = \varphi(y).$$

That is, φ inverts f. Also by the implicit function theorem, φ is differentiable at b with derivative

$$\varphi'(b) = -f'(a)^{-1}(-I_n) = f'(a)^{-1}$$

(as it must be), and we have recovered the inverse function theorem. In a nutshell, the argument converts the graph $y = f(x)$ into a level set $g(x, y) = 0$, and then the implicit function theorem says that locally the level set is also the graph of $x = \varphi(y)$. (See Figure 5.14.)

Rederiving the inverse function theorem so easily from the implicit function theorem is not particularly impressive, since proving the implicit function theorem without citing the inverse function theorem would be just as hard as the route we took of proving the inverse function theorem first. The point is that the two theorems have essentially the same content.

We end this section with one more example. Consider the function

$$g : \mathbb{R}^2 \longrightarrow \mathbb{R}, \quad g(x, y) = (x^2 + y^2)^2 - x^2 + y^2$$

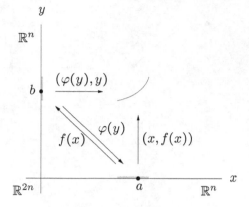

Figure 5.14. The inverse function theorem from the implicit function theorem

and the corresponding level set, a curve in the plane,

$$L = \{(x,y) \in \mathbb{R}^2 : g(x,y) = 0\}.$$

The implicit function theorem lets us analyze L qualitatively. The derivative matrix of g is

$$g'(x,y) = 4[x((x^2 + y^2) - 1/2) \quad y((x^2 + y^2) + 1/2)].$$

By the theorem, L is locally the graph of a function $y = \varphi(x)$ except possibly at its points where $y((x^2 + y^2) + 1/2) = 0$, which is to say $y = 0$. To find all such points is to find all x such that $g(x,0) = 0$. This condition is $x^4 - x^2 = 0$, or $x^2(x^2 - 1) = 0$, and so the points of L where locally it might not be the graph of $y = \varphi(x)$ are $(0,0)$ and $(\pm 1, 0)$. Provisionally we imagine L to have vertical tangents at these points.

Similarly, L is locally the graph of a function $x = \varphi(y)$ except possibly at its points where $x((x^2 + y^2) - 1/2) = 0$, which is to say $x = 0$ or $x^2 + y^2 = 1/2$. The condition $g(0,y) = 0$ is $y^4 + y^2 = 0$, whose only solution is $y = 0$. And if $x^2 + y^2 = 1/2$ then $g(x,y) = 1/4 - x^2 + y^2 = 3/4 - 2x^2$, which vanishes for $x = \pm\sqrt{3/8}$, also determining $y = \pm\sqrt{1/8}$. Thus the points of L where locally it might not be the graph of $x = \varphi(y)$ are $(0,0)$ and $(\pm\sqrt{3/8}, \pm\sqrt{1/8})$ with the two signs independent. Provisionally we imagine L to have horizontal tangents at these points.

However, since also we imagined a vertical tangent at $(0,0)$, this point requires further analysis. Keeping only the lowest-order terms of the relation $g(x,y) = 0$ gives $y^2 \approx x^2$, or $y \approx \pm x$, and so L looks like two crossing lines of slopes ± 1 near $(0,0)$. This analysis suffices to sketch L, as shown in Figure 5.15. The level set L is called a *lemniscate*. The lemniscate originated in astronomy, and the study of its arc length led to profound mathematical ideas by Gauss, Abel, and many others.

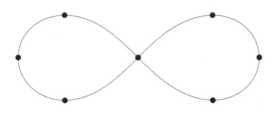

Figure 5.15. Lemniscate

Exercises

5.3.1. Does the relation $x^2 + y + \sin(xy) = 0$ implicitly define y as a function of x near the origin? If so, what is its best affine approximation? How about x as a function of y and its affine approximation?

5.3.2. Does the relation $xy - z \ln y + e^{xz} = 1$ implicitly define z as a function of (x, y) near $(0, 1, 1)$? How about y as a function of (x, z)? When possible, give the affine approximation to the function.

5.3.3. Do the simultaneous conditions $x^2(y^2 + z^2) = 5$ and $(x - z)^2 + y^2 = 2$ implicitly define (y, z) as a function of x near $(1, -1, 2)$? If so, then what is the function's affine approximation?

5.3.4. Same question for the conditions $x^2 + y^2 = 4$ and $2x^2 + y^2 + 8z^2 = 8$ near $(2, 0, 0)$.

5.3.5. Do the simultaneous conditions $xy + 2yz = 3xz$ and $xyz + x - y = 1$ implicitly define (x, y) as a function of z near $(1, 1, 1)$? How about (x, z) as a function of y? How about (y, z) as a function of x? Give affine approximations when possible.

5.3.6. Do the conditions $xy^2 + xzu + yv^2 = 3$ and $u^3yz + 2xv - u^2v^2 = 2$ implicitly define (u, v) in terms of (x, y, z) near the point $(1, 1, 1, 1, 1)$? If so, what is the derivative matrix of the implicitly defined mapping at $(1, 1, 1)$?

5.3.7. Do the conditions $x^2 + yu + xv + w = 0$ and $x + y + uvw = -1$ implicitly define (x, y) in terms of (u, v, w) near $(x, y, u, v, w) = (1, -1, 1, 1, -1)$? If so, what is the best affine approximation to the implicitly defined mapping?

5.3.8. Do the conditions

$$2x + y + 2z + u - v = 1$$
$$xy + z - u + 2v = 1$$
$$yz + xz + u^2 + v = 0$$

define the first three variables (x, y, z) as a function $\varphi(u, v)$ near the point $(x, y, z, u, v) = (1, 1, -1, 1, 1)$? If so, find the derivative matrix $\varphi'(1, 1)$.

5.3.9. Define $g : \mathbb{R}^2 \longrightarrow \mathbb{R}$ by $g(x,y) = 2x^3 - 3x^2 + 2y^3 + 3y^2$ and let L be the level set $\{(x,y) : g(x,y) = 0\}$. Find those points of L about which y need not be defined implicitly as a function of x, and find the points about which x need not be defined implicitly as a function of y. Describe L precisely—the result should explain the points you found.

5.4 Lagrange Multipliers: Geometric Motivation and Specific Examples

How close does the intersection of the planes $x+y+z = 1$ and $x-y+2z = -1$ in $\mathbb{R}^3$ come to the origin? This question is an example of an *optimization problem with constraints*. The goal in such problems is to maximize or minimize some function, but with relations imposed on its variables. Equivalently, the problem is to optimize some function whose domain is a level set.

A geometric solution of the sample problem just given is that the planes intersect in a line through the point $p = (0,1,0)$ in the direction $d = (1,1,1) \times (1,-1,2)$, so the point-to-line distance formula from Exercise 3.10.12 answers the question. This method is easy and efficient.

A more generic method of solution is via substitution. The equations of the constraining planes are $x + y = 1 - z$ and $x - y = -1 - 2z$; adding gives $x = -3z/2$, and subtracting gives $y = 1 + z/2$. To finish the problem, minimize the function $d^2(z) = (-3z/2)^2 + (1 + z/2)^2 + z^2$, where d^2 denotes distance squared from the origin. Minimizing d^2 rather than d avoids square roots.

Not all constrained problems yield readily to either of these methods. The more irregular the conditions, the less amenable they are to geometry, and the more tangled the variables, the less readily they distill. Merely adding more variables to the previous problem produces a nuisance: How close does the intersection of the planes $v + w + x + y + z = 1$ and $v - w + 2x - y + z = -1$ in $\mathbb{R}^5$ come to the origin? Now no geometric procedure lies conveniently at hand. As for substitution, linear algebra shows that

$$\begin{bmatrix} 1 & 1 & 1 & 1 & 1 \\ 1 & -1 & 2 & -1 & 1 \end{bmatrix} \begin{bmatrix} v \\ w \\ x \\ y \\ z \end{bmatrix} = \begin{bmatrix} 1 \\ -1 \end{bmatrix}$$

implies

$$\begin{bmatrix} v \\ w \end{bmatrix} = \begin{bmatrix} 1 & 1 \\ 1 & -1 \end{bmatrix}^{-1} \left(\begin{bmatrix} 1 \\ -1 \end{bmatrix} - \begin{bmatrix} 1 & 1 & 1 \\ 2 & -1 & 1 \end{bmatrix} \begin{bmatrix} x \\ y \\ z \end{bmatrix} \right) = \begin{bmatrix} -3x/2 - z \\ 1 + x/2 - y \end{bmatrix}.$$

Since the resulting function $d^2(x,y,z) = (-3x/2 - z)^2 + (1 + x/2 - y)^2 + x^2 + y^2 + z^2$ is quadratic, partial differentiation and more linear algebra will find its critical points. But the process is getting tedious.

Let's step back from specifics (but we will return to the currently unresolved example soon) and consider in general the necessary nature of a critical point in a constrained problem. The discussion will take place in two stages: first we consider the domain of the problem, and then we consider the critical point.

The domain of the problem is the points in n-space that satisfy a set of c constraints. To satisfy the constraints is to meet a condition

$$g(x) = \mathbf{0}_c,$$

where $g : A \longrightarrow \mathbb{R}^c$ is a $\mathcal{C}^1$-mapping, with $A \subset \mathbb{R}^n$ an open set. That is, the constrained set forming the domain in the problem is a level set L, the intersection of the level sets of the component functions g_i of g. (See Figures 5.16 and 5.17. The first figure shows two individual level sets for scalar-valued functions on $\mathbb{R}^3$, and the second figure shows them together and then shows their intersection, the level set for a vector-valued mapping.)

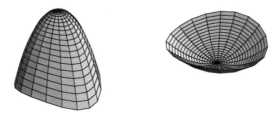

Figure 5.16. Level sets for two scalar-valued functions on $\mathbb{R}^3$

At every point $p \in L$, the set L must be locally orthogonal to each gradient $\nabla g_i(p)$. (See Figures 5.18 and 5.19. The first figure shows the level sets for the component functions of the constraint mapping, and the gradients of the component functions at p, while the second figure shows the tangent line and the normal plane to the level set at p. In the first figure, neither gradient is tangent to the other surface, and so in the second figure the two gradients are not normal to each other.) Therefore:

- L is orthogonal at p to every linear combination of the gradients,

$$\sum_{i=1}^{c} \lambda_i \nabla g_i(p) \quad \text{where } \lambda_1, \ldots, \lambda_c \text{ are scalars.}$$

Equivalently:

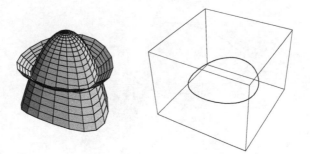

Figure 5.17. The intersection is a level set for a vector-valued mapping on $\mathbb{R}^3$

- Every such linear combination of gradients is orthogonal to L at p.

But we want to turn this idea around and assert the converse, that:

- Every vector that is orthogonal to L at p is such a linear combination.

However, the converse does not always follow. Intuitively, the argument is that if the gradients $\nabla g_1(p), \ldots, \nabla g_c(p)$ are linearly independent (i.e., they point in c nonredundant directions) then the implicit function theorem should say that the level set L therefore looks $(n-c)$-dimensional near p, so the space of vectors orthogonal to L at p is c-dimensional, and so every such vector is indeed a linear combination of the gradients. This intuitive argument is not a proof, but for now it is a good heuristic.

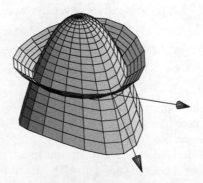

Figure 5.18. Gradients to the level sets at a point of intersection

Proceeding to the second stage of the discussion, now suppose that p is a critical point of the restriction to L of some $\mathcal{C}^1$-function $f : A \longrightarrow \mathbb{R}$. (Thus f

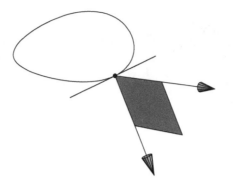

Figure 5.19. Tangent line and normal plane to the intersection

has the same domain $A \subset \mathbb{R}^n$ as g.) Then for every unit vector d describing a direction in L at p, the directional derivative $D_d f(p)$ must be 0. But $D_d f(p) = \langle \nabla f(p), d \rangle$, so this means that:

- $\nabla f(p)$ must be orthogonal to L at p.

This observation combines with our description of the most general vector orthogonal to L at p, in the third bullet above, to give Lagrange's condition:

> *Suppose that p is a critical point of the function f restricted to the level set $L = \{x : g(x) = \mathbf{0}_c\}$ of g. If the gradients $\nabla g_i(p)$ are linearly independent, then*

$$\nabla f(p) = \sum_{i=1}^{c} \lambda_i \nabla g_i(p) \quad \textit{for some scalars } \lambda_1, \ldots, \lambda_c,$$

> *and since p is in the level set, also*

$$g(p) = \mathbf{0}_c.$$

Approaching a constrained problem by setting up these conditions and then working with the new variables $\lambda_1, \ldots, \lambda_c$ is sometimes easier than the other methods. The λ_i are *useful but irrelevant constants.*

This discussion has derived the Lagrange multiplier criterion for the linearized version of the constrained problem. The next section will use the implicit function theorem to derive the criterion for the actual constrained problem, and then it will give some general examples. The remainder of this section is dedicated to specific examples.

Returning to the unresolved second example at the beginning of this section, the functions in question are

$$f(v, w, x, y, z) = v^2 + w^2 + x^2 + y^2 + z^2$$
$$g_1(v, w, x, y, z) = v + w + x + y + z - 1$$
$$g_2(v, w, x, y, z) = v - w + 2x - y + z + 1$$

and the corresponding Lagrange condition and constraints are (after absorbing a 2 into the λ's, whose particular values are irrelevant anyway)

$$(v, w, x, y, z) = \lambda_1(1, 1, 1, 1, 1) + \lambda_2(1, -1, 2, -1, 1)$$
$$= (\lambda_1 + \lambda_2, \lambda_1 - \lambda_2, \lambda_1 + 2\lambda_2, \lambda_1 - \lambda_2, \lambda_1 + \lambda_2)$$
$$v + w + x + y + z = 1$$
$$v - w + 2x - y + z = -1.$$

Substitute the expressions from the Lagrange condition into the constraints to get $5\lambda_1 + 2\lambda_2 = 1$ and $2\lambda_1 + 8\lambda_2 = -1$. That is,

$$\begin{bmatrix} 5 & 2 \\ 2 & 8 \end{bmatrix} \begin{bmatrix} \lambda_1 \\ \lambda_2 \end{bmatrix} = \begin{bmatrix} 1 \\ -1 \end{bmatrix},$$

and so, inverting the matrix to solve the system,

$$\begin{bmatrix} \lambda_1 \\ \lambda_2 \end{bmatrix} = \frac{1}{36} \begin{bmatrix} 8 & -2 \\ -2 & 5 \end{bmatrix} \begin{bmatrix} 1 \\ -1 \end{bmatrix} = \begin{bmatrix} 10/36 \\ -7/36 \end{bmatrix}.$$

Note how much more convenient the two λ's are to work with than the five original variables. Their values are auxiliary to the original problem, but substituting back now gives the nearest point to the origin,

$$(v, w, x, y, z) = \frac{1}{36}(3, 17, -4, 17, 3),$$

and its distance from the origin is $\sqrt{612}/36$. This example is just one instance of a general problem of finding the nearest point to the origin in $\mathbb{R}^n$ subject to c affine constraints. We will solve the general problem in the next section.

An example from geometry is Euclid's least area problem. Given an angle ABC and a point P interior to the angle as shown in Figure 5.20, what line through P cuts off from the angle the triangle of least area?

Draw the line L through P parallel to AB and let D be its intersection with AC. Let a denote the distance AD and let h denote the altitude from AC to P. Both a and h are constants. Given any other line L' through P, let x denote its intersection with AC and H denote the altitude from AC to the intersection of L' with AB. (See Figure 5.21.) The shaded triangle and its subtriangle in the figure are similar, giving the relation $x/H = (x - a)/h$.

The problem is now to minimize the function $f(x, H) = \frac{1}{2}xH$ subject to the constraint $g(x, H) = 0$ where $g(x, H) = (x-a)H - xh = 0$. Lagrange's condition $\nabla f(x, H) = \lambda \nabla g(x, H)$ and the constraint $g(x, H) = 0$ become, after absorbing a 2 into λ,

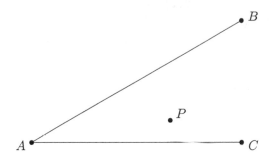

Figure 5.20. Setup for Euclid's least area problem

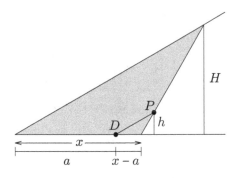

Figure 5.21. Construction for Euclid's least area problem

$$(H, x) = \lambda(H - h, x - a),$$
$$(x - a)H = xh.$$

The first relation quickly yields $(x-a)H = x(H-h)$. Combining this with the second shows that $H-h = h$, that is, $H = 2h$. The solution of Euclid's problem is, therefore, to take the segment that is *bisected* by P between the two sides of the angle. (See Figure 5.22.)

Euclid's least area problem has the interpretation of finding the point of tangency between the level set $g(x, H) = 0$, a hyperbola having asymptotes $x = a$ and $H = h$, and the level sets of $f(x, H) = (1/2)xH$, a family of hyperbolas having asymptotes $x = 0$ and $H = 0$. (See Figure 5.23, where the dashed asymptotes meet at (a, h) and the point of tangency is visibly $(x, H) = (2a, 2h)$.)

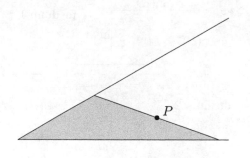

Figure 5.22. Solution of Euclid's least area problem

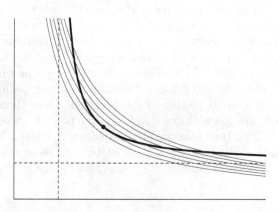

Figure 5.23. Level sets for Euclid's least area problem

An example from optics is Snell's law. A particle travels through medium 1 at speed v, and through medium 2 at speed w. If the particle travels from point A to point B as shown (Figure 5.24) in the least possible amount of time, what is the relation between angles α and β?

Because time is distance over speed, a little trigonometry shows that this problem is equivalent to minimizing $f(\alpha, \beta) = a \sec \alpha / v + b \sec \beta / w$ subject to the constraint $g(\alpha, \beta) = a \tan \alpha + b \tan \beta = d$ (g measures lateral distance traveled). The Lagrange condition $\nabla f(\alpha, \beta) = \lambda \nabla g(\alpha, \beta)$ is

$$\left(\frac{a}{v} \sin \alpha \sec^2 \alpha, \frac{b}{w} \sin \beta \sec^2 \beta \right) = \lambda (a \sec^2 \alpha, b \sec^2 \beta).$$

Therefore $\lambda = \sin \alpha / v = \sin \beta / w$, giving Snell's famous relation,

$$\frac{\sin \alpha}{\sin \beta} = \frac{v}{w}.$$

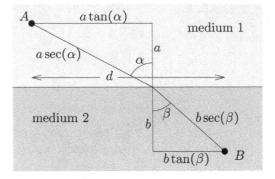

Figure 5.24. Geometry of Snell's law

Figure 5.25 depicts the situation using the variables $x = \tan \alpha$ and $y = \tan \beta$. The level set of possible configurations becomes the portion of the line $ax + by = d$ in the first quadrant, and the function to be optimized becomes $a\sqrt{1 + x^2}/v + b\sqrt{1 + y^2}/w$. A level set for a large value of the function passes through the point $(0, d/b)$, the configuration with $\alpha = 0$ in which the particle travels vertically in medium 1 and then travels a long path in medium 2, and a level set for a smaller value of the function passes through the point $(d/a, 0)$, the configuration with $\beta = 0$ in which the particle travels a long path in medium 1 and then travels vertically in medium 2, while a level set for an even smaller value of the function is tangent to the line segment at its point that describes the optimal configuration specified by Snell's law.

Figure 5.25. Level sets for the optics problem

For an example from analytic geometry, let the function f measure the square of the distance between the points $x = (x_1, x_2)$ and $y = (y_1, y_2)$ in the plane,

$$f(x_1, x_2, y_1, y_2) = (x_1 - y_1)^2 + (x_2 - y_2)^2.$$

Fix points $a = (a_1, a_2)$ and $b = (b_1, b_2)$ in the plane, and fix positive numbers r and s. Define

$$g_1(x_1, x_2) = (x_1 - a_1)^2 + (x_2 - a_2)^2 - r^2,$$
$$g_2(y_1, y_2) = (y_1 - b_1)^2 + (y_2 - b_2)^2 - s^2,$$
$$g(x_1, x_2, y_1, y_2) = (g_1(x_1, x_2), g_2(y_1, y_2)).$$

Then the set of four-tuples (x_1, x_2, y_1, y_2) such that

$$g(x_1, x_2, y_1, y_2) = (0, 0)$$

can be viewed as the set of pairs of points x and y that lie respectively on the circles centered at a and b with radii r and s. Thus, to optimize the function f subject to the constraint $g = \mathbf{0}$ is to optimize the distance between pairs of points on the circles. The rows of the 2×4 matrix

$$g'(x, y) = 2 \begin{bmatrix} x_1 - a_1 & x_2 - a_2 & 0 & 0 \\ 0 & 0 & y_1 - b_1 & y_2 - b_2 \end{bmatrix}$$

are linearly independent because $x \neq a$ and $y \neq b$. The Lagrange condition works out to

$$(x_1 - y_1, x_2 - y_2, y_1 - x_1, y_2 - x_2) = \lambda_1 (x_1 - a_1, x_2 - a_2, 0, 0)$$
$$- \lambda_2 (0, 0, y_1 - b_1, y_2 - b_2),$$

or

$$(x - y, y - x) = \lambda_1 (x - a, \mathbf{0}_2) - \lambda_2 (\mathbf{0}_2, y - b).$$

The second half of the vector on the left is the additive inverse of the first, so the condition can be rewritten as

$$x - y = \lambda_1 (x - a) = \lambda_2 (y - b).$$

If $\lambda_1 = 0$ or $\lambda_2 = 0$ then $x = y$ and both λ_i are 0. Otherwise, λ_1 and λ_2 are nonzero, forcing x and y to be distinct points such that

$$x - y \parallel x - a \parallel y - b,$$

and so the points x, y, a, and b are collinear. Granted, these results are obvious geometrically, but it is pleasing to see them follow so easily from the Lagrange multiplier condition. On the other hand, not all points x and y such that x, y, a, and b are collinear are solutions to the problem. For example, if both circles are bisected by the x-axis and neither circle sits inside the other, then x and y could be the leftmost points of the circles, neither the closest nor the farthest pair.

The last example of this section begins by maximizing the geometric mean of n nonnegative numbers,

$$f(x_1, \ldots, x_n) = (x_1 \cdots x_n)^{1/n}, \quad \text{each } x_i \geq 0,$$

subject to the constraint that their arithmetic mean is 1,

$$\frac{x_1 + \cdots + x_n}{n} = 1, \quad \text{each } x_i \geq 0.$$

The set of such $(x_1, \ldots, x_n)$-vectors is compact, being a closed subset of $[0, n]^n$. Since f is continuous on its domain $[0, \infty)^n$, it is continuous on the constrained set, and so it takes minimum and maximum values on the constrained set. At every constrained point set having some $x_i = 0$, the function-value $f = 0$ is the minimum. All other constrained points, having each $x_i > 0$, lie in the interior of the domain of f. The upshot is that we may assume that all x_i are positive and expect the Lagrange multiplier method to produce the maximum value of f among the values that it produces. Especially, if the Lagrange multiplier method produces only one value (as it will) then that value must be the maximum.

The constraining function is $g(x_1, \ldots, x_n) = (x_1 + \cdots + x_n)/n$, and the gradients of f and g are

$$\nabla f(x_1, \ldots, x_n) = \frac{f(x_1, \ldots, x_n)}{n} \left(\frac{1}{x_1}, \ldots, \frac{1}{x_n} \right),$$

$$\nabla g(x_1, \ldots, x_n) = \frac{1}{n}(1, \ldots, 1).$$

The Lagrange condition $\nabla f = \lambda \nabla g$ shows that all x_i are equal, and the constraint $g = 1$ forces their value to be 1. Therefore, the maximum value of the geometric mean when the arithmetic mean is 1 is the value

$$f(1, \ldots, 1) = (1 \cdots 1)^{1/n} = 1.$$

This Lagrange multiplier argument provides most of the proof of the following theorem.

Theorem 5.4.1 (Arithmetic–geometric mean inequality). *The geometric mean of n positive numbers is at most their arithmetic mean:*

$$(a_1 \cdots a_n)^{1/n} \leq \frac{a_1 + \cdots + a_n}{n} \qquad \textit{for all nonnegative } a_1, \ldots, a_n.$$

Proof. If any $a_i = 0$ then the inequality is clear. Given positive numbers $a_1, \ldots, a_n$, let $a = (a_1 + \cdots + a_n)/n$ and let $x_i = a_i/a$ for $i = 1, \ldots, n$. Then $(x_1 + \cdots + x_n)/n = 1$, and therefore

$$(a_1 \cdots a_n)^{1/n} = a(x_1 \cdots x_n)^{1/n} \leq a = \frac{a_1 + \cdots + a_n}{n}.$$

$\square$

Despite these pleasing examples, Lagrange multipliers are in general no computational panacea. Some problems of optimization with constraint are solved at least as easily by geometry or substitution. Nonetheless, Lagrange's method provides a unifying idea that addresses many different types of optimization problem without reference to geometry or physical considerations. In the following exercises, use whatever methods you find convenient.

Exercises

5.4.1. Find the nearest point to the origin on the intersection of the hyperplanes $x + y + z - 2w = 1$ and $x - y + z + w = 2$ in $\mathbb{R}^4$.

5.4.2. Find the nearest point on the ellipse $x^2 + 2y^2 = 1$ to the line $x + y = 4$.

5.4.3. Minimize $f(x, y, z) = z$ subject to the constraints $2x + 4y = 5$, $x^2 + z^2 = 2y$.

5.4.4. Maximize $f(x, y, z) = xy + yz$ subject to the constraints $x^2 + y^2 = 2$, $yz = 2$.

5.4.5. Find the extrema of $f(x, y, z) = xy + z$ subject to the constraints $x \geq 0$, $y \geq 0$, $xz + y = 4$, $yz + x = 4$.

5.4.6. Find the rectangular box of greatest volume, having sides parallel to the coordinate axes, that can be inscribed in the ellipsoid $\left(\frac{x}{a}\right)^2 + \left(\frac{y}{b}\right)^2 + \left(\frac{z}{c}\right)^2 = 1$.

5.4.7. The lengths of the twelve edges of a rectangular block sum to 4, and the areas of the six faces sum to 4α. Find the lengths of the edges when the excess of the block's volume over that of a cube with edge equal to the least edge of the block is greatest.

5.4.8. A cylindrical can (with top and bottom) has volume V. Subject to this constraint, what dimensions give it the least surface area?

5.4.9. Find the distance in the plane from the point $(0, 1)$ to the parabola $y = ax^2$ where $a > 0$. Note: the answer depends on whether $a > 1/2$ or $0 < a \leq 1/2$.

5.4.10. This exercise extends the arithmetic–geometric mean inequality. Let $e_1, \ldots, e_n$ be positive numbers with $\sum_{i=1}^{n} e_i = 1$. Maximize the function $f(x_1, \ldots, x_n) = x_1^{e_1} \cdots x_n^{e_n}$ (where each $x_i \geq 0$) subject to the constraint $\sum_{i=1}^{n} e_i x_i = 1$. Use your result to derive the weighted arithmetic–geometric mean inequality,

$$a_1^{e_1} \cdots a_n^{e_n} \leq e_1 a_1 + \cdots + e_n a_n \qquad \text{for all nonnegative } a_1, \ldots, a_n.$$

What values of the weights, $e_1, \ldots, e_n$ reduce this to the basic arithmetic–geometric mean inequality?

5.4.11. Let p and q be positive numbers satisfying the equation $\frac{1}{p} + \frac{1}{q} = 1$. Maximize the function of $2n$ variables $f(x_1, \ldots, x_n, y_1, \ldots, y_n) = \sum_{i=1}^{n} x_i y_i$ subject to the constraints $\sum_{i=1}^{n} x_i^p = 1$ and $\sum_{i=1}^{n} y_i^q = 1$. Derive **Hölder's inequality:** For all nonnegative $a_1, \ldots, a_n, b_1, \ldots, b_n$,

$$\sum_{i=1}^{n} a_i b_i \leq \left(\sum_{i=1}^{n} a_i^p \right)^{1/p} \left(\sum_{i=1}^{n} b_i^q \right)^{1/q}.$$

5.5 Lagrange Multipliers: Analytic Proof and General Examples

Recall that the environment for optimization with constraints consists of

- an open set $A \subset \mathbb{R}^n$,
- a constraining $\mathcal{C}^1$-mapping $g : A \longrightarrow \mathbb{R}^c$,
- the corresponding level set $L = \{v \in A : g(v) = \mathbf{0}_c\}$,
- and a $\mathcal{C}^1$-function $f : A \longrightarrow \mathbb{R}$ to optimize on L.

We have argued geometrically, and not fully rigorously, that if f on L is optimized at a point $p \in L$ then the gradient $f'(p)$ is orthogonal to L at p. Also, every linear combination of the gradients of the component functions of g is orthogonal to L at p. We want to assert the converse, that every vector that is orthogonal to L at p is such a linear combination. The desired converse assertion does not always hold, but if it does then it gives the Lagrange condition,

$$\nabla f(p) = \sum_{i=1}^{c} \lambda_i \nabla g_i(p).$$

Here is the rigorous analytic justification that the Lagrange multiplier method usually works. The implicit function theorem will do the heavy lifting, and it will reaffirm that the method is guaranteed only where the gradients of the component functions of g are linearly independent. The theorem makes the rigorous proof of the Lagrange criterion easier and more persuasive—at least in the author's opinion—than the heuristic argument given earlier.

Theorem 5.5.1 (Lagrange multiplier condition). *Let n and c be positive integers with $n > c$. Let $g : A \longrightarrow \mathbb{R}^c$ (where $A \subset \mathbb{R}^n$) be a mapping that is continuously differentiable at each interior point of A. Consider the level set*

$$L = \{x \in A : g(x) = \mathbf{0}_c\}.$$

Let $f : A \longrightarrow \mathbb{R}$ be a function. Suppose that the restriction of f to L has an extreme value at a point $p \in L$ that is an interior point of A. Suppose that f is differentiable at p, and suppose that the $c \times n$ derivative matrix $g'(p)$ contains a $c \times c$ block that is invertible. Then the following conditions hold:

$$\nabla f(p) = \lambda g'(p) \quad \textit{for some row vector } \lambda \in \mathbb{R}^c,$$
$$g(p) = \mathbf{0}_c.$$

The proof will culminate the ideas in this chapter as follows. The inverse function theorem says:

If the linearized inversion problem is solvable then the actual inversion problem is locally solvable.

The inverse function theorem is equivalent to the implicit function theorem:

If the linearized level set is a graph then the actual level set is locally a graph.

And finally, the idea for proving the Lagrange condition is:

Although the graph is a curved space, where the techniques of Chapter 4 do not apply, its domain is a straight space, where they do.

That is, the implicit function theorem lets us reduce optimization on the graph to optimization on the domain, which we know how to do.

Proof. The second condition holds since p is a point in L. The first condition needs to be proved. Let $r = n - c$, the number of variables that should remain free under the constraint $g(x) = \mathbf{0}_c$, and notate the point p as $p = (a, b)$, where $a \in \mathbb{R}^r$ and $b \in \mathbb{R}^c$. Using this notation, we have $g(a, b) = \mathbf{0}_c$ and $g'(a, b) = \begin{bmatrix} M & N \end{bmatrix}$ where M is $c \times r$ and N is $c \times c$ and invertible. (We may assume that N is the invertible block in the hypotheses to the theorem because we may freely permute the variables.) The implicit function theorem gives a mapping $\varphi : A_0 \longrightarrow \mathbb{R}^c$ (where $A_0 \subset \mathbb{R}^r$ and a is an interior point of A_0) with $\varphi(a) = b$, $\varphi'(a) = -N^{-1}M$, and for all points $(x, y) \in A$ near (a, b), $g(x, y) = \mathbf{0}_c$ if and only if $y = \varphi(x)$.

Make f depend only on the free variables by defining

$$f_0 = f \circ (\mathrm{id}_r, \varphi) : A_0 \longrightarrow \mathbb{R}, \quad f_0(x) = f(x, \varphi(x)).$$

(See Figure 5.26.) Since the domain of f_0 doesn't curve around in some larger space, f_0 is optimized by the techniques from Chapter 4. That is, the implicit function theorem has reduced optimization on the curved set to optimization in Euclidean space. Specifically, the multivariable critical point theorem says that f_0 has a critical point at a,

$$\nabla f_0(a) = \mathbf{0}_r.$$

Our task is to express the previous display in terms of the given data f and g. Doing so will produce the Lagrange condition.

Because $f_0 = f \circ (\mathrm{id}_r, \varphi)$ is a composition, the chain rule says that the condition $\nabla f_0(a) = \mathbf{0}_r$ is $\nabla f(a, \varphi(a)) \cdot (\mathrm{id}_r, \varphi)'(a) = \mathbf{0}_r$, or

$$\nabla f(a, b) \begin{bmatrix} I_r \\ \varphi'(a) \end{bmatrix} = \mathbf{0}_r.$$

Let $\nabla f(a,b) = (u,v)$ where $u \in \mathbb{R}^r$ and $v \in \mathbb{R}^c$ are row vectors, and recall that $\varphi'(a) = -N^{-1}M$. The previous display becomes

$$[u \; v]\begin{bmatrix} I_r \\ -N^{-1}M \end{bmatrix} = \mathbf{0}_r,$$

giving $u = vN^{-1}M$. This expression for u and the trivial identity $v = vN^{-1}N$ combine to give in turn

$$[u \; v] = vN^{-1}[M \; N].$$

But $[u \; v] = \nabla f(a,b)$ and $[M \; N] = g'(a,b)$ and $(a,b) = p$. So set $\lambda = vN^{-1}$ (a row vector in $\mathbb{R}^c$), and the previous display is precisely Lagrange's condition,

$$\nabla f(p) = \lambda g'(p).$$

$\square$

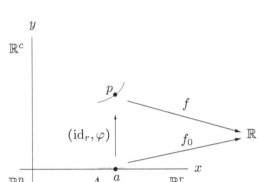

Figure 5.26. The Lagrange multiplier criterion from the implicit function theorem

We have seen that the Lagrange multiplier condition is necessary but not sufficient for an extreme value. That is, it can report a false positive, as in the two-circle problem in the previous section. False positives are not a serious problem, since inspecting all the points that meet the Lagrange condition will determine which of them give the true extrema of f. A false negative would be a worse situation, giving us no indication that an extreme value might exist, much less how to find it. The following example shows that the false negative scenario can arise without the invertible $c \times c$ block required in Theorem 5.5.1.

Let the temperature in the plane be given by

$$f(x,y) = x,$$

and consider a plane set defined by one constraint on two variables,

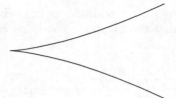

Figure 5.27. Curve with cusp

$$L = \{(x, y) \in \mathbb{R}^2 : y^2 = x^3\}.$$

(See Figure 5.27.) Since temperature increases as we move to the right, the coldest point of L is its leftmost point, the cusp at $(0,0)$. However, the Lagrange condition does not find this point. Indeed, the constraining function is $g(x,y) = x^3 - y^2$ (which does have continuous derivatives, notwithstanding that its level set has a cusp: the graph of a smooth function is smooth, but the level set of a smooth function need not be smooth—this is exactly the issue addressed by the implicit function theorem). Therefore the Lagrange condition and the constraint are

$$(1,0) = \lambda(3x^2, -2y),$$
$$x^3 = y^2.$$

These equations have no solution. The problem is that the gradient at the cusp is $\nabla g(0,0) = (0,0)$, and neither of its 1×1 subblocks is invertible. In general, the Lagrange multiplier condition will not report a false negative as long as we remember that it only claims to check for extrema at the *nonsingular* points of L, the points p such that $g'(p)$ has an invertible $c \times c$ subblock.

The previous section gave specific examples of the Lagrange multiplier method. This section now gives some general families of examples.

Recall that the previous section discussed the problem of optimizing the distance between two points in the plane, each point lying on an associated circle. Now, as the first general example of the Lagrange multiplier method, let $(x,y) \in \mathbb{R}^n \times \mathbb{R}^n$ denote a pair of points each from $\mathbb{R}^n$, and let the function f measure the square of the distance between such a pair,

$$f : \mathbb{R}^n \times \mathbb{R}^n \longrightarrow \mathbb{R}, \qquad f(x,y) = |x - y|^2.$$

Note that $\nabla f(x,y) = [x - y \; y - x]$, viewing x and y as row vectors. Given two mappings $g_1 : \mathbb{R}^n \longrightarrow \mathbb{R}^{c_1}$ and $g_2 : \mathbb{R}^n \longrightarrow \mathbb{R}^{c_2}$, define

$$g : \mathbb{R}^n \times \mathbb{R}^n \longrightarrow \mathbb{R}^{c_1 + c_2}, \qquad g(x,y) = (g_1(x), g_2(y)).$$

To optimize the function f subject to the constraint $g(x,y) = (\mathbf{0}_{c_1}, \mathbf{0}_{c_2})$ is to optimize the distance between pairs of points x and y on the respective level sets cut out of $\mathbb{R}^n$ by the c_1 conditions $g_1(x) = \mathbf{0}_{c_1}$ and the c_2 conditions $g_2(y) = \mathbf{0}_{c_2}$. Assuming that the Lagrange condition holds for the optimizing pair, it is

$$[x - y \; y - x] = \lambda g'(x, y) = \begin{bmatrix} \lambda_1 & -\lambda_2 \end{bmatrix} \begin{bmatrix} g_1'(x) & \mathbf{0}_{c_2 \times n} \\ \mathbf{0}_{c_1 \times n} & g_2'(y) \end{bmatrix}$$

$$= \lambda_1(g_1'(x), \mathbf{0}_{c_2 \times n}) - \lambda_2(\mathbf{0}_{c_1 \times n}, g_2'(y)),$$

where $\lambda_1 \in \mathbb{R}^{c_1}$ and $\lambda_2 \in \mathbb{R}^{c_2}$ are row vectors. The symmetry of ∇f reduces this equality of $2n$-vectors to an equality of n-vectors,

$$x - y = \lambda_1 g_1'(x) = \lambda_2 g_2'(y).$$

That is, either $x = y$ or the line through x and y is normal to the first level set at x and normal to the second level set at y, generalizing the result from the two-circle problem. With this result in mind, you may want to revisit Exercise 0.0.1 from the preface to these notes.

The remaining general Lagrange multiplier methods optimize a linear function or a quadratic function subject to affine constraints or a quadratic constraint. We gather the results in one theorem.

Theorem 5.5.2 (Low-degree optimization with constraints).

(1) *Let* $f(x) = a^\mathsf{T} x$ *(where* $a \in \mathbb{R}^n$*) subject to the constraint* $Mx = b$ *(where* $M \in \mathrm{M}_{c,n}(\mathbb{R})$ *has linearly independent rows, with* $c < n$, *and* $b \in \mathbb{R}^c$*). Check whether* $a^\mathsf{T} M^\mathsf{T} (MM^\mathsf{T})^{-1} M = a^\mathsf{T}$. *If so, then* f *subject to the constraint is identically* $a^\mathsf{T} M^\mathsf{T} (MM^\mathsf{T})^{-1} b$; *otherwise,* f *subject to the constraint has no optima.*

(2) *Let* $f(x) = x^\mathsf{T} A x$ *(where* $A \in \mathrm{M}_n(\mathbb{R})$ *is symmetric and invertible) subject to the constraint* $Mx = b$ *(where* $M \in \mathrm{M}_{c,n}(\mathbb{R})$ *has linearly independent rows, with* $c < n$, *and* $b \in \mathbb{R}^c$*). The* x *that optimizes* f *subject to the constraint and the optimal value are*

$$x = A^{-1} M^\mathsf{T} (MA^{-1}M^\mathsf{T})^{-1} b \quad and \quad f(x) = b^\mathsf{T} (MA^{-1}M^\mathsf{T})^{-1} b.$$

Especially when $A = I$, *the point* x *such that* $Mx = b$ *closest to the origin and its square distance from the origin are*

$$x = M^\mathsf{T} (MM^\mathsf{T})^{-1} b \quad and \quad |x|^2 = b^\mathsf{T} (MM^\mathsf{T})^{-1} b.$$

(3) *Let* $f(x) = a^\mathsf{T} x$ *(where* $a \in \mathbb{R}^n$*) subject to the constraint* $x^\mathsf{T} M x = b$ *(where* $M \in \mathrm{M}_n(\mathbb{R})$ *is symmetric and invertible, and* $b \in \mathbb{R}$ *is nonzero). Check whether* $a^\mathsf{T} M^{-1} a b > 0$. *If so, then the optimizing inputs and the optimal values are*

$$x = \pm M^{-1} a b / \sqrt{a^\mathsf{T} M^{-1} a b} \quad and \quad f(x) = \pm \sqrt{a^\mathsf{T} M^{-1} a b}.$$

Otherwise, f *subject to the constraint has no optima.*

(4) *Let $f(x) = x^T A x$ (where $A \in M_n(\mathbb{R})$ is symmetric) subject to the constraint $x^T M x = b$ (where $M \in M_n(\mathbb{R})$ is symmetric and invertible, and $b \in \mathbb{R}$ is nonzero). The possible optimal values of f subject to the constraint are*

$$f(x) = \lambda b \quad \text{where } \lambda \text{ is an eigenvalue of } M^{-1}A.$$

(The term "eigenvalue" will be explained in the proof.) Especially when $A = I$, the nearest square-distances from the origin on the quadratic surface $x^T M x = b$ take the form λb where λ is an eigenvalue of M^{-1}.

Proof. (1) The data are (viewing vectors as columns)

$$f : \mathbb{R}^n \longrightarrow \mathbb{R}, \quad f(x) = a^T x \quad \text{where } a \in \mathbb{R}^n,$$
$$g : \mathbb{R}^n \longrightarrow \mathbb{R}^c, \quad g(x) = Mx - b \text{ where } M \in M_{c,n}(\mathbb{R}) \text{ and } b \in \mathbb{R}^c.$$

Here we assume that $c < n$, i.e., there are fewer constraints than variables. Also, we assume that the c rows of M are linearly independent in $\mathbb{R}^n$, or equivalently (invoking a result from linear algebra), that some c columns of M are a basis of $\mathbb{R}^c$, or equivalently, that some $c \times c$ subblock of M (not necessarily contiguous columns) has nonzero determinant. The Lagrange condition and the constraints are

$$a^T = \lambda^T M \quad \text{where } \lambda \in \mathbb{R}^c,$$
$$Mx = b.$$

Before solving the problem, we need to consider the two relations in the previous display.

- The Lagrange condition $a^T = \lambda^T M$ is solvable for λ exactly when a^T is a linear combination of the rows of M. Since M has c rows, each of which is a vector in $\mathbb{R}^n$, and since $c < n$, generally a^T is not a linear combination of the rows of M, so the Lagrange conditions cannot be satisfied. That is:
  Generally the constrained function has no optimum.
  However, we will study the exceptional case, that a^T is a linear combination of the rows of M. In this case, the linear combination of the rows that gives a^T is unique because the rows are linearly independent. That is, if λ exists then it is uniquely determined.
  To find the only candidate λ, note that the Lagrange condition $a^T = \lambda^T M$ gives $a^T M^T = \lambda^T M M^T$, and thus $\lambda^T = a^T M^T (M M^T)^{-1}$. This calculation's first step is not reversible, and so the calculation does not always show that λ exists. But it does show that to check whether a^T is a linear combination of the rows of M, one checks whether $a^T M^T (M M^T)^{-1} M = a^T$, in which case $\lambda^T = a^T M^T (M M^T)^{-1}$.
  Note that furthermore, the Lagrange condition $a^T = \lambda^T M$ makes no reference to x.
- The constraining condition $Mx = b$ has solutions x only if b is a linear combination of the columns of M. Our assumptions about M guarantee that this is the case.

With a^T being a linear combination of the rows of M and with b being a linear combination of the columns of M, the Lagrange condition and the constraints immediately show that for every x in the constrained set,

$$f(x) = a^\mathsf{T} x = \lambda^\mathsf{T} M x = \lambda^\mathsf{T} b = a^\mathsf{T} M^\mathsf{T} (MM^\mathsf{T})^{-1} b.$$

That is, f subject to the constraint $g = b$ is the constant $= a^\mathsf{T} M^\mathsf{T} (MM^\mathsf{T})^{-1} b$.

For geometric insight into the calculation, envision the space of linear combinations of the rows of M (a c-dimensional subspace of $\mathbb{R}^n$) as a plane, and envision the space of vectors $\tilde{x}$ such that $M\tilde{x} = \mathbf{0}_c$ (an $(n-c)$-dimensional subspace of $\mathbb{R}^n$) as an axis orthogonal to the plane. The condition $a^\mathsf{T} = \lambda^\mathsf{T} M$ says that a lies in the plane, and the condition $Mx = b$ says that x lies on an axis parallel to the $\tilde{x}$-axis. (From linear algebra, the solutions of $Mx = b$ are the vectors

$$x = x_0 + \tilde{x},$$

where x_0 is the unique linear combination of the rows of M such that $Mx_0 = b$, and $\tilde{x}$ is any vector such that $M\tilde{x} = \mathbf{0}_c$.) The constant value of f is $a^\mathsf{T} x$ for every x on the axis. In particular, the value is $a^\mathsf{T} x_0$ where x_0 is the point where the axis meets the plane.

(2) Now we optimize a quadratic function subject to affine constraints. Here the data are

$$f : \mathbb{R}^n \longrightarrow \mathbb{R}, \quad f(x) = x^\mathsf{T} A x \quad \text{where } A \in \mathrm{M}_n(\mathbb{R}) \text{ is symmetric,}$$
$$g : \mathbb{R}^n \longrightarrow \mathbb{R}^c, \quad g(x) = Mx - b \text{ where } M \in \mathrm{M}_{c,n}(\mathbb{R}) \text{ and } b \in \mathbb{R}^c.$$

As in (1), we assume that $c < n$, and we assume that the c rows of M are linearly independent in $\mathbb{R}^n$, i.e., some c columns of M are a basis of $\mathbb{R}^c$, i.e., some $c \times c$ subblock of M has nonzero determinant. Thus the constraints $Mx = b$ have solutions x for every $b \in \mathbb{R}^c$.

To set up the Lagrange condition, we need to differentiate the quadratic function f. Compute that

$$f(x+h) - f(x) = (x+h)^\mathsf{T} A(x+h) - x^\mathsf{T} A x = 2x^\mathsf{T} A h + h^\mathsf{T} A h,$$

and so the best linear approximation of this difference is $T(h) = 2x^\mathsf{T} A h$. It follows that

$$\nabla f(x) = 2x^\mathsf{T} A.$$

Returning to the optimization problem, the Lagrange condition and the constraints are

$$x^\mathsf{T} A = \lambda^\mathsf{T} M \quad \text{where } \lambda \in \mathbb{R}^c,$$
$$Mx = b.$$

Having solved a particular problem of this sort in Section 5.4, we use its particular solution to guide our solution of the general problem. The first step was to express x in terms of λ, so here we transpose the Lagrange condition to get $Ax = M^{\mathsf{T}}\lambda$, then assume that A is invertible and thus get $x = A^{-1}M^{\mathsf{T}}\lambda$. The second step was to write the constraint in terms of λ and then solve for λ, so here we have $b = Mx = MA^{-1}M^{\mathsf{T}}\lambda$, so that $\lambda = (MA^{-1}M^{\mathsf{T}})^{-1}b$, assuming that the $c \times c$ matrix $MA^{-1}M^{\mathsf{T}}$ is invertible. Now the optimizing input $x = A^{-1}M^{\mathsf{T}}\lambda$ is

$$x = A^{-1}M^{\mathsf{T}}(MA^{-1}M^{\mathsf{T}})^{-1}b,$$

and the optimal function value $f(x) = x^{\mathsf{T}}Ax = \lambda^{\mathsf{T}}Mx = \lambda^{\mathsf{T}}b$ is

$$f(x) = b^{\mathsf{T}}(MA^{-1}M^{\mathsf{T}})^{-1}b.$$

In particular, letting $A = I$, the closest point x to the origin such that $Mx = b$ and the square of its distance from the origin are

$$x = M^{\mathsf{T}}(MM^{\mathsf{T}})^{-1}b, \qquad |x|^2 = b^{\mathsf{T}}(MM^{\mathsf{T}})^{-1}b.$$

(3) Next we optimize a linear function subject to a quadratic constraint. The data are

$$f : \mathbb{R}^n \longrightarrow \mathbb{R}, \quad f(x) = a^{\mathsf{T}}x \qquad \text{where } a \in \mathbb{R}^n,$$

$$g : \mathbb{R}^n \longrightarrow \mathbb{R}, \quad g(x) = x^{\mathsf{T}}Mx - b \ \text{ where } \begin{cases} M \in \mathrm{M}_n(\mathbb{R}) \text{ is symmetric,} \\ b \in \mathbb{R} \text{ is nonzero.} \end{cases}$$

The Lagrange condition and the constraint are

$$a^{\mathsf{T}} = \lambda x^{\mathsf{T}}M \quad \text{where } \lambda \in \mathbb{R},$$
$$x^{\mathsf{T}}Mx = b.$$

Therefore the possible optimized values of f are

$$f(x) = a^{\mathsf{T}}x = \lambda x^{\mathsf{T}}Mx = \lambda b,$$

and so to find these values it suffices to find the possible values of λ. Assuming that M is invertible, the Lagrange condition is $a^{\mathsf{T}}M^{-1} = \lambda x^{\mathsf{T}}$, and hence

$$a^{\mathsf{T}}M^{-1}ab = \lambda x^{\mathsf{T}}ab = \lambda^2 b^2 = f(x)^2.$$

Thus (assuming that $a^{\mathsf{T}}M^{-1}ab > 0$) the optimal values are

$$f(x) = \pm\sqrt{a^{\mathsf{T}}M^{-1}ab}.$$

The penultimate display also shows that $\lambda = \pm\sqrt{a^{\mathsf{T}}M^{-1}ab}/b$, so that the Lagrange condition gives the optimizing x-values,

$$x = \pm M^{-1}ab/\sqrt{a^{\mathsf{T}}M^{-1}ab}.$$

One readily confirms that indeed $x^\mathsf{T} M x = b$ for these x.

As a small geometric illustration of the sign-issues in this context, suppose that $n = 2$ and $M = \left[\begin{smallmatrix} 0 & 1 \\ 1 & 0 \end{smallmatrix}\right]$, so that the quadratic constraint is $2x_1 x_2 = b$. For $b > 0$ the optimizing problem is thus set on a hyperbola in the first and third quadrants of the plane. The function to be optimized is $f(x, y) = a_1 x_1 + a_2 x_2$ for some $a_1, a_2 \in \mathbb{R}$. Since M is its own inverse, the quantity $a^\mathsf{T} M^{-1} a b$ under the square root is $2a_1 a_2 b$, and thus the constrained optimization problem has solutions only when $a_1 a_2 > 0$. Meanwhile, the level sets of f are lines of slope $-a_1/a_2$, meaning that the problem has solutions only when the level sets have negative slope. In that case, the solutions will be at the two points where the hyperbola is tangent to a level set: a pair of opposite points, one in the first quadrant and one in the third. For $b < 0$ the constraining hyperbola moves to the second and fourth quadrants, and the problem has solutions when the level sets of f have a positive slope.

(4) Finally, we optimize a quadratic function subject to a quadratic constraint. The data are

$$f : \mathbb{R}^n \longrightarrow \mathbb{R}, \quad f(x) = x^\mathsf{T} A x \qquad \text{where } A \in \mathrm{M}_n(\mathbb{R}) \text{ is symmetric,}$$

$$g : \mathbb{R}^n \longrightarrow \mathbb{R}, \quad g(x) = x^\mathsf{T} M x - b \ \text{ where } \begin{cases} M \in \mathrm{M}_n(\mathbb{R}) \text{ is symmetric,} \\ b \in \mathbb{R} \text{ is nonzero.} \end{cases}$$

The Lagrange condition and the constraint are

$$x^\mathsf{T} A = \lambda x^\mathsf{T} M \quad \text{where } \lambda \in \mathbb{R},$$
$$x^\mathsf{T} M x = b.$$

By the Lagrange condition and the constraint, the possible optimal values of f take the form

$$f(x) = x^\mathsf{T} A x = \lambda x^\mathsf{T} M x = \lambda b,$$

which we will know as soon as we find the possible values of λ, without needing to find x. Assuming that M is invertible, the Lagrange condition gives

$$M^{-1} A x = \lambda x.$$

In other words, x must satisfy the condition that *multiplying x by $M^{-1} A$ gives a scalar multiple of x*. Every nonzero vector x that satisfies this condition is called an *eigenvector* of $M^{-1} A$. The scalar multiple factor λ is the corresponding *eigenvalue*. We will end the section with a brief discussion of eigenvalues.

□

The eigenvalues of a square matrix B are found by a systematic procedure. The first step is to observe that the condition $Bx = \lambda x$ is

$$(B - \lambda I)x = \mathbf{0}.$$

Since every eigenvector x is nonzero by definition, $B - \lambda I$ is not invertible, i.e.,

$$\det(B - \lambda I) = 0.$$

Conversely, for every $\lambda \in \mathbb{R}$ satisfying this equation there is at least one eigenvector x of B, because the equation $(B - \lambda I)x = \mathbf{0}$ has nonzero solutions. And so the eigenvalues are the real roots of the polynomial

$$p_B(\lambda) = \det(B - \lambda I).$$

This polynomial is the *characteristic polynomial of* B, already discussed in Exercise 4.7.10. For example, part (a) of that exercise covered the case $n = 2$, showing that if $B = \left[\begin{smallmatrix} a & b \\ b & d \end{smallmatrix}\right]$ then

$$p_B(\lambda) = \lambda^2 - (a + d)\lambda + (ad - b^2).$$

The discriminant of this quadratic polynomial is

$$\Delta = (a + d)^2 - 4(ad - b^2) = (a - d)^2 + 4b^2.$$

Since Δ is nonnegative, all roots of the characteristic polynomial are real. And a result of linear algebra says that for every positive n, all roots of the characteristic polynomial of a symmetric $n \times n$ matrix B are real as well. However, returning to our example, even though the square matrices A and M are assumed to be symmetric, the product $M^{-1}A$ need not be.

As a particular case of Theorem 5.5.2, part (4), if $A = I$ then finding the eigenvectors of M encompasses finding the points of a quadric surface that are closest to the origin or farthest from the origin. For instance, if $n = 2$ and $M = \left[\begin{smallmatrix} a & b \\ b & d \end{smallmatrix}\right]$ then we are optimizing on the set of points $(x_1, x_2) \in \mathbb{R}^2$ such that, say,

$$ax_1^2 + 2bx_1x_2 + dx_2^2 = 1.$$

The displayed equation is the equation of a conic section. When $b = 0$ we have an unrotated ellipse or hyperbola, and the only possible optimal points will be the scalar multiples of e_1 and e_2 that lie on the curve. For an ellipse, a pair of points on one axis is closest to the origin, and a pair on the other axis is farthest; for a hyperbola, a pair on one axis is closest, and there are no points on the other axis. In the case of a circle, the matrix M is a scalar multiple of the identity matrix, and so all vectors are eigenvectors, compatibly with the geometry that all points are equidistant from the origin. Similarly, if $n = 3$ then L is a surface such as an ellipsoid or a hyperboloid.

Exercises

5.5.1. Let $f(x, y) = y$ and let $g(x, y) = y^3 - x^4$. Graph the level set $L = \{(x, y) : g(x, y) = 0\}$. Show that the Lagrange multiplier criterion does not find any candidate points where f is optimized on L. Optimize f on L nonetheless.

5.5.2. Consider the linear mapping

$$g(x, y, z) = (x + 2y + 3z, 4x + 5y + 6z).$$

(a) Use Theorem 5.5.2, part (1), to optimize the linear function $f(x, y, z) = 6x + 9y + 12z$ subject to the affine constraint $g(x, y, z) = (7, 8)$.

(b) Verify without using the Lagrange multiplier method that the function f subject to the constraint $g = (7, 8)$ (with f and g from part (a)) is constant, always taking the value that you found in part (a).

(c) Show that the function $f(x, y, z) = 5x + 7y + z$ cannot be optimized subject to any constraint $g(x, y, z) = b$.

5.5.3. (a) Use Theorem 5.5.2, part (2), to minimize the quadratic function $f(x, y) = x^2 + y^2$ subject to the affine constraint $3x + 5y = 8$.

(b) Use the same result to find the extrema of $f(x, y, z) = 2xy + z^2$ subject to the constraints $x + y + z = 1$, $x + y - z = 0$.

(c) Use the same result to find the nearest point to the origin on the intersection of the hyperplanes $x + y + z - 2w = 1$ and $x - y + z + w = 2$ in $\mathbb{R}^4$, reproducing your answer to Exercise 5.4.1.

5.5.4. (a) Use Theorem 5.5.2, part (3), to optimize $f(x, y, z) = x - 2y + 2z$ on the sphere of radius 3 centered at the origin.

(b) Use the same result to optimize the function $f(x, y, z, w) = x + y - z - w$ subject to the constraint $g(x, y, z, w) = 1$, $g(x, y, z, w) = x^2/2 - y^2 + z^2 - w^2$.

5.5.5. (a) Use Theorem 5.5.2, part (4), to optimize the function $f(x, y) = 2xy$ subject to the constraint $g(x, y) = 1$ where $g(x, y) = x^2 + 2y^2$.

(b) Use the same result to optimize the function $f(x, y, z) = 2(xy + yz + zx)$ subject to the constraint $g(x, y, z) = 1$ where $g(x, y, z) = x^2 + y^2 - z^2$.

Part II

Multivariable Integral Calculus

6

Integration

The integral of a scalar-valued function of many variables, taken over a box
of its inputs, is defined in Sections 6.1 and 6.2. Intuitively, the integral can
be understood as representing mass or volume, but the definition is purely
mathematical: the integral is a limit of sums, as in one-variable calculus.
Multivariable integration has many familiar properties—for example, the integral of a sum is the sum of the integrals. Section 6.3 shows that continuous
functions can be integrated over boxes. However, we want to carry out multivariable integration over more generally shaped regions. That is, the theory
has geometric aspects not present in the one-dimensional case, where integration is carried out over intervals. After a quick review of the one-variable
theory in Section 6.4, Section 6.5 shows that continuous functions can also be
integrated over nonboxes that have manageable shapes. The main tools for
evaluating multivariable integrals are Fubini's theorem (Section 6.6), which
reduces an n-dimensional integral to an n-fold nesting of one-dimensional integrals, and the change of variable theorem (Section 6.7), which replaces one
multivariable integral by another that may be easier to evaluate. Section 6.8
provides some preliminaries for the proof of the change of variable theorem,
and then Section 6.9 gives the proof.

6.1 Machinery: Boxes, Partitions, and Sums

The integral represents physical ideas such as volume or mass or work, but
defining it properly in purely mathematical terms requires some care. Here is
some terminology that is standard from the calculus of one variable, except
perhaps *compact* (meaning *closed and bounded*) from Section 2.4 of these
notes. The language describes a domain of integration and the machinery to
subdivide it.

Definition 6.1.1 (Compact interval, length, partition, subinterval).
A **nonempty compact interval** *in* $\mathbb{R}$ *is a set*

© Springer International Publishing AG 2016   253
J. Shurman, *Calculus and Analysis in Euclidean Space*,
Undergraduate Texts in Mathematics, DOI 10.1007/978-3-319-49314-5_6

$$I = [a, b] = \{x \in \mathbb{R} : a \le x \le b\},$$

where a and b are real numbers with a ≤ b. The **length** *of the interval is*

$$\text{length}(I) = b - a.$$

A **partition** *of I is a set of real numbers*

$$P = \{t_0, t_1, \dots, t_k\}$$

satisfying

$$a = t_0 < t_1 < \cdots < t_k = b.$$

Such a partition divides I into k **subintervals** $J_1, \dots, J_k$ *where*

$$J_j = [t_{j-1}, t_j], \quad j = 1, \dots, k.$$

A generic nonempty compact subinterval of I is denoted J. (See Figure 6.1.) Since the only intervals that we are interested in are nonempty and compact, either or both of these properties will often be tacit from now on, rather than stated again and again. As a special case, Definition 6.1.1 says that every length-zero interval $[a, a]$ has only one partition, $P = \{a\}$, which divides it into no subintervals.

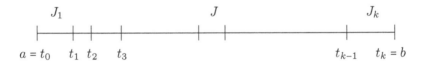

Figure 6.1. Interval and subintervals

The next definition puts an initial loose stipulation on functions to be integrated.

Definition 6.1.2 (Bounded function). *Let A be a subset of* $\mathbb{R}$*, and let* $f : A \longrightarrow \mathbb{R}$ *be a function. Then f is* **bounded** *if its range,* $\{f(x) : x \in A\}$*, is bounded as a set in* $\mathbb{R}$*, as in Definition 2.4.6. That is, f is bounded if there exists some R > 0 such that* $|f(x)| < R$ *for all* $x \in A$*.*

Visually, a function is bounded if its graph is contained inside a horizontal strip. On the other hand, the graph of a bounded function needn't be contained in a vertical strip, because the domain (and therefore the graph) need not be bounded. For example, these functions are bounded:

$$f(x) = \sin x, \qquad f(x) = 1/(1 + x^2), \qquad f(x) = \arctan x,$$

and these functions are not:

$$f(x) = e^x, \qquad f(x) = 1/x \text{ for } x \neq 0.$$

However, since we want to integrate a bounded function over a compact interval, the entire process is set inside a rectangle in the plane.

The next definition describes approximations of the integral by finite sums, the integral to be a limit of such sums if it exists at all. The summands involve limits, so already these sums are analytic constructs despite being finite.

Definition 6.1.3 (One-dimensional lower sum and upper sum). *Let I be a nonempty compact interval in* $\mathbb{R}$, *and let* $f : I \longrightarrow \mathbb{R}$ *be a bounded function. For every nonempty subinterval J of I, the greatest lower bound of the values taken by f on J is denoted* $m_J(f)$,

$$m_J(f) = \inf \{f(x) : x \in J\},$$

and similarly, the least upper bound is denoted $M_J(f)$,

$$M_J(f) = \sup \{f(x) : x \in J\}.$$

Let P be a partition of I into subintervals J. The **lower sum** *of f over P is*

$$L(f,P) = \sum_J m_J(f) \operatorname{length}(J),$$

and the **upper sum** *of f over P is*

$$U(f,P) = \sum_J M_J(f) \operatorname{length}(J).$$

If the interval I in Definition 6.1.3 has length zero, then the lower and upper sums are empty, and so they are assigned the value 0 by convention.

The function f in Definition 6.1.3 is not required to be differentiable or even continuous, only bounded. Even so, the values $m_J(f)$ and $M_J(f)$ in the previous definition exist by the set-bound phrasing of the principle that the real number system is complete. To review this idea, see Theorem 1.1.3. When f is in fact continuous, the extreme value theorem (Theorem 2.4.15) justifies substituting *min* and *max* for *inf* and *sup* in the definitions of $m_J(f)$ and $M_J(f)$, since each subinterval J is nonempty and compact. It may be easiest at first to understand $m_J(f)$ and $M_J(f)$ by imagining f to be continuous and mentally substituting appropriately. But we will need to integrate discontinuous functions f. Such functions may take no minimum or maximum on J, and so we may run into a situation like the one pictured in Figure 6.2, in which the values $m_J(f)$ and $M_J(f)$ are not actual outputs of f. Thus the definition must be as given to make sense.

The technical properties of inf and sup will figure in Lemmas 6.1.6, 6.1.8, and 6.2.2. To see them in isolation first, we rehearse them now. So, let S

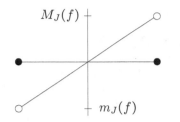

Figure 6.2. Sup and inf but no max or min

and T be nonempty sets of real numbers, both bounded. In the context of integration, S and T will be sets of outputs of a bounded function f. This specific description of S and T is irrelevant for the moment, but it may help you to see later how these ideas are used in context if you now imagine S and T on a vertical axis, as in Figure 6.2, rather than on a horizontal one. In any case, the necessary results are as follows.

- $\inf(S) \leq \sup(S)$. In fact *every* lower bound of S is at most as big as *every* upper bound, because every element of S lies between them. In particular, this argument applies to the greatest lower bound $\inf(S)$ and the least upper bound $\sup(S)$, giving the stated inequality.

- If $S \subset T$ then $\inf(T) \leq \inf(S) \leq \sup(S) \leq \sup(T)$. We already have the middle inequality. To establish the others, the idea is that since S is a subset, the bounds on S are innately at least as tight as those on T. More specifically, since $\inf(T)$ is a lower bound of T, it is a lower bound of the subset S, and because $\inf(S)$ is the *greatest* lower bound of S, the first inequality follows. The third inequality is similar.

  In particular, let I be a compact interval, let $f : I \longrightarrow \mathbb{R}$ be a bounded function, let J be a subinterval of I, let J' be a subinterval of J in turn, and then take S and T to be sets of output-values of f,

  $$S = \{f(x) : x \in J'\}, \qquad T = \{f(x) : x \in J\}.$$

  Then $S \subset T$ because S is a set of fewer outputs than T, and so this bullet has shown that

  $$m_J(f) \leq m_{J'}(f) \leq M_{J'}(f) \leq M_J(f).$$

- If $s \leq t$ for all $s \in S$ and $t \in T$ then $\sup(S) \leq \inf(T)$. Imprecisely, the idea is that S is entirely below T on the vertical axis, and so the smallest number that traps S from above is still below the largest number that traps T from below. A more careful proof is in the next section.

Graphing f over I in the usual fashion and interpreting the lower and upper sum as sums of rectangle-areas shows that they are respectively too small and too big to be the area under the graph. (See Figure 6.3.) Alternatively,

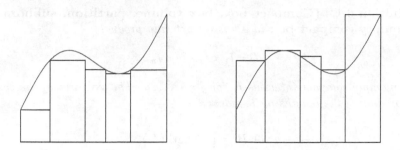

Figure 6.3. Too small and too big

thinking of f as the density function of a wire stretched over the interval I shows that the lower and upper sums are too small and too big to be the mass of the wire. The hope is that the lower and upper sums are trapping a yet-unknown quantity (possibly to be imagined as area or mass) from each side, and that as the partition P becomes finer, the lower and upper sums will actually converge to this value.

All the terminology so far generalizes easily from one dimension to many, i.e., from $\mathbb{R}$ to $\mathbb{R}^n$. Recall that if S_1, S_2, ..., S_n are subsets of $\mathbb{R}$ then their **Cartesian product** is a subset of $\mathbb{R}^n$,

$$S_1 \times S_2 \times \cdots \times S_n = \{(s_1, s_2, \ldots, s_n) : s_1 \in S_1, s_2 \in S_2, \ldots, s_n \in S_n\}.$$

(See Figure 6.4, in which $n = 2$, and S_1 has two components, and S_2 has one component, so that the Cartesian product $S_1 \times S_2$ has two components.)

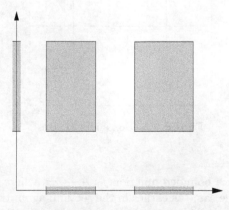

Figure 6.4. Cartesian product

Definition 6.1.4 (Compact box, box volume, partition, subbox). *A* **nonempty compact box** *in* $\mathbb{R}^n$ *is a Cartesian product*

$$B = I_1 \times I_2 \times \cdots \times I_n$$

of nonempty compact intervals I_j *for* $j = 1, \ldots, n$. *The* **volume** *of the box is the product of the lengths of its sides,*

$$\mathrm{vol}(B) = \prod_{j=1}^{n} \mathrm{length}(I_j).$$

A **partition** *of* B *is a Cartesian product of partitions* P_j *of* I_j *for* $j = 1, \ldots, n$,

$$P = P_1 \times P_2 \times \cdots \times P_n.$$

Such a partition divides B *into* **subboxes** J, *each such subbox being a Cartesian product of subintervals. By a slight abuse of language, these are called the* **subboxes of** P.

(See Figure 6.5, and imagine its three-dimensional Rubik's cube counterpart.) Every nonempty compact box in $\mathbb{R}^n$ has partitions, even such boxes with some length-zero sides. This point will arise at the very beginning of the next section.

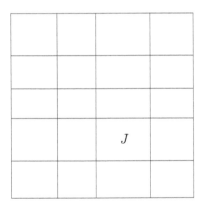

Figure 6.5. Box and subboxes

The definition of a bounded function $f : A \longrightarrow \mathbb{R}$, where now A is a subset of $\mathbb{R}^n$, is virtually the same as earlier in the section: again the criterion is that its range must be bounded as a set. (In fact, the definition extends just as easily to mappings $f : A \longrightarrow \mathbb{R}^m$, but we need only scalar-valued functions here.)

Definition 6.1.5 (n-dimensional lower sum and upper sum). *Let B be a nonempty compact box in $\mathbb{R}^n$, and let $f : B \longrightarrow \mathbb{R}$ be a bounded function. For every nonempty subbox J of B, define $m_J(f)$ and $M_J(f)$ analogously as before,*

$$m_J(f) = \inf\{f(x) : x \in J\} \qquad and \qquad M_J(f) = \sup\{f(x) : x \in J\}.$$

Let P be a partition of B into subboxes J. The **lower sum** *and* **upper sum** *of f over P are similarly*

$$L(f,P) = \sum_J m_J(f)\,\mathrm{vol}(J) \qquad and \qquad U(f,P) = \sum_J M_J(f)\,\mathrm{vol}(J).$$

With minor grammatical modifications, this terminology includes the previous definition as a special case when $n = 1$ (e.g., *volume* reverts to *length*, as it should revert to *area* when $n = 2$), so from now on we work in $\mathbb{R}^n$. However, keeping the cases $n = 1$ and $n = 2$ in mind should help to make the pandimensional ideas of multivariable integration geometrically intuitive. If the box B in Definition 6.1.5 has any sides of length zero then the upper and lower sums are 0.

Graphing f over B in the usual fashion when $n = 2$ and interpreting the lower and upper sum as sums of box-volumes shows that they are respectively too small and too big to be the volume under the graph. (See Figure 6.6.) Alternatively, if $n = 2$ or $n = 3$, then thinking of f as the density of a plate or a block occupying the box B shows that the lower and upper sums are too small and too big to be the object's mass. Again, the hope is that as the partitions become finer, the lower and upper sums will converge to a common value that they are trapping from either side.

Figure 6.6. Too small and too big

The first result supports this intuition.

Lemma 6.1.6. *For every box B, every partition P of B, and every bounded function $f : B \longrightarrow \mathbb{R}$,*

$$L(f,P) \leq U(f,P).$$

Proof. For every subbox J of P, $m_J(f) \le M_J(f)$ by the first bullet from earlier in this section with $S = \{f(x) : x \in J'\}$, while also $\mathrm{vol}(J) \ge 0$, and therefore $m_J(f)\,\mathrm{vol}(J) \le M_J(f)\,\mathrm{vol}(J)$. Sum this relation over all subboxes J to get the result.   □

The next thing to do is express the notion of taking a finer partition.

Definition 6.1.7 (Refinement). *Let P and P' be partitions of B. Then P' is a* **refinement** *of P if $P' \supset P$.*

Figure 6.7 illustrates the fact that if P' refines P then every subbox of P' is contained in a subbox of P. The literal manifestation in the figure of the containment $P' \supset P$ is that the set of points where a horizontal line segment and a vertical line segment meet in the right side of the figure subsumes the set of such points in the left side.

Refining a partition brings the lower and upper sums nearer each other:

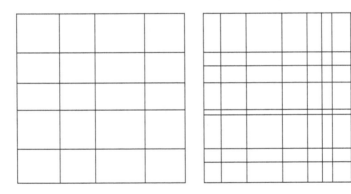

Figure 6.7. Refinement

Lemma 6.1.8. *Suppose that P' refines P as a partition of the box B. Then*

$$L(f, P) \le L(f, P') \qquad and \qquad U(f, P') \le U(f, P).$$

See Figure 6.8 for a picture-proof for lower sums when $n = 1$, thinking of the sums in terms of area. The formal proof is just a symbolic rendition of the figure's features.

Proof. Every subbox J of P divides further under the refinement P' into subboxes J'. Since each $J' \subset J$, we have $m_{J'}(f) \ge m_J(f)$ by the second bullet from earlier in this section, but even without reference to the bullet the idea is that

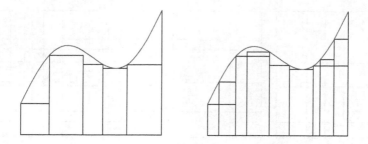

Figure 6.8. Lower sum increasing under refinement

$m_{J'}(f) \geq m_J(f)$ *because f has less opportunity to be small on the subbox J' of J.*

Thus

$$\sum_{J' \subset J} m_{J'}(f) \operatorname{vol}(J') \geq \sum_{J' \subset J} m_J(f) \operatorname{vol}(J')$$
$$= m_J(f) \sum_{J' \subset J} \operatorname{vol}(J') = m_J(f)\operatorname{vol}(J).$$

Sum the relation $\sum_{J' \subset J} m_{J'}(f) \operatorname{vol}(J') \geq m_J(f) \operatorname{vol}(J)$ over all subboxes J of P to get $L(f, P') \geq L(f, P)$. The argument is similar for upper sums.   □

The proof uncritically assumes that the volumes of a box's subboxes sum to the volume of the box. This assumption is true, and left as an exercise. The emphasis here isn't on boxes (which are straightforward), but on defining the integral of a function f whose domain is a box. The next result helps investigate whether the lower and upper sums indeed trap some value from both sides. First we need a definition.

Definition 6.1.9 (Common refinement). *Given two partitions of B,*

$$P = P_1 \times P_2 \times \cdots \times P_n \quad and \quad P' = P'_1 \times P'_2 \times \cdots \times P'_n,$$

their **common refinement** *is the partition*

$$P'' = (P_1 \cup P'_1) \times (P_2 \cup P'_2) \times \cdots \times (P_n \cup P'_n).$$

(See Figure 6.9.) The common refinement of two partitions P and P' is certainly a partition that refines both P and P', and it is the smallest such partition. The union $P \cup P'$ is not taken as the definition of the common refinement because it need not be a partition at all. The common refinement does all the work for the next result.

Proposition 6.1.10 (Lower sums are at most upper sums). *Let P and P' be partitions of the box B, and let $f : B \longrightarrow \mathbb{R}$ be any bounded function. Then*

$$L(f, P) \leq U(f, P').$$

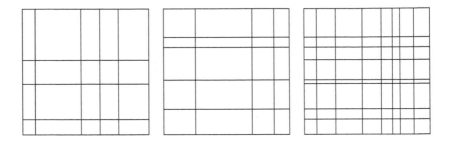

Figure 6.9. Common refinement

Proof. Let P'' be the common refinement of P and P'. By the two lemmas,

$$L(f, P) \le L(f, P'') \le U(f, P'') \le U(f, P'),$$

proving the result. □

Exercises

6.1.1. (a) Let $I = [0, 1]$, let $P = \{0, 1/2, 1\}$, let $P' = \{0, 3/8, 5/8, 1\}$, and let P'' be the common refinement of P and P'. What are the subintervals of P, and what are their lengths? Same question for P'. Same question for P''.

(b) Let $B = I \times I$, let $Q = P \times \{0, 1/2, 1\}$, let $Q' = P' \times \{0, 1/2, 1\}$, and let Q'' be the common refinement of Q and Q'. What are the subboxes of Q and what are their areas? Same question for Q'. Same question for Q''.

6.1.2. Show that the lengths of the subintervals of every partition of $[a, b]$ sum to the length of $[a, b]$. Same for the areas of the subboxes of $[a, b] \times [c, d]$. Generalize to $\mathbb{R}^n$.

6.1.3. Let $J = [0, 1]$. Compute $m_J(f)$ and $M_J(f)$ for each of the following functions $f : J \longrightarrow \mathbb{R}$.

(a) $f(x) = x(1 - x)$,

(b) $f(x) = \begin{cases} 1 & \text{if } x \text{ is irrational,} \\ 1/m & \text{if } x = n/m \text{ in lowest terms, } n, m \in \mathbb{Z} \text{ and } m > 0, \end{cases}$

(c) $f(x) = \begin{cases} (1 - x)\sin(1/x) & \text{if } x \ne 0, \\ 0 & \text{if } x = 0. \end{cases}$

6.1.4. (a) Let I, P, P', and P'' be as in Exercise 6.1.1(a), and let $f(x) = x^2$ on I. Compute the lower sums $L(f, P)$, $L(f, P')$, $L(f, P'')$ and the corresponding upper sums, and check that they conform to Lemma 6.1.6, Lemma 6.1.8, and Proposition 6.1.10.

(b) Let B, Q, Q', and Q'' be as in Exercise 6.1.1(b), and define $f : B \longrightarrow \mathbb{R}$ by

$$f(x, y) = \begin{cases} 0 & \text{if } 0 \le x < 1/2, \\ 1 & \text{if } 1/2 \le x \le 1. \end{cases}$$

Compute $L(f, Q)$, $L(f, Q')$, $L(f, Q'')$, and the corresponding upper sums, and check that they conform to Lemma 6.1.6, Lemma 6.1.8, and Proposition 6.1.10.

6.1.5. Draw the Cartesian product $([a_1, b_1] \cup [c_1, d_1]) \times ([a_2, b_2] \cup [c_2, d_2]) \subset \mathbb{R}^2$ where $a_1 < b_1 < c_1 < d_1$ and similarly for the other subscript.

6.1.6. When is a Cartesian product empty?

6.1.7. Show that the union of partitions of a box B need not be a partition of B.

6.1.8. Draw a picture illustrating the proof of Proposition 6.1.10 when $n = 1$.

6.2 Definition of the Integral

Fix a nonempty compact box B and a bounded function $f : B \longrightarrow \mathbb{R}$. The set of lower sums of f over all partitions P of B,

$$\{L(f, P) : P \text{ is a partition of } B\},$$

is nonempty because such partitions exist (as observed in the previous section), and similarly for the set of upper sums. Proposition 6.1.10 shows that the set of lower sums is bounded above by every upper sum, and similarly the set of upper sums is bounded below. Thus the next definition is natural.

Definition 6.2.1 (Lower integral, upper integral, integrability, integral). *The **lower integral** of f over B is the least upper bound of the lower sums of f over all partitions P,*

$$L \int_B f = \sup \{L(f, P) : P \text{ is a partition of } B\}.$$

*Similarly, the **upper integral** of f over B is the greatest lower bound of the upper sums of f over all partitions P,*

$$U \int_B f = \inf \{U(f, P) : P \text{ is a partition of } B\}.$$

*The function f is called **integrable over** B if the lower and upper integrals are equal, i.e., if $L \int_B f = U \int_B f$. In this case, their shared value is called the **integral of f over** B and written $\int_B f$.*

So we have a quantitative definition that seems appropriate. The integral, if it exists, is at least as big as every lower sum and at least as small as every upper sum; and it is specified as the common value that is approached from below by lower sums and from above by upper sums. Less formally, if quantities that we view as respectively too small and too big approach a common value, then that value must be what we're after.

The following lemma shows that $L\int_B f \leq U\int_B f$. Its proof provides an example of how to work with lower and upper bounds. Note that the argument does not require a contradiction or an ε, but rather it goes directly to the point.

Lemma 6.2.2 (Persistence of order). *Let $\mathcal{L}$ and $\mathcal{U}$ be nonempty sets of real numbers such that*

$$\ell \leq u \quad \text{for all } \ell \in \mathcal{L} \text{ and } u \in \mathcal{U}. \tag{6.1}$$

Then $\sup(\mathcal{L})$ and $\inf(\mathcal{U})$ exist, and they satisfy

$$\sup(\mathcal{L}) \leq \inf(\mathcal{U}).$$

Proof. The given condition (6.1) can be rephrased as

$$\text{for each } \ell \in \mathcal{L}, \quad \ell \leq u \text{ for all } u \in \mathcal{U},$$

meaning precisely that

$$\text{each } \ell \in \mathcal{L} \text{ is a lower bound of } \mathcal{U}.$$

Since $\mathcal{U}$ is nonempty and has lower bounds, it has a greatest lower bound $\inf(\mathcal{U})$. Since each $\ell \in \mathcal{L}$ is a lower bound and $\inf(\mathcal{U})$ is the greatest lower bound,

$$\ell \leq \inf(\mathcal{U}) \quad \text{for each } \ell \in \mathcal{L},$$

meaning precisely that

$$\inf(\mathcal{U}) \text{ is an upper bound of } \mathcal{L}.$$

Since $\mathcal{L}$ is nonempty and has an upper bound, it has a least upper bound $\sup(\mathcal{L})$. Since $\sup(\mathcal{L})$ is the least upper bound and $\inf(\mathcal{U})$ is an upper bound,

$$\sup(\mathcal{L}) \leq \inf(\mathcal{U}).$$

This is the desired result. □

Again let a nonempty compact box B and a bounded function $f : B \longrightarrow \mathbb{R}$ be given. The lemma shows that $L\int_B f \leq U\int_B f$ (exercise). Therefore, to show that $\int_B f$ exists, it suffices to show only that the reverse inequality holds, $L\int_B f \geq U\int_B f$.

Not all bounded functions $f : B \longrightarrow \mathbb{R}$ are integrable. The standard counterexample is the interval $B = [0, 1]$ and the function

$$f : B \longrightarrow \mathbb{R}, \qquad f(x) = \begin{cases} 1 & \text{if } x \text{ is rational,} \\ 0 & \text{if } x \text{ is irrational.} \end{cases}$$

Chasing through the definitions shows that for this B and f, every lower sum is $L(f,P) = 0$, so the lower integral is $L \int_B f = \sup\{0\} = 0$. Similarly, $U \int_B f = 1$. Since the upper and lower integrals don't agree, $\int_B f$ does not exist.

So the questions are, what functions *are* integrable, or at least, what are some general classes of integrable functions, and how does one evaluate their integrals? Working from the definitions, as in the last example, is a good exercise in simple cases to get familiar with the machinery, but as a general procedure it is hopelessly unwieldy. Here is one result that will help us in the next section to show that continuous functions are integrable.

Proposition 6.2.3 (Integrability criterion). *Let B be a box, and let $f : B \longrightarrow \mathbb{R}$ be a bounded function. Then f is integrable over B if and only if for every $\varepsilon > 0$, there exists a partition P of B such that $U(f,P) - L(f,P) < \varepsilon$.*

Proof. ($\Longrightarrow$) Let f be integrable over B and let $\varepsilon > 0$ be given. Since $\int_B f - \varepsilon/2$ is less than the least upper bound of the lower sums, it is not an upper bound of the lower sums, and similarly $\int_B f + \varepsilon/2$ is not a lower bound of the upper sums. Thus there exist partitions P and P' of B such that

$$L(f,P) > \int_B f - \varepsilon/2 \quad \text{and} \quad U(f,P') < \int_B f + \varepsilon/2.$$

Let P'' be the common refinement of P and P'. Then since refining increases lower sums and decreases upper sums, also

$$L(f,P'') > \int_B f - \varepsilon/2 \quad \text{and} \quad U(f,P'') < \int_B f + \varepsilon/2.$$

This shows that $U(f,P'') - L(f,P'') < \varepsilon$, as required.

($\Longleftarrow$) We need to show that $U \int_B f - L \int_B f = 0$. To do so, use the little principle that to prove that a nonnegative number is zero, it suffices to show that it is less than every positive number. Let $\varepsilon > 0$ be given. By assumption there exists a partition P such that

$$U(f,P) - L(f,P) < \varepsilon,$$

and by the definition of upper and lower integral, also

$$L(f,P) \le L \int_B f \le U \int_B f \le U(f,P).$$

The last two displays combine to give

$$U \int_B f - L \int_B f < \varepsilon.$$

Since the positive number ε is arbitrary, $U \int_B f - L \int_B f = 0$ as desired. $\quad\square$

Here is an example of using the integrability criterion. It subsumes the result from one-variable calculus that if $\int_a^b f$ exists then also $\int_a^c f$ and $\int_c^b f$ exist for every c between a and b, and they they sum to $\int_a^b f$.

Proposition 6.2.4. *Let B be a box, let $f : B \longrightarrow \mathbb{R}$ be a bounded function, and let P be a partition of B. If f is integrable over B then f is integrable over each subbox J of P, in which case*

$$\sum_J \int_J f = \int_B f.$$

Proof. Consider any partition P' of B that refines P. For each subbox J of P, let $P'_J = P' \cap J$, a partition of J. Let the symbol J' denote subboxes of P', and compute that

$$L(f, P') = \sum_{J'} m_{J'}(f) \operatorname{vol}(J') = \sum_J \sum_{J' \subset J} m_{J'}(f) \operatorname{vol}(J') = \sum_J L(f, P'_J).$$

Similarly, $U(f, P') = \sum_J U(f, P'_J)$.

Suppose that f is integrable over B. Let an arbitrary $\varepsilon > 0$ be given. By "$\Longrightarrow$" of the integrability criterion, there exists a partition P' of B such that

$$U(f, P') - L(f, P') < \varepsilon.$$

Since refining a partition cannot increase the difference between the upper and lower sums, we may replace P' by its common refinement with P and thus assume that P' refines P. Therefore the formulas from the previous paragraph show that

$$\sum_J (U(f, P'_J) - L(f, P'_J)) < \varepsilon,$$

and so

$$U(f, P'_J) - L(f, P'_J) < \varepsilon \quad \text{for each subbox } J \text{ of } B.$$

Therefore f is integrable over each subbox J of B by "$\Longleftarrow$" of the integrability criterion.

Now assume that f is integrable over B and hence over each subbox J. Still letting P' be any partition of B that refines P, the integral over each subbox J lies between the corresponding lower and upper sums, and so

$$L(f, P') = \sum_J L(f, P'_J) \le \sum_J \int_J f \le \sum_J U(f, P'_J) = U(f, P').$$

Thus $\sum_J \int_J f$ is an upper bound of all lower sums $L(f, P')$ and a lower bound of all upper sums $U(f, P')$, giving

$$L \int_B f \le \sum_J \int_J f \le U \int_B f.$$

But $L \int_B f = U \int_B f = \int_B f$ because f is integrable over B, and so the inequalities in the previous display collapse to give the desired result.   □

Similar techniques show that the converse of the proposition holds as well, so that given B, f, and P, f is integrable over B if and only if f is integrable over each subbox J, but we do not need this full result. Each of the proposition and its converse requires both implications of the integrability criterion.

The symbol B denotes a box in the next set of exercises.

Exercises

6.2.1. Let $f : B \longrightarrow \mathbb{R}$ be a bounded function. Explain how Lemma 6.2.2 shows that $L \int_B f \le U \int_B f$.

6.2.2. Let U and L be real numbers satisfying $U \ge L$. Show that $U = L$ if and only if for all $\varepsilon > 0$, $U - L < \varepsilon$.

6.2.3. Let $f : B \longrightarrow \mathbb{R}$ be the constant function $f(x) = k$ for all $x \in B$. Show that f is integrable over B and $\int_B f = k \cdot \mathrm{vol}(B)$.

6.2.4. Granting that every interval of positive length contains both rational and irrational numbers, fill in the details in the argument that the function $f : [0,1] \longrightarrow \mathbb{R}$ with $f(x) = 1$ for rational x and $f(x) = 0$ for irrational x is not integrable over $[0,1]$.

6.2.5. Let $B = [0,1] \times [0,1] \subset \mathbb{R}^2$. Define a function $f : B \longrightarrow \mathbb{R}$ by

$$f(x,y) = \begin{cases} 0 & \text{if } 0 \le x < 1/2, \\ 1 & \text{if } 1/2 \le x \le 1. \end{cases}$$

Show that f is integrable and $\int_B f = 1/2$.

6.2.6. This exercise shows that integration is linear. Let $f : B \longrightarrow \mathbb{R}$ and $g : B \longrightarrow \mathbb{R}$ be integrable.

(a) Let P be a partition of B and let J be some subbox of P. Show that

$$m_J(f) + m_J(g) \le m_J(f+g) \le M_J(f+g) \le M_J(f) + M_J(g).$$

Show that consequently,

$$L(f,P) + L(g,P) \le L(f+g,P) \le U(f+g,P) \le U(f,P) + U(g,P).$$

(b) Part (a) of this exercise obtained comparisons between lower and upper sums, analogously to the first paragraph of the proof of Proposition 6.2.4. Argue analogously to the rest of the proof to show that $\int_B (f+g)$ exists and equals $\int_B f + \int_B g$. (One way to begin is to use the integrability criterion twice and then a common refinement to show that there exists a partition P of B such that $U(f,P) - L(f,P) < \varepsilon/2$ and $U(g,P) - L(g,P) < \varepsilon/2$.)

(c) Let $c \ge 0$ be any constant. Let P be any partition of B. Show that for every subbox J of P,

$$m_J(cf) = c\, m_J(f) \quad \text{and} \quad M_J(cf) = c\, M_J(f).$$

Explain why consequently

$$L(cf, P) = c\, L(f, P) \quad \text{and} \quad U(cf, P) = c\, U(f, P).$$

Explain why consequently

$$L \int_B cf = c\, L \int_B f \quad \text{and} \quad U \int_B cf = c\, U \int_B f.$$

Explain why consequently $\int_B cf$ exists and

$$\int_B cf = c \int_B f.$$

(d) Let P be any partition of B. Show that for every subbox J of P,

$$m_J(-f) = -M_J(f) \quad \text{and} \quad M_J(-f) = -m_J(f).$$

Explain why consequently

$$L(-f, P) = -U(f, P) \quad \text{and} \quad U(-f, P) = -L(f, P).$$

Explain why consequently

$$L \int_B (-f) = -U \int_B f \quad \text{and} \quad U \int_B (-f) = -L \int_B f.$$

Explain why consequently $\int_B (-f)$ exists and

$$\int_B (-f) = - \int_B f.$$

Explain why the work so far here in part (d) combines with part (c) to show that for every $c \in \mathbb{R}$ (positive, zero, or negative), $\int_B cf$ exists and

$$\int_B cf = c \int_B f.$$

6.2.7. This exercise shows that integration preserves order. Let $f : B \longrightarrow \mathbb{R}$ and $g : B \longrightarrow \mathbb{R}$ both be integrable, and suppose that $f \leq g$, meaning that $f(x) \leq g(x)$ for all $x \in B$. Show that $\int_B f \leq \int_B g$. (Comment: Even though $f(x) \leq g(x)$ for all x, upper sums for f can be bigger than lower sums for g (!), so the argument requires a little finesse. Perhaps begin by explaining why the previous exercise lets us show instead that $\int_B (g - f) \geq 0$. That is, introducing the function $h = g - f$, we have $h(x) \geq 0$ for all x and we need to show that $\int_B h \geq 0$. This is precisely the original problem with $g = h$ and $f = 0$, so once one has assimilated this idea, one often says in similar contexts, "We may take $f = 0$.")

6.2.8. Suppose that $f : B \longrightarrow \mathbb{R}$ is integrable, and that so is $|f|$. Show that $|\int_B f| \leq \int_B |f|$.

6.2.9. Prove the converse to Proposition 6.2.4: Let B be a box, let $f : B \longrightarrow \mathbb{R}$ be a bounded function, and let P be a partition of B. If f is integrable over each subbox J of P then f is integrable over B. (You may quote the formulas from the first paragraph of the proof in the text, since that paragraph makes no assumptions of integrability. It may help to let b denote the number of subboxes J, so that this quantity has a handy name.)

6.3 Continuity and Integrability

Although the integrability criterion gives a test for the integrability of any specific function f, it is cumbersome to apply case by case. But handily, it will provide the punchline of the proof of the next theorem, which says that a natural class of functions is integrable.

Theorem 6.3.1 (Continuity implies integrability). *Let B be a box, and let $f : B \longrightarrow \mathbb{R}$ be a continuous function. Then f is integrable over B.*

To prove this theorem, as we will at the end of this section, we first need to sharpen our understanding of continuity on boxes. The version of continuity that we're familiar with isn't strong enough to prove certain theorems, this one in particular. Formulating the stronger version of continuity requires first revising the grammar of the familiar brand.

Definition 6.3.2 (Sequential continuity). *Let $S \subset \mathbb{R}^n$ be a set, and let $f : S \longrightarrow \mathbb{R}^m$ be a mapping. For every $x \in S$, f is **sequentially continuous** at x if for every sequence $\{x_\nu\}$ in S converging to x, the sequence $\{f(x_\nu)\}$ converges to $f(x)$. The mapping f is **sequentially continuous on S** if f is sequentially continuous at each point x in S.*

Definition 6.3.3 (ε-δ continuity). *Let $S \subset \mathbb{R}^n$ be a set, and let $f : S \longrightarrow \mathbb{R}^m$ be a mapping. For every $x \in S$, f is ε-δ **continuous** at x if for every $\varepsilon > 0$ there exists some $\delta > 0$ such that*

$$\text{if } \tilde{x} \in S \text{ and } |\tilde{x} - x| < \delta \text{ then } |f(\tilde{x}) - f(x)| < \varepsilon.$$

*The mapping f is ε-δ **continuous on S** if f is ε-δ continuous at each point x in S.*

Both definitions of continuity at a point x capture the idea that as inputs to f approach x, the corresponding outputs from f should approach $f(x)$. This idea is exactly the substance of sequential continuity. (See Figure 6.10.)

For ε-δ continuity at x, imagine that someone has drawn a ball of radius ε (over which you have no control, and it's probably quite small) about the

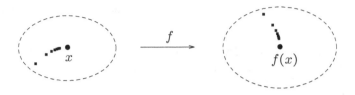

Figure 6.10. Sequential continuity

point $f(x)$ in $\mathbb{R}^m$. The idea is that in response, you can draw a ball of some radius—this is the δ in the definition—about the point x in S such that every point in the δ-ball about x gets taken by f into the ε-ball about $f(x)$. (See Figure 6.11.)

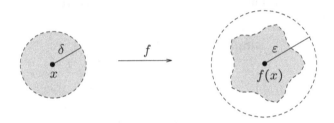

Figure 6.11. ε-δ continuity

For example, the function $f : \mathbb{R}^n \longrightarrow \mathbb{R}$ given by $f(x) = 2|x|$ is ε-δ continuous on $\mathbb{R}^n$. To show this, consider any point $x \in \mathbb{R}^n$, and let $\varepsilon > 0$ be given. Set $\delta = \varepsilon/2$. Then whenever $|\tilde{x} - x| < \delta$, a calculation that uses the generalized triangle inequality at the third step shows that

$$|f(\tilde{x}) - f(x)| = |2|\tilde{x}| - 2|x|| = 2||\tilde{x}| - |x|| \leq 2|\tilde{x} - x| < 2\delta = \varepsilon,$$

as needed. Thus f is ε-δ continuous at x, and since x is arbitrary, f is ε-δ continuous on $\mathbb{R}^n$.

For another example, to prove that the function $f : \mathbb{R} \longrightarrow \mathbb{R}$ given by $f(x) = x^2$ is ε-δ continuous on $\mathbb{R}$, consider any $x \in \mathbb{R}$ and let $\varepsilon > 0$ be given. This time set

$$\delta = \min\{1, \varepsilon/(1 + 2|x|)\}.$$

This choice of δ may look strange, but its first virtue is that since $\delta \leq 1$, for every $\tilde{x} \in \mathbb{R}$ with $|\tilde{x} - x| < \delta$, we have $|\tilde{x} + x| = |\tilde{x} - x + 2x| \leq |\tilde{x} - x| + 2|x| < 1 + 2|x|$; and its second virtue is that also $\delta \leq \varepsilon/(1 + 2|x|)$. These conditions fit perfectly into the following calculation,

$$|f(\tilde{x}) - f(x)| = |\tilde{x}^2 - x^2|$$
$$= |\tilde{x} + x|\,|\tilde{x} - x|$$
$$< (1 + 2|x|)\frac{\varepsilon}{1 + 2|x|} \quad \text{by the two virtues of } \delta$$
$$= \varepsilon.$$

And this is exactly what we needed to show that f is ε-δ continuous at x. Since x is arbitrary, f is ε-δ continuous on $\mathbb{R}$.

The tricky part of writing this sort of proof is finding the right δ. Doing so generally requires some preliminary fiddling around on scratch paper. For the proof just given, the initial scratch calculation would be

$$|f(\tilde{x}) - f(x)| = |\tilde{x}^2 - x^2| = |(\tilde{x} + x)(\tilde{x} - x)| = |\tilde{x} + x|\,|\tilde{x} - x|,$$

exhibiting the quantity that we need to bound by ε as a product of two terms, the second bounded directly by whatever δ we choose. The idea is initially to make the first term reasonably small by stipulating that δ be at most 1, giving as in the previous paragraph

$$|\tilde{x} + x| = |\tilde{x} - x + 2x| \le |\tilde{x} - x| + 2|x| < 1 + 2|x|.$$

Now $|f(\tilde{x}) - f(x)| \le (1 + 2|x|)|\tilde{x} - x|$. Next we constrain δ further to make this estimate less than ε when $|\tilde{x} - x| < \delta$. Stipulating that δ be at most $\varepsilon/(1 + 2|x|)$ does so. Hence the choice of δ in the proof.

To prove instead that the function $f : \mathbb{R} \longrightarrow \mathbb{R}$ given by $f(x) = x^2$ is sequentially continuous on $\mathbb{R}$, again take any $x \in \mathbb{R}$. Consider any sequence $\{x_\nu\}$ in $\mathbb{R}$ converging to x. To show that the sequence $\{f(x_\nu)\}$ in $\mathbb{R}$ converges to $f(x)$, compute that by sequence limit properties,

$$\{f(x_\nu)\} = \{x_\nu^2\} \overset{\nu}{\to} x^2 = f(x).$$

Since x is arbitrary, f is sequentially continuous on $\mathbb{R}$. Note how much easier this is than the ϵ-δ argument. Sequential continuity can be easier to establish, as shown here, but also it can be harder to exploit.

In fact, there is no need to continue distinguishing between sequential continuity and ε-δ continuity, because each type of continuity implies the other.

Proposition 6.3.4 (Sequential and ε-δ continuity are equivalent). *For every set $S \subset \mathbb{R}^n$ and every mapping $f : S \longrightarrow \mathbb{R}^m$, f is sequentially continuous on S if and only if f is ε-δ continuous on S.*

Proof. Let x be any point of S.

$(\Longleftarrow)$ Suppose that f is ε-δ continuous at x. We need to show that f is sequentially continuous at x. So, let $\{x_\nu\}$ be a sequence in S converging to x.

To show that $\{f(x_\nu)\}$ converges to $f(x)$ means that given an arbitrary $\varepsilon > 0$, we need to exhibit a starting index N such that

$$\text{for all } \nu > N, \ |f(x_\nu) - f(x)| < \varepsilon.$$

The definition of ε-δ continuity gives a δ such that

$$\text{if } \tilde{x} \in S \text{ and } |\tilde{x} - x| < \delta \text{ then } |f(\tilde{x}) - f(x)| < \varepsilon.$$

And since $\{x_\nu\}$ converges in S to x, there is some starting index N such that

$$\text{for all } \nu > N, \ |x_\nu - x| < \delta.$$

The last two displays combine to imply the first display, showing that f is sequentially continuous at x.

($\Longrightarrow$) Now suppose that f is not ε-δ continuous at x. Then for some $\varepsilon > 0$, no $\delta > 0$ satisfies the relevant conditions. In particular, $\delta = 1/\nu$ fails the conditions for $\nu = 1, 2, 3, \ldots$. So there is a sequence $\{x_\nu\}$ in S such that

$$|x_\nu - x| < 1/\nu \quad \text{and} \quad |f(x_\nu) - f(x)| \geq \varepsilon, \quad \nu = 1, 2, 3, \ldots.$$

The display shows that f is not sequentially continuous at x.

Since the two types on continuity imply each other at each point x of S, they imply each other on S.   □

The fact that the second half of this proof has to proceed by contraposition, whereas the first half is straightforward, shows that ε-δ continuity is a little more powerful than sequential continuity on the face of it, until we do the work of showing that they are equivalent. Also, the very definition of ε-δ continuity seems harder for students than the definition of sequential continuity, which is why these notes have used sequential continuity up to now. However, the exceptionally alert reader may have recognized that the second half of this proof is essentially identical to the proof of the persistence of inequality principle (Proposition 2.3.10). Thus, the occasional arguments in these notes that cited the persistence of inequality were tacitly using ε-δ continuity already, because sequential continuity was not transparently strong enough for their purposes. The reader who dislikes redundancy is encouraged to rewrite the second half of this proof to quote the persistence of inequality rather than re-prove it.

The reason that we bother with this new ε-δ type of continuity, despite its equivalence to sequential continuity meaning that it is nothing new, is that its grammar generalizes to describe the more powerful continuity that we need. The two examples above of ε-δ continuity differed: in the example $f(x) = x^2$, the choice of $\delta = \min\{1, \varepsilon/(2|x| + 1)\}$ for any given x and ε to satisfy the definition of ε-δ continuity at x depended not only on ε but on x as well. In the example $f(x) = 2|x|$, the choice of $\delta = \varepsilon/2$ for any given x and ε depended only on ε, i.e., it was independent of x. Here, one value of δ works simultaneously at all values of x once ε is specified. This technicality has enormous consequences.

Definition 6.3.5 (Uniform continuity). *Let $S \subset \mathbb{R}^n$ be a set, and let $f :$ $S \longrightarrow \mathbb{R}^m$ be a mapping. Then f is* **uniformly continuous on** S *if for every $\varepsilon > 0$ there exists some $\delta > 0$ such that*

$$\text{if } x, \tilde{x} \in S \text{ and } |\tilde{x} - x| < \delta \text{ then } |f(\tilde{x}) - f(x)| < \varepsilon.$$

The nomenclature *uniformly continuous on S* is meant to emphasize that given $\varepsilon > 0$, a single, *uniform* value of δ works in the definition of ε-δ continuity simultaneously for all points $x \in S$. The scope of its effectiveness is large-scale. Uniform continuity depends on both the mapping f and the set S.

A visual image may help distinguish between the old notion of continuity (henceforth called **pointwise continuity**) and the new, stronger notion of uniform continuity. Imagine the graph of a function $f : S \longrightarrow \mathbb{R}$ (where $S \subset \mathbb{R}$), and take some input point x. Then f is pointwise continuous at x if for every $\varepsilon > 0$, one can draw a rectangle of height 2ε centered at the point $(x, f(x))$ that is narrow enough that the graph of f protrudes only from the sides of the rectangle, not the top or bottom. The base of the rectangle is 2δ, where δ comes from ε-δ continuity. Note that for a given ε, one may need rectangles of various widths at different points. A rectangle that works at x may not be narrow enough to work again at some other point $\tilde{x}$. (See Figure 6.12, where ever-narrower rectangles are required as we move to the left on the graph.) On the other hand, the function f is uniformly continuous if given $\varepsilon > 0$, there is a single $2\varepsilon \times 2\delta$ rectangle that can slide along the entire graph of f with its centerpoint on the graph, and the graph never protruding from the top or bottom. (See Figure 6.13. A tacit assumption here is that the graph of f either doesn't extend beyond the picture frame, or it continues to rise and fall tamely if it does.) By contrast, no single rectangle will work in Figure 6.12.

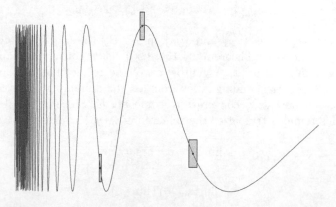

Figure 6.12. One ε can require different values of δ at different points x

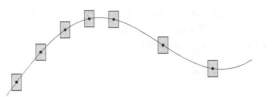

Figure 6.13. Or one δ can work uniformly for ε at all x

The domain of the nonuniformly continuous function $f(x) = \sin(1/x)$ in Figure 6.12 is not compact, not being closed at its left endpoint. We are about to prove that on a compact domain, uniform continuity follows for free from pointwise continuity. In conjunction with the compactness of the boxes B over which we integrate, this is the crucial ingredient for proving Theorem 6.3.1 (continuous functions are integrable over boxes), the goal of this section.

Theorem 6.3.6 (Continuity on compact sets is uniform). *Let $K \subset \mathbb{R}^n$ be compact, and let $f : K \longrightarrow \mathbb{R}^m$ be pointwise continuous on K. Then f is uniformly continuous on K.*

As with the proof that sequential continuity implies ε-δ continuity, we proceed by contraposition. That is, we show that in the case of a compact domain, if f is not uniformly continuous then f cannot be continuous either.

Proof. Suppose that f is not uniformly continuous. Then for some $\varepsilon > 0$ there exists no suitable uniform δ, and so in particular no reciprocal positive integer $1/\nu$ will serve as δ in the definition of uniform continuity. Thus for each $\nu \in \mathbb{Z}^+$ there exist points x_ν and y_ν in K such that

$$|x_\nu - y_\nu| < 1/\nu \quad \text{and} \quad |f(x_\nu) - f(y_\nu)| \geq \varepsilon. \qquad (6.2)$$

Consider the sequences $\{x_\nu\}$ and $\{y_\nu\}$ in K. By the sequential characterization of compactness (Theorem 2.4.13), $\{x_\nu\}$ has a convergent subsequence converging in K; call it $\{x_{\nu_k}\}$. Throw away the rest of the x_ν's and throw away the y_ν's of corresponding index, reindex the remaining terms of the two sequences, and now $\{x_\nu\}$ converges to some $p \in K$. Since $|x_\nu - y_\nu| < 1/\nu$ for each ν (this remains true after the reindexing), $\{y_\nu\}$ converges to p as well. So

$$\lim x_\nu = p = \lim y_\nu,$$

and thus

$$f(\lim x_\nu) = f(\lim y_\nu).$$

But the second condition in (6.2) shows that

$$\lim f(x_\nu) \neq \lim f(y_\nu),$$

i.e., even if both limits exist then they still cannot be equal. (If they both exist and they agree then $\lim(f(x_\nu) - f(y_\nu)) = 0$, but this is incompatible with the second condition in (6.2), $|f(x_\nu) - f(y_\nu)| \geq \varepsilon$ for all ν.) The previous two displays combine to show that

$$\lim f(x_\nu) \neq f(\lim x_\nu) \quad \text{or} \quad \lim f(y_\nu) \neq f(\lim y_\nu),$$

i.e., at least one of the left sides in the previous display doesn't match the corresponding right side or doesn't exist at all. Thus f is not continuous at p.

$\square$

Recall the main result that we want: If B is a box in $\mathbb{R}^n$ and $f : B \longrightarrow \mathbb{R}$ is continuous then $\int_B f$ exists. The result is easy to prove now. The crucial line of the proof is the opener.

Proof (of Theorem 6.3.1). The continuity of f on B is uniform. Thus, given $\varepsilon > 0$, there exists $\delta > 0$ such that

$$\text{if } x, \tilde{x} \in B \text{ and } |\tilde{x} - x| < \delta \text{ then } |f(\tilde{x}) - f(x)| < \frac{\varepsilon}{\text{vol}(B)}.$$

(We may take $\text{vol}(B) > 0$, making the volume safe to divide by, since otherwise all lower sums and upper sums are 0, making the integral 0 as well, and there is nothing to prove.) Take a partition P of B whose subboxes J have sides of length less than δ/n. By the size bounds (Proposition 2.2.7), all points x and $\tilde{x}$ in a given subbox J satisfy $|\tilde{x} - x| < \delta$, so

$$\text{if } x, \tilde{x} \in J \text{ then } |f(\tilde{x}) - f(x)| < \frac{\varepsilon}{\text{vol}(B)}.$$

Let x and $\tilde{x}$ vary over J, and cite the extreme value theorem (Theorem 2.4.15) to show that

$$M_J(f) - m_J(f) < \frac{\varepsilon}{\text{vol}(B)}.$$

Multiply by $\text{vol}(J)$ to get

$$M_J(f)\text{vol}(J) - m_J(f)\text{vol}(J) < \frac{\varepsilon \, \text{vol}(J)}{\text{vol}(B)},$$

and sum this relation over subboxes J to get

$$U(f, P) - L(f, P) < \varepsilon.$$

The integrability criterion now shows that $\int_B f$ exists.

$\square$

Integration synthesizes local data at each point of a domain into one whole. The idea of this section is that integrating a continuous function over a box is more than a purely local process: it requires the uniform continuity of the function all through the box, a large-scale simultaneous estimate that holds in consequence of the box being compact.

Exercises

6.3.1. Reread the proof that sequential and ε-δ continuity are equivalent; then redo the proof with the book closed.

6.3.2. Let $f : \mathbb{R} \longrightarrow \mathbb{R}$ be the cubing function $f(x) = x^3$. Give a direct proof that f is ε-δ continuous on $\mathbb{R}$. (Hint: $A^3 - B^3 = (A - B)(A^2 + AB + B^2)$.)

6.3.3. Here is a proof that the squaring function $f(x) = x^2$ is not uniformly continuous on $\mathbb{R}$. Suppose that some $\delta > 0$ satisfies the definition of uniform continuity for $\varepsilon = 1$. Set $x = 1/\delta$ and $\tilde{x} = 1/\delta + \delta/2$. Then certainly $|\tilde{x} - x| < \delta$, but

$$|f(\tilde{x}) - f(x)| = \left|\left(\frac{1}{\delta} + \frac{\delta}{2}\right)^2 - \frac{1}{\delta^2}\right| = \left|\frac{1}{\delta^2} + 1 + \frac{\delta^2}{4} - \frac{1}{\delta^2}\right| = 1 + \frac{\delta^2}{4} > \varepsilon.$$

This contradicts uniform continuity.

Is the cubing function of the previous exercise uniformly continuous on $\mathbb{R}$? On $[0, 500]$?

6.3.4. (a) Show that if $I \subset \mathbb{R}$ is an interval (possibly all of $\mathbb{R}$), $f : I \longrightarrow \mathbb{R}$ is differentiable, and there exists a positive constant R such that $|f'(x)| \le R$ for all $x \in I$ then f is uniformly continuous on I.

(b) Prove that sine and cosine are uniformly continuous on $\mathbb{R}$.

6.3.5. Let $f : [0, +\infty) \longrightarrow \mathbb{R}$ be the square root function $f(x) = \sqrt{x}$. You may take for granted that f is ε-δ continuous on $[0, +\infty)$.

(a) What does part (a) of the previous problem say about the uniform continuity of f?

(b) Is f uniformly continuous?

6.3.6. Let J be a box in $\mathbb{R}^n$ with sides of length less than δ/n. Show that all points x and $\tilde{x}$ in J satisfy $|\tilde{x} - x| < \delta$.

6.3.7. For $\int_B f$ to exist, it is sufficient that $f : B \longrightarrow \mathbb{R}$ be continuous, but it is not necessary. What preceding exercise provides an example of this? Here is another example. Let $B = [0, 1]$ and let $f : B \longrightarrow \mathbb{R}$ be monotonic increasing, meaning that if $x_1 < x_2$ in B then $f(x_1) \le f(x_2)$. Show that such a function is bounded, though it need not be continuous. Use the integrability criterion to show that $\int_B f$ exists.

6.3.8. The natural logarithm is defined as an integral. Let $r : \mathbb{R}^+ \longrightarrow \mathbb{R}$ be the reciprocal function, $r(x) = 1/x$ for $x > 0$. The natural logarithm is

$$\ln : \mathbb{R}^+ \longrightarrow \mathbb{R}, \qquad \ln(x) = \begin{cases} \int_{[1,x]} r & \text{if } x \ge 1, \\ -\int_{[x,1]} r & \text{if } 0 < x < 1. \end{cases}$$

We know that the integrals in the previous display exist, because the reciprocal function is continuous.

(a) Show that $\lim_{x\to\infty} \ln x/x = 0$ as follows. Let some small $\varepsilon > 0$ be given. For $x > 2/\varepsilon$, let $u(x,\varepsilon)$ denote the sum of the areas of the boxes $[1, 2/\varepsilon] \times [0, 1]$ and $[2/\varepsilon, x] \times [0, \varepsilon/2]$. Show that $u(x, \varepsilon) \geq \ln x$. (Draw a figure showing the boxes and the graph of r, and use the words *upper sum* in your answer.) Compute $\lim_{x\to\infty} u(\varepsilon, x)/x$ (here ε remains fixed), and use your result to show that $u(\varepsilon, x)/x < \varepsilon$ for all large enough x. This shows that $\lim_{x\to\infty} \ln x/x = 0$.

(b) Let $a > 0$ and $b > 1$ be fixed real numbers. Part (a) shows that

$$\ln x/x < \ln b/(a + 1) \quad \text{for all large } x.$$

Explain why consequently

$$x^a/b^x < 1/x \quad \text{for all large } x.$$

This proves that *exponential growth dominates polynomial growth*,

$$\lim_{x\to\infty} \frac{x^a}{b^x} = 0, \quad a > 0, \ b > 1.$$

Thus, for example,

$$\lim_{x\to\infty} \frac{x^{1000000}}{1.0000001^x} = 0,$$

even though the values of $x^{1000000}/1.0000001^x$ are enormous as x begins to grow.

6.4 Integration of Functions of One Variable

In a first calculus course one learns to do computations such as the following: to evaluate

$$\int_{x=1}^{e} \frac{(\ln x)^2}{x} \, dx,$$

let $u = \ln x$; then $du = dx/x$, and as x goes from 1 to e, u goes from 0 to 1, so the integral equals

$$\int_{u=0}^{1} u^2 \, du = \frac{1}{3} u^3 \Big|_0^1 = \frac{1}{3}.$$

Or such as this: to evaluate

$$\int_0^9 \frac{dx}{\sqrt{1 + \sqrt{x}}},$$

let $u = \sqrt{1 + \sqrt{x}}$. Then some algebra shows that $x = (u^2 - 1)^2$, and so $dx = 4(u^2 - 1)u \, du$. Also, when $x = 0$, $u = 1$, and when $x = 9$, $u = 2$. Therefore the integral is

$$\int_0^9 \frac{dx}{\sqrt{1+\sqrt{x}}} = 4 \int_1^2 \frac{(u^2-1)u}{u}\, du = 4 \int_1^2 (u^2-1)\, du$$

$$= 4\left(\frac{1}{3}u^3 - u\right)\Bigg|_1^2 = \frac{16}{3}.$$

Although both of these examples use substitution, they differ from each other in a way that a first calculus course may not explain. The first substitution involved picking an x-dependent u (i.e., $u = \ln x$) where $u'(x)$ (i.e., $1/x$) was present in the integral and got absorbed by the substitution. The second substitution took an opposite form to the first: this time the x-dependent u was inverted to produce a u-dependent x, and the factor $u'(x)$ was introduced into the integral rather than eliminated from it. Somehow, two different things are going on under the guise of *u-substitution*.

In this section we specialize our theory of multivariable integration to $n = 1$ and review two tools for evaluating one-dimensional integrals, the fundamental theorem of integral calculus (FTIC) and the change of variable theorem. Writing these down precisely will clarify the examples we just worked. More importantly, generalizing these results appropriately to n dimensions is the subject of the remainder of these notes.

The multivariable integral notation of this chapter, specialized to one dimension, is $\int_{[a,b]} f$. For familiarity, replace this by the usual notation,

$$\int_a^b f = \int_{[a,b]} f \quad \text{for } a \le b.$$

As matters stand, the redefined notation $\int_a^b f$ makes sense only when $a \le b$, so extend its definition to

$$\int_a^b f = -\int_b^a f \quad \text{for } a > b.$$

Once this is done, the same relation between *signed integrals* holds regardless of which (if either) of a and b is larger,

$$\int_a^b f = -\int_b^a f \quad \text{for all } a \text{ and } b.$$

Something nontrivial is happening here: when the multivariable integration of this chapter is specialized to one dimension, it can be extended to incorporate a sign convention to represent the order on $\mathbb{R}$. If $a < b$ then $\int_a^b$ describes positive traversal along the real line from a up to b, while $\int_b^a$ describes negative traversal from b down to a. This sort of thing does not obviously generalize to higher dimensions, because $\mathbb{R}^n$ is not ordered.

Casewise inspection shows that for every three points $a, b, c \in \mathbb{R}$ in any order, and for every integrable function $f : [\min\{a,b,c\}, \max\{a,b,c\}] \longrightarrow \mathbb{R}$,

$$\int_a^c f = \int_a^b f + \int_b^c f.$$

Also, if $f : [\min\{a,b\}, \max\{a,b\}] \longrightarrow \mathbb{R}$ takes the constant value k then

$$\int_a^b f = k(b-a),$$

again regardless of which of a and b is larger. These facts generalize Proposition 6.2.4 and Exercise 6.2.3 to signed one-variable integration.

Each of the next two theorems describes a sense in which one-variable differentiation and integration are inverse operations. Both are called the fundamental theorem of integral calculus, but the second is more deserving of the title because of how far it generalizes.

Theorem 6.4.1. *Let the function* $f : [a,b] \longrightarrow \mathbb{R}$ *be continuous. Define a function*

$$F : [a,b] \longrightarrow \mathbb{R}, \qquad F(x) = \int_a^x f.$$

Then F *is differentiable on* $[a,b]$, *and* $F' = f$.

Proof. Let x and $x+h$ lie in $[a,b]$ with $h \neq 0$. Study the difference quotient

$$\frac{F(x+h) - F(x)}{h} = \frac{\int_a^{x+h} f - \int_a^x f}{h} = \frac{\int_x^{x+h} f}{h}.$$

If $h > 0$ then $m_{[x,x+h]}(f) \cdot h \leq \int_x^{x+h} f \leq M_{[x,x+h]}(f) \cdot h$, and dividing through by h shows that the difference quotient lies between $m_{[x,x+h]}(f)$ and $M_{[x,x+h]}(f)$. Thus the difference quotient is forced to $f(x)$ as h goes to 0, since f is continuous. A similar analysis applies when $h < 0$.

Alternatively, an argument using the characterizing property of the derivative and the Landau–Bachmann notation does not require separate cases depending on the sign of h. Compute that

$$F(x+h) - F(x) - f(x)h = \int_x^{x+h} (f - f(x)) = \int_x^{x+h} o(1) = o(h),$$

But here the reader needs to believe, or check, the last equality.   □

The alert reader will recall the convention in these notes that a mapping can be differentiable only at an interior point of its domain. In particular, the derivative of a function $F : [a,b] \longrightarrow \mathbb{R}$ is undefined at a and b. Hence the statement of Theorem 6.4.1 is inconsistent with our usage, and strictly speaking the theorem should conclude that F is continuous on $[a,b]$ and differentiable on (a,b) with derivative $F' = f$. The given proof does show this, since the existence of the one-sided derivative of F at each endpoint makes F continuous there.

However, we prohibited derivatives at endpoints only to tidy up our statements. An alternative would have been to make the definition that for every compact, connected set $K \subset \mathbb{R}^n$ (both of these terms were discussed in Section 2.4), a mapping $f : K \longrightarrow \mathbb{R}^m$ is differentiable on K if there exist an open set $A \subset \mathbb{R}^n$ containing K and an extension of f to a differentiable mapping $f : A \longrightarrow \mathbb{R}^m$. Here the word *extension* means that the new function f on A has the same behavior on K as the old f. One reason that we avoided this slightly more general definition is that it is tortuous to track through the material in Chapter 4, especially for the student who is seeing the ideas for the first time. Also, this definition requires that the critical point theorem (stating that the extrema of a function occur at points where its derivative is 0) be fussily rephrased to say that this criterion applies only to the extrema that occur at the interior points of the domain. From the same preference for tidy statements over fussy ones, we now allow the more general definition of the derivative.

Proving the FTIC from Theorem 6.4.1 requires the observation that if two functions $F_1, F_2 : [a, b] \longrightarrow \mathbb{R}$ are differentiable, and $F_1' = F_2'$, then $F_1 = F_2 + c$ for some constant c. The observation follows from the mean value theorem and is an exercise.

Theorem 6.4.2 (Fundamental theorem of integral calculus). *Suppose that the function $F : [a, b] \longrightarrow \mathbb{R}$ is differentiable and F' is continuous. Then*

$$\int_a^b F' = F(b) - F(a).$$

Proof. Define $F_2 : [a, b] \longrightarrow \mathbb{R}$ by $F_2(x) = \int_a^x F'$. Then $F_2' = F'$ by the preceding theorem, so (Exercise 6.4.3) there exists a constant c such that for all $x \in [a, b]$,

$$F_2(x) = F(x) + c. \tag{6.3}$$

Plug $x = a$ into (6.3) to get $0 = F(a) + c$, so $c = -F(a)$. Next plug in $x = b$ to get $F_2(b) = F(b) - F(a)$. Since $F_2(b) = \int_a^b F'$ by definition, the proof is complete. $\square$

One can also prove the fundamental theorem with no reference to Theorem 6.4.1, letting the mean value theorem do all the work instead. Compute that for every partition P of $[a, b]$, whose points are $a = t_0 < t_1 < \cdots < t_k = b$,

$$F(b) - F(a) = \sum_{i=1}^k F(t_i) - F(t_{i-1}) \quad \text{(telescoping sum)}$$

$$= \sum_{i=1}^k F'(c_i)(t_i - t_{i-1}) \quad \text{with each } c_i \in (t_{i-1}, t_i), \text{ by the MVT}$$

$$\leq U(F', P).$$

Since P is arbitrary, $F(b) - F(a)$ is a lower bound of the upper sums and hence is at most the upper integral $U \int_a^b F'$. Since F' is continuous, its integral exists and the upper integral is the integral. That is,

$$F(b) - F(a) \le \int_a^b F'.$$

A similar argument with lower sums gives the opposite inequality.

In one-variable calculus one learns various techniques to find antiderivatives; i.e., given continuous f, one finds F such that $F' = f$. Once this is done, evaluating $\int_a^b f$ is merely plugging in to the FTIC. But since not all continuous functions have antiderivatives that are readily found, or even possible to write in an elementary form (for example, try $f(x) = e^{-x^2}$ or $f(x) = \sin(x^2)$), the FTIC has its limitations.

Another tool for evaluating one-dimensional integrals is the change of variable theorem. The idea is to transform one integral to another that may be better suited to the FTIC.

Theorem 6.4.3 (Change of variable theorem; forward substitution formula). *Let $\phi : [a, b] \longrightarrow \mathbb{R}$ be differentiable with continuous derivative and let $f : \phi[a, b] \longrightarrow \mathbb{R}$ be continuous. Then*

$$\int_a^b (f \circ \phi) \cdot \phi' = \int_{\phi(a)}^{\phi(b)} f. \tag{6.4}$$

Proof. Use Theorem 6.4.1 to define $F : \phi[a, b] \longrightarrow \mathbb{R}$ such that $F' = f$. By the chain rule, $F \circ \phi$ has derivative $(F \circ \phi)' = (F' \circ \phi) \cdot \phi' = (f \circ \phi) \cdot \phi'$, which is continuous on $[a, b]$. Thus by the FTIC twice,

$$\int_a^b (f \circ \phi) \cdot \phi' = \int_a^b (F \circ \phi)' = (F \circ \phi)(b) - (F \circ \phi)(a)$$

$$= F(\phi(b)) - F(\phi(a)) = \int_{\phi(a)}^{\phi(b)} F' = \int_{\phi(a)}^{\phi(b)} f.$$

$\square$

One way to apply the change of variable theorem to an integral $\int_a^b g$ is to recognize that the integrand takes the form $g = (f \circ \phi) \cdot \phi'$, giving the left side of (6.4) for suitable f and ϕ such that the right side $\int_{\phi(a)}^{\phi(b)} f$ is easier to evaluate. This method is called **integration by forward substitution**. For instance, for the first integral $\int_{x=1}^e ((\ln x)^2)/x \, dx$ at the beginning of this section, take

$$g : \mathbb{R}^+ \longrightarrow \mathbb{R}, \qquad g(x) = (\ln x)^2/x.$$

To evaluate $\int_1^e g$, define

$$\phi : \mathbb{R}^+ \longrightarrow \mathbb{R}, \qquad \phi(x) = \ln x$$

and
$$f : \mathbb{R} \longrightarrow \mathbb{R}, \qquad f(u) = u^2.$$

Then $g = (f \circ \phi) \cdot \phi'$, and $\phi(1) = 0$, $\phi(e) = 1$, so by the change of variable theorem,
$$\int_1^e g = \int_1^e (f \circ \phi) \cdot \phi' = \int_{\phi(1)}^{\phi(e)} f = \int_0^1 f.$$

Since f has antiderivative F where $F(u) = u^3/3$, the last integral equals $F(1) - F(0) = 1/3$ by the FTIC.

The second integral at the beginning of the section was evaluated not by the change of variable theorem as given, but by a consequence of it:

Corollary 6.4.4 (Inverse substitution formula). *Let $\phi : [a,b] \longrightarrow \mathbb{R}$ be continuous and let $f : \phi[a,b] \longrightarrow \mathbb{R}$ be continuous. Suppose further that ϕ is invertible and that ϕ^{-1} is differentiable with continuous derivative. Then*
$$\int_a^b (f \circ \phi) = \int_{\phi(a)}^{\phi(b)} f \cdot (\phi^{-1})'.$$

The formula in the corollary is the formula for **integration by inverse substitution**. To obtain it from (6.4), consider the diagrams for forward and inverse substitution:

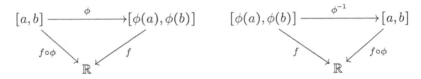

Noting where the various elements of the left diagram occur in the forward substitution formula $\int_a^b (f \circ \phi) \cdot \phi' = \int_{\phi(a)}^{\phi(b)} f$ shows that applying the forward substitution suitably to the right diagram gives $\int_{\phi(a)}^{\phi(b)} f \cdot (\phi^{-1})' = \int_a^b (f \circ \phi)$, the inverse substitution formula as claimed.

To apply the formula in Corollary 6.4.4 to an integral $\int_a^b g$, write the integrand as $g = f \circ \phi$, giving the left side, and then invert ϕ and differentiate the inverse to see whether the right side is easier to evaluate. For instance, for the second integral $\int_0^9 dx/\sqrt{1 + \sqrt{x}}$ at the beginning of the section, define
$$\phi : \mathbb{R}_{\geq 0} \longrightarrow \mathbb{R}_{\geq 1}, \qquad \phi(x) = \sqrt{1 + \sqrt{x}}$$

and
$$f : \mathbb{R}_{\geq 1} \longrightarrow \mathbb{R}, \qquad f(u) = 1/u.$$

Then the integral is
$$\int_0^9 \frac{dx}{\sqrt{1 + \sqrt{x}}} = \int_0^9 (f \circ \phi).$$

Let
$$u = \phi(x) = \sqrt{1 + \sqrt{x}}.$$
Then a little algebra gives
$$x = (u^2 - 1)^2 = \phi^{-1}(u),$$
so that
$$(\phi^{-1})'(u) = 4u(u^2 - 1).$$
Since $\phi(0) = 1$ and $\phi(9) = 2$, the integral becomes
$$\int_0^9 \frac{dx}{\sqrt{1 + \sqrt{x}}} = \int_0^9 (f \circ \phi) = \int_1^2 f \cdot (\phi^{-1})' = 4 \int_1^2 \frac{u(u^2 - 1)\, du}{u},$$

and as before, this evaluates easily to 16/3.

The variable-based notation used to work the two integrals at the beginning of this section, with x and u and dx and du, is much easier mnemonically than the function-based notation used to rework them with the change of variable theorem and its corollary. But a purist would object to it on two counts. First, expressions such as $(\ln x)^2/x$ and u^2 are not functions, they are the outputs of functions, so strictly speaking we can't integrate them. The problem is not serious, it is mere pedantry: we simply need to loosen our notation to let $\int_{x=a}^b f(x)$ be synonymous with $\int_a^b f$, at the cost of an unnecessary new symbol x. This x is called a *dummy variable*, because another symbol would do just as well: $\int_{y=a}^b f(y)$ and $\int_{\heartsuit=a}^b f(\heartsuit)$ also denote $\int_a^b f$. At the theoretical level, where we deal with functions as functions, this extra notation is useless and cumbersome, but in any down-to-earth example it is in fact a convenience because describing functions by formulas is easier and more direct than introducing new symbols to name them.

The second, more serious, objection to the variable-based notation is to the dx, the du, and mysterious relations such as $du = dx/x$ between them. What kind of objects are dx and du? In a first calculus course they are typically described as infinitesimally small changes in x and u, but our theory of integration is not based on such hazy notions; in fact, it was created in the nineteenth century to answer objections to their validity. (Though infinitesimals were revived and put on a firm footing in the 1960s, we have no business with them here.) An alternative is to view dx and du as formal symbols that serve, along with the integral sign $\int$, as bookends around the expression for the function being integrated. This viewpoint leaves notation such as $du = dx/x$ still meaningless in its own right. In a first calculus course it may be taught as a procedure with no real justification, whereas by contrast, the revisited versions of the two integral-calculations of this section are visibly applications of results that have been proved. However, the classical method is probably easier for most of us, its notational conventions dovetailing with the change of variable theorem and its corollary so well. So feel free to continue using it. (And remember to switch the limits of integration when you do.)

However, to underscore that dx is an unnecessary, meaningless symbol, it will generally not be used in these notes until it is defined in Chapter 9, as something called a *differential form*.

Exercises

6.4.1. (a) Show that for three points $a, b, c \in \mathbb{R}$ in any order, and every integrable function $f : [\min\{a,b,c\}, \max\{a,b,c\}] \longrightarrow \mathbb{R}$, $\int_a^c f = \int_a^b f + \int_b^c f$.
   (b) Show that if $f : [\min\{a,b\}, \max\{a,b\}] \longrightarrow \mathbb{R}$ takes the constant value k then $\int_a^b f = k(b-a)$, regardless of which of a and b is larger.

6.4.2. Complete the proof of Theorem 6.4.1 by analyzing the case $h < 0$.

6.4.3. Show that if $F_1, F_2 : [a, b] \longrightarrow \mathbb{R}$ are differentiable and $F_1' = F_2'$, then $F_1 = F_2 + C$ for some constant C. This result was used in this section to prove the fundamental theorem of calculus (Theorem 6.4.2), so do not use that theorem to address this exercise. However, this exercise does require a theorem. Reducing to the case $F_2 = 0$, as in the comment in Exercise 6.2.7, will make this exercise a bit tidier.

6.4.4. (a) Suppose that $0 \le a \le b$ and $f : [a^2, b^2] \longrightarrow \mathbb{R}$ is continuous. Define $F : [a, b] \longrightarrow \mathbb{R}$ by $F(x) = \int_{a^2}^{x^2} f$. Does F' exist, and if so then what is it?
   (b) More generally, suppose $f : \mathbb{R} \longrightarrow \mathbb{R}$ is continuous, and $\alpha, \beta : \mathbb{R} \longrightarrow \mathbb{R}$ are differentiable. Define $F : \mathbb{R} \longrightarrow \mathbb{R}$ by $F(x) = \int_{\alpha(x)}^{\beta(x)} f$. Does F' exist, and if so then what is it?

6.4.5. Let $f : [0, 1] \longrightarrow \mathbb{R}$ be continuous and suppose that for all $x \in [0, 1]$, $\int_0^x f = \int_x^1 f$. What is f?

6.4.6. Find all differentiable functions $f : \mathbb{R}_{\ge 0} \longrightarrow \mathbb{R}$ such that for all $x \in \mathbb{R}_{\ge 0}$, $(f(x))^2 = \int_0^x f$.

6.4.7. Define $f : \mathbb{R}^+ \longrightarrow \mathbb{R}$ by $f(u) = e^{(u + \frac{1}{u})}/u$ and $F : \mathbb{R}^+ \longrightarrow \mathbb{R}$ by $F(x) = \int_1^x f$. Show that F behaves somewhat like a logarithm in that $F(1/x) = -F(x)$ for all $x \in \mathbb{R}^+$. Interpret this property of F as a statement about area under the graph of f. (Hint: define $\phi : \mathbb{R}^+ \longrightarrow \mathbb{R}^+$ by $\phi(u) = 1/u$, and show that $(f \circ \phi) \cdot \phi' = -f$.)

6.5 Integration over Nonboxes

So far, we know that $\int_B f$ exists if B is a box and $f : B \longrightarrow \mathbb{R}$ is continuous (Theorem 6.3.1). With some more work, the theorem can be refined to relax these requirements. The basic idea is that $\int_B f$ still exists if f is discontinuous on a small enough subset of B. The idea isn't hard conceptually, but its justification requires some bookkeeping. Once it is established, integration over compact sets K other than boxes is easy to define, provided that their boundaries are suitably small.

To quantify the notion of small, and more generally the notion of set size, let a set $S \subset \mathbb{R}^n$ be given. The **characteristic function of** S is

$$\chi_S : \mathbb{R}^n \longrightarrow \mathbb{R}, \qquad \chi_S(x) = \begin{cases} 1 & \text{if } x \in S, \\ 0 & \text{otherwise.} \end{cases}$$

Suppose that S is bounded, meaning that S sits in some box B.

Definition 6.5.1 (Volume of a set). *The* **volume** *of a bounded set* $S \subset \mathbb{R}^n$ *is*

$$\text{vol}(S) = \int_B \chi_S \quad \text{where } B \text{ is any box containing } S,$$

if this integral exists.

This definition requires several comments. At first glance it seems ill-posed. Conceivably, $\int_B \chi_S$ could exist for some boxes B containing S but not others, and it could take different values for the various B where it exists. In fact, some technique shows that if $\int_B \chi_S$ exists for *some* box B containing S then it exists for *every* such box and always takes the same value, so the definition makes sense after all. See the exercises. Also, an exercise shows that the volume of a box B is the same under Definition 6.5.1 as under Definition 6.1.4, as it must be for grammatical consistency. Finally, note that not all sets have volume, only those whose characteristic functions are integrable.

Sets of volume zero are small enough that they don't interfere with integration. To prove such a result explicitly, we first translate the definition of volume zero into statements about the machinery of the integral. Let $S \subset \mathbb{R}^n$ sit in a box B, and let P be a partition of B. The subboxes J of P consist of two types:

$$\text{type I} : J \text{ such that } J \cap S \neq \varnothing$$

and

$$\text{type II} : J \text{ such that } J \cap S = \varnothing.$$

Thus S sits in the union of subboxes J of type I, and the sum of their volumes gives an upper sum for $\int_B \chi_S$.

For example, Figure 6.14 shows a circle S inside a box B, and a partition P of B, where the type I subboxes of the partition are shaded. The shaded boxes visibly have a small total area. Similarly, Figure 6.15 shows a smooth piece of surface in $\mathbb{R}^3$, then shows it inside a partitioned box, and Figure 6.16 shows some of the type I subboxes of the partition. Figure 6.16 also shows a smooth arc in $\mathbb{R}^3$ and some of the type I rectangles that cover it, with the ambient box and the rest of the partition now tacit. Figure 6.16 is meant to show that all the type I boxes, which combine to cover the surface or the arc, have a small total volume.

The following fact is convenient.

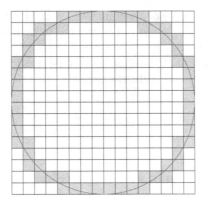

Figure 6.14. Circle, box, partition, and type I subboxes

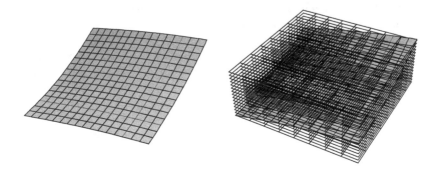

Figure 6.15. A two-dimensional set in $\mathbb{R}^3$; the set inside a partitioned box

Proposition 6.5.2 (Volume-zero criterion). *A set S contained in a box B has volume zero if and only if for every $\varepsilon > 0$ there exists a partition P of B such that*

$$\sum_{J:\text{type I}} \text{vol}(J) < \varepsilon.$$

The proof is an exercise. This criterion makes it plausible that every bounded smooth arc in $\mathbb{R}^2$ has volume zero, and similarly for a bounded smooth arc or smooth piece of surface in $\mathbb{R}^3$. The next result uses the criterion to provide a general class of volume-zero sets. Recall that for every set $S \subset \mathbb{R}^k$ and every mapping $\varphi : S \longrightarrow \mathbb{R}^\ell$, the **graph** of φ is a subset of $\mathbb{R}^{k+\ell}$,

$$\text{graph}(\varphi) = \{(x, \varphi(x)) : x \in S\}.$$

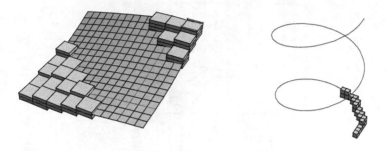

Figure 6.16. Some type I subboxes of the partition, and for an arc in $\mathbb{R}^3$

Proposition 6.5.3 (Graphs have volume zero). *Let B be a box in $\mathbb{R}^m$, and let $\varphi: B \longrightarrow \mathbb{R}$ be continuous. Then graph(φ) has volume zero.*

The idea is that the graph of the function φ in the proposition will describe some of the points of discontinuity of a different function f that we want to integrate. Thus the dimension m in the proposition is typically $n-1$, where the function f that we want to integrate has n-dimensional input.

Proof. The continuity of φ on B is uniform, and the image of φ, being compact, sits in some interval I.

Let $\varepsilon > 0$ be given. Set ε' equal to any positive number less than $\varepsilon/(2\mathrm{vol}(B))$ such that length(I)/ε' is an integer. There exist a partition Q of I whose subintervals K have length ε' and a $\delta > 0$ such that for all $x, \tilde{x} \in B$,

$$|\tilde{x} - x| < \delta \quad \Longrightarrow \quad |\varphi(\tilde{x}) - \varphi(x)| < \varepsilon'. \tag{6.5}$$

Now take a partition P of B whose subboxes J have sides of length less than δ/m, so that if two points are in a common subbox J then the distance between them is less than δ. Consider the partition $P \times Q$ of $B \times I$. For each subbox J of P there exist at most two subboxes $J \times K$ of $P \times Q$ over J that intersect the graph of φ, i.e., subboxes of type I. To see this, note that if we have three or more such subboxes, then some pair $J \times K$ and $J \times K'$ are not vertical neighbors, and so every hypothetical pair of points of the graph, one in each subbox, are less than distance δ apart horizontally but at least distance ε' apart vertically. But by (6.5), this is impossible. (See Figure 6.17. The horizontal direction in the figure is only a schematic of the m-dimensional box B, but the vertical direction accurately depicts the one-dimensional codomain of φ.)

Now, working with subboxes $J \times K$ of $P \times Q$, compute that

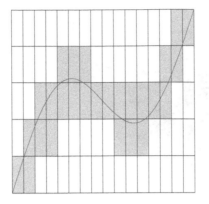

Figure 6.17. The graph meets at most two boxes over each base

$$\sum_{\text{type I}} \text{vol}(J \times K) = \sum_{\text{type I}} \text{vol}(J) \cdot \varepsilon' \qquad \text{since length}(K) = \varepsilon'$$

$$\leq 2 \sum_{J} \text{vol}(J) \cdot \varepsilon' \qquad \text{by the preceding paragraph}$$

$$= 2\text{vol}(B) \cdot \varepsilon' < \varepsilon \qquad \text{since } \varepsilon' < \varepsilon/(2\text{vol}(B)),$$

and the proof is complete by the volume-zero criterion. $\square$

An exercise shows that every finite union of sets of volume zero also has volume zero, and another exercise shows that every subset of a set of volume zero also has volume zero. These facts and the preceding proposition are enough to demonstrate that many regions have boundaries of volume zero. The boundary of a set consists of all points simultaneously near the set and near its complement—roughly speaking, its edge. (Unfortunately, the mathematical terms *bounded* and *boundary* need have nothing to do with each other. A set with a boundary need not be bounded, and a bounded set need not have any boundary points nor contain any of its boundary points if it does have them.) For example, the set in Figure 6.18 has a boundary consisting of four graphs of functions on one-dimensional boxes, i.e., on intervals. Two of the boundary pieces are graphs of functions $y = \varphi(x)$, and the other two are graphs of functions $x = \varphi(y)$. Two of the four functions are constant functions.

The main result of this section is that discontinuity on a set of volume zero does not interfere with integration.

Theorem 6.5.4 (Near-continuity implies integrability). *Let $B \subset \mathbb{R}^n$ be a box. Let $f : B \longrightarrow \mathbb{R}$ be bounded, and continuous except on a set $S \subset B$ of volume zero. Then $\int_B f$ exists.*

Proof. Let $\varepsilon > 0$ be given.

The proof involves two partitions. Because f is bounded, there exists a positive number R such that $|f(x)| < R$ for all $x \in B$. Take a partition P

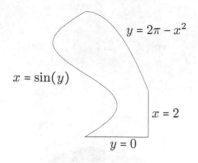

$$y = 2\pi - x^2$$

$$x = \sin(y)$$

$$x = 2$$

$$y = 0$$

Figure 6.18. Boundary with area zero

of B whose subboxes J of type I (those intersecting the set S where f is discontinuous) have volumes adding to less than $\varepsilon/(4R)$. (See Figure 6.19, in which the function f is the dome shape over the unit disk but is 0 outside the unit disk, making it discontinuous on the unit circle.)

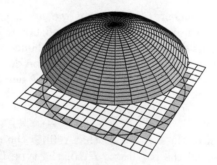

Figure 6.19. Type I subboxes of small total area

Consider some yet unspecified refinement P' of P dividing each subbox J of P into further subboxes J'. (See Figure 6.20, in which the original boxes J of type I remain shaded, but each box J of either type has been further partitioned.) On every J', $M_{J'}(f) - m_{J'}(f) \leq 2R$, and so a short calculation shows that regardless of how the refinement P' is to be specified, its subboxes J' that sit inside type I subboxes J of P make only a small contribution to the difference between the lower sum and the upper sum of f over P',

$$\sum_{J \,:\, \text{type I}} \sum_{J' \subset J} (M_{J'}(f) - m_{J'}(f)) \operatorname{vol}(J')$$

$$\leq 2R \sum_{J \,:\, \text{type I}} \sum_{J' \subset J} \operatorname{vol}(J') = 2R \sum_{J \,:\, \text{type I}} \operatorname{vol}(J) < 2R \frac{\varepsilon}{4R} = \frac{\varepsilon}{2}. \tag{6.6}$$

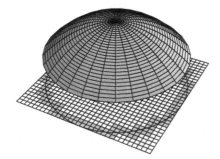

Figure 6.20. Refinement of the partition

To specify the refinement P' of P that we need, consider the type II subboxes J of P, i.e., the union of the unshaded boxes in Figure 6.19. The function f is continuous on each such subbox and hence integrable over it by Theorem 6.3.1. Let the number of these subboxes be denoted N. By ($\Longrightarrow$) of the integrability criterion, each type II subbox J has a partition P'_J such that

$$U(f, P'_J) - L(f, P'_J) < \frac{\varepsilon}{2N}.$$

Let P' be a partition of the full box B that refines the original partition P and also incorporates all the partitions P'_J of the type II subboxes J. Thus the intersection of P' with any particular type II subbox J refines P'_J. Since refinement cannot increase the distance between lower and upper sums, another short calculation shows that the subboxes J' of P' that sit inside type II subboxes J of P also make only a small contribution to the difference between the lower sum and the upper sum of f over P',

$$\sum_{J \,:\, \text{type II}} \sum_{J' \subset J} (M_{J'}(f) - m_{J'}(f)) \operatorname{vol}(J')$$

$$\leq \sum_{J \,:\, \text{type II}} U(f, P'_J) - L(f, P'_J) < N \cdot \frac{\varepsilon}{2N} = \frac{\varepsilon}{2}. \tag{6.7}$$

Finally, combining (6.6) and (6.7) shows that $U(f, P') - L(f, P') < \varepsilon$, and so by ($\Longleftarrow$) of the integrability criterion, $\int_B f$ exists. $\square$

To recapitulate the argument: The fact that f is bounded means that its small set of discontinuities can't cause much difference between lower and upper sums, and the continuity of f on the rest of its domain poses no obstacle to integrability either. The only difficulty was making the ideas fit into our box-counting definition of the integral. The reader could well object that proving Theorem 6.5.4 shouldn't have to be this complicated. Indeed, the theory of integration being presented here, *Riemann integration*, involves laborious proofs precisely because it uses such crude technology: finite sums over boxes. More powerful theories of integration exist, with stronger theorems and more graceful arguments. However, those theories also entail the startup cost of assimilating a larger, more abstract set of working ideas, making them difficult to present as quickly as Riemann integration.

Now we can discuss integration over nonboxes.

Definition 6.5.5 (Known-integrable function). *A function*

$$f : K \longrightarrow \mathbb{R}$$

is **known-integrable** *if K is a compact subset of $\mathbb{R}^n$ having boundary of volume zero, and if f is bounded on K and is continuous on all of K except possibly a subset of volume zero.*

For example, let $K = \{(x,y) : |(x,y)| \le 1\}$ be the closed unit disk in $\mathbb{R}^2$, and define

$$f : K \longrightarrow \mathbb{R}, \qquad f(x,y) = \begin{cases} 1 & \text{if } x \ge 0, \\ -1 & \text{if } x < 0. \end{cases}$$

To see that this function is known-integrable, note that the boundary of K is the union of the upper and lower unit semicircles, which are graphs of continuous functions on the same 1-dimensional box,

$$\varphi_\pm : [-1,1] \longrightarrow \mathbb{R}, \qquad \varphi_\pm(x) = \pm\sqrt{1 - x^2}.$$

Thus the boundary of K has area zero. Furthermore, f is bounded on K, and f is continuous on all of K except the vertical interval $\{0\} \times [-1,1]$, which has area zero by the 2-dimensional box area formula.

Definition 6.5.6 (Integral over a nonbox). *Let*

$$f : K \longrightarrow \mathbb{R}$$

be a known-integrable function. Extend its domain to $\mathbb{R}^n$ by defining a new function

$$\tilde{f} : \mathbb{R}^n \longrightarrow \mathbb{R}, \qquad \tilde{f}(x) = \begin{cases} f(x) & \text{if } x \in K, \\ 0 & \text{if } x \notin K. \end{cases}$$

Then the integral of f over K is

$$\int_K f = \int_B \tilde{f} \quad \text{where } B \text{ is any box containing } K.$$

For the example just before the definition, the extended function is

$$\tilde{f} : \mathbb{R}^2 \longrightarrow \mathbb{R}, \qquad f(x,y) = \begin{cases} 1 & \text{if } |(x,y)| \le 1 \text{ and } x \ge 0, \\ -1 & \text{if } |(x,y)| \le 1 \text{ and } x < 0, \\ 0 & \text{if } |(x,y)| > 1, \end{cases}$$

and to integrate the original function over the disk, we integrate the extended function over the box $B = [0,1] \times [0,1]$.

Returning to generality, the integral on the right side of the equality in the definition exists because $\tilde{f}$ is bounded and discontinuous on a set of volume zero, as required for Theorem 6.5.4. In particular, the definition of volume is now, sensibly enough,

$$\mathrm{vol}(K) = \int_K 1.$$

Naturally, the result of Proposition 6.2.4, that the integral over the whole is the sum of the integrals over the pieces, is not particular to boxes and subboxes.

Proposition 6.5.7. *Let $K \subset \mathbb{R}^n$ be a compact set whose boundary has volume zero. Let $f : K \longrightarrow \mathbb{R}$ be continuous. Further, let $K = K_1 \cup K_2$ where each K_j is compact and the intersection $K_1 \cap K_2$ has volume zero. Then f is integrable over K_1 and K_2, and*

$$\int_{K_1} f + \int_{K_2} f = \int_K f.$$

Proof. Define

$$f_1 : K \longrightarrow \mathbb{R}, \qquad f_1(x) = \begin{cases} f(x) & \text{if } x \in K_1, \\ 0 & \text{otherwise.} \end{cases}$$

Then f_1 is known-integrable on K, and so $\int_K f_1$ exists and equals $\int_{K_1} f_1$. Define a corresponding function $f_2 : K \longrightarrow \mathbb{R}$, for which the corresponding conclusions hold. It follows that

$$\int_{K_1} f_1 + \int_{K_2} f_2 = \int_K f_1 + \int_K f_2 = \int_K (f_1 + f_2).$$

But $f_1 + f_2$ equals f except on the volume-zero set $K_1 \cap K_2$, which contributes nothing to the integral. The result follows.   □

Exercises

6.5.1. (a) Suppose that $I_1 = [a_1, b_1]$, $I_2 = [a_2, b_2]$, ... are intervals in $\mathbb{R}$. Show that their intersection $I_1 \cap I_2 \cap \cdots$ is another interval (possibly empty).

(b) Suppose that $S = S_1 \times \cdots \times S_n$, $T = T_1 \times \cdots \times T_n$, $U = U_1 \times \cdots \times U_n$, ... are Cartesian products of sets. Show that their intersection is

$$S \cap T \cap U \cap \cdots = (S_1 \cap T_1 \cap U_1 \cap \cdots) \times \cdots \times (S_n \cap T_n \cap U_n \cap \cdots).$$

(c) Show that every intersection of boxes in $\mathbb{R}^n$ is another box (possibly empty).

(d) If S is a set and T_1, T_2, T_3, ... are all sets that contain S, show that $T_1 \cap T_2 \cap T_3 \cap \cdots$ contains S.

6.5.2. Let S be a nonempty bounded subset of $\mathbb{R}^n$, let B be any box containing S, and let B' be the intersection of all boxes containing S. By the preceding problem, B' is also a box containing S. Use Proposition 6.2.4 to show that if either of $\int_B \chi_S$ and $\int_{B'} \chi_S$ exist then both exist and they are equal. It follows, as remarked in the text, that the definition of the volume of S is independent of the containing box B.

6.5.3. Let $B \subset \mathbb{R}^n$ be a box. Show that its volume under Definition 6.5.1 equals its volume under Definition 6.1.4. (Hint: Exercise 6.2.3.)

6.5.4. Let S be the set of rational numbers in $[0,1]$. Show that under Definition 6.5.1, the volume (i.e., length) of S does not exist.

6.5.5. Prove the volume-zero criterion.

6.5.6. If $S \subset \mathbb{R}^n$ has volume zero and R is a subset of S, show that R has volume zero. (Hint: $0 \le \chi_R \le \chi_S$.)

6.5.7. Prove that if S_1 and S_2 have volume zero, then so does $S_1 \cup S_2$. (Hint: $\chi_{S_1 \cup S_2} \le \chi_{S_1} + \chi_{S_2}$.)

6.5.8. Find an unbounded set with nonempty boundary, and a bounded set with empty boundary.

6.5.9. Review Figure 6.18 and its discussion in this section. Also review the example that begins after Definition 6.5.5 and continues after Definition 6.5.6. Similarly, use results from this section such as Theorem 6.5.4 and Proposition 6.5.3 to explain why for each set K and function $f : K \longrightarrow \mathbb{R}$ below, the integral $\int_K f$ exists. Draw a picture each time, taking $n = 3$ for the picture in part (f).

(a) $K = \{(x,y) : 2 \le y \le 3, \ 0 \le x \le 1 + \ln y / y\}$, $f(x,y) = e^{xy}$.

(b) $K = \{(x,y) : 1 \le x \le 4, \ 1 \le y \le \sqrt{x}\}$, $f(x,y) = e^{x/y^2} / y^5$.

(c) K = the region between the curves $y = 2x^2$ and $x = 4y^2$, $f(x,y) = 1$.

(d) $K = \{(x,y) : 1 \le x^2 + y^2 \le 2\}$, $f(x,y) = x^2$.

(e) K = the pyramid with vertices $(0,0,0)$, $(3,0,0)$, $(0,3,0)$, $(0,0,3/2)$, $f(x,y,z) = x$.

(f) $K = \{x \in \mathbb{R}^n : |x| \le 1\}$ (the solid unit ball in $\mathbb{R}^n$), $f(x_1,\ldots,x_n) = x_1 \cdots x_n$.

6.6 Fubini's Theorem

With existence theorems for the integral now in hand, this section and the next one present tools to compute integrals.

An n-**fold iterated integral** is n one-dimensional integrals nested inside each other, such as

$$\int_{x_1=a_1}^{b_1} \int_{x_2=a_2}^{b_2} \cdots \int_{x_n=a_n}^{b_n} f(x_1, x_2, \ldots, x_n),$$

for some function $f : [a_1, b_1] \times \cdots \times [a_n, b_n] \longrightarrow \mathbb{R}$. An iterated integral is definitely not the same sort of object as an n-dimensional integral. We can evaluate an iterated integral by working from the inside out. For the innermost integral, f is to be viewed as a function of the variable x_n with its other inputs treated as constants, and so on outward. For example,

$$\int_{x=0}^{1} \int_{y=0}^{2} xy^2 = \int_{x=0}^{1} \frac{1}{3} xy^3 \Big|_{y=0}^{2} = \int_{x=0}^{1} \frac{8}{3} x = \frac{4}{3} x^2 \Big|_{x=0}^{1} = \frac{4}{3}.$$

There are $n!$ different orders in which one can iterate n integrals, e.g., the example just worked is not the same object as $\int_{y=0}^{2} \int_{x=0}^{1} xy^2$. Regardless of order, each one-dimensional integral requires varying its particular input to f while holding the other inputs fixed. The upshot of all this variable-dependence is that there is no reasonable alternative to naming and writing the variables in an iterated integral.

In an inner integral, outer variables may figure not only as inputs to the integrand, but also in the limits of integration. For example, in the calculation

$$\int_{x=0}^{\pi} \int_{y=0}^{x} \cos(x+y) = \int_{x=0}^{\pi} \sin(x+y) \Big|_{y=0}^{x} = \int_{x=0}^{\pi} \sin(2x) - \sin(x) = -2,$$

each inner integral over y is being taken over a segment of x-dependent length as the outer variable x varies from 0 to π. (See Figure 6.21.)

Fubini's theorem says that under suitable conditions, the n-dimensional integral is equal to the n-fold iterated integral. The theorem thus provides an essential calculational tool for multivariable integration.

Theorem 6.6.1 (Fubini's theorem). *Let $B = [a, b] \times [c, d] \subset \mathbb{R}^2$, and let $f : B \longrightarrow \mathbb{R}$ be bounded, and continuous except on a subset $S \subset B$ of area zero, so $\int_B f$ exists. Suppose that for each $x \in [a, b]$, the cross-sectional integral $\int_{y=c}^{d} f(x, y)$ exists; this happens if the cross-sectional function $\varphi_x : [c, d] \longrightarrow \mathbb{R}$ given by $\varphi_x(y) = f(x, y)$ is continuous as a function of y except on a subset of length zero, and in particular this happens if S contains only finitely many points (possibly none) having first coordinate x. Then the iterated integral $\int_{x=a}^{b} \int_{y=c}^{d} f(x, y)$ also exists, and*

$$\int_B f = \int_{x=a}^{b} \int_{y=c}^{d} f(x, y).$$

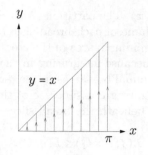

Figure 6.21. Variable range of inner integration

For notational convenience, the theorem is stated only in two dimensions. Replacing $[a, b]$ and $[c, d]$ by boxes gives a more general version with a virtually identical proof. Thinking geometrically in terms of area and volume makes the theorem plausible in two dimensions, because each inner integral is the area of a cross section of the volume under the graph of f. (See Figure 6.22.)

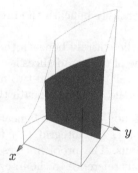

Figure 6.22. Inner integral as cross-sectional area

However, since the multiple integral and the iterated integral are defined analytically as limits of sums, our only available method for proving the theorem is analytic: we must compare approximating sums for the two integrals. We now discuss the ideas before giving the actual proof. A lower sum for the integral $\int_B f$ is shown geometrically on the left side of Figure 6.23. A partition $P \times Q$ divides the box $B = [a, b] \times [c, d]$ into subboxes $I \times J$, and the volume of each solid region in the figure is the area of a subbox times the minimum height of the graph over the subbox. By contrast, letting $g(x) = \int_{y=c}^{d} f(x, y)$ be the area of the cross section at x, the right side of Figure 6.23 shows a lower sum for the integral $\int_{x=a}^{b} g(x)$. The partition P divides the interval $[a, b]$ into subintervals I, and the volume of each bread-slice in the figure is the length of a subinterval times the minimum area of the cross sections orthogonal to I. The proof will show that because integrating in the y-direction is a finer diagnostic than summing minimal box-areas in the y-direction, the bread-slices on the right side of the figure are a superset of the boxes on the left side. Consequently, the volume beneath the bread-slices is at least the volume of the boxes,

$$L(f, P \times Q) \le L(g, P).$$

By similar reasoning for upper sums, in fact we expect that

$$L(f, P \times Q) \le L(g, P) \le U(g, P) \le U(f, P \times Q). \tag{6.8}$$

Since $L(f, P \times Q)$ and $U(f, P \times Q)$ converge to $\int_B f$ under a suitable refinement of $P \times Q$, so do $L(g, P)$ and $U(g, P)$. Thus the iterated integral exists and equals the double integral as desired. The details of turning the geometric intuition of this paragraph into a proof of Fubini's theorem work out fine, provided that we carefully tend to matters in just the right order. However, the need for care is genuine. A subtle point not illustrated by Figure 6.23 is that

- although the boxes lie entirely beneath the bread-slices (this is a relation between two sets),
- and although the boxes lie entirely beneath the graph (so is this),
- and although the volume of the bread-slices is at most the volume beneath the graph (but this is a relation between two numbers),
- the bread-slices need not lie entirely beneath the graph.

Since the bread-slices need not lie entirely beneath the graph, the fact that their volume $L(g, P)$ estimates the integral $\int_B f$ from below does not follow from pointwise considerations. The proof finesses this point by establishing the inequalities (6.8) without reference to the integral, only then bringing the integral into play as the limit of the extremal sums in (6.8).

Proof. For each $x \in [a, b]$, define the cross-sectional function

$$\varphi_x : [c, d] \longrightarrow \mathbb{R}, \qquad \varphi_x(y) = f(x, y).$$

The hypotheses of Fubini's theorem ensure that as x varies from a to b, each cross-sectional function φ_x is continuous except at finitely many points, and hence it is integrable on $[c, d]$. Give the cross-sectional integral a name,

$$g : [a, b] \longrightarrow \mathbb{R}, \qquad g(x) = \int_c^d \varphi_x.$$

The iterated integral $\int_{x=a}^{b} \int_{y=c}^{d} f(x, y)$ is precisely the integral $\int_a^b g$. We need to show that this exists and equals $\int_B f$.

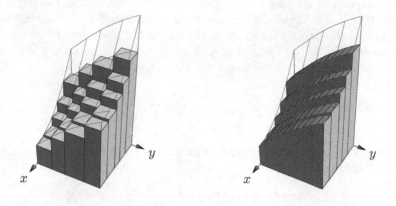

Figure 6.23. Geometry of two lower sums

Consider any partition $P \times Q$ of B into subboxes $J \times K$. Thus P partitions $[a, b]$ into subintervals J, and Q partitions $[c, d]$ into subintervals K. Take any subinterval J of P, and take any point x of J. Note that φ_x on each K samples f only on a cross section of $J \times K$, and so f has more opportunity to be small on $J \times K$ than φ_x has on K. That is,

$$m_{J \times K}(f) \le m_K(\varphi_x).$$

The lower sum of the cross-sectional function φ_x over the y-partition Q is a lower bound for the cross-sectional integral $g(x)$,

$$\sum_K m_K(\varphi_x) \operatorname{length}(K) = L(\varphi_x, Q) \le \int_c^d \varphi_x = g(x).$$

The previous two displays combine to give a lower bound for the cross-sectional integral $g(x)$, the lower bound making reference to the interval J on which x lies but independent of the particular point x of J,

$$\sum_K m_{J \times K}(f) \operatorname{length}(K) \le g(x) \quad \text{for all } x \in J.$$

That is, the left side of this last display is a lower bound of all values $g(x)$ as x varies through J. So it is at most the greatest lower bound,

$$\sum_K m_{J \times K}(f) \operatorname{length}(K) \le m_J(g).$$

Multiply through by the length of J to get

$$\sum_K m_{J \times K}(f) \operatorname{area}(J \times K) \le m_J(g) \operatorname{length}(J).$$

(This inequality says that each y-directional row of boxes in the left half of Figure 6.23 has at most the volume of the corresponding bread-slice in the right half of the figure.) As noted at the end of the preceding paragraph, the iterated integral is the integral of g. The estimate just obtained puts us in a position to compare lower sums for the double integral and the iterated integral,

$$L(f, P \times Q) = \sum_{J,K} m_{J \times K}(f) \operatorname{area}(J \times K) \le \sum_J m_J(g) \operatorname{length}(J) = L(g, P).$$

Concatenating a virtually identical argument with upper sums gives the anticipated chain of inequalities,

$$L(f, P \times Q) \le L(g, P) \le U(g, P) \le U(f, P \times Q).$$

The outer terms converge to $\int_B f$ under a suitable refinement of $P \times Q$, and hence so do the inner terms, showing that $\int_a^b g$ exists and equals $\int_B f$.   □

Since we will use Fubini's theorem to evaluate actual examples, all the notational issues discussed in Section 6.4 arise here again. A typical notation for examples is

$$\int_B f(x, y) = \int_{x=a}^b \int_{y=c}^d f(x, y),$$

where the left side is a 2-dimensional integral, the right side is an iterated integral, and $f(x, y)$ is an expression defining f. For example, by Fubini's theorem and the calculation at the beginning of this section,

$$\int_{[0,1] \times [0,2]} xy^2 = \int_{x=0}^1 \int_{y=0}^2 xy^2 = \frac{4}{3}.$$

Of course, an analogous theorem asserts that $\int_B f(x, y) = \int_{y=c}^d \int_{x=a}^b f(x, y)$, provided that the set S of discontinuity meets horizontal segments at only finitely many points too. In other words, the double integral also equals the other iterated integral, and consequently the two iterated integrals agree. For example, $\int_{y=0}^2 \int_{x=0}^1 xy^2$ also works out easily to $4/3$.

In many applications, the integral over B is really an integral over a non-rectangular compact set K, as defined at the end of the previous section. If K is the area between the graphs of continuous functions $\varphi_1, \varphi_2 : [a, b] \longrightarrow \mathbb{R}$, i.e., if

$$K = \{(x, y) : a \le x \le b, \varphi_1(x) \le y \le \varphi_2(x)\},$$

then one iterated integral takes the form $\int_{x=a}^b \int_{y=\varphi_1(x)}^{\varphi_2(x)} f(x, y)$. Similarly, if

$$K = \{(x, y) : c \le y \le d, \theta_1(y) \le x \le \theta_2(y)\},$$

then the other iterated integral is $\int_{y=c}^d \int_{x=\theta_1(y)}^{\theta_2(y)} f(x, y)$. (See Figure 6.24.)

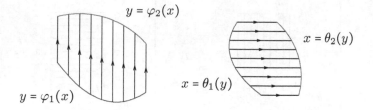

Figure 6.24. Setting up nonrectangular double integrals

The interchangeability of the order of integration leads to a fiendish class of iterated integral problems in which one switches order to get a workable integrand. For example, the iterated integral

$$\int_{y=0}^{2} \int_{x=y/2}^{1} e^{-x^2}$$

looks daunting because the integrand e^{-x^2} has no convenient antiderivative, but after exchanging the order of the integrations and then carrying out a change of variable, it becomes

$$\int_{x=0}^{1} \int_{y=0}^{2x} e^{-x^2} = \int_{x=0}^{1} 2xe^{-x^2} = \int_{u=0}^{1} e^{-u} = 1 - e^{-1}.$$

Interchanging the order of integration can be tricky in such cases; often one has to break K up into several pieces first, e.g.,

$$\int_{x=1}^{2} \int_{y=1/x}^{2} = \int_{y=1/2}^{1} \int_{x=1/y}^{2} + \int_{y=1}^{2} \int_{x=1}^{2}.$$

A carefully labeled diagram facilitates this process. For example, Figure 6.25 shows the sketch that arises from the integral on the left side, and then the resulting sketch that leads to the sum of two integrals on the right side.

Interchanging the outer two integrals in a triply iterated integral is no different from the double case, but interchanging the inner two is tricky, because of the constant-but-unknown value taken by the outer variable. Sketching a generic two-dimensional cross section usually makes the substitutions clear. For example, consider the iterated integral

$$\int_{x=0}^{1} \int_{y=x^3}^{x^2} \int_{z=y}^{x^2}. \tag{6.9}$$

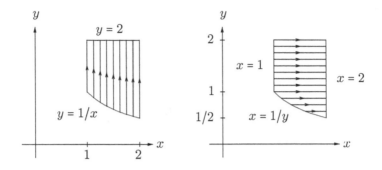

Figure 6.25. Sketches for iterated integrals

(The function being integrated is irrelevant to this discussion of how to exchange the order of integration, so it is omitted from the notation.) Exchanging the outer two integrals is carried out via the first diagram in Figure 6.26. The diagram leads to the iterated integral

$$\int_{y=0}^{1} \int_{x=\sqrt{y}}^{\sqrt[3]{y}} \int_{z=y}^{x^2}.$$

On the other hand, to exchange the inner integrals of (6.9), think of x as fixed but generic between 0 and 1 and consider the second diagram in Figure 6.26. This diagram shows that (6.9) is also the iterated integral

$$\int_{x=0}^{1} \int_{z=x^3}^{x^2} \int_{y=x^3}^{z}. \tag{6.10}$$

Switching the outermost and innermost integrals of (6.9) while leaving the middle one in place requires three successive switches of adjacent integrals. For instance, switching the inner integrals as we just did and then doing an outer exchange on (6.10) virtually identical to the outer exchange of a moment earlier (substitute z for y in the first diagram of Figure 6.26) shows that (6.9) is also

$$\int_{z=0}^{1} \int_{x=\sqrt{z}}^{\sqrt[3]{z}} \int_{y=x^3}^{z}.$$

Finally, the first diagram of Figure 6.27 shows how to exchange the inner integrals once more. The result is

$$\int_{z=0}^{1} \int_{y=z^{3/2}}^{z} \int_{x=\sqrt{z}}^{\sqrt[3]{y}}.$$

The second diagram of Figure 6.27 shows the three-dimensional figure that our iterated integral has traversed in various fashions. It is satisfying to see how

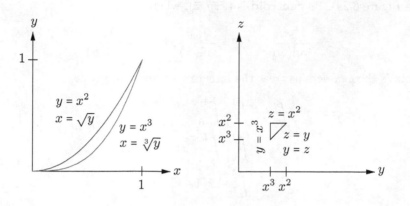

Figure 6.26. Sketches for a triply iterated integral

this picture is compatible with the cross-sectional sketches, and to determine which axis is which. However, the three-dimensional figure is unnecessary for exchanging the order of integration. The author of these notes finds using two-dimensional cross sections easier and more reliable than trying to envision an entire volume at once. Also, the two-dimensional cross-section technique will work in an n-fold iterated integral for every $n \geq 3$, even when the whole situation is hopelessly beyond visualizing.

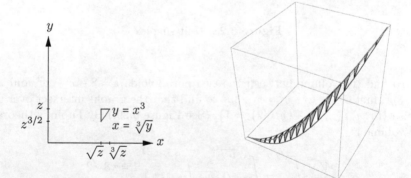

Figure 6.27. Another cross section and the three-dimensional region

The **unit simplex in** $\mathbb{R}^3$ is the set

$$S = \{(x, y, z) : x \geq 0, \, y \geq 0, \, z \geq 0, \, x + y + z \leq 1\}$$

(see Figure 6.28). Its **centroid** is $(\bar{x}, \bar{y}, \bar{z})$, where

$$\bar{x} = \frac{\int_S x}{\text{vol}(S)}, \qquad \bar{y} = \frac{\int_S y}{\text{vol}(S)}, \qquad \bar{z} = \frac{\int_S z}{\text{vol}(S)}.$$

Fubini's theorem lets us treat the integrals as iterated, giving

$$\int_S x = \int_{x=0}^1 \int_{y=0}^{1-x} \int_{z=0}^{1-x-y} x$$

$$= \int_{x=0}^1 \int_{y=0}^{1-x} x(1-x-y)$$

$$= \int_{x=0}^1 \tfrac{1}{2} x(1-x)^2 = \frac{1}{24},$$

where the routine one-variable calculations are not shown in detail. Similarly, $\text{vol}(S) = \int_S 1$ works out to $1/6$, so $\bar{x} = 1/4$. By symmetry, $\bar{y} = \bar{z} = 1/4$ also. See the exercises for an n-dimensional generalization of this result.

Figure 6.28. Unit simplex

To find the volume between the two paraboloids $z = 8 - x^2 - y^2$ and $z = x^2 + 3y^2$, first set $8 - x^2 - y^2 = x^2 + 3y^2$ to find that the graphs intersect over the ellipse $\{(x,y) : (x/2)^2 + (y/\sqrt{2})^2 = 1\}$. (See Figure 6.29.) By Fubini's theorem the volume is

$$V = \int_{y=-\sqrt{2}}^{\sqrt{2}} \int_{x=-\sqrt{4-2y^2}}^{\sqrt{4-2y^2}} \int_{z=x^2+3y^2}^{8-x^2-y^2} 1 = \pi 8 \sqrt{2}$$

where again the one-dimensional calculations are omitted.

Another example is to find the volume of the region K common to the cylinders $x^2 + y^2 = 1$ and $x^2 + z^2 = 1$. For each x-value between -1 and 1, y and z vary independently between $-\sqrt{1-x^2}$ and $\sqrt{1-x^2}$. That is, the intersection of the two cylinders is a union of squares, whose corners form two tilted ellipses. (See Figure 6.30.) By the methods of this section, the integral has the same value as the iterated integral, which is

Figure 6.29. Volume between two graphs

$$\int_{x=-1}^{1} \int_{y=-\sqrt{1-x^2}}^{\sqrt{1-x^2}} \int_{z=-\sqrt{1-x^2}}^{\sqrt{1-x^2}} 1 = 4 \int_{x=-1}^{1} \left(1 - x^2\right) = \frac{16}{3}.$$

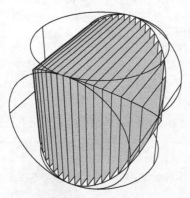

Figure 6.30. Volume common to two cylinders

Finally, we end the section with a more theoretical example.

Proposition 6.6.2 (Differentiation under the integral sign). *Consider a function*

$$f : [a, b] \times [c, d] \longrightarrow \mathbb{R}.$$

Suppose that f and D_1f are continuous. Also consider the cross-sectional integral function,

$$g : [a, b] \longrightarrow \mathbb{R}, \qquad g(x) = \int_{y=c}^{d} f(x, y).$$

Then g is differentiable, and $g'(x) = \int_{y=c}^{d} D_1 f(x, y)$. *That is,*

$$\frac{\mathrm{d}}{\mathrm{d}x} \int_{y=c}^{d} f(x, y) = \int_{y=c}^{d} \frac{\partial}{\partial x} f(x, y).$$

Proof. Compute for $x \in [a, b]$, using the fundamental theorem of integral calculus (Theorem 6.4.2) for the second equality and then Fubini's theorem for the fourth,

$$g(x) = \int_{y=c}^{d} f(x, y)$$

$$= \int_{y=c}^{d} \left(\int_{t=a}^{x} D_1 f(t, y) \quad + \quad f(a, y) \right)$$

$$= \int_{y=c}^{d} \int_{t=a}^{x} D_1 f(t, y) + C \quad (\text{where } C = \int_{y=c}^{d} f(a, y))$$

$$= \int_{t=a}^{x} \int_{y=c}^{d} D_1 f(t, y) + C.$$

We show that $\int_{y=c}^{d} D_1 f(t, y)$ is a continuous function of t. Fix t, and let $\varepsilon > 0$ be given. The continuity of $D_1 f$ on its compact domain $[a, b] \times [c, d]$ is uniform, so for some $\delta > 0$, for all $\tilde{t}$ such that $|\tilde{t} - t| < \delta$, we have $|D_1 f(\tilde{t}, y) - D_1 f(t, y)| < \varepsilon / (d - c)$ for all $y \in [c, d]$. Thus for all such $\tilde{t}$,

$$\left| \int_{y=c}^{d} D_1 f(\tilde{t}, y) - \int_{y=c}^{d} D_1 f(t, y) \right| \le \int_{y=c}^{d} |D_1 f(\tilde{t}, y) - D_1 f(t, y)| < \varepsilon.$$

This proves the claimed continuity. Now Theorem 6.4.1 says that the derivative of the iterated integral is the inner integral evaluated at $t = x$,

$$g'(x) = \int_{y=c}^{d} D_1 f(x, y).$$

This is the desired result. □

See Exercise 6.6.10 for another example in this spirit.

Exercises

6.6.1. Let S be the set of points $(x, y) \in \mathbb{R}^2$ between the x-axis and the sine curve as x varies between 0 and 2π. Since the sine curve has two arches between 0 and 2π, and since the area of an arch of the sine function is 2,

$$\int_{S} 1 = 4.$$

On the other hand,

$$\int_{x=0}^{2\pi} \int_{y=0}^{\sin x} 1 = \int_{x=0}^{2\pi} \sin x = 0.$$

Why doesn't this contradict Fubini's theorem?

6.6.2. Exchange the order of integration in $\int_{x=a}^{b} \int_{y=a}^{x} f(x,y)$.

6.6.3. Exchange the inner order of integration in $\int_{x=0}^{1} \int_{y=0}^{1-x} \int_{z=0}^{x+y} f$.

6.6.4. Exchange the inner order of integration in $\int_{x=0}^{1} \int_{y=0}^{1} \int_{z=0}^{x^2+y^2} f$. Sketch the region of integration.

6.6.5. Evaluate $\int_K f$ from parts (a), (b), (c), (f) of Exercise 6.5.9, except change K to $[0,1]^n$ for part (f).

6.6.6. Find the volume of the region K bounded by the coordinate planes, $x + y = 1$, and $z = x^2 + y^2$. Sketch K.

6.6.7. Evaluate $\int_K (1 + x + y + z)^{-3}$ where K is the unit simplex.

6.6.8. Find the volume of the region K in the first octant bounded by $x = 0$, $z = 0$, $z = y$, and $x = 4 - y^2$. Sketch K.

6.6.9. Find the volume of the region K between $z = x^2 + 9y^2$ and $z = 18 - x^2 - 9y^2$. Sketch K.

6.6.10. Let $f : \mathbb{R}^2 \longrightarrow \mathbb{R}$ have continuous mixed second-order partial derivatives, i.e., let $D_{12}f$ and $D_{21}f$ exist and be continuous. Rederive the familiar fact that $D_{12}f = D_{21}f$ as follows. If $D_{12}f(p,q) - D_{21}f(p,q) > 0$ at some point (p,q) then $D_{12}f - D_{21}f > 0$ on some rectangle $B = [a,b] \times [c,d]$ containing (p,q), so $\int_B (D_{12}f - D_{21}f) > 0$. Obtain a contradiction by evaluating this integral.

6.6.11. Let K and L be compact subsets of $\mathbb{R}^n$ with boundaries of volume zero. Suppose that for each $x_1 \in \mathbb{R}$, the cross-sectional sets

$$K_{x_1} = \{(x_2, \ldots, x_n) : (x_1, x_2, \ldots, x_n) \in K\}$$
$$L_{x_1} = \{(x_2, \ldots, x_n) : (x_1, x_2, \ldots, x_n) \in L\}$$

have equal $(n-1)$-dimensional volumes. Show that K and L have the same volume. (Hint: Use Fubini's theorem to decompose the n-dimensional volume-integral as the iteration of a 1-dimensional integral of $(n-1)$-dimensional integrals.) Illustrate for $n = 2$.

6.6.12. Let x_0 be a positive real number, and let $f : [0, x_0] \longrightarrow \mathbb{R}$ be continuous. Show that

$$\int_{x_1=0}^{x_0} \int_{x_2=0}^{x_1} \cdots \int_{x_n=0}^{x_{n-1}} f(x_n) = \frac{1}{(n-1)!} \int_{t=0}^{x_0} (x_0 - t)^{n-1} f(t).$$

(Use induction. The base case $n = 1$ is easy; then the induction hypothesis applies to the inner $(n-1)$-fold integral.)

6.6.13. Let $n \in \mathbb{Z}^+$ and $r \in \mathbb{R}_{\geq 0}$. The **$n$-dimensional simplex of side** r is

$$S_n(r) = \{(x_1, \ldots, x_n) : 0 \leq x_1, \ldots, 0 \leq x_n, x_1 + \cdots + x_n \leq r\}.$$

(a) Sketch $S_n(r)$ for $n = 1, 2, 3$, with your sketches for $n = 2$ and $n = 3$ showing that $S_n(r)$ is a disjoint union of cross-sectional $(n-1)$-dimensional simplices of side $r - x_n$ at height x_n as x_n varies from 0 to r. Explain this symbolically for general $n > 1$. That is, explain why

$$S_n(r) = \bigsqcup_{x_n \in [0,r]} S_{n-1}(r - x_n) \times \{x_n\}.$$

(b) Prove that $\mathrm{vol}(S_1(r)) = r$. Use part (a) and Fubini's theorem (cf. the hint to Exercise 6.6.11) to prove that

$$\mathrm{vol}(S_n(r)) = \int_{x_n=0}^{r} \mathrm{vol}(S_{n-1}(r - x_n)) \qquad \text{for } n > 1,$$

and show by induction that $\mathrm{vol}(S_n(r)) = r^n/n!$.
 (c) Use Fubini's theorem to show that

$$\int_{S_n(r)} x_n = \int_{x_n=0}^{r} x_n \frac{(r - x_n)^{n-1}}{(n-1)!}.$$

Work this integral by substitution or by parts to get $\int_{S_n(r)} x_n = r^{n+1}/(n+1)!$.
 (d) The centroid of $S_n(r)$ is $(\bar{x}_1, \ldots, \bar{x}_n)$, where $\bar{x}_j = \int_{S_n(r)} x_j / \mathrm{vol}(S_n(r))$ for each j. What are these coordinates explicitly? (Make sure your answer agrees with the case in the text.)

6.7 Change of Variable

Every point $p \in \mathbb{R}^2$ with Cartesian coordinates (x, y) is also specified by its **polar coordinates** (r, θ), where r is the distance from the origin to p, and θ is the angle from the positive x-axis to p. (See Figure 6.31.)

The angle θ is defined only up to multiples of 2π, and it isn't defined at all when $p = (0, 0)$. Trigonometry expresses (x, y) in terms of (r, θ),

$$x = r \cos \theta, \qquad y = r \sin \theta. \tag{6.11}$$

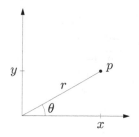

Figure 6.31. Polar coordinates

But expressing (r, θ) in terms of (x, y) is a little more subtle. Certainly

$$r = \sqrt{x^2 + y^2}.$$

Also, $\tan\theta = y/x$ provided that $x \neq 0$, but this doesn't mean that $\theta = \arctan(y/x)$. Indeed, arctan isn't even a well-defined function until its range is specified, e.g., as $(-\pi/2, \pi/2)$. With this particular restriction, the actual formula for θ, even given that not both x and y are 0, is not $\arctan(y/x)$, but

$$\theta = \begin{cases} \arctan(y/x) & \text{if } x > 0 \text{ and } y \geq 0 \text{ (this lies in } [0, \pi/2)), \\ \pi/2 & \text{if } x = 0 \text{ and } y > 0, \\ \arctan(y/x) + \pi & \text{if } x < 0 \text{ (this lies in } (\pi/2, 3\pi/2)), \\ 3\pi/2 & \text{if } x = 0 \text{ and } y < 0, \\ \arctan(y/x) + 2\pi & \text{if } x > 0 \text{ and } y < 0 \text{ (this lies in } (3\pi/2, 2\pi)). \end{cases}$$

The formula is unwieldy, to say the least. (The author probably would not read through the whole thing if he were instead a reader. In any case, see Figure 6.32.) A better approach is that given (x, y), the polar radius r is the unique nonnegative number such that

$$r^2 = x^2 + y^2,$$

and then, if $r \neq 0$, the polar angle θ is the unique number in $[0, 2\pi)$ such that (6.11) holds. But still, going from polar coordinates (r, θ) to Cartesian coordinates (x, y) as in (6.11) is considerably more convenient than conversely. This is good, since as we will see, doing so is also more natural.

The change of variable mapping from polar to Cartesian coordinates is

$$\Phi : \mathbb{R}_{\geq 0} \times [0, 2\pi] \longrightarrow \mathbb{R}^2, \qquad \Phi(r, \theta) = (r\cos\theta, r\sin\theta).$$

The mapping is injective except that the half-lines $\mathbb{R}_{\geq 0} \times \{0\}$ and $\mathbb{R}_{\geq 0} \times \{2\pi\}$ both map to the nonnegative x-axis, and the vertical segment $\{0\} \times [0, 2\pi]$ is squashed to the point $(0, 0)$. Each horizontal half-line $\mathbb{R}_{\geq 0} \times \{\theta\}$ maps to the

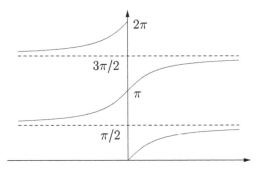

Figure 6.32. The angle θ between 0 and 2π

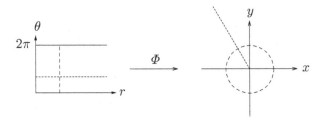

Figure 6.33. The polar coordinate mapping

ray of angle θ with the positive x-axis, and each vertical segment $\{r\} \times [0, 2\pi]$ maps to the circle of radius r. (See Figure 6.33.)

It follows that regions in the (x, y)-plane defined by radial or angular constraints are images under Φ of (r, θ)-regions defined by rectangular constraints. For example, the Cartesian disk

$$D_b = \{(x, y) : x^2 + y^2 \le b^2\}$$

is the Φ-image of the polar rectangle

$$R_b = \{(r, \theta) : 0 \le r \le b, 0 \le \theta \le 2\pi\}.$$

(See Figure 6.34.) Similarly, the Cartesian annulus and quarter disk

$$A_{a,b} = \{(x, y) : a^2 \le x^2 + y^2 \le b^2\},$$
$$Q_b = \{(x, y) : x \ge 0, y \ge 0, x^2 + y^2 \le b^2\},$$

are the images of rectangles. (See figures 6.35 and 6.36.)

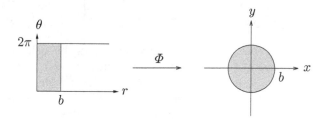

Figure 6.34. Rectangle to disk under the polar coordinate mapping

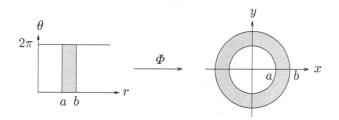

Figure 6.35. Rectangle to annulus under the polar coordinate mapping

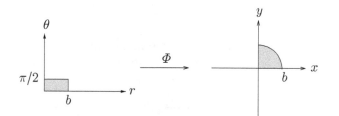

Figure 6.36. Rectangle to quarter disk under the polar coordinate mapping

Iterated integrals over rectangles are especially convenient to evaluate, because the limits of integration for the two one-variable integrals are constants rather than variables that interact. For example,

$$\int_{r=a}^{b} \int_{\theta=0}^{2\pi} = \int_{\theta=0}^{2\pi} \int_{r=a}^{b} .$$

These tidy (r, θ) limits describe the (x, y) annulus $A_{a,b}$ indirectly via Φ, while the more direct approach of an (x, y)-iterated integral over $A_{a,b}$ requires four messy pieces,

$$\int_{x=-b}^{-a} \int_{y=-\sqrt{b^2-x^2}}^{\sqrt{b^2-x^2}} + \int_{x=-a}^{a} \left[\int_{y=-\sqrt{b^2-x^2}}^{-\sqrt{a^2-x^2}} + \int_{y=\sqrt{a^2-x^2}}^{\sqrt{b^2-x^2}} \right] + \int_{x=a}^{b} \int_{y=-\sqrt{b^2-x^2}}^{\sqrt{b^2-x^2}}.$$

Thus, since Fubini's theorem equates integrals over two-dimensional regions to twofold iterated integrals, it would be a real convenience to reduce integrating over the (x, y)-annulus to integrating over the (r, θ) rectangle that maps to it under Φ. The change of variable theorem will do so. This is the sense in which it is natural to map from polar to Cartesian coordinates rather than in the other direction.

The change of variable theorem says in some generality how to transform an integral from one coordinate system to another. Recall that given a set $A \subset \mathbb{R}^n$ and a differentiable mapping $\Phi : A \longrightarrow \mathbb{R}^n$, the $n \times n$ matrix of partial derivatives of Φ is denoted Φ',

$$\Phi' = [D_j \Phi_i]_{i,j=1,\ldots,n}.$$

A differentiable mapping whose partial derivatives are all continuous is called a C^1-**mapping**. Also, for every set $K \subset \mathbb{R}^n$, an **interior point** of K is a point of K that is not a boundary point, and the **interior** of K is the set of all such points,

$$K^\circ = \{\text{interior points of } K\}.$$

We will discuss boundary points and interior points more carefully in the next section. In the specific sorts of examples that arise in calculus, they are easy enough to recognize.

Theorem 6.7.1 (Change of variable theorem for multiple integrals).
Let $K \subset \mathbb{R}^n$ be a compact and connected set having boundary of volume zero. Let A be an open superset of K, and let

$$\Phi : A \longrightarrow \mathbb{R}^n$$

be a C^1-mapping such that

$$\Phi \text{ is injective on } K^\circ \quad \text{and} \quad \det \Phi' \neq 0 \text{ on } K^\circ.$$

Let

$$f : \Phi(K) \longrightarrow \mathbb{R}$$

be a continuous function. Then

$$\int_{\Phi(K)} f = \int_K (f \circ \Phi) \cdot |\det \Phi'|.$$

This section will end with a heuristic argument to support Theorem 6.7.1, and then Section 6.9 will prove the theorem after some preliminaries in Section 6.8. In particular, Section 6.8 will explain why the left side integral in the theorem exists. (The right-side integral exists because the integrand is continuous on K, which is compact and has boundary of volume zero, but the fact that $\Phi(K)$ is nice enough for the left-side integral to exist requires some discussion.) From now to the end of this section, the focus is on how the theorem is used. Generally, the idea is to carry out substitutions of the sort that were called inverse substitutions in the one-variable discussion of Section 6.4. That is, to apply the theorem to an integral $\int_D f$, find a suitable set K and mapping Φ such that $D = \Phi(K)$ and the integral $\int_K (f \circ \Phi) \cdot |\det \Phi'|$ is easier to evaluate. The new integral most likely will be easier because K has a nicer shape than D (this wasn't an issue in the one-variable case), but also possibly because the new integrand is more convenient.

For example, to integrate the function $f(x,y) = x^2 + y^2$ over the annulus $A_{a,b}$, recall the polar coordinate mapping $\Phi(r,\theta) = (r\cos\theta, r\sin\theta)$, and recall that under this mapping, the annulus is the image of a box,

$$A_{a,b} = \Phi([a,b] \times [0,2\pi]).$$

The composition of the integrand with Φ is

$$(f \circ \Phi)(r,\theta) = r^2,$$

and the polar coordinate has derivative matrix

$$\Phi' = \begin{bmatrix} \cos\theta & -r\sin\theta \\ \sin\theta & r\cos\theta \end{bmatrix},$$

with absolute determinant

$$|\det \Phi'| = r.$$

So by the change of variable theorem, the desired integral is instead an integral over a box in polar coordinate space,

$$\int_{A_{a,b}} f = \int_{[a,b]\times[0,2\pi]} r^2 \cdot r.$$

By Fubini's theorem, the latter integral can be evaluated as an iterated integral,

$$\int_{[a,b]\times[0,2\pi]} r^3 = \int_{\theta=0}^{2\pi} \int_{r=a}^{b} r^3 = \frac{\pi}{2}(b^4 - a^4).$$

Similarly, the half disk $H_b = \Phi([0,b] \times [0,\pi])$ has centroid $(0,\bar{y})$ where

$$\bar{y} = \frac{\int_{H_b} y}{\text{area}(H_b)} = \frac{\int_{\theta=0}^{\pi} \int_{r=0}^{b} r\sin\theta \cdot r}{\pi b^2/2} = \frac{2b^3/3}{\pi b^2/2} = \frac{4}{3\pi}b.$$

Indeed, $4/(3\pi)$ is somewhat less than $1/2$, in conformance with our physical intuition of the centroid of a region as its balancing point.

Subtle aspects of Theorem 6.7.1 were in play for the previous two examples. The polar change of coordinate mapping $\Phi(r,\theta)$ isn't injective on all of the box $[a, b] \times [0, 2\pi]$ that parametrizes the annulus: the 2π-periodic behavior of Φ as a function of θ maps the top and bottom edges of the box to the same segment $[a, b]$ of the x-axis. Furthermore, on the box $[0, b] \times [0, \pi]$ that parametrizes the half disk, not only does Φ collapse the left edge of the box to the origin in the (x, y)-plane, but also $\det \Phi' = 0$ on the left edge of the box. Thus we really do require the theorem's hypotheses that Φ need be injective only on the interior of K, and that the condition $\det \Phi' \neq 0$ need hold only on the interior of K.

Just as polar coordinates are convenient for radial symmetry in $\mathbb{R}^2$, **cylindrical coordinates** in $\mathbb{R}^3$ conveniently describe regions with symmetry about the z-axis. A point $p \in \mathbb{R}^3$ with Cartesian coordinates (x, y, z) has cylindrical coordinates (r, θ, z) where (r, θ) are the polar coordinates for the point (x, y). (See Figure 6.37.)

Figure 6.37. Cylindrical coordinates

The cylindrical change of variable mapping is thus

$$\Phi : \mathbb{R}_{\geq 0} \times [0, 2\pi] \times \mathbb{R} \longrightarrow \mathbb{R}^3$$

given by

$$\Phi(r, \theta, z) = (r \cos \theta, r \sin \theta, z).$$

That is, Φ is just the polar coordinate mapping on z cross sections, so like the polar map, it is mostly injective. Its derivative matrix is

$$\Phi' = \begin{bmatrix} \cos \theta & -r \sin \theta & 0 \\ \sin \theta & r \cos \theta & 0 \\ 0 & 0 & 1 \end{bmatrix},$$

and again
$$|\det \Phi'| = r.$$

So, for example, to integrate $f(x, y, z) = y^2 z$ over the cylinder $C : x^2 + y^2 \le 1$, $0 \le z \le 2$, note that $C = \Phi([0, 1] \times [0, 2\pi] \times [0, 2])$, and therefore by the change of variable theorem and then Fubini's theorem,

$$\int_C f = \int_{\theta=0}^{2\pi} \int_{r=0}^{1} \int_{z=0}^{2} r^2 \sin^2 \theta \cdot z \cdot r = \int_{\theta=0}^{2\pi} \sin^2 \theta \cdot \frac{r^4}{4}\Big|_{r=0}^{1} \cdot \frac{z^2}{2}\Big|_{z=0}^{2} = \frac{\pi}{2}.$$

From now on, Fubini's theorem no longer necessarily warrants comment.

For another example, we evaluate the integral $\int_S \sqrt{x^2 + y^2}$ where S is the region bounded by $z^2 = x^2 + y^2$, $z = 0$, and $z = 1$. (This region looks like an ice cream cone with the ice cream licked down flat.) The change of variable theorem transforms the integral into (r, θ, z)-coordinates,

$$\int_S \sqrt{x^2 + y^2} = \int_{r=0}^{1} r^2 \int_{\theta=0}^{2\pi} \int_{z=r}^{1} 1 = \frac{\pi}{6}.$$

Spherical coordinates in $\mathbb{R}^3$ are designed to exploit symmetry about the origin. A point $p = (x, y, z) \in \mathbb{R}^3$ has spherical coordinates (ρ, θ, φ) where the spherical radius ρ is the distance from the origin to p, the longitude θ is the angle from the positive x-axis to the (x, y)-projection of p, and the colatitude φ is the angle from the positive z-axis to p. By some geometry, the spherical coordinate mapping is

$$\Phi : R_{\ge 0} \times [0, 2\pi] \times [0, \pi] \longrightarrow \mathbb{R}^3$$

given by

$$\Phi(\rho, \theta, \varphi) = (\rho \cos \theta \sin \varphi, \rho \sin \theta \sin \varphi, \rho \cos \varphi).$$

The spherical coordinate mapping has derivative matrix

$$\Phi' = \begin{bmatrix} \cos \theta \sin \varphi & -\rho \sin \theta \sin \varphi & \rho \cos \theta \cos \varphi \\ \sin \theta \sin \varphi & \rho \cos \theta \sin \varphi & \rho \sin \theta \cos \varphi \\ \cos \varphi & 0 & -\rho \sin \varphi \end{bmatrix},$$

with determinant (using column-linearity)

$$\det \Phi' = -\rho^2 \sin \varphi \det \begin{bmatrix} \cos \theta \sin \varphi & \sin \theta & \cos \theta \cos \varphi \\ \sin \theta \sin \varphi & -\cos \theta & \sin \theta \cos \varphi \\ \cos \varphi & 0 & -\sin \varphi \end{bmatrix}$$

$$= -\rho^2 \sin \varphi \left(\begin{array}{c} \cos^2 \theta \sin^2 \varphi + \sin^2 \theta \cos^2 \varphi \\ + \cos^2 \theta \cos^2 \varphi + \sin^2 \theta \sin^2 \varphi \end{array} \right)$$

$$= -\rho^2 \sin \varphi,$$

so that since $0 \le \varphi \le \pi$,

$$|\det \Phi'| = \rho^2 \sin \varphi.$$

That is, the spherical coordinate mapping reverses orientation. It can be redefined to preserve orientation by changing φ to the latitude angle, varying from $-\pi/2$ to $\pi/2$, rather than the colatitude.

Figure 6.38 shows the image under the spherical coordinate mapping of some (θ, φ)-rectangles, each having a fixed value of ρ, and similarly for Figure 6.39 for some fixed values of θ, and Figure 6.40 for some fixed values of φ. Thus the spherical coordinate mapping takes boxes to regions with these sorts of walls, such as the half ice cream cone with a bite taken out of its bottom in Figure 6.41.

Figure 6.38. Spherical coordinates for some fixed spherical radii

For an example of the change of variable theorem using spherical coordinates, the solid ball of radius r in $\mathbb{R}^3$ is

$$B_3(r) = \Phi([0, r] \times [0, 2\pi] \times [0, \pi]),$$

and therefore its volume is

$$\mathrm{vol}(B_3(r)) = \int_{B_3(r)} 1 = \int_{\theta=0}^{2\pi} \int_{\rho=0}^{r} \int_{\varphi=0}^{\pi} \rho^2 \sin \varphi = 2\pi \cdot \frac{1}{3} r^3 \cdot 2 = \frac{4}{3} \pi r^3.$$

It follows that the cylindrical shell $B_3(b) - B_3(a)$ has volume $4\pi(b^3 - a^3)/3$. See Exercises 6.7.12 through 6.7.14 for the lovely formula giving the volume of the n-ball for arbitrary n.

The change of variable theorem and spherical coordinates work together to integrate over the solid ellipsoid of (positive) axes a, b, c,

$$E_{a,b,c} = \{(x, y, z) : (x/a)^2 + (y/b)^2 + (z/c)^2 \le 1\}.$$

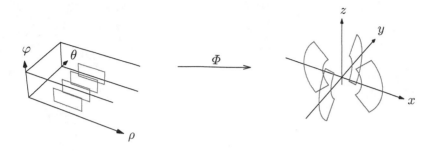

Figure 6.39. Spherical coordinates for some fixed longitudes

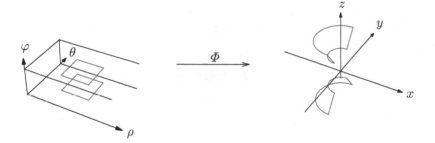

Figure 6.40. Spherical coordinates for some fixed colatitudes

For example, to compute the integral

$$\int_{E_{a,b,c}} (Ax^2 + By^2 + Cz^2),$$

first define a change of variable mapping that stretches the unit sphere into the ellipsoid,

$$\Phi : B_3(1) \longrightarrow E_{a,b,c}, \qquad \Phi(u,v,w) = (au, bv, cw).$$

The absolute determinant of the derivative matrix of Φ is the obvious volume-dilation constant,

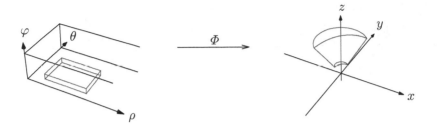

Figure 6.41. The spherical coordinate mapping on a box

$$\Phi' = \begin{bmatrix} a & 0 & 0 \\ 0 & b & 0 \\ 0 & 0 & c \end{bmatrix}, \qquad |\det \Phi'| = abc.$$

Let $f(x, y, z) = z^2$. Then because $E_{a,b,c} = \Phi(B_3(1))$ and $(f \circ \Phi)(u, v, w) = c^2 w^2$, part of the integral is

$$\int_{\Phi(B_3(1))} f = \int_{B_3(1)} (f \circ \Phi) \cdot |\det \Phi'| = abc \cdot c^2 \int_{B_3(1)} w^2.$$

Apply the change of variable theorem again, using the spherical coordinate mapping into (u, v, w)-space,

$$\int_{B_3(1)} w^2 = \int_{\rho=0}^{1} \int_{\theta=0}^{2\pi} \int_{\varphi=0}^{\pi} \rho^2 \cos^2 \varphi \cdot \rho^2 \sin \varphi = \frac{4\pi}{15}.$$

By the symmetry of the symbols in the original integral, its overall value is therefore

$$\int_{E_{a,b,c}} (Ax^2 + By^2 + Cz^2) = \frac{4\pi}{15} abc(a^2 A + b^2 B + c^2 C).$$

Another example is to find the centroid of upper hemispherical shell

$$S = (B_3(b) - B_3(a)) \cap \{z \geq 0\}.$$

By symmetry, $\overline{x} = \overline{y} = 0$. As for $\overline{z}$, compute using spherical coordinates that

$$\int_S z = \int_{\rho=a}^{b} \int_{\theta=0}^{2\pi} \int_{\varphi=0}^{\pi/2} \rho \cos \varphi \cdot \rho^2 \sin \varphi = \frac{\pi}{4}(b^4 - a^4).$$

This integral needs to be divided by the volume $2\pi(b^3 - a^3)/3$ of S to give

$$\overline{z} = \frac{3(b^4 - a^4)}{8(b^3 - a^3)}.$$

In particular, the centroid of the solid hemisphere is 3/8 of the way up. It is perhaps surprising that π does not figure in this formula, as it did in the two-dimensional case.

Here is a heuristic argument to support the change of variable theorem. Suppose that K is a box. Recall the theorem's assertion: under certain conditions,

$$\int_{\Phi(K)} f = \int_K (f \circ \Phi) \cdot |\det \Phi'|.$$

To argue that this equality holds, take a partition P dividing K into subboxes J, and in each subbox choose a point x_J. If the partition is fine enough, then each J maps under Φ to a small patch A of volume $\text{vol}(A) \approx |\det \Phi'(x_J)|\text{vol}(J)$ (cf. Section 3.8), and each x_J maps to a point $y_A \in A$. (See Figure 6.42.) Since the integral is a limit of weighted sums, it follows that

$$\int_{\Phi(K)} f \approx \sum_A f(y_A)\text{vol}(A)$$
$$\approx \sum_J f(\Phi(x_J))|\det \Phi'(x_J)|\text{vol}(J)$$
$$\approx \int_K (f \circ \Phi) \cdot |\det \Phi'|,$$

and these should become equalities in the limit as P becomes finer. What makes this reasoning incomplete is that the patches A are not boxes, as are required for our theory of integration.

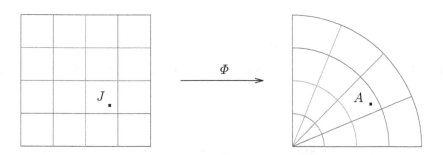

Figure 6.42. Change of variable

Recall from Sections 3.8 and 3.9 that the absolute value of $\det \Phi'(x)$ describes how the mapping Φ scales volume at x, while the sign of $\det \Phi'(x)$ says whether the mapping locally preserves or reverses orientation. The factor $|\det \Phi'|$ in the n-dimensional change of variable theorem (rather than the signed $\det \Phi'$) reflects the fact that n-dimensional integration does not take orientation into account. This unsigned result is less satisfying than the corresponding result in one-variable theory, which does consider orientation and therefore comes with a signed change of variable theorem, $\int_{\phi(a)}^{\phi(b)} f = \int_a^b (f \circ \phi) \cdot \phi'$. An orientation-sensitive n-dimensional integration theory will be developed in Chapter 9.

Exercises

6.7.1. Evaluate $\int_S x^2 + y^2$ where S is the region bounded by $x^2 + y^2 = 2z$ and $z = 2$. Sketch S.

6.7.2. Find the volume of the region S above $x^2 + y^2 = 4z$ and below $x^2 + y^2 + z^2 = 5$. Sketch S.

6.7.3. Find the volume of the region between the graphs of $z = x^2 + y^2$ and $z = (x^2 + y^2 + 1)/2$.

6.7.4. Derive the spherical coordinate mapping.

6.7.5. Let Φ be the spherical coordinate mapping. Describe $\Phi(K)$ where

$$K = \{(\rho, \theta, \varphi) : 0 \le \theta \le 2\pi, \, 0 \le \varphi \le \pi/2, \, 0 \le \rho \le \cos\varphi\}.$$

(Hint: Along with visualizing the geometry, set $\theta = 0$ and consider the condition $\rho^2 = \rho \cos\varphi$ in Cartesian coordinates.) Same question for

$$K = \{(\rho, \theta, \varphi) : 0 \le \theta \le 2\pi, \, 0 \le \varphi \le \pi, \, 0 \le \rho \le \sin\varphi\}.$$

6.7.6. Evaluate $\int_S xyz$ where S is the first octant of $B_3(1)$.

6.7.7. Find the mass of a solid figure filling the spherical shell

$$S = B_3(b) - B_3(a)$$

with density $\delta(x, y, z) = x^2 + y^2 + z^2$.

6.7.8. A solid sphere of radius b has density $\delta(x, y, z) = e^{-(x^2 + y^2 + z^2)^{3/2}}$. Find its mass, $\int_{B_3(b)} \delta$.

6.7.9. Find the centroid of the region $S = B_3(a) \cap \{x^2 + y^2 \le z^2\} \cap \{z \ge 0\}$. Sketch S.

6.7.10. (a) Prove **Pappus's theorem**: Let K be a compact set in the (x, z)-plane lying to the right of the z-axis and with boundary of area zero. Let S be the solid obtained by rotating K about the z-axis in $\mathbb{R}^3$. Then

$$\mathrm{vol}(S) = 2\pi\bar{x} \cdot \mathrm{area}(K),$$

where as always, $\bar{x} = \int_K x/\mathrm{area}(K)$. (Use cylindrical coordinates.)
(b) What is the volume of the torus $T_{a,b}$ of cross-sectional radius a and major radius b from the center of rotation to the center of the cross-sectional disk? (See Figure 6.43.)

Figure 6.43. Torus

6.7.11. Prove the **change of scale principle**: if the set $K \subset \mathbb{R}^n$ has volume v then for every $r \geq 0$, the set $rK = \{rx : x \in K\}$ has volume $r^n v$. (Change variables by $\Phi(x) = rx$.)

6.7.12. (Volume of the n-ball, first version.) Let $n \in \mathbb{Z}^+$ and $r \in \mathbb{R}_{\geq 0}$. The **$n$-dimensional ball of radius r** is

$$B_n(r) = \{x : x \in \mathbb{R}^n \mid |x| \leq r\} = \{(x_1, \ldots, x_n) : x_1^2 + \cdots + x_n^2 \leq r^2\}.$$

Let

$$v_n = \text{vol}(B_n(1)).$$

(a) Explain how Exercise 6.7.11 reduces computing the volume of $B_n(r)$ to computing v_n.

(b) Explain why $v_1 = 2$ and $v_2 = \pi$.

(c) Let D denote the unit disk $B_2(1)$. Explain why for $n > 2$,

$$B_n(1) = \bigsqcup_{(x_1, x_2) \in D} \{(x_1, x_2)\} \times B_{n-2}(\sqrt{1 - x_1^2 - x_2^2}).$$

That is, the unit n-ball is a union of cross-sectional $(n-2)$-dimensional balls of radius $\sqrt{1 - x_1^2 - x_2^2}$ as (x_1, x_2) varies through the unit disk. Make a sketch for $n = 3$, the only value of n for which we can see this.

(d) Explain why for $n > 2$,

$$v_n = v_{n-2} \int_{(x_1, x_2) \in D} (1 - x_1^2 - x_2^2)^{\frac{n}{2} - 1}$$

$$= v_{n-2} \int_{\theta=0}^{2\pi} \int_{r=0}^{1} (1 - r^2)^{\frac{n}{2} - 1} \cdot r$$

$$= v_{n-2} \pi / (n/2).$$

(Use the definition of volume at the end of Section 6.5, Fubini's theorem, the definition of volume again, the change of scale principle from the previous exercise, and the change of variable theorem.)

(e) Prove by induction the *for n even* case of the formula

$$v_n = \begin{cases} \dfrac{\pi^{n/2}}{(n/2)!} & \text{for } n \text{ even,} \\[3mm] \dfrac{\pi^{(n-1)/2} 2^n ((n-1)/2)!}{n!} & \text{for } n \text{ odd.} \end{cases}$$

(The *for n odd* case can be proved by induction as well, but the next two exercises provide a better, more conceptual, approach to the volumes of odd-dimensional balls.)

6.7.13. This exercise computes the *improper integral* $I = \int_{x=0}^{\infty} e^{-x^2}$, defined as the limit $\lim_{R \to \infty} \int_{x=0}^{R} e^{-x^2}$. Let $I(R) = \int_{x=0}^{R} e^{-x^2}$ for $R \geq 0$.

(a) Use Fubini's theorem to show that $I(R)^2 = \int_{S(R)} e^{-x^2-y^2}$, where $S(R)$ is the square

$$S(R) = \{(x,y) : 0 \leq x \leq R, \, 0 \leq y \leq R\}.$$

(b) Let $Q(R)$ be the quarter disk

$$Q(R) = \{(x,y) : 0 \leq x, \, 0 \leq y, \, x^2 + y^2 \leq R^2\},$$

and similarly for $Q(\sqrt{2}\,R)$. Explain why

$$\int_{Q(R)} e^{-x^2-y^2} \leq \int_{S(R)} e^{-x^2-y^2} \leq \int_{Q(\sqrt{2}\,R)} e^{-x^2-y^2}.$$

(c) Change variables, and evaluate $\int_{Q(R)} e^{-x^2-y^2}$ and $\int_{Q(\sqrt{2}\,R)} e^{-x^2-y^2}$. What are the limits of these two quantities as $R \to \infty$?

(d) What is I?

6.7.14. (Volume of the *n*-ball, improved version) Define the gamma function as an integral,

$$\Gamma(s) = \int_{x=0}^{\infty} x^{s-1} e^{-x} \, dx, \quad s > 0.$$

(This *improper integral* is well behaved, even though it is not being carried out over a bounded region and even though the integrand is unbounded near $x = 0$ when $0 < s < 1$. We use dx here because this exercise is computational.)

(a) Show: $\Gamma(1) = 1$, $\Gamma(1/2) = \sqrt{\pi}$, $\Gamma(s+1) = s\Gamma(s)$. (Substitute and see the previous exercise for the second identity, integrate by parts for the third.)

(b) Use part (a) to show that $n! = \Gamma(n+1)$ for $n = 0, 1, 2, \dots$. Accordingly, define $x! = \Gamma(x+1)$ for all real numbers $x > -1$, not only nonnegative integers.

(c) Use Exercise 6.7.12(b), Exercise 6.7.12(d), and the extended definition of the factorial in part (b) of this exercise to obtain a uniform formula for the volume of the unit *n*-ball,

$$v_n = \frac{\pi^{n/2}}{(n/2)!}, \quad n = 1, 2, 3, \dots.$$

(We already have this formula for *n* even. For *n* odd, the argument is essentially identical to Exercise 6.7.12(e) but starting at the base case $n = 1$.) Thus the *n*-ball of radius r has volume

$$\text{vol}(B_n(r)) = \frac{\pi^{n/2}}{(n/2)!} r^n, \quad n = 1, 2, 3, \ldots .$$

(d) The *Legendre duplication formula* for the gamma function is

$$\Gamma(2s) = 2^{2s-1}\pi^{-1/2}\Gamma(s)\Gamma(s + 1/2).$$

For odd n, what value of s shows that the values of v_n from part (c) of this exercise and from part (e) of Exercise 6.7.12 are equal?

(e) (Read-only. While the calculation of v_n in these exercises shows the effectiveness of our integration toolkit, the following heuristic argument illustrates that we would profit from an even more effective theory of integration.) Decompose Euclidean space $\mathbb{R}^n$ into concentric n-spheres (the n-sphere is the boundary of the n-ball), each having radius r and differential radial thickness dr. Since each such n-sphere is obtained by removing the n-ball of radius r from the n-ball of radius $r + dr$, its differential volume is

$$v_n(r + dr)^n - v_n r^n \approx v_n n r^{n-1} \, dr.$$

Here we ignore the higher powers of dr on the grounds that they are so much smaller than the dr-term. Thus, reusing some ideas from a moment ago, and using informal notation,

$$\pi^{n/2} = \left(\int_{\mathbb{R}} e^{-x^2} \, dx \right)^n \qquad \text{since the integral equals } \sqrt{\pi}$$

$$= \int_{\mathbb{R}^n} e^{-|x|^2} \, dV \qquad \text{by Fubini's theorem}$$

$$= v_n n \int_{r=0}^{\infty} r^{n-1} e^{-r^2} \, dr \qquad \text{integrating over spherical shells}$$

$$= v_n \, n/2 \int_{t=0}^{\infty} t^{n/2-1} e^{-t} \, dt \qquad \text{substituting } t = r^2$$

$$= v_n \, n/2 \, \Gamma(n/2)$$

$$= v_n \, (n/2)!.$$

The formula $v_n = \pi^{n/2}/(n/2)!$ follows immediately. The reason that this induction-free argument lies outside our theoretical framework is that it integrates directly (rather than by the change of variable theorem) even as it decomposes $\mathbb{R}^n$ into small pieces that aren't boxes. Although we would prefer a more flexible theory of integration that allows such procedures, developing it takes correspondingly more time.

6.7.15. This exercise heuristically derives *Stirling's formula*,

$$n! \sim \sqrt{2\pi n} \, (n/e)^n, \quad n \gg 0.$$

(a) Show that because $n! = \Gamma(n + 1)$, it follows that $n! = \int_{t=0}^{\infty} e^{n \ln t - t} \, dt$.

(b) With n fixed and t variable, show that the quantity $n \ln t - t$ takes its maximum value $n \ln n - n$ at $t = n$, where its first derivative is 0 and its second derivative is $-1/n$. Thus the quantity's quadratic approximation about its maximizing point is $n \ln n - n - \frac{1}{2n}(t-n)^2$.

(c) In the integral expression of $n!$ from (a), replace $n \ln t - t$ by its quadratic approximation from (b) to get

$$\Gamma(n+1) \sim (n/e)^n \int_{t=0}^{\infty} e^{-\frac{1}{2n}(t-n)^2} \, dt.$$

The quantity $t - n$ runs through $(-n, \infty)$ as t runs through $(0, \infty)$. Thus, assuming that $n \gg 0$, replace $t - n$ by t and extend the integration to all of $\mathbb{R}$ to get

$$\Gamma(n+1) \sim (n/e)^n \int_{t=-\infty}^{\infty} e^{-\frac{1}{2n}t^2} \, dt.$$

Replace t by $\sqrt{2n}\,t$, and use exercise 6.7.13 to evaluate the resulting integral and obtain Stirling's formula.

6.7.16. This exercise evaluates the improper integral

$$I_s = \int_{x=-\infty}^{\infty} \frac{dx}{(1+x^2)^s} \quad \text{(for every real number } s > 1/2\text{).}$$

(a) For $\alpha > 0$, make a substitution in the integral $\int_{t=0}^{\infty} t^s e^{-\alpha t} \frac{dt}{t}$ to show that it equals $\Gamma(s)\alpha^{-s}$. Thus

$$\alpha^{-s} = \frac{1}{\Gamma(s)} \int_{t=0}^{\infty} t^s e^{-\alpha t} \frac{dt}{t}, \quad \alpha > 0.$$

(b) Explain how a particular choice of α in (a) leads to

$$I_s = \frac{1}{\Gamma(s)} \int_{x=-\infty}^{\infty} \int_{t=0}^{\infty} t^s e^{-(1+x^2)t} \frac{dt}{t} \, dx.$$

(c) Explain how after exchanging the order of integration, a few other steps lead to

$$I_s = \frac{1}{\Gamma(s)} \int_{t=0}^{\infty} t^{s-1/2} e^{-t} \frac{dt}{t} \int_{x=-\infty}^{\infty} e^{-x^2} \, dx.$$

(d) Use earlier exercises to conclude that

$$I_s = \sqrt{\pi} \, \frac{\Gamma(s-1/2)}{\Gamma(s)}.$$

Can you check this formula for $s = 1$?

6.7.17. Let A and B be positive real numbers. This exercise evaluates the improper integral

$$I_s = \int_{x=-\infty}^{\infty} \frac{dx}{(Ae^{2x} + Be^{-2x})^s} \quad \text{(for every real number } s > 0\text{)}.$$

(a) Recall from Exercise 6.7.16(a) that $\alpha^{-s} = \frac{1}{\Gamma(s)} \int_{t=0}^{\infty} t^s e^{-\alpha t} \frac{dt}{t}$ for all $\alpha > 0$. Explain how a particular choice of α leads to

$$I_s = \frac{1}{\Gamma(s)} \int_{x=-\infty}^{\infty} \int_{t=0}^{\infty} t^s e^{-(Ae^{2x} + Be^{-2x})t} \frac{dt}{t} \, dx.$$

(b) Let $x = \frac{1}{2} \log u$ (natural logarithm) and show that

$$I_s = \frac{1}{2\Gamma(s)} \int_{u=0}^{\infty} \int_{t=0}^{\infty} t^s e^{-(Au + Bu^{-1})t} \frac{dt}{t} \frac{du}{u}.$$

Replace t by ut to get

$$I_s = \frac{1}{2\Gamma(s)} \int_{u=0}^{\infty} \int_{t=0}^{\infty} t^s u^s e^{-(Au^2 + B)t} \frac{dt}{t} \frac{du}{u}.$$

Replace u by $\sqrt{u}$ to get

$$I_s = \frac{1}{4\Gamma(s)} \int_{u=0}^{\infty} \int_{t=0}^{\infty} t^s u^{s/2} e^{-(Au + B)t} \frac{dt}{t} \frac{du}{u}.$$

(c) Exchange the order of integration and replace u by u/t to get

$$I_s = \frac{1}{4\Gamma(s)} \int_{t=0}^{\infty} \int_{u=0}^{\infty} t^{s/2} u^{s/2} e^{-(Au + Bt)} \frac{du}{u} \frac{dt}{t}.$$

Replace u by u/A and t by t/B to get

$$I_s = A^{-s/2} B^{-s/2} \frac{1}{4\Gamma(s)} \int_{t=0}^{\infty} t^{s/2} e^{-t} \frac{dt}{t} \int_{u=0}^{\infty} u^{s/2} e^{-u} \frac{du}{u}.$$

Thus the integral is

$$\int_{x=-\infty}^{\infty} \frac{dx}{(Ae^{2x} + Be^{-2x})^s} = \frac{\Gamma(s/2)\Gamma(s/2)}{4\Gamma(s)} A^{-s/2} B^{-s/2}, \quad s > 0.$$

6.7.18. (Read-only. This exercise makes use not only of the gamma function but of some results beyond our scope, in the hope of interesting the reader in those ideas.)

(a) Consider any $x \in \mathbb{R}_{>0}$, $\xi \in \mathbb{R}$, and $s \in \mathbb{R}_{>1}$. We show that

$$\int_{y=-\infty}^{\infty} \frac{e^{i\xi y}}{(x + iy)^s} \, dy = \begin{cases} \frac{2\pi}{\Gamma(s)} e^{-x\xi} \xi^{s-1} & \text{if } \xi > 0, \\ 0 & \text{if } \xi \le 0. \end{cases}$$

Indeed, replacing ξ by $x\xi$ in the gamma function integral gives a variant expression of gamma that incorporates x,

$$\Gamma(s) = \int_{\xi=0}^{\infty} e^{-\xi}\xi^s \frac{d\xi}{\xi} = x^s \int_{\xi=0}^{\infty} e^{-x\xi}\xi^s \frac{d\xi}{\xi}.$$

A result from complex analysis says that this formula extends from the open half-line of positive x-values to the open half-plane of complex numbers $x+iy$ with x positive. That is, for every $y \in \mathbb{R}$,

$$\Gamma(s) = (x+iy)^s \int_{\xi=0}^{\infty} e^{-(x+iy)\xi}\xi^s \frac{d\xi}{\xi}.$$

This is

$$\frac{\Gamma(s)}{(x+iy)^s} = \int_{\xi=0}^{\infty} e^{-iy\xi}\varphi_x(\xi)\,d\xi \quad \text{where} \quad \varphi_x(\xi) = \begin{cases} e^{-x\xi}\xi^{s-1} & \text{if } \xi > 0, \\ 0 & \text{if } \xi \leq 0. \end{cases}$$

The integral here is a Fourier transform. That is, letting $\mathcal{F}$ denote the Fourier transform operator, the previous display says that

$$\frac{\Gamma(s)}{(x+iy)^s} = (\mathcal{F}\varphi_x)(y), \quad y \in \mathbb{R}.$$

The integral $\Gamma(s)\int_{y=-\infty}^{\infty} e^{i\xi y}(x+iy)^{-s}\,dy$ is consequently the inverse Fourier transform at ξ of the Fourier transform of φ_x. Fourier inversion says that the inverse Fourier transform of the Fourier transform is the original function multiplied by 2π. Putting all of this together gives the value of the integral at the beginning of the exercise.

(b) We introduce an n-dimensional gamma function for every positive integer n. Let

$$\mathcal{C}_n = \{n \times n \text{ symmetric positive definite matrices}\}.$$

The set $\mathcal{C}_n$ is so denoted because it forms a structure called a *cone*: it is closed under addition and under dilation by positive real numbers. For $n > 1$, Exercise 4.7.11 gives a decomposition

$$\mathbb{R}^{n-1} \times \mathbb{R}_{>0} \times \mathcal{C}_{n-1} \approx \mathcal{C}_n, \quad c \times a \times \xi_2 \approx \begin{bmatrix} a & c^{\mathsf{T}} \\ c & a^{-1}cc^{\mathsf{T}} + \xi_2 \end{bmatrix}.$$

The nth gamma function is

$$\Gamma_n(s) = \int_{\xi \in \mathcal{C}_n} e^{-\operatorname{tr}\xi}(\det \xi)^s \frac{d\xi}{(\det \xi)^{(n+1)/2}},$$

in which $d\xi = \prod_{i \leq j} d\xi_{ij}$ is the product of the differentials of the diagonal and superdiagonal elements of ξ, where we recall that because ξ is symmetric the subdiagonal entries are redundant. The decomposition of $\mathcal{C}_n$ combines with some other facts (which the reader is encouraged to identify, if not prove) to show that

$$\Gamma_n(s) = \int_{c\in\mathbb{R}^{n-1}} \int_{a\in\mathbb{R}_{>0}} \int_{\xi_2\in\mathcal{C}_{n-1}} \left(\begin{array}{c} e^{-a^{-1}|c|^2 - a - \operatorname{tr}\xi_2} a^s (\det\xi_2)^s \\ \cdot \dfrac{\mathrm{d}\xi_2\, \mathrm{d}a\, \mathrm{d}c}{a^{(n+1)/2}(\det\xi_2)^{(n+1)/2}} \end{array} \right).$$

Replacing c by $a^{1/2}c$ (and thus $\mathrm{d}c$ by $a^{(n-1)/2}\,\mathrm{d}c$) lets the integral be separated,

$$\Gamma_n(s) = \int_{c\in\mathbb{R}^{n-1}} e^{-|c|^2}\,\mathrm{d}c \cdot \int_{a\in\mathbb{R}_{>0}} e^{-a}a^s \frac{\mathrm{d}a}{a}$$

$$\cdot \int_{\xi_2\in\mathcal{C}_{n-1}} e^{-\operatorname{tr}\xi_2}(\det\xi_2)^{s-1/2} \frac{\mathrm{d}\xi_2}{(\det\xi_2)^{n/2}}$$

$$= \pi^{(n-1)/2}\Gamma(s)\Gamma_{n-1}(s-\tfrac{1}{2}).$$

And iterating the argument gives the value of the nth gamma function in terms of the basic gamma function,

$$\Gamma_n(s) = \pi^{(n-1)n/4}\Gamma(s)\Gamma(s-\tfrac{1}{2})\Gamma(s-\tfrac{2}{2})\cdots\Gamma(s-\tfrac{n-2}{2})\Gamma(s-\tfrac{n-1}{2}).$$

Similarly to part (a), one now can evaluate an integral over the vector space $\mathcal{V}_n$ of $n \times n$ symmetric matrices for a given $\xi \in \mathcal{V}_n$,

$$\int_{y\in\mathcal{V}_n} \frac{e^{i\operatorname{tr}(\xi y)}}{\det(x+iy)^s}\,\mathrm{d}y = \begin{cases} \dfrac{(2\pi)^n \pi^{(n-1)n/2}}{\Gamma_n(s)} e^{-\operatorname{tr}(x\xi)}(\det\xi)^{s-(n+1)/2} & \text{if } \xi \in \mathcal{C}_n, \\ 0 & \text{otherwise,} \end{cases}$$

using the fact that the constant for Fourier inversion over the space of $n \times n$ symmetric matrices is $(2\pi)^n \pi^{(n-1)n/2}$.

Figure 6.44. Geodesic dome

6.7.19. Figure 6.44 shows a geodesic dome with 5-fold vertices and 6-fold vertices. (A *geodesic* of the sphere is a great circle.) Figure 6.45 shows a bird's-eye view of the dome. The thinner edges emanate from the 5-vertices, while four of the six edges emanating from each 6-vertex are thicker. The five triangles that meet at a 5-vertex are isosceles, while two of the six triangles that meet at a 6-vertex are equilateral. This exercise uses vector algebra and the spherical coordinate system to work out the lengths and angles of the dome. Integration and the change of variable theorem play no role in this exercise.

Figure 6.45. Geodesic dome, bird's-eye view

(a) Take all vertices to lie on a sphere of radius 1. The ten thick edges around the equator form a regular 10-gon. Show that consequently the thick edges have length

$$a = 2\sin(\pi/10) = 2\cos(2\pi/5).$$

This famous number from geometry goes back to Euclid. Note that $a = \zeta_5 + \zeta_5^{-1}$ where $\zeta_5 = e^{2\pi i/5} = \cos(2\pi/5) + i\sin(2\pi/5)$ is the fifth root of unity one-fifth of the way counterclockwise around the complex unit circle. Thus $a^2 + a - 1 = \zeta_5^2 + 2 + \zeta_5^3 + \zeta_5 + \zeta_5^4 - 1$, and the right side is 0 by the finite geometric sum formula. That is,

$$a^2 + a - 1 = 0, \quad a > 0,$$

and so the length of the thick edges is

$$a = \frac{-1 + \sqrt{5}}{2} = 0.618033988\ldots.$$

This number is a variant of the so-called golden ratio.

(b) The dome has a point at the north pole $(0, 0, 1)$; then a layer of five points p_0 through p_4 around the north pole at some colatitude φ; then a layer of ten points q_0 through q_9, five at colatitude 2φ and the other five at some second colatitude ϕ; and finally the layer of ten equatorial points r_0 through r_9. The colatitude φ must be such that the triangle with vertices n, q_0, and q_2 is equilateral. These vertices may be taken to be

$$n = (0,0,1),$$
$$q_0, q_2 = (\cos(\pi/5)\sin(2\varphi), \mp\sin(\pi/5)\sin(2\varphi), \cos(2\varphi)).$$

Show that the equilateral condition $|n - q_0|^2 = |q_2 - q_0|^2$ gives the condition $\cos^2(\varphi) = 1/(2-a)$, then $\sin^2(\varphi) = (1-a)/(2-a)$, then $\tan^2(\varphi) = a^2$, so that the colatitude of the five points about the north pole is

$$\varphi = \arctan(a) = 31.7174\ldots^\circ.$$

Use the cross-sectional triangle having vertices 0, n, p_0 and the law of cosines to show that the shorter segments have length

$$b = \sqrt{2(1 - 1/\sqrt{2-a})} = 0.546533057\ldots.$$

(Alternatively, one can find φ and b using the triangle with vertices n, p_0, p_1.) For reference in part (e), show that

$$2\varphi = \arctan(2) = 63.4349\ldots^\circ.$$

(c) Show that the angle of an isosceles triangle where its equal sides meet at a 5-vertex is
$$\alpha = 2\arcsin(a/(2b)) = 68.8619\ldots^\circ,$$

and the angles where its unequal sides meet at 6-vertices are

$$\beta = \arccos(a/(2b)) = 55.5690\ldots^\circ.$$

(d) Show that the angle where two a-segments meet along a geodesic is $180° - 36°$. Show that the angle where two b-segments meet along a geodesic (this happens at the 6-vertices but not at the 5-vertices) is $180° - \varphi$.
(e) To find the colatitude ϕ of $q_1, q_3, \ldots, q_9$, take q_9 and q_1 to be

$$q_9, q_1 = (\cos(\pi/5)\sin(2\varphi), \mp\sin(\pi/5)\sin(2\varphi), \cos(2\varphi)),$$

and consider the geodesic containing them. Their cross product is normal to the plane of the geodesic. Show that this cross product is

$$q_9 \times q_1 = 2\sin(\pi/5)\sin(2\varphi)(-\cos(2\varphi), 0, \cos(\pi/5)\sin(2\varphi)).$$

Show by illustration that the latitude of this cross product is the colatitude ϕ of q_9 and q_1. Show that $\phi = \arctan(\sqrt{2+a})$. Show further that $(a+1)^2 = 2+a$, so that in fact,
$$\phi = \arctan(a + 1) = 58.2825\ldots^\circ.$$

6.8 Topological Preliminaries for the Change of Variable Theorem

This section establishes some topological results to prepare for proving the change of variable theorem (Theorem 6.7.1), and then the next section gives the proof. Both sections are technical, and so the reader is invited to skim as feels appropriate. For instance, one might focus on the discussion, the statements, and the figures, but go light on the proofs.

In preparation for proving the change of variable theorem, we review its statement. The statement includes the terms *boundary* and *interior*, which we have considered only informally so far, but we soon will discuss them more carefully. The statement also includes the term *open*, and the reader is reminded that a set is called open if its complement is closed; we soon will review the definition of a closed set. The statement includes the term C^1-*mapping*, meaning a mapping such that all partial derivatives of all of its component functions exist and are continuous. And the statement includes the notation K° for the interior of a set K. The theorem says:

Let $K \subset \mathbb{R}^n$ be a compact and connected set having boundary of volume zero. Let A be an open superset of K, and let

$$\Phi : A \longrightarrow \mathbb{R}^n$$

be a C^1-mapping such that

$$\Phi \text{ is injective on } K^\circ \quad \text{and} \quad \det \Phi' \neq 0 \text{ on } K^\circ.$$

Let

$$f : \Phi(K) \longrightarrow \mathbb{R}$$

be a continuous function. Then

$$\int_{\Phi(K)} f = \int_K (f \circ \Phi) \cdot |\det \Phi'|.$$

Thus the obvious data for the theorem are K, Φ, and f. (The description of Φ subsumes A, and in any case the role of A is auxiliary.) But also, although the dimension n is conceptually generic but fixed, in fact the proof of the theorem will entail induction on n, so that we should view n as a variable part of the setup as well. Here are some comments about the data.

- The continuous image of a compact set is compact (Theorem 2.4.14), so that $\Phi(K)$ is again compact. Similarly, by an invocation in Section 2.4, the continuous image of a connected set is connected, so that $\Phi(K)$ is again connected. The reader who wants to minimize invocation may instead assume that that K is path-connected, so that $\Phi(K)$ is again path-connected (see Exercise 2.4.10 for the definition of path-connectedness and the fact that path-connectedness is a topological property); the distinction

between connectedness and path-connectedness is immaterial for every example that will arise in calculus. We soon will see that the image $\Phi(K)$
also has boundary of volume zero, so that in fact $\Phi(K)$ inherits all of the
assumed properties of K.

- Thus both integrals in the change of variable theorem exist, because in
  each case the integrand is continuous on the domain of integration and
  the domain of integration is compact and has boundary of volume zero.

- The hypotheses of the theorem can be weakened or strengthened in various ways with no effect on the outcome. Indeed, the proof of the theorem
  proceeds partly by strengthening the hypotheses. The hypotheses in Theorem 6.7.1 were chosen to make the theorem fit the applications that arise
  in calculus. Especially, parametrizations by polar, cylindrical, or spherical coordinates often degenerate on the boundary of the parameter-box,
  hence the conditions that Φ is injective and $\det \Phi' \neq 0$ being required
  only on the interior K°. See Figure 6.46. In the figure, the polar coordinate mapping collapses the left side of the parametrizing rectangle to the
  origin in the parametrized disk, and it takes the top and bottom sides
  of the parametrizing rectangle to the same portion of the x-axis in the
  parametrized disk. Furthermore, neither the origin nor the portion of the
  x-axis is on the boundary of the parametrized disk even though they both
  come from the boundary of the parametrizing rectangle. On the other
  hand, every nonboundary point of the parametrizing rectangle is taken
  to a nonboundary point of the parametrized disk, so that every boundary point of the parametrized disk comes from a boundary point of the
  parametrizing rectangle.

- While the hypotheses about Φ are weaker than necessary in order to make
  the theorem easier to use, the hypothesis that f is continuous is stronger
  than necessary in order to make the theorem easier to prove. The theorem
  continues to hold if f is assumed only to be integrable, but then the proof
  requires more work. In calculus examples, f is virtually always continuous.
  This subject will be revisited at the end of Chapter 7.

This section places a few more topological ideas into play to set up the
proof of the change of variable theorem in the next section. The symbols K, A,
Φ, and f denoting the set, the open superset, the change of variable, and the
function in the theorem will retain their meanings throughout the discussion.
Symbols such as S will denote other sets, symbols such as Ψ will denote other
transformations, and symbols such as g will denote other functions.

Recall some topological ideas that we have already discussed.

- For every point $a \in \mathbb{R}^n$ and every positive real number $r > 0$, the open ball
  centered at a of radius r is the set

$$B(a,r) = \{x \in \mathbb{R}^n : |x - a| < r\}.$$

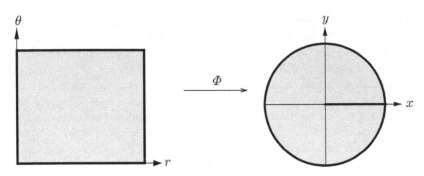

Figure 6.46. The change of variable mapping need not behave well on the boundary

- A point $a \in \mathbb{R}^n$ is called a limit point of a set $S \in \mathbb{R}^n$ if every open ball centered at a contains some point $x \in S$ such that $x \neq a$. A subset A of $\mathbb{R}^n$ is called closed if it contains all of its limit points.

Definition 6.8.1. *Let S be a subset of $\mathbb{R}^n$. Its **closure** $\overline{S}$ is the smallest closed superset of S.*

Here *smallest* is taken in the sense of set-containment. The intersection of closed sets is closed (Exercise 6.8.1(a)), and so $\overline{S}$ is the intersection of all closed supersets of S, including $\mathbb{R}^n$. Thus $\overline{S}$ exists and is unique. The special-case definition

$$\overline{B(a,r)} = \{x \in \mathbb{R}^n : |x - a| \leq r\}$$

from Section 5.1 is consistent with Definition 6.8.1.

Closed sets can also be described in terms of *boundary points* rather than limit points.

Definition 6.8.2. *Let S be a subset of $\mathbb{R}^n$. A point $p \in \mathbb{R}^n$ is called a **boundary point** of S if for every $r > 0$ the open ball $B(p,r)$ contains a point from S and a point from the complement S^c. The **boundary** of S, denoted ∂S, is the set of boundary points of S.*

A boundary point of a set need not be a limit point of the set, and a limit point of a set need not be a boundary point of the set (Exercise 6.8.1(b)). Nonetheless, similarly to the definition of closed set in the second bullet before Definition 6.8.1, a set is closed if and only if it contains all of its boundary points (Exercise 6.8.1(c)). The boundary of every set is closed (Exercise 6.8.1(d)). Since the definition of boundary point is symmetric in the set and its complement, the boundary of the set is also the boundary of the complement,

$$\partial S = \partial(S^c).$$

The closure of a set is the union of the set and its boundary (Exercise 6.8.2(a)),

$$\overline{S} = S \cup \partial S.$$

If S is bounded then so is its closure $\overline{S}$ (Exercise 6.8.2(b)), and therefore the closure of a bounded set is compact. The special-case definition

$$\partial \overline{B(a,r)} = \{x \in \mathbb{R}^n : |x - a| = r\}$$

from Section 6.1 is consistent with Definition 6.8.2.

Definition 6.8.3. *An* **open box** *in* $\mathbb{R}^n$ *is a set of the form*

$$J = (a_1, b_1) \times (a_2, b_2) \times \cdots \times (a_n, b_n).$$

The word box, *unmodified, continues to mean a closed box.*

Proposition 6.8.4 (Finiteness property of compact sets: special case of the Heine–Borel theorem). *Consider a compact set $K \subset \mathbb{R}^n$. Suppose that some collection of open boxes J_i covers K. Then a finite subcollection of the open boxes J_i covers K.*

Proof (Sketch). Suppose that no finite collection of the open boxes J_i covers K. Let B_1 be a box that contains K. Partition B_1 into 2^n subboxes $\widetilde{B}$ by bisecting it in each direction. If for each subbox $\widetilde{B}$, some finite collection of the open boxes J_i covers $K \cap \widetilde{B}$, then the 2^n-fold collection of these finite collections in fact covers all of K. Thus no finite collection of the open boxes J_i covers $K \cap \widetilde{B}$ for at least one subbox $\widetilde{B}$ of B_1. Name some such subbox B_2, repeat the argument with B_2 in place of B_1, and continue in this fashion, obtaining nested boxes

$$B_1 \supset B_2 \supset B_3 \supset \cdots$$

whose sides are half as long at each succeeding generation, and such that no $K \cap B_j$ is covered by a finite collection of the open boxes J_i. The intersection $K \cap B_1 \cap B_2 \cap \cdots$ contains at most one point, because the boxes B_j eventually shrink smaller than the distance between any two given distinct points. On the other hand, since each $K \cap B_j$ is nonempty (otherwise the empty subcollection of the open boxes J_i would cover it), there is a sequence $\{c_j\}$ with each $c_j \in K \cap B_j$; and since K is compact and each B_j is compact and the B_j are nested, the sequence $\{c_j\}$ has a subsequence that converges in K and in each B_j, hence converging in the intersection $K \cap B_1 \cap B_2 \cap \cdots$. Thus the intersection is a single point c. Some open box J_i covers c because $c \in K$, and so because the boxes B_j shrink to c, also J_i covers B_j for all high enough indices j. This contradicts the fact that no $K \cap B_j$ is covered by finitely many J_i. Thus the initial supposition that no finite collection of the open boxes J_i covers K is untenable. $\square$

Although the finiteness property of compact sets plays only a small role in these notes, the idea is important and far-reaching. For example, it lies at the heart of sequence-free proofs that the continuous image of a compact set is compact, the continuous image of a connected set is connected, and continuity on compact sets is uniform.

The following lemma is similar to the difference magnification lemma (Lemma 5.1.3). Its content is that although passing a box through a mapping needn't give another box, if the box is somewhat uniform in its dimensions and if the mapping has bounded derivatives then the mapping takes the box into a second box that isn't too much bigger than the original.

Lemma 6.8.5 (Box-volume magnification lemma). *Let B be a box in $\mathbb{R}^n$ whose longest side is at most twice its shortest side. Let g be a differentiable mapping from an open superset of B in $\mathbb{R}^n$ to $\mathbb{R}^n$. Suppose that there is a number c such that $|D_j g_i(x)| \le c$ for all $i, j \in \{1, \ldots, n\}$ and all $x \in B$. Then $g(B)$ sits in a box B' such that $\mathrm{vol}(B') \le (2nc)^n \mathrm{vol}(B)$.*

Proof. Let x be the centerpoint of B and let $\tilde{x}$ be any point of B. Make the line segment connecting x to $\tilde{x}$ the image of a function of one variable,

$$\gamma : [0, 1] \longrightarrow \mathbb{R}^n, \qquad \gamma(t) = x + t(\tilde{x} - x).$$

Fix any $i \in \{1, \ldots, n\}$. Identically to the proof of the difference magnification lemma, we have for some $t \in (0, 1)$,

$$g_i(\tilde{x}) - g_i(x) = \langle g_i'(\gamma(t)), \tilde{x} - x \rangle.$$

For each j, the jth entry of the vector $g_i'(\gamma(t))$ is $D_j g_i(\gamma(t))$, and we are given that $|D_j g_i(\gamma(t))| \le c$. Also, the jth entry of the vector $\tilde{x} - x$ satisfies $|\tilde{x}_j - x_j| \le \ell/2$, where ℓ is the longest side of B. Thus

$$|g_i(\tilde{x}) - g_i(x)| \le nc\ell/2,$$

and so

$$g_i(B) \subset [g_i(x) - nc\ell/2, g_i(x) + nc\ell/2].$$

Apply this argument for each $i \in \{1, \ldots, n\}$ to show that $g(B)$ lies in the box B' centered at $g(x)$ having sides $nc\ell$ and therefore having volume

$$\mathrm{vol}(B') = (nc\ell)^n.$$

On the other hand, since the shortest side of B is at least $\ell/2$,

$$\mathrm{vol}(B) \ge (\ell/2)^n.$$

The result follows. $\qquad\qquad\qquad\qquad\qquad\qquad\qquad\qquad\qquad\qquad\qquad\qquad$ □

Using the previous two results, we can show that the property of having volume zero is preserved under mappings that are well enough behaved. However, we need to assume more than just continuity. The property of having volume zero is not a topological property.

Proposition 6.8.6 (Volume zero preservation under $\mathcal{C}^1$-mappings). *Let $S \subset \mathbb{R}^n$ be a compact set having volume zero. Let A be an open superset of S, and let*

$$\Phi : A \longrightarrow \mathbb{R}^n$$

be a $\mathcal{C}^1$-mapping. Then $\Phi(S)$ again has volume zero.

Proof. For each $s \in S$ there exists an $r_s > 0$ such that the copy of the box $[-r_s, r_s]^n$ centered at s lies in A (Exercise 6.8.5(a)). Let J_s denote the corresponding open box, i.e., a copy of $(-r_s, r_s)^n$ centered at s. By the finiteness property of compact sets, a collection of finitely many of the open boxes J_s covers S, so certainly the corresponding collection U of the closed boxes does so as well. As a finite union of compact sets, U is compact (Exercise 6.8.1(f)). Therefore the partial derivatives $D_j \Phi_i$ for $i, j = 1, \ldots, n$ are uniformly continuous on U, and so some constant c bounds all $D_j \Phi_i$ on U.

Let $\varepsilon > 0$ be given. Cover S by finitely many boxes B_i having total volume less than $\varepsilon/(2nc)^n$. After replacing each box by its intersections with the boxes of U, we may assume that the boxes all lie in U. (Here it is relevant that the intersection of two boxes is a box.) And after further subdividing the boxes if necessary, we may assume that the longest side of each box is at most twice the shortest side (Exercise 6.8.6(b)). By the box-volume magnification lemma, the Φ-images of the boxes lie in a union of boxes B_i' having volume

$$\sum_i \operatorname{vol}(B_i') \leq (2nc)^n \sum_i \operatorname{vol}(B_i) < \varepsilon.$$

$\square$

The last topological preliminary that we need is the formal definition of *interior*.

Definition 6.8.7 (Interior point, interior of a set). *Let $S \subset \mathbb{R}^n$ be a set. Every nonboundary point of S is an* **interior point** *of S. Thus x is an interior point of S if some open ball $B(x, r)$ lies entirely in S. The* **interior** *of S is*

$$S^\circ = \{interior\ points\ of\ S\}.$$

The interior of every set S is open (Exercise 6.8.6(a)). Every set decomposes as the disjoint union of its interior points and its boundary points (Exercise 6.8.6(b)),

$$S = S^\circ \cup (S \cap \partial S), \qquad S^\circ \cap \partial S = \varnothing.$$

As anticipated at the beginning of this section, we now can complete the argument that the properties of the set K in the change of variable theorem are preserved by the mapping Φ in the theorem.

Proposition 6.8.8. *Let $K \subset \mathbb{R}^n$ be a compact and connected set having boundary of volume zero. Let A be an open superset of K, and let $\Phi : A \longrightarrow \mathbb{R}^n$ be a $\mathcal{C}^1$-mapping such that $\det \Phi' \neq 0$ everywhere on K°. Then $\Phi(K)$ is again a compact and connected set having boundary of volume zero.*

Proof. We have discussed the fact that $\Phi(K)$ is again compact and connected. Restrict Φ to K. The inverse function theorem says that Φ maps interior points of K to interior points of $\Phi(K)$, and thus $\partial(\Phi(K)) \subset \Phi(\partial K)$. By the volume-zero preservation proposition, $\mathrm{vol}(\Phi(\partial K)) = 0$. So $\mathrm{vol}(\partial(\Phi(K))) = 0$ as well.

□

Exercises

6.8.1. (a) Show that every intersection—not just twofold intersections and not even just finite-fold intersections—of closed sets is closed. (Recall from Proposition 2.4.5 that a set S is closed if and only if every sequence in S that converges in $\mathbb{R}^n$ in fact converges in S.)

(b) Show by example that a boundary point of a set need not be a limit point of the set. Show by example that a limit point of a set need not be a boundary point of the set.

(c) Show that a set is closed if and only if it contains each of its boundary points. (Again recall the characterization of closed sets mentioned in part (a).)

(d) Show that the boundary of every set is closed.

(e) Show that every union of two closed sets is closed. It follows that every union of finitely many closed sets is closed. Recall that by definition, a set is open if its complement is closed. Explain why consequently every intersection of finitely many open sets is open.

(f) Explain why every union of finitely many compact sets is compact.

6.8.2. Let S be any subset of $\mathbb{R}^n$.

(a) Show that its closure is its union with its boundary, $\overline{S} = S \cup \partial S$.

(b) Show that if S is bounded then so is $\overline{S}$.

6.8.3. (a) Which points of the proof of Proposition 6.8.4 are sketchy? Fill in the details.

(b) Let S be an unbounded subset of $\mathbb{R}^n$, meaning that S is not contained in any ball. Find a collection of open boxes J_i that covers S but such that no finite subcollection of the open boxes J_i covers S.

(c) Let S be a bounded but nonclosed subset of $\mathbb{R}^n$, meaning that S is bounded but missing a limit point. Find a collection of open boxes J_i that covers S but such that no finite subcollection of the open boxes J_i covers S.

6.8.4. Let $\varepsilon > 0$. Consider the box $B = [0,1] \times [0,\varepsilon] \subset \mathbb{R}^2$, and consider the mapping $g : \mathbb{R}^2 \longrightarrow \mathbb{R}^2$ given by $g(x,y) = (x,x)$. What is the smallest box B' containing $g(B)$? What is the ratio $\mathrm{vol}(B')/\mathrm{vol}(B)$? Discuss the relationship between this example and Lemma 6.8.5.

6.8.5. The following questions are about the proof of Proposition 6.8.6.

(a) Explain why for each $s \in S$ there exists an $r_s > 0$ such that the copy of the box $[-r_s, r_s]^n$ centered at s lies in A.

(b) Explain why every box (with all sides assumed to be positive) can be subdivided into boxes whose longest side is at most twice the shortest side.

6.8.6. Let $S \subset \mathbb{R}^n$ be any set.

(a) Show that the interior S° is open.

(b) Show that S decomposes as the disjoint union of its interior points and its boundary points.

6.9 Proof of the Change of Variable Theorem

Again recall the statement of the change of variable theorem:

> Let $K \subset \mathbb{R}^n$ be a compact and connected set having boundary of volume zero. Let A be an open superset of K, and let $\Phi : A \longrightarrow \mathbb{R}^n$ be a C^1-mapping such that Φ is injective on K° and $\det \Phi' \neq 0$ on K°. Let $f : \Phi(K) \longrightarrow \mathbb{R}$ be a continuous function. Then
>
> $$\int_{\Phi(K)} f = \int_K (f \circ \Phi) \cdot |\det \Phi'|.$$

We begin chipping away at the theorem by strengthening its hypotheses.

Proposition 6.9.1 (Optional hypothesis-strengthening). *To prove the change of variable theorem, it suffices to prove the theorem subject to any combination of the following additional hypotheses:*

- *K is a box.*
- *Φ is injective on all of A,*
- *$\det \Phi' \neq 0$ on all of A.*

Before proceeding to the proof of the proposition, it deserves comment that we will not always want K to be a box. But once the proposition is proved, we may take K to be a box or not as convenient.

Proof. Let $\varepsilon > 0$ be given.

Let B be a box containing K, and let P be a partition of B into subboxes J. Define three types of subbox,

$$\text{type I}\ \ : J \text{ such that } J \subset K^\circ,$$
$$\text{type II}\ : J \text{ such that } J \cap \partial K \neq \varnothing \text{ (and thus } J \cap \partial(B \backslash K) \neq \varnothing),$$
$$\text{type III} : J \text{ such that } J \subset B - (K \cup \partial K).$$

(In the left side of Figure 6.47, the type I subboxes are shaded and the type II subboxes are white. There are no type III subboxes in the figure, but type III subboxes play no role in the pending argument anyway.) The three types of box are exclusive and exhaustive (Exercise 6.9.2(a)).

Also define a function

$$g : B \longrightarrow \mathbb{R}, \qquad g(x) = \begin{cases} (f \circ \Phi)(x) \cdot |\det \Phi'(x)| & \text{if } x \in K, \\ 0 & \text{if } x \notin K. \end{cases}$$

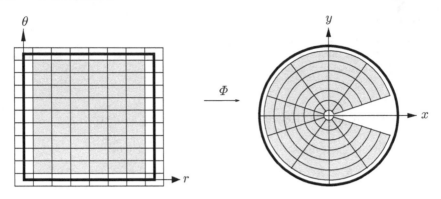

Figure 6.47. Type I and type II subboxes, image of the type I subboxes

The continuous function f is necessarily bounded on $\Phi(K)$, say by R. The partial derivatives $D_j\Phi_i$ of the component functions of Φ are continuous on K, and so the continuous function $|\det \Phi'|$ is bounded on the compact set K, say by $\widetilde{R}$. Thus $R\widetilde{R}$ bounds g on B.

As in the proof of the volume zero preservation proposition (Proposition 6.8.6), we can cover the subset K of A by a collection U of finitely many boxes that is again a subset of A, and so the continuous partial derivatives $D_j\Phi_i$ of the component functions of Φ are bounded on the compact set U, say by c. We may assume that the partition P is fine enough that all subboxes J of type I and type II lie in U (Exercise 6.9.2(b)). And we may assume that the longest side of each subbox J is at most twice the shortest side. Recall that $\varepsilon > 0$ has been given. Because the boundary of K has volume zero, we may further assume that the partition P is fine enough that

$$\sum_{J:\text{type II}} \text{vol}(J) < \min\left\{ \frac{\varepsilon}{R(2nc)^n}, \frac{\varepsilon}{R\widetilde{R}} \right\}$$

(Exercise 6.9.2(c)).

Let

$$\Phi(K)_\text{I} = \bigcup_{J:\text{type I}} \Phi(J), \qquad \Phi(K)_\text{II} = \Phi(K)\backslash\Phi(K)_\text{I}.$$

(Thus $\Phi(K)_\text{I}$ is shaded in the right side of Figure 6.47, while $\Phi(K)_\text{II}$ is white.) Then the integral on the left side of the equality in the change of variable theorem decomposes into two parts,

$$\int_{\Phi(K)} f = \int_{\Phi(K)_\text{I}} f + \int_{\Phi(K)_\text{II}} f,$$

and because Φ is injective on $K°$, the previous display can be rewritten as

$$\int_{\Phi(K)} f = \sum_{J\,:\,\text{type I}} \int_{\Phi(J)} f + \int_{\Phi(K)_\text{II}} f. \qquad (6.12)$$

Also,

$$\Phi(K)_{\mathrm{II}} \subset \bigcup_{J \,:\, \text{type II}} \Phi(J),$$

so that

$$\left| \int_{\Phi(K)_{\mathrm{II}}} f \right| \le \int_{\Phi(K)_{\mathrm{II}}} |f| \le \sum_{J \,:\, \text{type II}} \int_{\Phi(J)} |f|.$$

By the box-volume magnification lemma (Lemma 6.8.5), for each box J of type II, $\mathrm{vol}(\Phi(J)) \le (2nc)^n \, \mathrm{vol}(J)$. Thus, by the bounds on f and on the sum of the type II box-volumes, it follows that

$$\left| \int_{\Phi(K)_{\mathrm{II}}} f \right| < \varepsilon.$$

That is, the second term on the right side of (6.12) contributes as negligibly as desired to the integral on the left side, which is the integral on the left side of the change of variable theorem. In terms of Figure 6.47, the idea is that if the boxes in the left half of the figure are refined until the sum of the white box-areas is small enough then the integral of f over the corresponding small white region in the right half of the figure becomes negligible.

Meanwhile, the integral on the right side of the equality in the change of variable theorem also decomposes into two parts,

$$\int_K (f \circ \Phi) \cdot |\det \Phi'| = \sum_{J \,:\, \text{type I}} \int_J g + \sum_{J \,:\, \text{type II}} \int_J g. \qquad (6.13)$$

By the bounds on g and on the sum of the type II box-volumes,

$$\left| \sum_{J \,:\, \text{type II}} \int_J g \right| \le \sum_{J \,:\, \text{type II}} \int_J |g| < \varepsilon.$$

That is, the second term on the right side of (6.13) contributes as negligibly as desired to the integral on the left side, which is the integral on the right side of the change of variable theorem. In terms of Figure 6.47, the idea is that if the boxes in the left half of the figure are refined until the sum of the white box-areas is small enough then the integral of $(f \circ \Phi) \cdot |\det \Phi'|$ over the white boxes becomes negligible. That is, it suffices to prove the change of variable theorem for boxes like the shaded boxes in the left half of the figure.

The type I subboxes J of the partition of the box B containing the original K (which is not assumed to be a box) satisfy all of the additional hypotheses in the statement of the proposition: each J is a box, and we may shrink the domain of Φ to the open superset K° of each J, where Φ is injective and where $\det \Phi' \ne 0$. Thus, knowing the change of variable theorem subject to any of the additional hypotheses says that the first terms on the right sides of (6.12) and (6.13) are equal, making the integrals on the left sides lie within ε of each other. Since ε is arbitrary, the integrals are in fact equal. In sum, it suffices to prove the change of variable theorem assuming any of the additional hypotheses, as desired. $\square$

Proposition 6.9.2 (Alternative optional hypothesis-strengthening).
To prove the change of variable theorem, it suffices to prove the theorem subject to the following additional hypotheses:

- $\Phi(K)$ *is a box (but now we may not assume that K is a box).*
- Φ *is injective on all of A.*
- $\det \Phi' \neq 0$ *on all of A.*

Similarly to the remark after Proposition 6.9.1, we will not always want the additional hypotheses.

Proof. With the previous proposition in play, the idea now is to run through its proof in reverse, starting from the strengthened hypotheses that it grants us. Thus we freely assume that K is a box, that the change of variable mapping Φ is injective on all of A, and that $\det \Phi' \neq 0$ on all of A. By the inverse function theorem, the superset $\Phi(A)$ of $\Phi(K)$ is open and $\Phi : A \longrightarrow \Phi(A)$ has a C^1 inverse

$$\Phi^{-1} : \Phi(A) \longrightarrow A.$$

Let $\varepsilon > 0$ be given.

Let B be a box containing $\Phi(K)$, and let P be a partition of B into subboxes J. Define three types of subbox,

type I : J such that $J \subset \Phi(K)^{\circ}$,

type II : J such that $J \cap \partial \Phi(K) \neq \varnothing$ (and thus $J \cap \partial(B \backslash \Phi(K)) \neq \varnothing$),

type III : J such that $J \subset B - (\Phi(K) \cup \partial \Phi(K))$.

These three types of box are exclusive and exhaustive. Also, define as before

$$g : B \longrightarrow \mathbb{R}, \qquad g(x) = \begin{cases} (f \circ \Phi)(x) \cdot |\det \Phi'(x)| & \text{if } x \in K, \\ 0 & \text{if } x \notin K. \end{cases}$$

Again, f is bounded on $\Phi(K)$, say by R, and $|\det \Phi'|$ is bounded on K, say by $\widetilde{R}$, so that $R\widetilde{R}$ bounds g on B. (See Figure 6.48, in which the type I subboxes cover nearly all of $\Phi(K)$ and their inverse images cover nearly all of K.)

Cover the subset $\Phi(K)$ of $\Phi(A)$ by a collection U of finitely many boxes that is again a subset of $\Phi(A)$. Then the continuous partial derivatives $D_j \Phi_i^{-1}$ of the component functions of Φ^{-1} are bounded on the compact set U, say by c. We may assume that the partition P is fine enough that all subboxes J of type I and type II lie in U. And we may assume that the longest side of each subbox J is at most twice the shortest side. Recall that $\varepsilon > 0$ has been given. Because the boundary of $\Phi(K)$ has volume zero, we may further assume that the partition P is fine enough that

$$\sum_{J:\text{type II}} \text{vol}(J) < \min\left\{ \frac{\varepsilon}{R}, \frac{\varepsilon}{R\widetilde{R}(2nc)^n} \right\}.$$

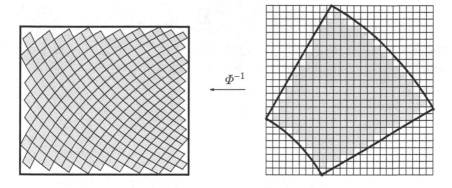

Figure 6.48. Type I, II, and III subboxes, inverse image of the type I subboxes

Let

$$K_{\mathrm{I}} = \bigcup_{J:\text{type I}} \Phi^{-1}(J), \qquad K_{\mathrm{II}} = K \backslash K_{\mathrm{I}}.$$

Then the integral on the left side of the equality in the change of variable theorem decomposes into two parts,

$$\int_{\Phi(K)} f = \sum_{J \,:\, \text{type I}} \int_J f + \sum_{J \,:\, \text{type II}} \int_J f. \qquad (6.14)$$

By the bounds on f and on the sum of the type II box-volumes,

$$\left| \sum_{J \,:\, \text{type II}} \int_J f \right| \le \sum_{J \,:\, \text{type II}} \int_J |f| < \varepsilon.$$

That is, the second term on the right side of (6.14) contributes as negligibly as desired to the integral on the left side, which is the integral on the left side of the change of variable theorem.

Meanwhile, the integral on the right side of the equality in the change of variable theorem also decomposes into two parts,

$$\int_K (f \circ \Phi) \cdot |\det \Phi'| = \int_{K_{\mathrm{I}}} g + \int_{K_{\mathrm{II}}} g,$$

and because Φ^{-1} is injective, the previous display can be rewritten as

$$\int_K (f \circ \Phi) \cdot |\det \Phi'| = \sum_{J \,:\, \text{type I}} \int_{\Phi^{-1}(J)} g + \int_{K_{\mathrm{II}}} g. \qquad (6.15)$$

Also,

$$K_{\mathrm{II}} \subset \bigcup_{J \,:\, \text{type II}} \Phi^{-1}(J),$$

so that

$$\left|\int_{K_{\mathrm{II}}} g\right| \le \int_{K_{\mathrm{II}}} |g| \le \sum_{J \,:\, \text{type II}} \int_{\Phi^{-1}(J)} |g|.$$

For each box J of type II, $\operatorname{vol}(\Phi^{-1}(J)) \le (2nc)^n \operatorname{vol}(J)$. Thus, by the bounds on g and on the sum of the type II box-volumes, it follows that

$$\left|\int_{K_{\mathrm{II}}} g\right| < \varepsilon.$$

That is, the second term on the right side of (6.15) contributes as negligibly as desired to the integral on the left side, which is the integral on the right side of the change of variable theorem.

The type I subboxes J of the partition of the box B containing the original $\Phi(K)$ (which is not assumed to be a box) satisfy the new additional hypothesis in the statement of the proposition. The other two additional hypotheses in the statement of the proposition are already assumed. Thus, knowing the change of variable theorem subject to the additional hypotheses says that the first terms on the right sides of (6.14) and (6.15) are equal, making the integrals on the left sides lie within ε of each other. Since ε is arbitrary, the integrals are in fact equal. In sum, it suffices to prove the change of variable theorem assuming the additional hypotheses, as desired.   □

Proposition 6.9.3 (Further optional hypothesis-strengthening). *To prove the change of variable theorem, it suffices to prove the theorem subject to the additional hypothesis that f is identically 1.*

As with the other hypothesis-strengthenings, we will not always want f to be identically 1, but we may take it to be so when convenient.

Proof. We assume the strengthened hypotheses given us by Proposition 6.9.2. Let P be a partition of the box $\Phi(K)$ into subboxes J. For each subbox J, view the quantity $M_J(f) = \sup\{f(x) : x \in J\}$ both as a number and as a constant function. Assume that the change of variable theorem holds for the constant function 1 and therefore for every constant function, and compute

$$\int_K (f \circ \Phi) \cdot |\det \Phi'| = \sum_J \int_{\Phi^{-1}(J)} (f \circ \Phi) \cdot |\det \Phi'|$$
$$\le \sum_J \int_{\Phi^{-1}(J)} (M_J(f) \circ \Phi) \cdot |\det \Phi'|$$
$$= \sum_J \int_J M_J(f) \quad \text{by the assumption}$$
$$= \sum_J M_J(f) \operatorname{vol}(J)$$
$$= U(f, P).$$

As a lower bound of the upper sums, $\int_K (f \circ \Phi) \cdot |\det \Phi'|$ is at most the integral,

$$\int_K (f \circ \Phi) \cdot |\det \Phi'| \le \int_{\Phi(K)} f.$$

A similar argument gives the opposite inequality, making the integrals equal as desired. □

The next result will allow the proof of the change of variable theorem to decompose the change of variable mapping.

Proposition 6.9.4 (Persistence under composition). *In the change of variable theorem, suppose that the change of variable mapping is a composition*

$$\Phi = \Gamma \circ \Psi$$

where the mappings

$$\Psi : A \longrightarrow \mathbb{R}^n$$

and

$$\Gamma : \widetilde{A} \longrightarrow \mathbb{R}^n \quad (where \ \widetilde{A} \ is \ an \ open \ superset \ of \ \Psi(K))$$

satisfy the hypotheses of the change of variable theorem. If

$$\int_{\Psi(K)} g = \int_K (g \circ \Psi) \cdot |\det \Psi'| \quad for \ continuous \ functions \ g : \Psi(K) \longrightarrow \mathbb{R}$$

and

$$\int_{\Gamma(\Psi(K))} 1 = \int_{\Psi(K)} |\det \Gamma'|$$

then also

$$\int_{\Phi(K)} 1 = \int_K |\det \Phi'|.$$

Proof. The argument is a straightforward calculation using the definition of Φ, the second given equality, the first given equality, the multiplicativity of the determinant, the chain rule, and again the definition of Φ,

$$\int_{\Phi(K)} 1 = \int_{\Gamma(\Psi(K))} 1 = \int_{\Psi(K)} |\det \Gamma'|$$

$$= \int_K |\det(\Gamma' \circ \Psi)| \cdot |\det \Psi'| = \int_K |\det((\Gamma' \circ \Psi) \cdot \Psi')|$$

$$= \int_K |\det(\Gamma \circ \Psi)'| = \int_K |\det \Phi'|.$$

□

Proposition 6.9.5 (Linear change of variable). *The change of variable theorem holds for invertible linear mappings.*

Proof. Let

$$T : \mathbb{R}^n \longrightarrow \mathbb{R}^n$$

be an invertible linear mapping having matrix M. Thus $T'(x) = M$ for all x. Also, T is a composition of recombines, scales, and transpositions, and so by the persistence of the change of variable theorem under composition, it suffices to prove the theorem assuming that T is a recombine or a scale or a transposition. In each case, Propositions 6.9.1 and 6.9.3 allow us to assume that K is a box B and $f = 1$. Thus the desired result is simply

$$\mathrm{vol}(T(B)) = |\det M| \cdot \mathrm{vol}(B),$$

and we established this formula back in Section 3.8.   □

The change of variable theorem is proved partially by induction on the dimension n.

Proposition 6.9.6 (Base case for the induction). *The change of variable theorem holds if* $n = 1$.

Proof. Because $n = 1$, K is an interval $[a, b] \subset \mathbb{R}$ where $a \leq b$. Here is where we use the hypothesis that K is connected. Since we have not studied connected sets closely, the reader is being asked to take for granted that every compact and connected subset of $\mathbb{R}$ is a closed and bounded interval. (Or see Exercise 6.9.1 for a proof that every compact and *path-connected* subset of $\mathbb{R}$ is a closed and bounded interval.) The continuous function

$$\Phi' : [a, b] \longrightarrow \mathbb{R}$$

can take the value 0 only at a and b. Thus by the intermediate value theorem, Φ' never changes sign on $[a, b]$. If $\Phi' \geq 0$ on $[a, b]$ then Φ is increasing, and so (using Theorem 6.4.3 for the second equality)

$$\int_{\Phi([a,b])} f = \int_{\Phi(a)}^{\Phi(b)} f = \int_a^b (f \circ \Phi) \cdot \Phi' = \int_{[a,b]} (f \circ \Phi) \cdot |\Phi'|.$$

If $\Phi' \leq 0$ on $[a, b]$ then Φ is decreasing, and so

$$\int_{\Phi([a,b])} f = \int_{\Phi(b)}^{\Phi(a)} f = -\int_{\Phi(a)}^{\Phi(b)} f = -\int_a^b (f \circ \Phi) \cdot \Phi' = \int_{[a,b]} (f \circ \Phi) \cdot |\Phi'|.$$

Thus in either case the desired result holds.   □

Proposition 6.9.7 (Bootstrap induction step). *For every* $n > 1$, *if the change of variable theorem holds in dimension* $n - 1$ *then it holds in dimension* n *subject to the additional hypothesis that the transformation* Φ *fixes at least one coordinate.*

A 3-dimensional transformation Φ that fixes the third coordinate is shown in Figure 6.49. The figure makes the proof of Proposition 6.9.7 inevitable: the desired result holds for each slice because we are assuming the change of variable theorem in dimension $n - 1$, and so Fubini's theorem gives the result for the entire figure.

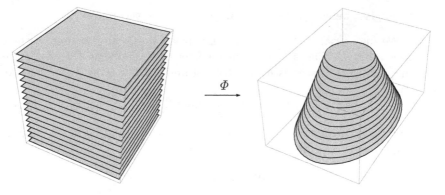

Figure 6.49. A transformation that fixes the third coordinate

Proof. Propositions 6.9.1 and 6.9.3 allow us to assume that K is a box B, that Φ is injective on B, that $\det \Phi' \neq 0$ on B, and that $f = 1$. Also, we may assume that the coordinate fixed by Φ is the last coordinate. There exist a box $B_{n-1} \subset \mathbb{R}^{n-1}$ and an interval $I = [a, b] \subset \mathbb{R}$ such that

$$B = \bigcup_{t \in I} B_{n-1} \times \{t\}.$$

By assumption, Φ is a $\mathcal{C}^1$-mapping on an open superset A of B. For each $t \in I$ let A_t denote the cross section of A with last coordinate t,

$$A_t = \{x \in \mathbb{R}^{n-1} : (x, t) \in A\}.$$

Then A_t is an open superset of B_{n-1} in $\mathbb{R}^{n-1}$. For each $t \in I$ define a mapping

$$\Psi_t : A_t \longrightarrow \mathbb{R}^{n-1}, \qquad \Psi_t(x) = (\Phi_1(x, t), \dots, \Phi_{n-1}(x, t)).$$

Each Ψ_t is a $\mathcal{C}^1$-mapping on an open superset of B_{n-1}, and

$$\Phi(B) = \bigcup_{t \in I} \Psi_t(B_{n-1}) \times \{t\}.$$

Since Φ is injective on B and $\det \Phi' \neq 0$ on B, it follows that each Ψ_t is injective on B_{n-1}, and the formula

$$|\det \Psi_t'(x)| = |\det \Phi'(x, t)|, \quad (x, t) \in B \tag{6.16}$$

(Exercise 6.9.3) shows that $\det \Psi_t' \neq 0$ on B_{n-1}. Thus for each t, the set B_{n-1} and the transformation Ψ_t satisfy the change of variable theorem hypotheses in dimension $n - 1$. Compute, using Fubini's theorem, quoting the change of variable theorem in dimension $n - 1$, and citing formula (6.16) and again using Fubini's theorem, that

$$\int_{\Phi(B)} 1 = \int_{t \in I} \int_{\Psi_t(B_{n-1})} 1 = \int_{t \in I} \int_{B_{n-1}} |\det \Psi_t'| = \int_B |\det \Phi'|.$$

$\square$

At long last we can prove the change of variable theorem for $n > 1$.

Proof. We may assume the result for dimension $n - 1$, and we may assume that K is a box B, that A is an open superset of B, and that $\Phi : A \longrightarrow \mathbb{R}^n$ is a C^1-mapping such that Φ is injective on A and $\det \Phi' \neq 0$ on A. We need to show that

$$\int_{\Phi(B)} 1 = \int_B |\det \Phi'|. \tag{6.17}$$

To prove the theorem, we will partition B into subboxes J, each J having an open superset A_J on which Φ is a composition

$$\Phi = T \circ \Gamma \circ \Psi,$$

where Ψ and Γ are C^1-mappings that fix at least one coordinate and T is a linear transformation. Note that Ψ, Γ, and T inherit injectivity and nonzero determinant-derivatives from Φ, so that in particular, T is invertible. Since the theorem holds for each of Ψ, Γ, and T, it holds for their composition. In more detail,

$$
\begin{aligned}
\int_{T(\Gamma(\Psi(J)))} 1 &= \int_{\Gamma(\Psi(J))} |\det T'| & \text{by Proposition 6.9.5} \\
&= \int_{\Psi(J)} |\det(T' \circ \Gamma)| \, |\det \Gamma'| & \text{by Proposition 6.9.7} \\
&= \int_{\Psi(J)} |\det(T \circ \Gamma)'| & \text{by the chain rule} \\
&= \int_J |\det \left((T \circ \Gamma)' \circ \Psi \right)| \, |\det \Psi'| & \text{by Proposition 6.9.7} \\
&= \int_J |\det(T \circ \Gamma \circ \Psi)'| & \text{by the chain rule.}
\end{aligned}
$$

That is, for each J,

$$\int_{\Phi(J)} 1 = \int_J |\det \Phi'|,$$

and so summing over all subboxes J finally gives (6.17).

To obtain the subboxes J, proceed as follows for each point $x \in B$. Let

$$T = D\Phi_x$$

and define

$$\widetilde{\Phi} = T^{-1} \circ \Phi,$$

so that $D\widetilde{\Phi}_x = \mathrm{id}_n$ is the n-dimensional identity map. Introduce the nth projection function, $\pi_n(x_1, \ldots, x_n) = x_n$, and further define

$$\Psi : A \longrightarrow \mathbb{R}^n, \qquad \Psi = (\widetilde{\Phi}_1, \ldots, \widetilde{\Phi}_{n-1}, \pi_n),$$

so that $D\Psi_x = \mathrm{id}_n$ as well. By the inverse function theorem, Ψ is locally invertible. Let J_x be a subbox of B containing x having an open superset A_x such that Ψ^{-1} exists on $\Psi(A_x)$. Now define

$$\Gamma : \Psi(A_x) \longrightarrow \mathbb{R}^n, \qquad \Gamma = (\pi_1, \ldots, \pi_{n-1}, \widetilde{\Phi}_n \circ \Psi^{-1}).$$

Then $\Gamma \circ \Psi = \widetilde{\Phi} = T^{-1} \circ \Phi$ on A_x, so that $T \circ \Gamma \circ \Psi = \Phi$ on A_x, and thus Ψ, Γ, and T have the desired properties. (Figure 6.50 illustrates the decomposition for the polar coordinate mapping. In the figure, Ψ changes only the first coordinate, Γ changes only the second, and then the linear mapping T completes the polar coordinate change of variable.)

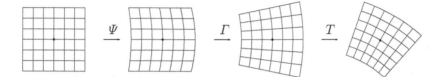

Figure 6.50. Local decomposition of the polar coordinate mapping

Cover B by the collection of open interiors of the boxes J_x. By the finiteness property of B, some finite collection of the interiors covers B, and so certainly the corresponding finite collection of the boxes J_x themselves covers B. Partition B into subboxes J such that each J lies in one of the finitely many J_x, and the process is complete.   □

In contrast to all of this, recall the much easier proof of the one-dimensional change of variable theorem, using the construction of an antiderivative by integrating up to a variable endpoint (Theorem 6.4.1, sometimes called the first fundamental theorem of integral calculus) and using the (second) fundamental theorem of integral calculus twice,

$$\int_a^b (f \circ \phi) \cdot \phi' = \int_a^b (F' \circ \phi) \cdot \phi' \qquad \text{where } F(x) = \int_a^x f, \text{ so } F' = f$$

$$= \int_a^b (F \circ \phi)' \qquad \text{by the chain rule}$$

$$= (F \circ \phi)(b) - (F \circ \phi)(a) \qquad \text{by the FTIC}$$

$$= F(\phi(b)) - F(\phi(a)) \qquad \text{by definition of composition}$$

$$= \int_{\phi(a)}^{\phi(b)} F' \qquad \text{by the FTIC again}$$

$$= \int_{\phi(a)}^{\phi(b)} f \qquad \text{since } F' = f.$$

We see that the one-variable fundamental theorem of integral calculus is doing the bulk of the work. Chapter 9 will give us a multivariable fundamental theorem, after which we can sketch a proof of the multivariable change of variable theorem in the spirit of the one-variable argument just given. A fully realized version of that proof still has to handle topological issues, but even so it is more efficient than the long, elementary method of this section.

Exercises

6.9.1. Let K be a nonempty compact subset of $\mathbb{R}$. Explain why the quantities $a = \min\{x : x \in K\}$ and $b = \max\{x : x \in K\}$ exist. Now further assume that K is path-connected, so that in particular there is a continuous function

$$\gamma : [0,1] \longrightarrow \mathbb{R}$$

such that $\gamma(0) = a$ and $\gamma(1) = b$. Explain why consequently $K = [a,b]$.

6.9.2. (a) Explain to yourself why the three types of rectangle in the proof of Proposition 6.9.1 are exclusive. Now suppose that the three types are not exhaustive, i.e., some rectangle J lies partly in K° and partly in $(B \backslash K)^\circ$ without meeting the set $\partial K = \partial(B \backslash K)$. Supply details as necessary for the following argument. Let $x \in J$ lie in K° and let $\tilde{x} \in J$ lie in $(B \backslash K)^\circ$. Define a function from the unit interval to $\mathbb{R}$ by mapping the interval to the line segment from x to $\tilde{x}$, and then mapping each point of the segment to 1 if it lies in K and to -1 if it lies in $B \backslash K$. The resulting function is continuous on the interval, and it changes sign on the interval, but it does not take the value 0. This is impossible, so the rectangle J cannot exist.

(b) In the proof of Proposition 6.9.1, show that we may assume that the partition P is fine enough that all subboxes J of type I and type II lie in U.

(c) In the proof of Proposition 6.9.1, show that given $\varepsilon > 0$, we may assume that the partition P is fine enough that

$$\sum_{J:\text{type II}} \text{vol}(J) < \min\left\{ \frac{\varepsilon}{R(2nc)^n}, \frac{\varepsilon}{R\widetilde{R}} \right\}.$$

6.9.3. In the proof of Proposition 6.9.7, establish formula (6.16).

6.9.4. Here is a sketched variant of the endgame of the change of variable proof: *A slightly easier variant of Proposition 6.9.7 assumes that the transformation Φ changes at most one coordinate, and then the process of factoring Φ locally as a composition can be iterated until each factor is either linear or changes at most one coordinate.* Fill in the details.

7

Approximation by Smooth Functions

Let k be a nonnegative integer. Recall that a C^k-function on $\mathbb{R}^n$ is a function all of whose partial derivatives up through order k exist and are continuous. That is, to say that a function

$$f : \mathbb{R}^n \longrightarrow \mathbb{R}$$

is C^k is to say that f, and $D_j f$ for $j = 1, \ldots, n$, and $D_{jj'} f$ for $j, j' = 1, \ldots, n$, and so on up to all $D_{j_1 \cdots j_k} f$ exist and are continuous on $\mathbb{R}^n$. Various ideas that we have discussed so far have required different values of k:

- If f is C^1 then f is differentiable in the multivariable sense of derivative (Theorem 4.5.3).
- If f is C^2 then its mixed second-order derivatives $D_{12} f$ and $D_{21} f$ are equal (Theorem 4.6.1).
- The multivariable max/min test (Proposition 4.7.8) assumes a C^2-function.
- The inverse function theorem says that if $A \subset \mathbb{R}^n$ is open and $f : A \longrightarrow \mathbb{R}^n$ is componentwise C^1 and its derivative Df_a is invertible at a point a then f is locally invertible about a, and the local inverse is again C^1 (Theorem 5.2.1).
- A C^0-mapping from the unit interval can fill the square, but a C^1-mapping cannot.
- If f (again scalar-valued now) is C^0 then it is integrable over every compact set having boundary of volume zero (Section 6.5).
- In the change of variable formula $\int_{\Phi(K)} f = \int_K (f \circ \Phi) \cdot |\det \Phi'|$ for multiple integrals (Theorem 6.7.1), the change of variable mapping Φ is assumed to be C^1, and for now the integrand f is assumed to be C^0. We will return to this example at the very end of this chapter.

Meanwhile, a *smooth* function is a function on $\mathbb{R}^n$ all of whose partial derivatives of all orders exist. Smooth functions are also called C^∞-functions, an appropriate notation because the derivatives of each order are continuous in consequence of the derivatives of one-higher order existing. This chapter

© Springer International Publishing AG 2016
J. Shurman, *Calculus and Analysis in Euclidean Space*,
Undergraduate Texts in Mathematics, DOI 10.1007/978-3-319-49314-5_7

briefly touches on the fact that for functions that vanish off a compact set, C^0-functions and C^1-functions and C^2-functions are well approximated by C^∞-functions.

The approximation technology is an integral called the *convolution*. The idea is as follows. Suppose that we had a function

$$\delta : \mathbb{R}^n \longrightarrow \mathbb{R}$$

with the following properties:

(1) $\delta(x) = 0$ for all $x \neq \mathbf{0}$,
(2) $\int_{x \in \mathbb{R}^n} \delta(x) = 1$.

So conceptually the graph of δ is an infinitely high, infinitely narrow spike above $\mathbf{0}$ having total volume 1. No such function exists, at least not in the usual sense of function. (The function δ, known as the *Dirac delta function*, is an example of a *distribution*, distributions being objects that generalize functions.) Nonetheless, if δ were sensible then for every function $f : \mathbb{R}^n \longrightarrow \mathbb{R}$ and for every $x \in \mathbb{R}^n$, we would have in consequence that the graph of the product of f and the x-translate of δ is an infinitely high, infinitely narrow spike above x having total volume $f(x)$,

(1) $f(y)\delta(x - y) = 0$ for all $y \neq x$,
(2) $\int_{y \in \mathbb{R}^n} f(y)\delta(x - y) = f(x)$.

That is, granting the Dirac delta function, every function f can be expressed as an integral. The idea motivating convolution is that if we replace the idealized delta function by a smooth pulse φ, tall but finitely high, narrow but positively wide, and having total volume 1, and if f is well enough behaved (e.g., f is continuous and vanishes off a compact set) then we should still recover a close approximation of f from the resulting integral,

$$\int_{y \in \mathbb{R}^n} f(y)\varphi(x - y) \approx f(x).$$

The approximating integral on the left side of the previous display is the convolution of f and φ evaluated at x. Although f is assumed only to be continuous, the convolution is smooth. Indeed, every x_i-derivative passes through the y-integral and φ is smooth, so that

$$\frac{\partial}{\partial x_i} \int_y f(y)\varphi(x - y) = \int_y f(y)\frac{\partial \varphi}{\partial x_i}(x - y),$$

and similarly for higher derivatives.

One can see convolution in action visually by comparing graphs of convolutions to the graph of the original function. And the conceptual framework for establishing the properties of convolution analytically is not difficult. Having discussed approximation by convolution, we will freely assume in the remaining chapters of these notes that our functions are C^∞, i.e., that they are smooth.

7.1 Spaces of Functions

To begin, we quantify the phrase *functions that vanish off a compact set* from the chapter introduction.

Definition 7.1.1 (Support). *Consider a function*

$$f : \mathbb{R}^n \longrightarrow \mathbb{R}.$$

The **support** *of f is the closure of the set of its inputs that produce nonzero outputs,*

$$\mathrm{supp}(f) = \overline{\{x \in \mathbb{R}^n : f(x) \neq 0\}}.$$

The function f is **compactly supported** *if its support is compact. The class of compactly supported C^k-functions is denoted $C_c^k(\mathbb{R}^n)$. Especially, $C_c^0(\mathbb{R}^n)$ denotes the class of compactly supported continuous functions.*

Each class $C_c^k(\mathbb{R}^n)$ of functions forms a vector space over $\mathbb{R}$ (Exercise 7.1.1). Figure 7.1 shows a compactly supported C^0-function on $\mathbb{R}$ and its support. The graph has some corners, so the function is not C^1.

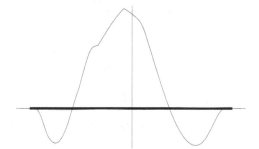

Figure 7.1. Compactly supported continuous function on $\mathbb{R}$ and its support

The spaces of compactly supported functions shrink as their member-functions are required to have more derivatives,

$$C_c^0(\mathbb{R}^n) \supset C_c^1(\mathbb{R}^n) \supset C_c^2(\mathbb{R}^n) \supset \cdots,$$

and we will see that all of the containments are proper.

Definition 7.1.2 (Test function). *A* **test function** *is a compactly supported smooth function. The class of test functions is denoted $C_c^\infty(\mathbb{R}^n)$.*

The class of test functions sits at the end of the chain of containments of function-spaces from a moment ago,

$$\mathcal{C}_c^\infty(\mathbb{R}^n) = \bigcap_{k \geq 0} \mathcal{C}_c^k(\mathbb{R}^n),$$

and as an intersection of vector spaces over $\mathbb{R}$, the test functions $\mathcal{C}_c^\infty(\mathbb{R}^n)$ again form a vector space over $\mathbb{R}$. In the chain of containments

$$\mathcal{C}_c^0(\mathbb{R}^n) \supset \mathcal{C}_c^1(\mathbb{R}^n) \supset \mathcal{C}_c^2(\mathbb{R}^n) \supset \cdots \supset \mathcal{C}_c^\infty(\mathbb{R}^n),$$

all of the containments are proper. Indeed, for a vivid example of the first containment, Weierstrass showed how to construct a function f of one variable, having support $[0, 1]$, that is continuous everywhere but differentiable nowhere on its support. The function of n variables

$$f_0(x_1, x_2, \ldots, x_n) = f(\|(x_1, x_2, \ldots, x_n)\|)$$

thus lies in $\mathcal{C}_c^0(\mathbb{R}^n)$ but not in $\mathcal{C}_c^1(\mathbb{R}^n)$. Next, the function

$$f_1(x_1, x_2, \ldots, x_n) = \int_{t_1=0}^{x_1} f_0(t_1, x_2, \ldots, x_n)$$

lies in $\mathcal{C}_c^1(\mathbb{R}^n)$ but not $\mathcal{C}_c^2(\mathbb{R}^n)$, because its first partial derivative is f_0, which does not have a first partial derivative. Defining f_2 as a similar integral of f_1 gives a function that lies in $\mathcal{C}_c^2(\mathbb{R}^n)$ but not $\mathcal{C}_c^3(\mathbb{R}^n)$, and so on. Finally, none of the functions f_k just described lies in $\mathcal{C}_c^\infty(\mathbb{R}^n)$.

For every $k > 0$ and every $f \in \mathcal{C}_c^k(\mathbb{R}^n)$, the supports of the partial derivatives are contained in the support of the original function,

$$\operatorname{supp}(D_j f) \subset \operatorname{supp}(f), \quad j = 1, \ldots, n.$$

Thus the partial derivative operators D_j take $\mathcal{C}_c^k(\mathbb{R}^n)$ to $\mathcal{C}_c^{k-1}(\mathbb{R}^n)$ as sets. The operators are linear because

$$D_j(f + \tilde{f}) = D_j f + D_j \tilde{f}, \quad f, \tilde{f} \in \mathcal{C}_c^k(\mathbb{R}^n)$$

and

$$D_j(cf) = c D_j f, \quad f \in \mathcal{C}_c^k(\mathbb{R}^n), \ c \in \mathbb{R}.$$

In addition, more can be said about the D_j operators. Each space $\mathcal{C}_c^k(\mathbb{R}^n)$ of functions carries an absolute value function having properties similar to the absolute value on Euclidean space $\mathbb{R}^n$. With these absolute values in place, the partial differentiation operators are continuous.

Definition 7.1.3 ($\mathcal{C}_c^k(\mathbb{R}^n)$ absolute value). *The absolute value function on $\mathcal{C}_c^0(\mathbb{R}^n)$ is*

$$| \ | : \mathcal{C}_c^0(\mathbb{R}^n) \longrightarrow \mathbb{R}, \quad |f| = \sup\{|f(x)| : x \in \mathbb{R}^n\}.$$

Let k be a nonnegative integer. The absolute value function on $\mathcal{C}_c^k(\mathbb{R}^n)$ is

$$| \ |_k : \mathcal{C}_c^k(\mathbb{R}^n) \longrightarrow \mathbb{R}$$

given by

$$|f|_k = \max \left\{ \begin{array}{l} |f|, \\ |D_j f| \ for \ j = 1, \ldots, n, \\ |D_{jj'} f| \ for \ j, j' = 1, \ldots, n, \\ \vdots \\ |D_{j_1 \cdots j_k} f| \ for \ j_1, \ldots, j_k = 1, \ldots, n \end{array} \right\}.$$

That is, $|f|_k$ is the largest absolute value of f or of any derivative of f up to order k. In particular, $| \ |_0 = | \ |$.

The *largest absolute values* mentioned in the definition exist by the extreme value theorem, because the relevant partial derivatives are compactly supported and continuous. By contrast, we have not defined an absolute value on the space of test functions $\mathcal{C}_c^\infty(\mathbb{R}^n)$, because the obvious attempt to extend Definition 7.1.3 to test functions would involve the maximum of an infinite set, a maximum that certainly need not exist.

Proposition 7.1.4 ($\mathcal{C}_c^k(\mathbb{R}^n)$ absolute value properties).

(A1) *Absolute value is positive: $|f|_k \geq 0$ for all $f \in \mathcal{C}_c^k(\mathbb{R}^n)$, and $|f|_k = 0$ if and only if f is the zero function.*

(A2) *Scaling property: $|cf|_k = |c| \, |f|_k$ for all $c \in \mathbb{R}$ and $f \in \mathcal{C}_c^k(\mathbb{R}^n)$.*

(A3) *Triangle inequality: $|f + g|_k \leq |f|_k + |g|_k$ for all $f, g \in \mathcal{C}_c^k(\mathbb{R}^n)$.*

Proof. The first two properties are straightforward to check. For the third property, note that for every $f, g \in \mathcal{C}_c^0(\mathbb{R}^n)$ and every $x \in \mathbb{R}^n$,

$$|(f + g)(x)| \leq |f(x)| + |g(x)| \leq |f| + |g|.$$

Thus $|f| + |g|$ is an upper bound of all values $|(f + g)(x)|$, so that

$$|f + g| \leq |f| + |g|.$$

That is, $|f + g|_0 \leq |f|_0 + |g|_0$. If $f, g \in \mathcal{C}_c^1(\mathbb{R}^n)$ then the same argument shows that also $|D_j(f + g)| \leq |D_j f| + |D_j g|$ for $j = 1, \ldots, n$, so that

$$|f + g|_1 = \max \left\{ \begin{array}{l} |f + g|, \\ |D_j f + D_j g| \ for \ j = 1, \ldots, n \end{array} \right\}$$

$$\leq \max \left\{ \begin{array}{l} |f| + |g|, \\ |D_j f| + |D_j g| \ for \ j = 1, \ldots, n \end{array} \right\}$$

$$\leq \max \left\{ \begin{array}{l} |f|, \\ |D_j f| \ for \ j = 1, \ldots, n \end{array} \right\} + \max \left\{ \begin{array}{l} |g|, \\ |D_j g| \ for \ j = 1, \ldots, n \end{array} \right\}$$

$$= |f|_1 + |g|_1.$$

(For the second inequality, note for example that

$$\max(|f| + |g|) = (|f| + |g|)(\tilde{x}) \quad \text{for some } \tilde{x}$$
$$= |f|(\tilde{x}) + |g|(\tilde{x}) \leq \max |f| + \max |g|,$$

and similarly for each partial derivative.) The proof that $|f + g|_k \leq |f|_k + |g|_k$ for higher values of k is more of the same.   □

Now we can verify the anticipated continuity of the linear operators D_j from $\mathcal{C}_c^k(\mathbb{R}^n)$ to $\mathcal{C}_c^{k-1}(\mathbb{R}^n)$.

Proposition 7.1.5 (Continuity of differentiation). *For every $k \geq 1$, the partial differentiation mappings*

$$D_j : \mathcal{C}_c^k(\mathbb{R}^n) \longrightarrow \mathcal{C}_c^{k-1}(\mathbb{R}^n), \quad j = 1, \ldots, n$$

are continuous.

Proof. Consider any function $f \in \mathcal{C}_c^k(\mathbb{R}^n)$ and any sequence $\{f_m\}$ in $\mathcal{C}_c^k(\mathbb{R}^n)$. Suppose that

$$\lim_m |f_m - f|_k = 0.$$

Then

$$\lim_m |f_m - f| = 0,$$
$$\lim_m |D_j f_m - D_j f| = 0 \text{ for } j = 1, \ldots, n,$$
$$\lim_m |D_{jj'} f_m - D_{jj'} f| = 0 \text{ for } j, j' = 1, \ldots, n,$$
$$\vdots$$
$$\lim_m |D_{j_1 j_2 \ldots j_k} f_m - D_{j_1 j_2 \ldots j_k} f| = 0 \text{ for } j_1, j_2, \ldots, j_k = 1, \ldots, n.$$

Fix any $j \in \{1, \ldots, n\}$. As a subset of the information in the previous display,

$$\lim_m |D_j f_m - D_j f| = 0,$$
$$\lim_m |D_{jj'} f_m - D_{jj'} f| = 0 \text{ for } j' = 1, \ldots, n,$$
$$\vdots$$
$$\lim_m |D_{jj_2 \ldots j_k} f_m - D_{jj_2 \ldots j_k} f| = 0 \text{ for } j_2, \ldots, j_k = 1, \ldots, n.$$

That is,

$$\lim_m |D_j f_m - D_j f|_{k-1} = 0.$$

The implication that we have just proved,

$$\lim_m |f_m - f|_k = 0 \implies \lim_m |D_j f_m - D_j f|_{k-1} = 0,$$

is exactly the assertion that $D_j : \mathcal{C}_c^k(\mathbb{R}^n) \longrightarrow \mathcal{C}_c^{k-1}(\mathbb{R}^n)$ is continuous, and the proof is complete.   □

Again let $k \geq 1$. The fact that $|f|_{k-1} \leq |f|_k$ for every $f \in C_c^k(\mathbb{R}^n)$ (Exercise 7.1.2) shows that for every $f \in C_c^k(\mathbb{R}^n)$ and every sequence $\{f_m\}$ in $C_c^k(\mathbb{R}^n)$, if $\lim_m |f_m - f|_k = 0$ then $\lim_m |f_m - f|_{k-1} = 0$. That is, the inclusion mapping

$$i : C_c^k(\mathbb{R}^n) \longrightarrow C_c^{k-1}(\mathbb{R}^n), \quad i(f) = f$$

is continuous.

The space $C_c^\infty(\mathbb{R}^n)$ of test functions is closed under partial differentiation, meaning that the partial derivatives of a test function are again test functions (Exercise 7.1.3).

In this chapter we will show that just as every real number $x \in \mathbb{R}$ is approximated as closely as desired by rational numbers $q \in \mathbb{Q}$, every compactly supported continuous function $f \in C_c^k(\mathbb{R}^n)$ is approximated as closely as desired by test functions $g \in C_c^\infty(\mathbb{R}^n)$. More precisely, we will show that:

For every $f \in C_c^k(\mathbb{R}^n)$, there exists a sequence $\{f_m\}$ in $C_c^\infty(\mathbb{R}^n)$ such that $\lim_m |f_m - f|_k = 0$.

The fact that $\lim_m |f_m - f|_k = 0$ means that given any $\varepsilon > 0$, there exists a starting index m_0 such that f_m for all $m \geq m_0$ uniformly approximates f to within ε up to kth order. That is, for all $m \geq m_0$, simultaneously for all $x \in \mathbb{R}^n$,

$$|f_m(x) - f(x)| < \varepsilon,$$
$$|D_j f_m(x) - D_j f(x)| < \varepsilon \text{ for } j = 1, \ldots, n,$$
$$|D_{jj'} f_m(x) - D_{jj'} f(x)| < \varepsilon \text{ for } j, j' = 1, \ldots, n,$$
$$\vdots$$
$$|D_{j_1 \ldots j_k} f_m(x) - D_{j_1 \ldots j_k} f(x)| < \varepsilon \text{ for } j_1, \ldots, j_k = 1, \ldots, n.$$

The use of *uniform* here to connote that a condition holds simultaneously over a set of values is similar to its use in *uniform continuity*.

Exercises

7.1.1. Show that each class $C_c^k(\mathbb{R}^n)$ of functions forms a vector space over $\mathbb{R}$.

7.1.2. Verify that $|f|_{k-1} \leq |f|_k$ for every $f \in C_c^k(\mathbb{R}^n)$.

7.1.3. Explain why each partial derivative of a test function is again a test function.

7.1.4. Let $\{f_n\}$ be a sequence of functions in $C_c^0(\mathbb{R}^n)$, and suppose that the sequence converges, meaning that there exists a function $f : \mathbb{R}^n \longrightarrow \mathbb{R}$ such that $\lim_n f_n(x) = f(x)$ for all $x \in \mathbb{R}^n$. Must f have compact support? Must f be continuous?

7.2 Pulse Functions

A *pulse function* is a useful type of test function. To construct pulse functions, first consider the function

$$s : \mathbb{R} \longrightarrow \mathbb{R}, \qquad s(x) = \begin{cases} 0 & \text{if } x \le 0, \\ e^{-1/x} & \text{if } x > 0. \end{cases}$$

(See Figure 7.2.) Each $x < 0$ lies in an open interval on which s is the constant function 0, and each $x > 0$ lies in an open interval on which s is a composition of smooth functions, so in either case all derivatives $s^{(k)}(x)$ exist. More specifically, for every nonnegative integer k, there exists a polynomial $p_k(x)$ such that the kth derivative of s takes the form

$$s^{(k)}(x) = \begin{cases} 0 & \text{if } x < 0, \\ p_k(x) x^{-2k} e^{-1/x} & \text{if } x > 0, \\ ? & \text{if } x = 0. \end{cases}$$

Only $s^{(k)}(0)$ is in question. However, $s^{(0)}(0) = 0$, and if we assume that $s^{(k)}(0) = 0$ for some $k \ge 0$ then it follows (because exponential behavior dominates polynomial behavior) that

$$\lim_{h \to 0^+} \frac{s^{(k)}(h) - s^{(k)}(0)}{h} = \lim_{h \to 0^+} p_k(h) h^{-2k-1} e^{-1/h} = 0.$$

That is, $s^{(k+1)}(0)$ exists and equals 0 as well. By induction, $s^{(k)}(0) = 0$ for all $k \ge 0$. Thus s is smooth: each derivative exists, and each derivative is continuous because the next derivative exists as well. But s is not a test function, because its support is not compact: $\operatorname{supp}(s) = [0, \infty)$.

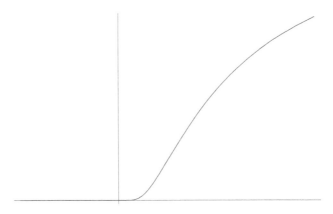

Figure 7.2. Smooth function

Now the pulse function is defined in terms of the smooth function,

$$p : \mathbb{R} \longrightarrow \mathbb{R}, \qquad p(x) = \frac{s(x+1)s(-x+1)}{\int_{x=-1}^{1} s(x+1)s(-x+1)}.$$

The graph of p (Figure 7.3) explains the name *pulse function*. As a product of compositions of smooth functions, p is smooth. The support of p is $[-1, 1]$, so p is a test function. Also, p is normalized so that

$$\int_{[-1,1]} p = 1.$$

The maximum pulse value $p(0)$ is therefore close to 1 because the pulse graph is roughly a triangle of base 2, but $p(0)$ is not exactly 1. The pulse function $p_2(x, y) = p(x)p(y)$ from $\mathbb{R}^2$ to $\mathbb{R}$, having support $[-1, 1]^2$, is shown in Figure 7.4. A similar pulse function p_3 on $\mathbb{R}^3$ can be imagined as a concentration of density in a box about the origin.

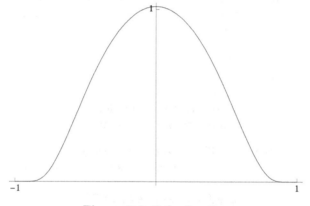

Figure 7.3. Pulse function

Exercises

7.2.1. Since the function s in this section is smooth, it has nth-degree Taylor polynomials $T_n(x)$ at $a = 0$ for all nonnegative integers n. (Here n does not denote the dimension of Euclidean space.) For what x does $s(x) = T_n(x)$?

7.2.2. Let p be the pulse function defined in this section. Explain why $\operatorname{supp}(p) = [-1, 1]$.

7.2.3. Let $p : \mathbb{R} \longrightarrow \mathbb{R}$ be the one-dimensional pulse function from this section.
   (a) Graph the function $q(x) = p(2a - b + x(b - a)))$, where $a < b$.

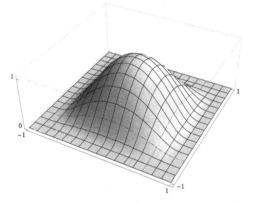

Figure 7.4. Two-dimensional pulse function

(b) Graph the function $r(x) = \int_{t=-1}^{x} p(t)$.

(c) Use the function r from part (b) to give a formula for a test function that is 0 for $x < a$, climbs from 0 to 1 for $a \le x \le b$, is 1 for $b < x < c$, drops from 1 to 0 for $c \le x \le d$, and is 0 for $d < x$.

7.3 Convolution

This section shows how to construct test functions from $\mathcal{C}_c^0(\mathbb{R}^n)$-functions. In preparation, we introduce a handy piece of notation.

Definition 7.3.1 (Sum, difference of two sets). *Let S and T be subsets of $\mathbb{R}^n$. Their **sum** is the set consisting of all sums of a point of S plus a point of T,*

$$S + T = \{s + t : s \in S,\ t \in T\}.$$

*Their **difference** is similarly*

$$S - T = \{s - t : s \in S,\ t \in T\}.$$

Visually, $S + T$ can be imagined as many copies of T, one based at each point of S, or vice versa. For example, if K is a three-dimensional box and B is a small ball about $\mathbf{0}_3$ then $K + B$ is slightly larger than K, again shaped like a box except that the edges and corners are rounded. Similarly, $\{\mathbf{0}\} - T$ is the reflection of T through the origin. The sum or difference of two compact sets is compact (Exercise 7.3.1(a)). The sum of of the open balls $B(a, r)$ and $B(b, s)$ is $B(a + b, r + s)$ (Exercise 7.3.1(b)). The reader is alerted that the set difference here is different from another, more common notion of set difference, that being the elements of one set that are not elements of another,

$$S \backslash T = \{s \in S : s \notin T\}.$$

Returning to $\mathcal{C}_c^0(\mathbb{R}^n)$-functions, every such function can be integrated over all of $\mathbb{R}^n$.

Definition 7.3.2 (Integral of a $\mathcal{C}_c^0(\mathbb{R}^n)$-function). *Let $f \in \mathcal{C}_c^0(\mathbb{R}^n)$. The integral of f is the integral of f over any box that contains its support,*

$$\int f = \int_B f \quad \text{where } \operatorname{supp}(f) \subset B.$$

In Definition 7.3.2 the integral on the right side exists by Theorem 6.3.1. Also, the integral on the right side is independent of the suitable box B, always being the integral over the intersection of all such boxes, the smallest suitable box. Thus the integral on the left side exists and is unambiguous. We do not bother writing $\int_{\mathbb{R}^n} f$ rather than $\int f$, because it is understood that by default we are integrating f over $\mathbb{R}^n$.

Definition 7.3.3 (Mollifying kernel). *Let $f \in \mathcal{C}_c^0(\mathbb{R}^n)$ be a compactly supported continuous function, and let $\varphi \in \mathcal{C}_c^\infty(\mathbb{R}^n)$ be a test function. The **mollifying kernel** associated to f and φ is the function*

$$\kappa : \mathbb{R}^n \times \mathbb{R}^n \longrightarrow \mathbb{R}, \qquad \kappa(x,y) = f(y)\varphi(x-y).$$

For every fixed $x \in \mathbb{R}^n$, the corresponding cross section of the mollifying kernel is denoted κ_x,

$$\kappa_x : \mathbb{R}^n \longrightarrow \mathbb{R}, \qquad \kappa_x(y) = \kappa(x,y).$$

For each $x \in \mathbb{R}^n$, the mollifying kernel $\kappa_x(y)$ can be nonzero only if $y \in \operatorname{supp}(f)$ and $x - y \in \operatorname{supp}(\varphi)$. It follows that

$$\operatorname{supp}(\kappa_x) \subset \operatorname{supp}(f) \cap (\{x\} - \operatorname{supp}(\varphi)).$$

Therefore κ_x is compactly supported. (Figure 7.5 shows an example of the multiplicands $f(y)$ and $\varphi(x-y)$ of $\kappa_x(y)$, and Figure 7.6 shows their compactly supported product.) Also, since f and φ are continuous, κ_x is continuous. That is, for each x, the mollifying kernel κ_x viewed as a function of y again lies in $\mathcal{C}_c^0(\mathbb{R}^n)$, making it integrable by Theorem 6.3.1.

The mollifying kernel is so named for good reason. First, it is a kernel in the sense that we integrate it to get a new function.

Definition 7.3.4 (Convolution). *Let $f \in \mathcal{C}_c^0(\mathbb{R}^n)$ and let $\varphi \in \mathcal{C}_c^\infty(\mathbb{R}^n)$. The **convolution** of f and φ is the function defined by integrating the mollifying kernel,*

$$f * \varphi : \mathbb{R}^n \longrightarrow \mathbb{R}, \qquad (f * \varphi)(x) = \int_y \kappa_x(y) = \int_y f(y)\varphi(x-y).$$

Second, although the mollifying kernel is only as well behaved as f, integrating it indeed mollifies f in the sense that the integral is as well behaved as φ, i.e., the integral is a test function. Even if f is nowhere differentiable, $f * \varphi$ has all partial derivatives of all orders while remaining compactly supported. Furthermore, the derivatives have the natural formula obtained by passing them through the integral.

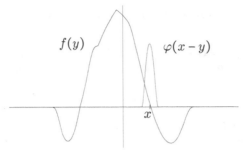

Figure 7.5. Multiplicands of the mollifying kernel

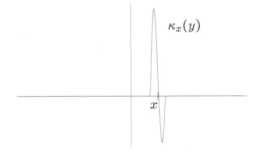

Figure 7.6. The mollifying kernel is compactly supported

Proposition 7.3.5 (Derivatives of the convolution). *Let $f \in C_c^0(\mathbb{R}^n)$ and let $\varphi \in C_c^\infty(\mathbb{R}^n)$. Then also $f * \varphi \in C_c^\infty(\mathbb{R}^n)$. Specifically, the partial derivatives of the convolution are the convolutions with the partial derivatives,*

$$D_j(f * \varphi) = f * D_j\varphi, \quad j = 1, \ldots, n,$$

and similarly for the higher-order partial derivatives.

The following result helps to prove Proposition 7.3.5. In its statement, the symbol φ, which usually denotes a test function, instead denotes a $C_c^1(\mathbb{R}^n)$-function. The reason for the weaker hypothesis will appear soon in the proof of Corollary 7.3.7.

Lemma 7.3.6 (Uniformity lemma for C^1-functions). *Let $\varphi \in C_c^1(\mathbb{R}^n)$. Given $\varepsilon > 0$, there exists a corresponding $\delta > 0$ such that for all $a \in \mathbb{R}^n$ and all nonzero $h \in \mathbb{R}$, and for every $j \in \{1, \ldots, n\}$,*

$$|h| < \delta \implies \left| \frac{\varphi(a + he_j) - \varphi(a)}{h} - D_j\varphi(a) \right| < \varepsilon.$$

Proof. Fix some j in $\{1, \ldots, n\}$. The mean value theorem at the jth coordinate gives for all $a \in \mathbb{R}^n$ and all nonzero $h \in \mathbb{R}$,

$$\left| \frac{\varphi(a + he_j) - \varphi(a)}{h} - D_j\varphi(a) \right| = |D_j\varphi(a + te_j) - D_j\varphi(a)| \text{ where } |t| < |h|.$$

Since $D_j\varphi$ is continuous on $\mathbb{R}^n$ and is compactly supported, it is uniformly continuous on $\mathbb{R}^n$, and so given any $\varepsilon > 0$ there exists a corresponding $\delta_j > 0$ such that for all $a \in \mathbb{R}^n$ and $t \in \mathbb{R}$,

$$|D_j\varphi(a + te_j) - D_j\varphi(a)| < \varepsilon \quad \text{if } |t| < \delta_j.$$

Thus

$$|h| < \delta_j \implies \left| \frac{\varphi(a + he_j) - \varphi(a)}{h} - D_j\varphi(a) \right| < \varepsilon.$$

After running the argument of the previous paragraph for $j = 1, \ldots, n$, define $\delta = \min\{\delta_1, \ldots, \delta_n\}$. Then for all nonzero $h \in \mathbb{R}$ and for each $j \in \{1, \ldots, n\}$, if $|h| < \delta$ then $|h| < \delta_j$. This implication combines with the previous display to give the result. $\square$

Now we can establish the derivative formula for the convolution.

Proof (of Proposition 7.3.5). To see that $f * \varphi$ is compactly supported, recall the observation that for a given x, the mollifying kernel $\kappa_x(y) = f(y)\varphi(x - y)$ can be nonzero only at y-values such that

$$y \in \mathrm{supp}(f) \cap (\{x\} - \mathrm{supp}(\varphi)).$$

Such y can exist only if x takes the form

$$x = y + z, \quad y \in \mathrm{supp}(f), \ z \in \mathrm{supp}(\varphi).$$

That is, the integrand is always zero if $x \notin \mathrm{supp}(f) + \mathrm{supp}(\varphi)$ (see Figure 7.7). Hence,

$$\mathrm{supp}(f * \varphi) \subset \mathrm{supp}(f) + \mathrm{supp}(\varphi).$$

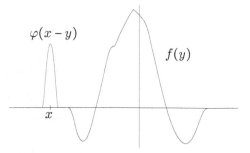

Figure 7.7. The mollifying kernel is zero for x outside $\mathrm{supp}(f) + \mathrm{supp}(\varphi)$

To show that $D_j(f * \varphi)$ exists and equals $f * D_j\varphi$ for $j = 1, \ldots, n$ is precisely to show that each x-derivative passes through the y-integral,

$$\frac{\partial}{\partial x_j} \int_y f(y)\varphi(x-y) = \int_y f(y)\frac{\partial\varphi}{\partial x_j}(x-y), \quad j = 1, \ldots, n.$$

Since the integral is being taken over some box B, the equality follows from Proposition 6.6.2. But we prove it using other methods, for reasons that will emerge later in the chapter. The function f is bounded, say by R, so we can estimate that for every $x \in \mathbb{R}^n$ and every nonzero $h \in \mathbb{R}$ and every j,

$$\left| \frac{(f * \varphi)(x + he_j) - (f * \varphi)(x)}{h} - (f * D_j\varphi)(x) \right|$$

$$= \left| \frac{\int_y f(y)\varphi(x + he_j - y) - \int_y f(y)\varphi(x-y)}{h} - \int_y f(y)D_j\varphi(x-y) \right|$$

$$= \left| \int_y f(y)\left(\frac{\varphi(x - y + he_j) - \varphi(x-y)}{h} - D_j\varphi(x-y) \right) \right|$$

$$\leq R \int_y \left| \frac{\varphi(x - y + he_j) - \varphi(x-y)}{h} - D_j\varphi(x-y) \right|.$$

Assuming that $|h| < 1$, the support of the integrand as a function of y lies in the bounded set

$$\{x + te_j : -1 < t < 1\} - \text{supp}(\varphi),$$

and therefore the integral can be taken over some box B. By the uniformity lemma, given any $\varepsilon > 0$, for all small enough h the integrand is less than $\varepsilon/(R\,\text{vol}(B))$ uniformly in y. Consequently the integral is less than ε/R. In sum, given any $\varepsilon > 0$, for all small enough h we have

$$\left| \frac{(f * \varphi)(x + he_j) - (f * \varphi)(x)}{h} - (f * D_j\varphi)(x) \right| < \varepsilon.$$

Since x is arbitrary, this gives the desired result for first-order partial derivatives,

$$D_j(f * \varphi) = f * D_j\varphi, \quad j = 1, \ldots, n.$$

As for higher-order partial derivatives, note that $D_j\varphi \in \mathcal{C}_c^\infty(\mathbb{R}^n)$ for each j. So the same result for second-order partial derivatives follows,

$$D_{jj'}(f * \varphi) = D_{j'}(f * D_j\varphi) = f * D_{jj'}\varphi, \quad j, j' = 1, \ldots, n,$$

and so on.   □

The proof of Proposition 7.3.5 required only that each κ_x be integrable, that f be bounded, and that φ lie in $\mathcal{C}_c^1(\mathbb{R}^n)$. We will make use of this observation in Section 7.5.

If the function f lies in the subspace $\mathcal{C}^1_c(\mathbb{R}^n)$ of $\mathcal{C}^0_c(\mathbb{R}^n)$ then the partial derivatives of the convolution pass through the integral to f as well as to φ. That is, for differentiable functions, the derivative of the convolution is the convolution of the derivative.

Corollary 7.3.7. *Let $k \geq 1$, let $f \in \mathcal{C}^k_c(\mathbb{R}^n)$, and let $\varphi \in \mathcal{C}^\infty_c(\mathbb{R}^n)$. Then*

$$D_{j_1 \dots j_k}(f * \varphi) = D_{j_1 \dots j_k} f * \varphi, \quad j_1, \dots, j_k = 1, \dots, n.$$

Proof. Since

$$(f * \varphi)(x) = \int_y f(y) \varphi(x - y),$$

it follows by the change of variable theorem (replace y by $x - y$) that also

$$(f * \varphi)(x) = \int_y f(x - y) \varphi(y).$$

Now the proof of the proposition works with the roles of f and φ exchanged to show that $D_j(f * \varphi) = D_j f * \varphi$ for $j = 1, \dots, n$. (Here is where it is relevant that the uniformity lemma requires only a $\mathcal{C}^1_c(\mathbb{R}^n)$-function rather than a test function.) Similarly, if $f \in \mathcal{C}^2_c(\mathbb{R}^n)$ then because $D_j f \in \mathcal{C}^1_c(\mathbb{R}^n)$ for $j = 1, \dots, n$, it follows that

$$D_{jj'}(f * \varphi) = D_{jj'} f * \varphi, \quad j, j' = 1, \dots, n.$$

The argument for higher derivatives is the same. $\qquad\square$

Consider a function $f \in \mathcal{C}^0_c(\mathbb{R}^n)$. Now that we know that every convolution $f * \varphi$ (where $\varphi \in \mathcal{C}^\infty_c(\mathbb{R}^n)$) lies in $\mathcal{C}^\infty_c(\mathbb{R}^n)$, the next question is to what extent the test function $f * \varphi$ resembles the original compactly supported continuous function f. As already noted, for every x, the integral

$$(f * \varphi)(x) = \int_y f(y) \varphi(x - y)$$

refers to values of f only on $\{x\} - \operatorname{supp}(\varphi)$. Especially, if $\operatorname{supp}(\varphi)$ is a small set about the origin then the convolution value $(f * \varphi)(x)$ depends only on the behavior of the original function f near x. The next section will construct useful test functions φ having small support, the idea being that convolutions $f * \varphi$ with such test functions will approximate the functions f being convolved. For example, in Figure 7.5, $f(x)$ is small and positive, while the integral of the mollifying kernel shown in Figure 7.6 is plausibly small and positive as well.

Exercises

7.3.1. (a) Show that the sum of two compact sets is compact.

(b) Let $B(a,r)$ and $B(b,s)$ be open balls. Show that their sum is $B(a + b, r + s)$.

(c) Recall that there are four standard axioms for addition, either in the context of a field or a vector space. Which of the four axioms are satisfied by set addition, and which are not?

(d) Let $0 < a < b$. Let A be the circle of radius b in the (x,y)-plane, centered at the origin. Let B be the closed disk of radius a in the (x,z)-plane, centered at $(b,0,0)$. Describe the sum $A + B$.

7.3.2. Let $f \in C_c^0(\mathbb{R}^n)$, and let $\varphi \in C_c^\infty(\mathbb{R}^n)$. Assume that $\varphi \geq 0$, i.e., all output values of φ are nonnegative, and assume that $\int \varphi = 1$. Suppose that R bounds f, meaning that $|f(x)| < R$ for all x. Show that R also bounds $f * \varphi$.

7.4 Test Approximate Identity and Convolution

Our next technical tool is a sequence of test functions whose graphs are ever taller and more narrow, each enclosing volume 1.

Definition 7.4.1 (Test approximate identity). *A* **test approximate identity** *is a sequence of test functions*

$$\{\varphi_m\} = \{\varphi_1, \varphi_2, \varphi_3, \dots\}$$

such that:

(1) *Each φ_m is nonnegative, i.e., each φ_m maps $\mathbb{R}^n$ to $\mathbb{R}_{\geq 0}$.*
(2) *Each φ_m has integral 1, i.e., $\int \varphi_m = 1$ for each m.*
(3) *The supports of the φ_m shrink to $\{\mathbf{0}\}$, i.e.,*

$$\operatorname{supp}(\varphi_1) \supset \operatorname{supp}(\varphi_2) \supset \cdots, \qquad \bigcap_{m=1}^{\infty} \operatorname{supp}(\varphi_m) = \{\mathbf{0}\}.$$

We can construct a test approximate identity using the pulse function p from Section 7.2. Define for $m = 1, 2, 3, \dots$

$$\varphi_m : \mathbb{R}^n \longrightarrow \mathbb{R}, \qquad \varphi_m(x) = m^n\, p(mx_1)\, p(mx_2) \cdots p(mx_n).$$

Then $\operatorname{supp}(\varphi_m) = [-1/m, 1/m]^n$ for each m. Here the coefficient m^n is chosen such that $\int \varphi_m = 1$ (Exercise 7.4.1). Figure 7.8 shows the graphs of φ_2, φ_4, φ_8, and φ_{15} when $n = 1$. The first three graphs have the same vertical scale, but not the fourth. Figure 7.9 shows the graphs of φ_1 through φ_4 when $n = 2$, all having the same vertical scale.

The *identity* being approximated by the sequence of test functions $\{\varphi_m\}$ is the Dirac delta function from the chapter introduction, denoted δ. To repeat

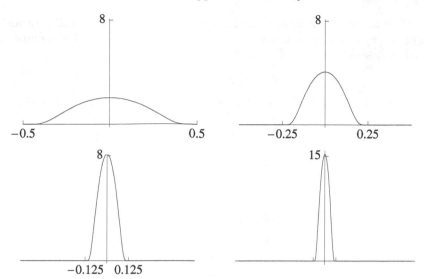

Figure 7.8. The functions φ_2, φ_4, φ_8, and φ_{15} from an approximate identity

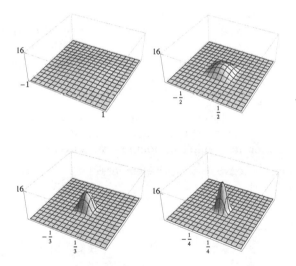

Figure 7.9. The functions φ_1 through φ_4 from a two-dimensional approximate identity

ideas from the introduction, δ is conceptually a unit point mass at the origin, and so its properties should be

$$\operatorname{supp}(\delta) = \{\mathbf{0}\}, \qquad \int \delta = 1.$$

No such function exists in the orthodox sense of the word *function*. But regardless of sense, for every function $f : \mathbb{R}^n \longrightarrow \mathbb{R}$ and every $x \in \mathbb{R}^n$, the mollifying kernel associated to f and δ,

$$\kappa_x(y) = f(y)\delta(x - y),$$

is conceptually a point of mass $f(x)$ at each x. That is, its properties should be

$$\text{supp}(\kappa_x) = \{x\}, \qquad (f * \delta)(x) = \int_y \kappa_x(y) = f(x).$$

Under a generalized notion of function, the Dirac delta makes perfect sense as an object called a distribution, defined by the integral in the previous display but only for a limited class of functions:

$$\text{for all } x, \quad (f * \delta)(x) = f(x) \text{ for test functions } f.$$

Yes, now it is f that is restricted to be a test function. The reason for this is that δ is not a test function, not being a function at all, and to get a good theory of distributions such as δ, we need to restrict the functions that they convolve with. In sum, the Dirac delta function is an identity in the sense that

$$f * \delta = f \text{ for test functions } f.$$

Distribution theory is beyond the scope of these notes, but we may conceive of the identity property of the Dirac delta function as the expected limiting behavior of any test approximate identity. That is, returning to the environment of $f \in C_c^0(\mathbb{R}^n)$ and taking any test approximate identity $\{\varphi_m\}$, we expect that

$$\lim_m (f * \varphi_m) = f \quad \text{for } C_c^0(\mathbb{R}^n)\text{-functions } f.$$

As explained in Section 7.1, this limit will be uniform, meaning that the values $(f * \varphi_m)(x)$ will converge to $f(x)$ at one rate simultaneously for all x in $\mathbb{R}^n$. See Exercise 7.4.3 for an example of nonuniform convergence.

For an example of convolution with elements of a test approximate identity, consider the sawtooth function

$$f : \mathbb{R} \longrightarrow \mathbb{R}, \qquad f(x) = \begin{cases} |x| & \text{if } |x| \le 1/4, \\ 1/2 - |x| & \text{if } 1/4 < |x| \le 1/2, \\ 0 & \text{if } 1/2 < |x|. \end{cases}$$

Recall the test approximate identity $\{\varphi_m\}$ from after Definition 7.4.1. Figure 7.10 shows f and its convolutions with φ_2, φ_4, φ_8, and φ_{15}. The convolutions approach the original function while smoothing its corners, and the convolutions are bounded by the bound on the original function as shown in Exercise 7.3.2. Also, the convolutions have larger supports than the original function, but the supports shrink toward the original support as m grows.

The following lemma says that if compact sets shrink to a point, then eventually they lie inside any given ball about the point. Specifically, the sets that we have in mind are the supports of a test approximate identity.

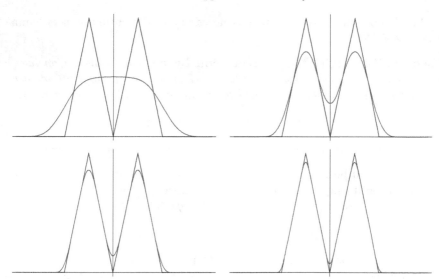

Figure 7.10. The sawtooth function convolved with various φ_m

Lemma 7.4.2 (Shrinking sets lemma). *Let*

$$\{S_m\} = \{S_1, S_2, S_3, \dots\}$$

be a sequence of compact subsets of $\mathbb{R}^n$ *such that*

$$S_1 \supset S_2 \supset S_3 \supset \cdots, \qquad \bigcap_{m=1}^{\infty} S_m = \{\mathbf{0}\}.$$

Then for every $\delta > 0$ *there exists some positive integer* m_0 *such that*

$$\text{for all } m \geq m_0, \quad S_m \subset B(\mathbf{0}, \delta).$$

Proof. Let $\delta > 0$ be given. If no S_m lies in $B(\mathbf{0}, \delta)$ then there exist points

$$x_1 \in S_1 \backslash B(\mathbf{0}, \delta),$$
$$x_2 \in S_2 \backslash B(\mathbf{0}, \delta),$$
$$x_3 \in S_3 \backslash B(\mathbf{0}, \delta),$$

and so on. The sequence $\{x_m\}$ lies in S_1, so it has a convergent subsequence. The containments $S_1 \supset S_2 \supset \cdots$ show that replacing the sequence by the subsequence preserves the displayed conditions, so we may assume that the original sequence converges. Let x denote its limit. For every $m \geq 1$, the terms of the sequence from index m onward lie in S_m, so $x \in S_m$. Thus $x \in \bigcap_m S_m = \{\mathbf{0}\}$, i.e., $x = \mathbf{0}$. But also, $|x_m| \geq \delta$ for each m, so $|x| \geq \delta$. This is a contradiction, so we are done. $\qquad\square$

The hypothesis of compactness is necessary in the shrinking sets lemma (Exercise 7.4.2).

Theorem 7.4.3 ($C_c^0(\mathbb{R}^n)$-approximation by convolutions). *Consider a function $f \in C_c^0(\mathbb{R}^n)$ and let $\{\varphi_m\} : \mathbb{R}^n \longrightarrow \mathbb{R}$ be a test approximate identity. Given $\varepsilon > 0$, there exists a positive integer m_0 such that for all integers m,*

$$m \geq m_0 \implies |f * \varphi_m - f| < \varepsilon.$$

That is, the convolutions $f * \varphi_m$ converge uniformly to the original function f.

Proof. Let $\varepsilon > 0$ be given. Since the support of f is compact, f is uniformly continuous on its support, and hence f is uniformly continuous on all of $\mathbb{R}^n$. So there exists some $\delta > 0$ such that for all $x, y \in \mathbb{R}^n$,

$$|y - x| < \delta \implies |f(y) - f(x)| < \varepsilon.$$

Because the supports of the approximate identity functions shrink to $\{\mathbf{0}\}$, the shrinking sets lemma says that there exists some positive integer m_0 such that for all integers $m \geq m_0$, $\text{supp}(\varphi_m) \subset B(\mathbf{0}, \delta)$. Note that m_0 depends only on δ, which in turn depends only on ε, all of this with no reference to any particular $x \in \mathbb{R}^n$. Now, for all $x, y \in \mathbb{R}^n$, and all $m \geq m_0$,

$$\begin{aligned} y \in x - \text{supp}(\varphi_m) &\implies y \in x - B(\mathbf{0}, \delta) = x + B(\mathbf{0}, \delta) \\ &\implies |y - x| < \delta \\ &\implies |f(y) - f(x)| < \varepsilon. \end{aligned}$$

Because the approximate identity functions φ_m have integral 1, we have for all $x \in \mathbb{R}^n$ and all positive integers m,

$$f(x) = \int_y f(x) \varphi_m(x - y).$$

Use the fact that the approximate identity functions φ_m are nonnegative to estimate that for all $x \in \mathbb{R}^n$ and all positive integers m,

$$\begin{aligned} |(f * \varphi_m)(x) - f(x)| &= \left| \int_y (f(y) - f(x)) \varphi_m(x - y) \right| \\ &\leq \int_y |f(y) - f(x)| \varphi_m(x - y). \end{aligned}$$

We may integrate only over y-values in $x - \text{supp}(\varphi_m)$, so that if $m \geq m_0$ then the integrand is less than $\varepsilon \varphi_m(x - y)$. That is, since the approximate identity functions have integral 1, we have for all $x \in \mathbb{R}^n$ and all positive integers m,

$$m \geq m_0 \implies |(f * \varphi_m)(x) - f(x)| < \varepsilon \int_y \varphi_m(x - y) = \varepsilon.$$

This is the desired result. Note how the argument has used all three defining properties of the approximate identity. $\qquad\square$

Corollary 7.4.4 ($\mathcal{C}_c^k(\mathbb{R}^n)$-approximation by convolutions). *Let k be a positive integer. Consider a function $f \in \mathcal{C}_c^k(\mathbb{R}^n)$ and let $\{\varphi_m\} : \mathbb{R}^n \longrightarrow \mathbb{R}$ be a test approximate identity. Given $\varepsilon > 0$, there exists a positive integer m_0 such that for all integers m,*

$$m \geq m_0 \implies |f * \varphi_m - f|_k < \varepsilon.$$

That is, the convolutions and their derivatives converge uniformly to the original function and its derivatives up to order k.

Proof. Recall from Corollary 7.3.7 that if $f \in \mathcal{C}_c^1(\mathbb{R}^n)$ then for every test function φ, the derivative of the convolution is the convolution of the derivative,

$$D_j(f * \varphi) = D_j f * \varphi, \quad j = 1, \dots, n.$$

Since the derivatives $D_j f$ lie in $\mathcal{C}_c^0(\mathbb{R}^n)$, the theorem says that their convolutions $D_j f * \varphi_m$ converge uniformly to the derivatives $D_j f$ as desired. The argument for higher derivatives is the same. $\qquad\square$

Exercises

7.4.1. Recall that $\int p = 1$ where $p : \mathbb{R}^n \longrightarrow \mathbb{R}$ is the pulse function from Section 7.2. Let m be any positive integer and recall the definition in this section,

$$\varphi_m(x) = m^n\, p(mx_1)\, p(mx_2) \cdots p(mx_n).$$

Explain why consequently $\int \varphi_m = 1$.

7.4.2. Find a sequence $\{S_m\}$ of subsets of $\mathbb{R}$ satisfying all of the hypotheses of the shrinking sets lemma except for compactness, and such that no S_m is a subset of the interval $B(0,1) = (-1,1)$.

7.4.3. This exercise illustrates a nonuniform limit. For each positive integer m, define

$$f_m : [0,1] \longrightarrow \mathbb{R}, \qquad f_m(x) = x^m.$$

Also define

$$f : [0,1] \longrightarrow \mathbb{R}, \qquad f(x) = \begin{cases} 0 & \text{if } 0 \leq x < 1, \\ 1 & \text{if } x = 1. \end{cases}$$

  (a) Using one set of axes, graph f_1, f_2, f_3, f_{10}, and f.
  (b) Show that for every $x \in [0,1]$, $\lim_m f_m(x) = f(x)$. That is, given $\varepsilon > 0$, there exists some positive integer m_0 such that for all positive integers m,

$$m \geq m_0 \implies |f_m(x) - f(x)| < \varepsilon.$$

Thus the function f is the limit of the sequence of functions $\{f_m\}$. That is,

$$\text{for each } x, \quad f(x) = \lim_m \{f_m(x)\}.$$

(c) Now let $\varepsilon = 1/2$. Show that for every positive integer m, no matter how large, there exists some corresponding $x \in [0,1]$ such that $|f_m(x) - f(x)| \geq \varepsilon$. That is,

$$\text{for each } m, \quad |f_m(x) - f(x)| \text{ fails to be small for some } x.$$

Thus the convergence of $\{f_m\}$ to f is not uniform, i.e., the functions do not converge to the limit-function at one rate simultaneously for all $x \in [0,1]$.

7.5 Known-Integrable Functions

Recall that the slogan-title of Theorem 6.5.4 is *near-continuity implies integrability*. The largest space of functions that we have considered so far in this chapter is $C_c^0(\mathbb{R}^n)$, so we have not yet discussed the entire class of functions that we know to be integrable. This section gives some results about convolution and approximation for such functions.

Recall also that a function is called bounded if its outputs form a bounded set.

Definition 7.5.1 (Known-integrable function). *A function*

$$f : \mathbb{R}^n \longrightarrow \mathbb{R}.$$

is **known-integrable** *if it is bounded, compactly supported, and continuous except on a set of volume zero. The class of known-integrable functions is denoted* $\mathcal{I}_c(\mathbb{R}^n)$.

Unsurprisingly, the class $\mathcal{I}_c(\mathbb{R}^n)$ forms a vector space over $\mathbb{R}$.

Let $f \in \mathcal{I}_c(\mathbb{R}^n)$. The integral of f is the integral of f over any box that contains its support,

$$\int f = \int_B f \quad \text{where supp}(f) \subset B.$$

Similarly to the remarks after Definition 7.3.2, the integral on the right side exists, but this time by Theorem 6.5.4. The integral on the right side is independent of the box B, and so the integral on the left side exists, is unambiguous, and is understood to be the integral of f over all of $\mathbb{R}^n$.

The convolution remains sensible when f is known-integrable. That is, if $f \in \mathcal{I}_c(\mathbb{R}^n)$ and $\varphi \in C_c^\infty(\mathbb{R}^n)$ then for each $x \in \mathbb{R}^n$ the mollifying kernel

$$\kappa_x : \mathbb{R}^n \longrightarrow \mathbb{R}, \quad \kappa_x(y) = f(y)\varphi(x-y)$$

again lies in $\mathcal{I}_c(\mathbb{R}^n)$. And so we may continue to define the convolution of f and φ as

$$f * \varphi : \mathbb{R}^n \longrightarrow \mathbb{R}, \quad (f * \varphi)(x) = \int_y \kappa_x(y).$$

The formulas for convolution derivatives remain valid as well. That is, if $f \in \mathcal{I}_c(\mathbb{R}^n)$ and $\varphi \in C_c^\infty(\mathbb{R}^n)$ then also $f * \varphi \in C_c^\infty(\mathbb{R}^n)$, and

$$D_j(f * \varphi) = f * \varphi_j, \quad j = 1, \ldots, n,$$
$$D_{jj'}(f * \varphi) = f * D_{jj'}\varphi_j, \quad j, j' = 1, \ldots, n,$$

and so on. Here is where it is relevant that our proof of Proposition 7.3.5 required only that each κ_x be integrable, that f be bounded, and that φ lie in $C_c^1(\mathbb{R}^n)$.

Given a known-integrable function $f \in \mathcal{I}_c(\mathbb{R}^n)$ and a test approximate identity $\{\varphi_m\}$, we would like the convolutions $\{f * \varphi_m\}$ to approximate f uniformly as m grows. But the following proposition shows that this is impossible when f has discontinuities.

Proposition 7.5.2 (The uniform limit of continuous functions is continuous). *Let*

$$\{f_m\} : \mathbb{R}^n \longrightarrow \mathbb{R}$$

be a sequence of continuous functions that converges uniformly to a limit function

$$f : \mathbb{R}^n \longrightarrow \mathbb{R}.$$

Then f is continuous as well.

Proof. For every two points $x, \tilde{x} \in \mathbb{R}^n$ and for every positive integer m we have

$$|f(\tilde{x}) - f(x)| = |f(\tilde{x}) - f_m(\tilde{x}) + f_m(\tilde{x}) - f_m(x) + f_m(x) - f(x)|$$
$$\leq |f(\tilde{x}) - f_m(\tilde{x})| + |f_m(\tilde{x}) - f_m(x)| + |f_m(x) - f(x)|.$$

Let $\varepsilon > 0$ be given. For all m large enough, the first and third terms are less than $\varepsilon/3$ regardless of the values of x and $\tilde{x}$. Fix such a value of m, and fix x. Then since f_m is continuous, the middle term is less than $\varepsilon/3$ if $\tilde{x}$ is close enough to x. It follows that

$$|f(\tilde{x}) - f(x)| < \varepsilon \quad \text{for all } \tilde{x} \text{ close enough to } x.$$

That is, f is continuous. $\qquad\qquad\qquad\qquad\qquad\qquad\qquad\qquad\qquad$ □

Thus the convergence property of convolutions must become more technical for known-integrable functions rather than compactly supported continuous functions. In preparation for proving the convergence property, the following lemma says that if K is a compact subset of an open set then so is the sum of K and some closed ball.

Lemma 7.5.3 (Thickening lemma). *Let K and A be subsets of $\mathbb{R}^n$ such that*

$$K \subset A, \quad K \text{ is compact}, \quad A \text{ is open}.$$

Then

$$\text{for some } r > 0, \quad K + \overline{B(0, r)} \subset A.$$

Proof. Since K is compact, it lies in some ball $B(\mathbf{0}, R)$. Solving the problem with the open set $A \cap B(\mathbf{0}, R)$ in place of A also solves the original problem.

Having replaced A by $A \cap B(\mathbf{0}, R)$, define a function on K that takes positive real values,

$$d : K \longrightarrow \mathbb{R}_{>0}, \qquad d(a) = \sup\{r : B(a, r) \subset A\}.$$

The fact that we have shrunk A (if necessary) to lie inside the ball has ensured that d is finite, because specifically $d(a) \le R$ for all a. Fix some $a \in K$ and let $r = d(a)$. Let $\{r_m\}$ be a strictly increasing sequence of positive real numbers such that $\lim_m \{r_m\} = r$. Then $B(a, r_m) \subset A$ for each m, and so

$$B(a, r) = \bigcup_{m=1}^{\infty} B(a, r_m) \subset A.$$

This argument shows that in fact,

$$d(a) = \max\{r : B(a, r) \subset A\}.$$

The function d is continuous. To see this, fix some point $a \in K$ and let $r = d(a)$. Consider also a second point $\tilde{a} \in K$ such that $|\tilde{a} - a| < r$, and let $\tilde{r} = d(\tilde{a})$. Then

$$B(\tilde{a}, r - |\tilde{a} - a|) \subset B(a, r) \subset A,$$

showing that $\tilde{r} \ge r - |\tilde{a} - a|$. Either $\tilde{r} \le r + |\tilde{a} - a|$, or $\tilde{r} > r + |\tilde{a} - a| \ge r$ so that also $|\tilde{a} - a| < \tilde{r}$ and the same argument shows that $r \ge \tilde{r} - |\tilde{a} - a|$, i.e., $\tilde{r} \le r + |\tilde{a} - a|$ after all. That is, we have shown that for every $a \in K$,

$$\left\{ \begin{matrix} \tilde{a} \in K \\ |\tilde{a} - a| < r(a) \end{matrix} \right\} \implies |d(\tilde{a}) - d(a)| \le |\tilde{a} - a|.$$

Thus d is continuous at a (given $\varepsilon > 0$, let $\delta = \min\{r(a), \varepsilon/2\}$), and since $a \in K$ is arbitrary, d is continuous on K as claimed.

Since K is compact and d is continuous, d takes a minimum value $\tilde{r} > 0$. Thus $K + B(\mathbf{0}, \tilde{r}) \subset A$. Finally, let $r = \tilde{r}/2$. Then $K + \overline{B(\mathbf{0}, \tilde{r})} \subset A$ as desired.   □

Now we can establish the convergence property of convolutions for known-integrable functions.

Theorem 7.5.4 ($\mathcal{I}_c(\mathbb{R}^n)$-approximation by convolutions). *Consider a function $f \in \mathcal{I}_c(\mathbb{R}^n)$ and let $\{\varphi_m\} : \mathbb{R}^n \longrightarrow \mathbb{R}$ be a test approximate identity. Let K be a compact subset of $\mathbb{R}^n$ such that f is continuous on an open superset of K. Given $\varepsilon > 0$, there exists a positive integer m_0 such that for all integers m,*

$$m \ge m_0 \implies |(f * \varphi_m)(x) - f(x)| < \varepsilon \text{ for all } x \in K.$$

That is, the convolutions converge uniformly to the original function on compact subsets of open sets where the function is continuous.

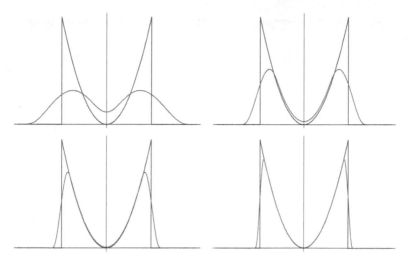

Figure 7.11. The truncated squaring function convolved with various φ_m

Proof. Let $\varepsilon > 0$ be given. By the thickening lemma, there exists some $r > 0$ such that f is continuous on $K + \overline{B(0,r)}$. Hence f is uniformly continuous on $K + \overline{B(0,r)}$. That is, there exists $\delta > 0$ (with $\delta < r$) such that for all $x \in K$ and all $y \in \mathbb{R}^n$,

$$|y - x| < \delta \implies |f(y) - f(x)| < \varepsilon.$$

There exists some positive integer m_0 such that for all integers $m \geq m_0$, $\mathrm{supp}(\varphi_m) \subset B(0,\delta)$. For all $x \in K$, all $y \in \mathbb{R}^n$, and all $m \geq m_0$,

$$y \in x - \mathrm{supp}(\varphi_m) \implies y \in x - B(0,\delta) = x + B(0,\delta)$$
$$\implies |y - x| < \delta$$
$$\implies |f(y) - f(x)| < \varepsilon.$$

From here, the proof is virtually identical to the proof of Theorem 7.4.3.   □

For example, consider the truncated squaring function

$$f : \mathbb{R} \longrightarrow \mathbb{R}, \qquad f(x) = \begin{cases} x^2 & \text{if } |x| \leq 1/2, \\ 0 & \text{if } 1/2 < |x|. \end{cases}$$

Note that f lies in $\mathcal{I}_c(\mathbb{R}^n)$ rather than in $\mathcal{C}_c^0(\mathbb{R}^n)$ because of its discontinuities at $x = \pm 1/2$. Figure 7.11 shows f and its convolutions with φ_2, φ_4, φ_8, and φ_{15}. The convolutions converge uniformly to the truncated parabola on compact sets away from the two points of discontinuity. But the convergence is not well behaved at or near those two points. Indeed, the function value $f(\pm 1/2) = 1/4$ rather than $f(\pm 1/2) = 0$ is arbitrary and has no effect on the convolution in any case. And again the convolutions are bounded by the bound on the original function, and their supports shrink toward the original support as m grows.

In consequence of $\mathcal{I}_c(\mathbb{R}^n)$-approximation by convolutions, every integral of a known-integrable function is approximated as closely as desired by the integral of a test function. Thus the hypothesis of a continuous integrand f in the change of variable theorem for multiple integrals (Theorem 6.7.1), mentioned in the last bullet of the chapter introduction, can now be weakened to a known-integrable integrand.

8

Parametrized Curves

This chapter introduces parametrized curves as a warmup for Chapter 9 to follow. The subject of Chapter 9 is integration over k-dimensional parametrized surfaces in n-dimensional space, and the parametrized curves of this chapter are the special case $k = 1$. Multivariable integration plays no role in this chapter. Aside from being one-dimensional surfaces, parametrized curves are interesting in their own right.

Section 8.1 leads into the subject of curves by introducing two specific curves that solve problems beyond the capabilities of classical straightedge and compass constructions. One striking idea here is the fact that by using algebra to study geometry, we can describe precisely how the classical constructions are limited. Section 8.2 begins the study of parametrized curves, meaning curves that we view not only as sets but as specified traversals of the sets. Section 8.3 discusses the canonical parametrization of a curve by arc length, the traversal at unit speed. Section 8.4 specializes the discussion to curves in the plane. In this case, a local parameter called the *curvature* gives a fairly complete description of curves in the large. Similarly, Section 8.5 discusses curves in three-dimensional space. Here a second local parameter called *torsion* is needed along with curvature to describe curves. Finally, Section 8.6 generalizes the idea of describing a curve in optimal local coordinates to n dimensions.

8.1 Euclidean Constructions and Two Curves

The *straightedge* constructs the line that passes through two given points in the Euclidean plane. The *compass* constructs the circle that is centered at a given point and has a given distance as its radius. A finite succession of straightedge and compass constructions is called a *Euclidean construction*.

Physical straightedge and compass constructions are imprecise. Furthermore, there is really no such thing as a straightedge: aside from having to be

© Springer International Publishing AG 2016   375
J. Shurman, *Calculus and Analysis in Euclidean Space*,
Undergraduate Texts in Mathematics, DOI 10.1007/978-3-319-49314-5_8

infinite, the line-constructor somehow requires a prior line for its own construction. But we don't concern ourselves with the details of actual tools for drawing lines and circles. Instead we imagine the constructions to be ideal, and we focus on the theoretical question of what Euclidean constructions can or cannot accomplish.

With computer graphics being a matter of course to us today, the technological power of Euclidean constructions, however idealized, is underwhelming, and so one might reasonably wonder why they deserve study. One point of this section is to use the study of Euclidean constructions to demonstrate the idea of *investigating the limitations of a technology*. That is, mathematical reasoning of one sort (in this case, algebra) can determine the capacities of some other sort of mathematical technique (in this case, Euclidean constructions). In a similar spirit, a subject called Galois theory uses the mathematics of finite group theory to determine the capacities of solving polynomial equations by radicals.

In a high-school geometry course one should learn that Euclidean constructions have the capacity to

- bisect an angle,
- bisect a segment,
- draw the line through a given point and perpendicular to a given line,
- and draw the line through a given point and parallel to a given line.

These constructions (Exercise 8.1.1) will be taken for granted here.

Two classical problems of antiquity are *trisecting the angle* and *doubling the cube*. This section will argue algebraically that neither of these problems can be solved by Euclidean constructions, and then the second point of this section is to introduce particular curves—and methods to generate them—that solve the classical problems where Euclidean constructions fail to do so.

Take any two distinct points in the plane and denote them 0 and 1. Use the straightedge to draw the line through them. We may as well take the line to be horizontal with 1 appearing to the right of 0. Now define a real number r as *Euclidean* if we can locate it on our number line with a Euclidean construction. For instance, it is clear how the compass constructs the integers from 0 to any specified n, positive or negative, in finitely many steps. Thus the integers are Euclidean. Further, we can add an orthogonal line through any integer. Repeating the process on such orthogonal lines gives us as much of the integer-coordinate grid as we want.

Proposition 8.1.1. *The Euclidean numbers form a subfield of $\mathbb{R}$. That is, 0 and 1 are Euclidean, and if r and s are Euclidean, then so are $r \pm s$, rs, and (if $s \neq 0$) r/s.*

Proof. We have already constructed 0 and 1, and given any r and s it is easy to construct $r \pm s$. If $s \neq 0$ then the construction shown in Figure 8.1 produces r/s. Finally, to construct rs when $s \neq 0$, first construct $1/s$, and then $rs = r/(1/s)$ is Euclidean as well.   □

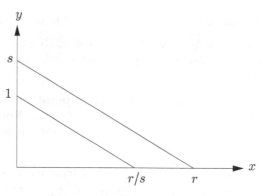

Figure 8.1. Constructing r/s

Let $\mathbb{E}$ denote the field of Euclidean numbers. Since $\mathbb{Q}$ is the smallest subfield of $\mathbb{R}$, it follows that $\mathbb{Q} \subset \mathbb{E} \subset \mathbb{R}$. The questions are whether $\mathbb{E}$ is no more than $\mathbb{Q}$, whether $\mathbb{E}$ is all of $\mathbb{R}$, and—assuming that in fact $\mathbb{E}$ lies properly between $\mathbb{Q}$ and $\mathbb{R}$—how we can describe the elements of $\mathbb{E}$. The next proposition shows that $\mathbb{E}$ is a proper superfield of $\mathbb{Q}$.

Proposition 8.1.2. *If $c \geq 0$ is constructible, i.e., if $c \in \mathbb{E}$, then so is $\sqrt{c}$.*

Proof. In the construction shown in Figure 8.2 we have a semicircle of radius $(c+1)/2$ centered at $((c+1)/2, 0)$. This semicircle contains the point $(1, y)$, where

$$y = \sqrt{((c+1)/2)^2 - ((c-1)/2)^2} = \sqrt{c}.$$

(Due to a tacit assumption in the figure, this proof isn't quite complete, but see Exercise 8.1.2.) □

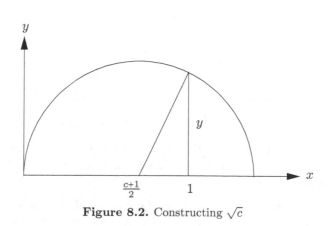

Figure 8.2. Constructing $\sqrt{c}$

Thus, every real number expressible in terms of finitely many square roots starting from $\mathbb{Q}$, such as $\sqrt{1 + \sqrt{2 + \sqrt{3}}}$, lies in $\mathbb{E}$. Next we show that the converse holds as well. That is, every number in $\mathbb{E}$ is expressible in finitely many square roots starting from $\mathbb{Q}$.

Definition 8.1.3. *Let $\mathbb{F}$ be any subfield of $\mathbb{R}$. A **point in** $\mathbb{F}$ is a point (x, y) in the plane whose coordinates x and y belong to $\mathbb{F}$. A **line in** $\mathbb{F}$ is a line through two points in $\mathbb{F}$. A **circle in** $\mathbb{F}$ is a circle whose center is a point in $\mathbb{F}$ and whose radius is a number in $\mathbb{F}$.*

Exercise 8.1.3 shows that every line in $\mathbb{F}$ has equation $ax + by + c = 0$ where $a, b, c \in \mathbb{F}$, and every circle in $\mathbb{F}$ has equation $x^2 + y^2 + ax + by + c = 0$ with $a, b, c \in \mathbb{F}$.

Proposition 8.1.4. *Let $\mathbb{F}$ be any subfield of $\mathbb{R}$. Let L_1, L_2 be any nonparallel lines in $\mathbb{F}$, and let C_1, C_2 be distinct circles in $\mathbb{F}$. Then:*

(1) *$L_1 \cap L_2$ is a point in $\mathbb{F}$.*
(2) *$C_1 \cap C_2$ is either empty or it is one or two points whose coordinates are expressible in terms of $\mathbb{F}$ and a square root of a value in $\mathbb{F}$.*
(3) *$C_1 \cap L_1$ is either empty or it is one or two points whose coordinates are expressible in terms of $\mathbb{F}$ and a square root of a value in $\mathbb{F}$.*

Proof. (1) is Exercise 8.1.4(a).

(2) reduces to (3), for if the circles

$$C_1 : x^2 + y^2 + a_1 x + b_1 y + c_1 = 0,$$
$$C_2 : x^2 + y^2 + a_2 x + b_2 y + c_2 = 0$$

intersect, then $C_1 \cap C_2 = C_1 \cap L$ where L is the line

$$L : (a_1 - a_2)x + (b_1 - b_2)y + (c_1 - c_2) = 0$$

(Exercise 8.1.4(b)). Since C_1 is a circle in $\mathbb{F}$, the equations for C_2 and L show that C_2 is a circle in $\mathbb{F}$ if and only if L is a line in $\mathbb{F}$.

To prove (3), keep the equation for the circle C_1 and suppose the line L_1 has equation $dx + ey + f = 0$. The case $d = 0$ is Exercise 8.1.4(c). Otherwise, we may take $d = 1$ after dividing through by d, an operation that keeps the other coefficients in $\mathbb{F}$. Thus $x = -ey - f$. Now, for (x, y) to lie in $C_1 \cap L_1$, we need

$$(-ey - f)^2 + y^2 + a_1(-ey - f) + b_1 y + c_1 = 0,$$

a condition of the form $Ay^2 + By + C = 0$ with $A, B, C \in \mathbb{F}$. Solving for y involves at most a square root over $\mathbb{F}$, and then $x = -ey - f$ involves only further operations in $\mathbb{F}$. $\square$

This result characterizes the field $\mathbb{E}$ of constructible numbers. Points in $\mathbb{E}$ are obtained by intersecting lines and circles, starting with lines and circles in $\mathbb{Q}$. By the proposition, this means taking a succession of square roots. Thus, the field $\mathbb{E}$ is the set of numbers expressible in finitely many field and square root operations starting from $\mathbb{Q}$.

Now we can dispense with the two classical problems mentioned earlier.

Theorem 8.1.5. *An angle of 60 degrees cannot be trisected by straightedge and compass.*

Proof. If we could construct a 20-degree angle then we could construct the number $\cos(20°)$ (Exercise 8.1.5(a)). From trigonometry,

$$\cos(3\theta) = 4\cos^3(\theta) - 3\cos(\theta)$$

(Exercise 8.1.5(b)), so in particular, $\cos(20°)$ satisfies the cubic polynomial relation

$$4x^3 - 3x - 1/2 = 0.$$

This cubic relation has no quadratic factors, so its root $\cos(20°)$ is not constructible. (Strictly speaking, this last statement requires some algebraic justification, but at least it should feel plausible.)   □

Theorem 8.1.6. *The side of a cube having volume 2 is not constructible.*

Proof. Indeed, the side satisfies the relation $x^3 - 2 = 0$, which again has no quadratic factors.   □

Thinking algebraically had made certain complicated-seeming geometric questions easy.

The second half of this section introduces curves to trisect the angle and to double the cube. The first curve, the *conchoid of Nicomedes*, is defined as follows. Fix a point O and a line L in the plane. For convenience, take $O = (0,0)$ and $L : \{y = b\}$ where $b > 0$ is constant. Fix a positive real number d. For each point $P \in \mathbb{R}^2$ with y-coordinate bigger than b, let $\ell(O,P)$ denote the line through O and P. The conchoid is then the set

$$\{P \in \mathbb{R}^2 : \ell(O,P) \text{ meets } L \text{ at a point distance } d \text{ from } P\}.$$

(See Figure 8.3.)

The conchoid can be organically generated, as shown in Figure 8.4. The lighter piece of the device in the figure swivels at the origin, and as it swivels, the tack at the lower end of the darker piece tracks the horizontal groove at $y = b$. Thus the lighter piece slides along the length of the darker one, and the pen at its upper end draws the conchoid.

The conchoid trisects angles, as shown in Figure 8.5. Given an angle $\angle AOB$ with $AB \perp OA$, construct the conchoid with $d = 2 \cdot OB$. (The conchoid in this figure is rotated 90 degrees clockwise from those in the previous two figures.) Then proceed as follows.

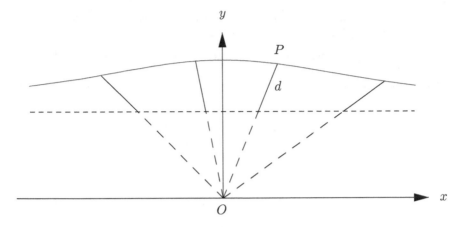

Figure 8.3. A conchoid

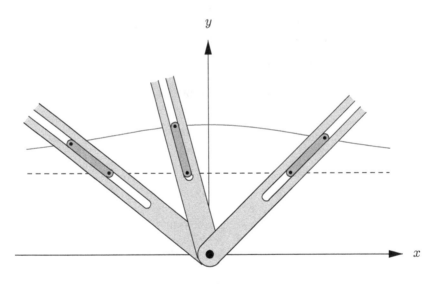

Figure 8.4. Organic generation of the conchoid

- Let E be the point on the conchoid with the same y-coordinate as B.
- Let C be the intersection point of AB and OE. Thus $CE = 2 \cdot OB$ by our choice of conchoid.
- Let D be the midpoint of CE. Thus $CD = DE = OB$, and also BD is the same length.
- Let $\alpha = \angle AOC$. Then also $\alpha = \angle BED$ and $\alpha = \angle EBD$.
- Let $\beta = \angle BOD$. Then also $\beta = \angle BDO$. The angle $\angle AOB$ that we want to trisect equals $\alpha + \beta$.

- So the other angle at D equals $\pi - 2\alpha$, because it is the remaining angle in triangle BDE, but also it is visibly $\pi - \beta$. Thus $\beta = 2\alpha$.
- The angle $\angle AOB = \alpha + \beta$ that we want to trisect now equals 3α, and so α is the desired trisection.

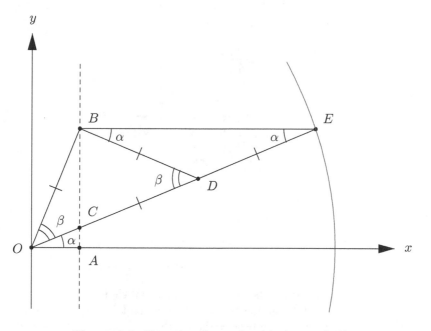

Figure 8.5. Trisecting the angle with the conchoid

The *cissoid of Diocles* is defined as follows. Take a circle of radius $a > 0$ centered at $(a, 0)$. Each ray emanating from the origin into the right half-plane intersects the circle at a point C and intersects the circle's right vertical tangent at a point B. Let P denote the the point on the ray such that $OP = CB$. The cissoid is the set of all such p (see Figure 8.6).

Newton showed how to generate the cissoid organically (see Figure 8.7). As the tack at the end of the shorter piece of the device in the figure tracks the vertical groove at $x = a$, the longer piece of the device slides past the bumper at $(-a, 0)$. Consequently, the pen in the center of the shorter piece draws the cissoid. Verifying that this construction indeed gives the cissoid is Exercise 8.1.6.

The cissoid doubles the cube. In the left half of Figure 8.8, M is the midpoint of the vertical segment from $(1, 0)$ to $(1, 1)$, so that the smaller right triangle has height-to-base ratio $1/2$. The line through $(2, 0)$ and M meets the point P on the cissoid, and the larger right triangle also has height-to-base ratio $1/2$. In the right side of the figure, the line through $(0, 0)$ and P

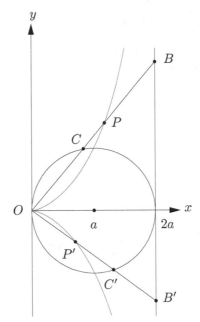

Figure 8.6. The cissoid

meets the circle, and the two horizontal distances labeled x are equal by the nature of the cissoid. Continuing to work in the right half of the figure, we see that the right triangle with base x and height y is similar to the two other right triangles, and the analysis of the left half of the figure has shown that the unlabeled vertical segment in the right half has height $(2-x)/2$. Thus the similar right triangles give the relations

$$\frac{y}{x} = \frac{2-x}{y} \quad \text{and} \quad \frac{y}{x} = \frac{x}{(2-x)/2}.$$

It follows that

$$\frac{y^2}{x} = 2-x \quad \text{and} \quad \frac{y}{x^2} = \frac{2}{2-x}.$$

Multiply the two equalities to get

$$\left(\frac{y}{x}\right)^3 = 2.$$

That is, multiplying the sides of a cube by y/x doubles the volume of the cube, as desired.

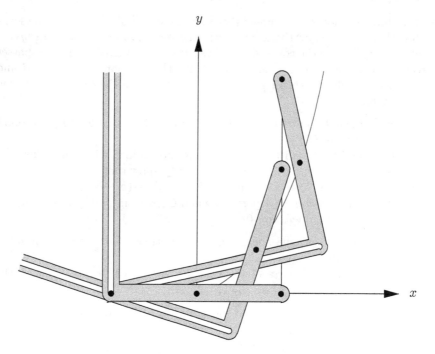

Figure 8.7. Organic generation of the cissoid

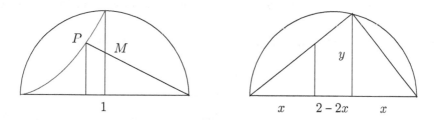

Figure 8.8. Doubling the cube with the cissoid

Exercises

8.1.1. Show how straightedge and compass constructions bisect an angle, bisect a segment, draw the line through point P perpendicular to line L, and draw the line through point P parallel to line L.

8.1.2. What tacit assumption does the proof of Proposition 8.1.2 make about c? Complete the proof for constructible $c \geq 0$ not satisfying the assumption.

8.1.3. Show that for every subfield $\mathbb{F}$ of $\mathbb{R}$, every line in $\mathbb{F}$ has equation $ax+by+c = 0$ with $a, b, c \in \mathbb{F}$; show that every circle in $\mathbb{F}$ has equation $x^2+y^2+ax+by+c = 0$ with $a, b, c \in \mathbb{F}$. Are the converses to these statements true? If the line passes through the point p in direction d, what are the relations between p, d and a, b, c? If the circle has center p and radius r, what are the relations between p, r and a, b, c?

8.1.4. (a) If L_1 and L_2 are nonparallel lines in $\mathbb{F}$, show that $L_1 \cap L_2$ is a point with coordinates in $\mathbb{F}$.

(b) If C_1 and C_2 are distinct intersecting circles in $\mathbb{F}$ with equations $x^2 + y^2 + a_1 x + b_1 y + c_1 = 0$ for C_1 and similarly for C_2, show that $C_1 \cap C_2$ is equal to $C_1 \cap L$ where L is the line with equation $(a_1 - a_2)x + (b_1 - b_2)y + (c_1 - c_2) = 0$.

(c) Prove Proposition 8.1.4 part (3) when C_1 is as in part (b) here and L_1 has equation $ey + f = 0$ with $e \neq 0$.

8.1.5. (a) Suppose that the angle θ is constructible. Show that the number $\cos \theta$ is constructible as well.

(b) Equate the real parts of the equality $e^{i3\alpha} = \left(e^{i\alpha}\right)^3$ to establish the trigonometric identity $\cos 3\alpha = 4\cos^3 \alpha - 3\cos \alpha$.

8.1.6. Show that Newton's organic construction really does generate the cissoid.

8.2 Parametrized Curves

For our purposes a curve is not specified as a subset of $\mathbb{R}^n$, but instead as a traversal of such a set.

Definition 8.2.1 (Parametrized curve). *A* **parametrized curve** *is a smooth mapping*

$$\alpha : I \longrightarrow \mathbb{R}^n$$

where $I \subset \mathbb{R}$ is a nonempty interval and $n \geq 1$.

Here *smooth* means that the mapping α has derivatives of all orders. A small technicality is that the definition should, strictly speaking, insist that if the interval I is not open then α extends smoothly to some open superinterval of I. We won't bother checking this in our examples.

The interval I in the definition is the **parameter interval** of α. Every point $t \in I$ is a **parameter value**, and the corresponding point $\alpha(t) \in \mathbb{R}^n$ is a **point on the curve**. Collectively, the set of points on the curve,

$$\widehat{\alpha} = \{\alpha(t) : t \in I\},$$

is the **trace** of the curve. So the nomenclature *point on the curve* is a slight abuse of language: a curve is a mapping and its trace is a set, and really $\alpha(t)$ is a point on the trace of the curve. But maintaining this distinction is pointlessly pedantic. Also, since all of our curves will be parametrized, we will refer to them simply as *curves*.

Definition 8.2.2 (Tangent vector, regular curve). *Let* $\alpha : I \longrightarrow \mathbb{R}^n$ *be a curve, and let* $t \in I$. *The* **tangent vector of** α **at** t *is* $\alpha'(t)$. *The curve* α *is* **regular** *if its tangent vector* $\alpha'(t)$ *is nonzero for all* $t \in I$.

It is often helpful to think of I as an interval of time, so that α describes a time-dependent motion through space. Thinking in this way suggests some more terminology.

- The tangent vector $\alpha'(t)$ is also called the **velocity vector of** α **at** t.
- The scalar magnitude $|\alpha'(t)|$ of the velocity vector is the **speed of** α **at** t.

Thus we may visualize $\alpha(t)$ as a point and the velocity $\alpha'(t)$ as an arrow emanating from the point in the direction of motion, the length of the arrow being the speed of the motion. The definition of a regular curve can be rephrased as the criterion that its time-dependent traversal never comes to a halt.

Definition 8.2.3 (Arc length of a curve). *Let* $\alpha : I \longrightarrow \mathbb{R}^n$ *be a curve, and let* t, t' *be points of* I *with* $t < t'$. *The* **arc length of** α **from** t **to** t' *is*

$$L(t, t') = \int_{\tau = t}^{t'} |\alpha'(\tau)| \, d\tau.$$

In physical terms, this definition is a curvy version of the familiar idea that distance equals speed times time. For a more purely mathematical definition of a curve's arc length, we should take the limit of the lengths of inscribed polygonal paths. Take a partition $t_0 < t_1 < \cdots < t_n$ of the parameter interval $[t, t']$, where $t_0 = t$ and $t_n = t'$. The partition determines the corresponding points on the curve, $\alpha(t_0), \alpha(t_1), \ldots, \alpha(t_n)$. The arc length should be the limit of the sums of the lengths of the line segments joining the points,

$$L(t, t') = \lim_{n \to \infty} \sum_{k=1}^{n} |\alpha(t_k) - \alpha(t_{k-1})|.$$

It is possible to show that for smooth curves—in fact, for $\mathcal{C}^1$-curves—the limit exists and is equal to the integral definition of arc length. (The details of the argument are too technical to deserve full explication here, but very briefly: since the integral is conceptually the length of an inscribed polygon with infinitely many sides, each infinitesimally long, and since the length of an inscribed polygon increases when any of its segments is replaced by more segments by adding more points of inscription, the definition of $L(t, t')$ as an integral should be at least as big as the definition of $L(t, t')$ as a limit of sums, and in fact this is easy to show. For the other inequality we need to argue that the limit of sums gets as close to the integral as we wish. Since the sums aren't quite Riemann sums for the integral, this is where things get slightly tricky.) Using the limit of sums as the definition of arc length is more general, since it makes no reference to the smoothness of α. A continuous curve for which the arc length (defined as the limit of inscribed polygon lengths) is finite is called **rectifiable**. Perhaps surprisingly, not all continuous curves are rectifiable. For that matter, the image of a continuous curve need not match our intuition of a curve. For instance, there is a continuous mapping from the closed interval $[0,1]$ to all of the square $[0,1] \times [0,1]$, a so-called area-filling curve. In any case, we will continue to assume that our curves are smooth, and we will use the integral definition of arc length.

For example, the **helix** is the curve $\alpha : \mathbb{R} \longrightarrow \mathbb{R}^3$ where

$$\alpha(t) = (a \cos t, a \sin t, bt).$$

Here $a > 0$ and $b > 0$ are constants. (See Figure 8.9.)

Figure 8.9. The helix

The velocity vector of the helix is

$$\alpha'(t) = (-a \sin t, a \cos t, b),$$

and so the speed is

$$|\alpha'(t)| = \sqrt{a^2 + b^2}.$$

For another example, the **cycloid** is the curve made by a point on a rolling wheel of radius 1. (See Figure 8.10.) Its parametrization, in terms of the angle θ through which the wheel has rolled, is

$$C(\theta) = (\theta - \sin \theta, 1 - \cos \theta), \quad 0 \le \theta \le 2\pi.$$

Its velocity vector is

$$C'(\theta) = (1 - \cos\theta, \sin\theta), \quad 0 \le \theta \le 2\pi,$$

and so its speed is

$$|C'(\theta)| = \sqrt{(1 - \cos\theta)^2 + (\sin\theta)^2} = \sqrt{2 - 2\cos\theta}$$

$$= \sqrt{4 \cdot \frac{1}{2}(1 - \cos\theta)} = \sqrt{4\sin^2(\theta/2)}$$

$$= 2|\sin(\theta/2)|$$

$$= 2\sin(\theta/2) \qquad \text{since } \sin \ge 0 \text{ on } [0, \pi].$$

So the speed of the cycloid is greatest—equal to 2—when $\theta = \pi$, i.e., when the point is at the top of the wheel. And it is least—equal to 0—when $\theta = 0$ and $\theta = 2\pi$. These results agree with what we see when we look at the wheel of a moving bicycle: a blur at the top and distinct spokes at the bottom.

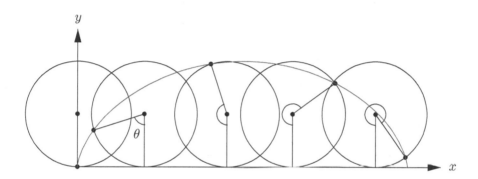

Figure 8.10. A rolling wheel

The length of the cycloid as the parameter varies from 0 to some angle θ is

$$L(0, \theta) = \int_{t=0}^{\theta} 2\sin(t/2)\, dt = 4 \int_{t=0}^{\theta} \sin(t/2)\, d(t/2) = 4 \int_{\tau=0}^{\theta/2} \sin(\tau)\, d\tau$$

$$= 4 - 4\cos(\theta/2), \qquad 0 \le \theta \le 2\pi.$$

In particular, a full arch of the cycloid has length 8.

The cycloid has amazing properties. Upside down, it is the **brachistochrone,** the curve of steepest descent, meaning that it is the curve between two given points along which a bead slides (without friction) most quickly. Upside down, it is also the **tautochrone,** meaning that a bead starting from any point slides (without friction) to the bottom in the same amount of time. For another property of the cycloid, suppose that a weight swings from a string 4 units long suspended at the origin, between two upside-down cycloids. The right-hand upside-down cycloid is

$$C(\theta) = (\theta - \sin\theta, \cos\theta - 1), \quad 0 \le \theta \le 2\pi.$$

Thus the weight's position when it is swinging to the right is (for $0 \le \theta \le \pi$)

$$\alpha(\theta) = C(\theta) + (4 - L(0, \theta))\frac{C'(\theta)}{|C'(\theta)|}$$

$$= (\theta - \sin\theta, \cos\theta - 1) + 4\cos(\theta/2)\frac{(1 - \cos\theta, -\sin\theta)}{2\sin(\theta/2)}$$

$$= (\theta - \sin\theta, \cos\theta - 1) + 2\cot(\theta/2)(1 - \cos\theta, -\sin\theta).$$

But since $0 \le \theta \le \pi$, we may carry out the following calculation, in which all quantities under square root signs are nonnegative and so is the evaluation of the square root at the last step,

$$\cot(\theta/2) = \frac{\cos(\theta/2)}{\sin(\theta/2)} = \frac{\sqrt{\frac{1}{2}(1 + \cos\theta)}}{\sqrt{\frac{1}{2}(1 - \cos\theta)}}$$

$$= \sqrt{\frac{(1 + \cos\theta)^2}{(1 - \cos\theta)(1 + \cos\theta)}} = \sqrt{\frac{(1 + \cos\theta)^2}{1 - \cos^2\theta}}$$

$$= \frac{1 + \cos\theta}{\sin\theta}.$$

And so now

$$\alpha(\theta) = (\theta - \sin\theta, \cos\theta - 1) + 2\frac{1 + \cos\theta}{\sin\theta}(1 - \cos\theta, -\sin\theta)$$

$$= (\theta - \sin\theta, \cos\theta - 1) + 2(\sin\theta, -1 - \cos\theta)$$

$$= (\theta + \sin\theta, -3 - \cos\theta).$$

Shift the weight's position rightward by π and upward by 2 to obtain

$$\alpha(\theta) + (\pi, 2) = (\pi + \theta + \sin\theta, -1 - \cos\theta), \quad 0 \le \theta \le \pi.$$

On the other hand, the right half of the original upside-down cycloid is

$$C(\pi + \theta) = (\pi + \theta - \sin(\pi + \theta), \cos(\pi + \theta) - 1)$$

$$= (\pi + \theta + \sin\theta, -1 - \cos\theta), \quad 0 \le \theta \le 2\pi.$$

These are identical: $\alpha(\theta) + (\pi, 2) = C(\theta + \pi)$ for $0 \le \theta \le \pi$. That is, the weight swings along the trace of a cycloid congruent to the two others. Since the the upside-down cycloid is the tautochrone, this idea was used by Huygens to attempt to design pendulum-clocks that would work on ships despite their complicated motion.

The area under one arch of the cycloid is the integral

$$\int_{x=0}^{2\pi} y(x)\, dx$$

where $y(x)$ is the function that takes the x-coordinate of a point of the cycloid and returns its y-coordinate. As the cycloid parameter θ varies from 0 to 2π, so does the x-coordinate of the cycloid-point,

$$x = x(\theta) = \theta - \sin\theta,$$

and the parametrization of the cycloid tells us that even without knowing $y(x)$, we know that

$$y(x(\theta)) = 1 - \cos\theta.$$

Thus the area under one arch of the cycloid is

$$\int_{x=0}^{2\pi} y(x)\,dx = \int_{\theta=0}^{2\pi} y(x(\theta))x'(\theta)\,d\theta = \int_{\theta=0}^{2\pi} (1-\cos\theta)^2\,d\theta,$$

and routine calculation shows that the area is 3π.

A parametrization for the conchoid of Nicomedes is

$$\alpha : (-\pi/2, \pi/2) \longrightarrow \mathbb{R}^2, \qquad \alpha(\theta) = (b\sec\theta + d)(\cos\theta, \sin\theta)$$

where now the line L is $\{x = b\}$, rotating the conchoid a quarter turn clockwise from before, and where the parameter θ is the usual angle from the polar coordinate system. Every point (x, y) on the conchoid satisfies the equation

$$(x^2 + y^2)(x - b)^2 = d^2 x^2.$$

A parametrization for the cissoid of Diocles is

$$\alpha : \mathbb{R} \longrightarrow \mathbb{R}^2, \qquad \alpha(t) = \left(\frac{2at^2}{1+t^2}, \frac{2at^3}{1+t^2} \right).$$

where the parameter t is $\tan\theta$, with θ being the usual angle from the polar coordinate system.

Exercises

8.2.1. (a) Let $\alpha : I \longrightarrow \mathbb{R}^n$ be a regular curve that doesn't pass through the origin, but has a point $\alpha(t_0)$ of nearest approach to the origin. Show that the position vector $\alpha(t_0)$ and the velocity vector $\alpha'(t_0)$ are orthogonal. (Hint: If $u, v : I \longrightarrow \mathbb{R}^n$ are differentiable then $\langle u, v \rangle' = \langle u', v \rangle + \langle u, v' \rangle$—this follows quickly from the one-variable product rule.) Does the result agree with your geometric intuition?

(b) Find a regular curve $\alpha : I \longrightarrow \mathbb{R}^n$ that does not pass through the origin and does not have a point of nearest approach to the origin. Does an example exist with I compact?

8.2.2. Let α be a regular parametrized curve with $\alpha''(t) = 0$ for all $t \in I$. What is the nature of α?

8.2.3. Let $\alpha : I \longrightarrow \mathbb{R}^n$ be a parametrized curve and let $v \in \mathbb{R}^n$ be a fixed vector. Assume that $\langle \alpha'(t), v \rangle = 0$ for all $t \in I$ and that $\langle \alpha(t_o), v \rangle = 0$ for some $t_0 \in I$. Prove that $\langle \alpha(t), v \rangle = 0$ for all $t \in I$. What is the geometric idea?

8.2.4. (a) Verify the parametrization of the conchoid given in this section.
(b) Verify the relation $(x^2 + y^2)(x - b)^2 = d^2 x^2$ satisfied by points on the conchoid.

8.2.5. (a) Verify the parametrization of the cissoid given in this section. Is this parametrization regular? What happens to $\alpha(t)$ and $\alpha'(t)$ as $t \to \infty$?
(b) Verify Newton's organic generation of the cissoid.

8.3 Parametrization by Arc Length

Recall that the trace of a curve is the set of points on the curve. Thinking of a curve as time-dependent traversal makes it clear that different curves may well have the same trace. That is, different curves can describe different motions along the same path. For example, the curves

$$\alpha : [0, 2\pi] \longrightarrow \mathbb{R}^2, \qquad \alpha(t) = (\cos t, \sin t)$$
$$\beta : [0, 2\pi] \longrightarrow \mathbb{R}^2, \qquad \beta(t) = (\cos 5t, \sin 5t)$$
$$\gamma : [0, 2\pi] \longrightarrow \mathbb{R}^2, \qquad \gamma(t) = (\cos t, -\sin t)$$
$$\delta : [0, \log(2\pi + 1)] \longrightarrow \mathbb{R}^2, \qquad \delta(t) = (\cos(e^t - 1), \sin(e^t - 1))$$

all have the unit circle as their trace, but their traversals of the circle are different: α traverses it once counterclockwise at unit speed, β traverses it five times counterclockwise at speed 5, γ traverses it once clockwise at unit speed, and δ traverses it once counterclockwise at increasing speed.

Among the four traversals, α and δ are somehow basically the same, moving from the same starting point to the same ending point in the same direction, never stopping or backing up. The similarity suggests that we should be able to modify one into the other. On the other hand, β and γ seem essentially different from α and from each other. The following definition describes the idea of adjusting a curve without changing its traversal in any essential way.

Definition 8.3.1 (Equivalence of curves). *Two curves* $\alpha : I \longrightarrow \mathbb{R}^n$ *and* $\beta : I' \longrightarrow \mathbb{R}^n$ *are* **equivalent**, *written*

$$\alpha \sim \beta,$$

if there exists a mapping $\phi : I \longrightarrow I'$, *smooth with smooth inverse, with* $\phi' > 0$ *on* I, *such that*

$$\alpha = \beta \circ \phi.$$

For example, consider the mapping

$$\phi : [0, 2\pi] \longrightarrow [0, \log(2\pi + 1)], \qquad \phi(s) = \log(s + 1).$$

This mapping is differentiable and so is its inverse,

$$\phi^{-1} : [0, \log(2\pi + 1)] \longrightarrow [0, 2\pi], \qquad \phi^{-1}(t) = e^t - 1.$$

Also, $\phi'(s) = 1/(s + 1)$ is positive for all $s \in I$. Again recalling the examples α and δ, the calculation

$$(\delta \circ \phi)(s) = (\cos(e^{\log(s+1)} - 1), \sin(e^{\log(s+1)} - 1)) = (\cos s, \sin s) = \alpha(s)$$

shows that $\alpha \sim \delta$, as expected.

A similar calculation with ϕ^{-1} shows that also $\delta \sim \alpha$. This symmetry is a particular instance of a general rule, whose proof is an exercise in formalism.

Proposition 8.3.2 (Properties of equivalence). *Let α, β, and γ be curves. Then:*

(1) $\alpha \sim \alpha$.
(2) *If $\alpha \sim \beta$ then $\beta \sim \alpha$.*
(3) *If $\alpha \sim \beta$ and $\beta \sim \gamma$ then $\alpha \sim \gamma$.*

*In words, the relation "$\sim$" is **reflexive**, **symmetric**, and **transitive**.*

Among a family of equivalent regular curves, one is canonical: the curve that traverses at unit speed. Recall that the arc length of a curve α from t to t' is

$$L(t, t') = \int_{\tau = t}^{t'} |\alpha'(\tau)| \, d\tau.$$

Definition 8.3.3 (Parametrization by arc length). *The curve γ is **parametrized by arc length** if for all points in $s, s' \in I$ with $s < s'$,*

$$L(s, s') = s' - s.$$

Equivalently, γ is parametrized by arc length if $|\gamma'(s)| = 1$ for all $s \in I$.

As in the definition just given, we adopt the convention that a curve parametrized by arc length is by default denoted γ rather than α, and its parameter denoted s rather than t.

To justify the intuition that every regular curve is equivalent to some curve parametrized by arc length, we need two familiar theorems. The first version of the one-variable fundamental theorem of integral calculus says:

Let $f : [a, b] \longrightarrow \mathbb{R}$ be continuous. Define a function

$$F : [a, b] \longrightarrow \mathbb{R}, \qquad F(x) = \int_a^x f.$$

Then F is differentiable on $[a, b]$ and $F' = f$.

And the one-variable inverse function theorem says:

> Let $f : I \longrightarrow \mathbb{R}$ have a continuous derivative on I with $f'(x) \neq 0$ for all $x \in I$. Then the image of f is an interval I', and f has a differentiable inverse $g : I' \longrightarrow I$. For each $y \in I'$, the derivative of the inverse at y is given by the formula $g'(y) = 1/f'(x)$ where $x = g(y)$.

These theorems let us reparametrize every regular curve by arc length.

Proposition 8.3.4. *Every regular curve is equivalent to a curve parametrized by arc length.*

Proof. Let $\alpha : I \longrightarrow \mathbb{R}^n$ be regular. Thus we are tacitly assuming that α is smooth, so that in particular α' is continuous. Pick any parameter value $t_0 \in I$ and let $p_0 = \alpha(t_0)$ be the corresponding point on the curve. Define the arc length function $\ell : I \longrightarrow \mathbb{R}$ by the formula

$$\ell(t) = \int_{\tau=t_0}^{t} |\alpha'(\tau)|\, d\tau.$$

By the fundamental theorem, ℓ is differentiable and $\ell'(t) = |\alpha'(t)|$. Thus ℓ' is continuous and never vanishes, so by the inverse function theorem ℓ has a differentiable inverse $\ell^{-1} : I' \longrightarrow I$ for some interval I'. Define a new curve $\gamma : I' \longrightarrow \mathbb{R}^n$ by $\gamma = \alpha \circ \ell^{-1}$. Thus α and γ are equivalent, and the following diagram commutes (meaning that either path around the triangle yields the same result):

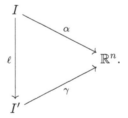

For all $t \in I$, letting $s = \ell(t)$, the chain rule gives an equality of vectors,

$$\alpha'(t) = (\gamma \circ \ell)'(t) = \gamma'(s)\,\ell'(t) = \gamma'(s)\,|\alpha'(t)|,$$

and then taking absolute values gives an equality of scalars,

$$|\alpha'(t)| = |\gamma'(s)|\,|\alpha'(t)|.$$

Since $|\alpha'(t)| > 0$ for all t because α is regular, it follows that

$$|\gamma'(s)| = 1 \quad \text{for all } s \in I'.$$

Thus γ is parametrized by arc length. $\square$

So every regular curve is equivalent to a curve parametrized by arc length. The next question about a regular curve is whether its equivalent curve that is parametrized by arc length is unique. The answer is essentially yes. The only choice is the starting point, determined by the choice of t_0 in the proof.

Explicitly reparametrizing by arc length can be a nuisance, because it requires computing the inverse function ℓ^{-1} that we invoked in the abstract during the course of reparametrizing. (This function can be doubly hard to write down in elementary terms, because not only is it an inverse function, but furthermore it is the inverse function of a forward function defined as an integral.) Since the theory guarantees that each regular curve is equivalent to a curve parametrized by arc length, when we prove theorems in the sequel, we may assume that we are given such curves. But on the other hand, since reparametrizing is nontrivial computationally, we want the formulas that we will derive later in the chapter not to assume parametrization by arc length, so that we can apply them to regular curves in general.

Exercises

8.3.1. Show that the equivalence "~" on curves is reflexive, symmetric, and transitive.

8.3.2. The parametrized curve

$$\alpha : [0, +\infty) \longrightarrow \mathbb{R}^2, \qquad \alpha(t) = (ae^{bt} \cos t, ae^{bt} \sin t)$$

(where $a > 0$ and $b < 0$ are real constants) is called a **logarithmic spiral**.
    (a) Show that as $t \to +\infty$, $\alpha(t)$ spirals in toward the origin.
    (b) Show that as $t \to +\infty$, $L(0, t)$ remains bounded. Thus the spiral has finite length.

8.3.3. Explicitly reparametrize each curve $\alpha : I \longrightarrow \mathbb{R}^n$ with a curve $\gamma : I' \longrightarrow \mathbb{R}^n$ parametrized by arc length.
    (a) The ray $\alpha : \mathbb{R}_{>0} \longrightarrow \mathbb{R}^n$ given by $\alpha(t) = t^2 v$ where v is some fixed nonzero vector.
    (b) The circle $\alpha : \mathbb{R} \longrightarrow \mathbb{R}^2$ given by $\alpha(t) = (\cos e^t, \sin e^t)$.
    (c) The helix $\alpha : [0, 2\pi] \longrightarrow \mathbb{R}^3$ given by $\alpha(t) = (a \cos t, a \sin t, bt)$.
    (d) The cycloid $\alpha : [\pi/2, 3\pi/2] \longrightarrow \mathbb{R}^2$ given by $\alpha(t) = (t - \sin t, 1 - \cos t)$.

8.4 Plane Curves: Curvature

Let $\gamma : I \longrightarrow \mathbb{R}^2$ be a plane curve parametrized by arc length s. We next specify a natural coordinate system at each point of γ. Its **tangent vector** $T(s)$ is

$$T = \gamma'.$$

So to first order, the curve is moving in the T-direction. Its **normal vector** $N(s)$ is the 90-degree counterclockwise rotation of $T(s)$. Thus the **Frenet frame** $\{T, N\}$ is a positive basis of $\mathbb{R}^2$ consisting of orthogonal unit vectors. Before proceeding, we need to establish two handy little facts that hold in every dimension n.

Lemma 8.4.1. (a) *Let $v : I \longrightarrow \mathbb{R}^n$ be a smooth mapping such that $|v(t)| = c$ (where c is constant) for all t. Then*

$$\langle v, v' \rangle = 0.$$

(b) *Let $v, w : I \longrightarrow \mathbb{R}^n$ be smooth mappings such that $\langle v(t), w(t) \rangle = c$ (where c is constant) for all t. Then*

$$\langle w', v \rangle = -\langle v', w \rangle.$$

Proof. (a) $\langle v, v' \rangle = \frac{1}{2} \langle v, v \rangle' = 0$. (b) $\langle w', v \rangle + \langle v', w \rangle = \langle v, w \rangle' = 0$. □

We return to dimension $n = 2$. Part (a) of the lemma shows that the derivative of the tangent vector is some scalar multiple of the normal vector,

$$T' = \kappa N, \quad \kappa = \kappa(s) \in \mathbb{R}.$$

The scalar-valued function $\kappa(s)$ is the **curvature** of γ. The curvature can be positive, negative, or zero depending on whether to second order the curve is bending counterclockwise toward N, clockwise away from N, or not at all.

In particular, if r is a positive real number then the curve

$$\gamma(s) = r(\cos(s/r), \sin(s/r)), \quad s \in \mathbb{R}$$

is a circle of radius r parametrized by arc length. The tangent vector $T(s) = \gamma'(s)$ and its derivative $T'(s) = \gamma''(s)$ are

$$T = (-\sin(s/r), \cos(s/r)), \qquad T' = \frac{1}{r}(-\cos(s/r), -\sin(s/r)) = \frac{1}{r}N,$$

showing that the curvature of the circle is the reciprocal of its radius,

$$\kappa(s) = \frac{1}{r}.$$

In general, the absolute curvature of a curve is the reciprocal of the radius of the best-fitting circle to γ. We omit the proof of this.

Plausibly, if we are told only that γ is some curve parametrized by arc length, that γ begins at some point p_0 with initial tangent vector T_0, and that γ has curvature function $\kappa(s)$, then we can reproduce the curve γ. This is true but beyond our scope to show here. Nonetheless it explains that:

> *The combination of a set of initial conditions and the local information of the curvature at each point of a curve is enough to recover the curve itself, a global object.*

Hence the local information—the curvature—is of interest.

To see how the Frenet frame continually adjusts itself as γ is traversed, we differentiate T and N. Since these are orthogonal unit vectors, their derivatives resolve nicely into components via the inner product,

$$T' = \langle T', T \rangle T + \langle T', N \rangle N,$$
$$N' = \langle N', T \rangle T + \langle N', N \rangle N.$$

The condition $T' = \kappa N$ shows that the top row inner products are $\langle T', T \rangle = 0$ and $\langle T', N \rangle = \kappa$. Since N is a unit vector, $\langle N', N \rangle = 0$ by part (a) of the lemma, and since T and N are orthogonal, $\langle N', T \rangle = -\langle T', N \rangle = -\kappa$ by part (b). Thus the **Frenet equations** for a curve parametrized by arc length can be formulated as

$$\begin{bmatrix} T' \\ N' \end{bmatrix} = \begin{bmatrix} 0 & \kappa \\ -\kappa & 0 \end{bmatrix} \begin{bmatrix} T \\ N \end{bmatrix}.$$

The geometric idea is that as we move along the curve at unit speed, the Frenet frame continually adjusts itself so that its first vector is tangent to the curve in the direction of motion and the second vector is ninety degrees counterclockwise to the first. The curvature is the rate (positive, negative, or zero) at which the first vector is bending toward the second while the second vector preserves the ninety-degree angle between them by bending away from the first vector as much as the first vector is bending toward it.

Since $\gamma' = T$ and thus $\gamma'' = T'$, the first and second derivatives of every curve γ parametrized by arc length are expressed in terms of the Frenet frame,

$$\begin{bmatrix} \gamma' \\ \gamma'' \end{bmatrix} = \begin{bmatrix} 1 & 0 \\ 0 & \kappa \end{bmatrix} \begin{bmatrix} T \\ N \end{bmatrix}.$$

This matrix relation shows that the local canonical form of a such a curve is, up to quadratic order,

$$\gamma(s_0 + s) \approx \gamma(s_0) + s\gamma'(s_0) + \frac{1}{2}s^2\gamma''(s_0)$$
$$= \gamma(s_0) + sT + \frac{\kappa}{2}s^2 N.$$

That is, in (T, N)-coordinates the curve is locally $(s, (\kappa/2)s^2)$, a parabola at the origin that opens upward or downward or not at all, depending on κ. If we view the curve in local coordinates as we traverse its length at unit speed, we see the parabola change its shape as κ varies, possibly narrowing and widening, or opening to a horizontal line and then bending the other way. This periscope-view of γ, along with knowing $\gamma(s)$ and $\gamma'(s)$ for one value s in the parameter domain, determines γ entirely.

We want a curvature formula for every regular smooth plane curve, not necessarily parametrized by arc length,

$$\alpha : I \longrightarrow \mathbb{R}^2.$$

To derive the formula, recall that the reparametrization of α by arc length is the curve γ characterized by a relation involving the arc length function of α,

$$\alpha = \gamma \circ \ell, \quad \text{where} \quad \ell(t) = \int^t |\alpha'| \quad \text{and so} \quad \ell' = |\alpha'|.$$

By the chain rule, and then by the product rule and again the chain rule,

$$\alpha' = (\gamma' \circ \ell) \cdot \ell',$$
$$\alpha'' = (\gamma' \circ \ell) \cdot \ell'' + (\gamma'' \circ \ell) \cdot (\ell')^2.$$

These relations and the earlier expressions of γ' and γ'' in terms of the Frenet frame combine to give

$$\begin{bmatrix} \alpha' \\ \alpha'' \end{bmatrix} = \begin{bmatrix} \ell' & 0 \\ \ell'' & \ell'^2 \end{bmatrix} \begin{bmatrix} \gamma' \circ \ell \\ \gamma'' \circ \ell \end{bmatrix} = \begin{bmatrix} \ell' & 0 \\ \ell'' & \ell'^2 \end{bmatrix} \begin{bmatrix} 1 & 0 \\ 0 & \kappa \end{bmatrix} \begin{bmatrix} T \\ N \end{bmatrix}.$$

Take determinants, recalling that $\ell' = |\alpha'|$,

$$\det(\alpha', \alpha'') = |\alpha'|^3 \kappa.$$

Thus the curvature is

$$\kappa = \frac{\det(\alpha', \alpha'')}{|\alpha'|^3} = \frac{x'y'' - x''y'}{\left((x')^2 + (y')^2 \right)^{3/2}} \qquad (\alpha = (x, y) \text{ regular}).$$

In particular, if a curve γ is parametrized by arc length then its curvature in coordinates is

$$\kappa = \det(\gamma', \gamma'') = x'y'' - x''y' \qquad (\gamma = (x, y) \text{ parametrized by arc length}).$$

The fact that a plane curve lies on a circle if and only if its curvature is constant cries out to be true. (If it isn't, then our definitions must be misguided.) And it is easy to prove using global coordinates. However, we prove it by working with the Frenet frame, in anticipation of the less obvious result for space curves to follow in the next section.

Proposition 8.4.2. *Let $\gamma : I \longrightarrow \mathbb{R}^2$ be regular. Then*

$$\gamma \text{ lies on a circle} \quad \Longleftrightarrow \quad \kappa(s) \text{ is a nonzero constant for all } s \in I.$$

When these conditions hold, $|\kappa| = 1/\rho$ where $\rho > 0$ is the radius of the circle.

Proof. We may assume that γ is parametrized by arc length.
($\Longrightarrow$) We will zoom in on the global condition that γ lies on a circle, differentiating repeatedly and using the Frenet frame as our coordinate system. In the argument, γ and its derivatives depend on the parameter s, and

so does the curvature κ, but we omit s from the notation in order to keep the presentation light. We are given that for some fixed point $p \in \mathbb{R}^2$ and some fixed radius $\rho > 0$,

$$|\gamma - p| = \rho.$$

And by the nature of the Frenet frame, $\gamma - p$ decomposes as

$$\gamma - p = \langle \gamma - p, T \rangle T + \langle \gamma - p, N \rangle N. \tag{8.1}$$

Since $|\gamma - p|$ is constant, Lemma 8.4.1(a) gives $\langle \gamma - p, \gamma' \rangle = 0$, and now Lemma 8.4.1(b) gives $\langle \gamma - p, \gamma'' \rangle = -\langle \gamma', \gamma' \rangle = -1$. Since $\gamma' = T$ and $\gamma'' = \kappa N$, these calculations have shown that $\langle \gamma - p, T \rangle = 0$ and $\langle \gamma - p, N \rangle = -1/\kappa$ with $\kappa \neq 0$. Thus (8.1) is simply

$$\gamma - p = -(1/\kappa)N.$$

But since $|\gamma - p| = \rho$, it follows that $1/\kappa = \pm\rho$ is constant, and so κ is constant, as desired.

($\Longleftarrow$) Assume that $\kappa(s)$ is a nonzero constant. To show that $\gamma - p = -(1/\kappa)N$, compute (using the Frenet equation $N' = -\kappa T$) the derivative

$$(\gamma + (1/\kappa)N)' = T + (1/\kappa)(-\kappa T) = 0.$$

So $\gamma + (1/\kappa)N$ is indeed some fixed vector p, and $\gamma - p = -(1/\kappa)N$, as expected. It follows that γ lies on the circle of radius $1/|\kappa|$ centered at p. □

Since $N = (1/\kappa)\gamma''$, the previous proof has shown that the differential equation

$$\gamma - p = -(1/\kappa)^2 \gamma''$$

arises from uniform circular motion of radius $1/|\kappa|$.

Exercises

8.4.1. (a) Let a and b be positive. Find the curvature of the ellipse $\alpha(t) = (a\cos(t), b\sin(t))$ for $t \in \mathbb{R}$.

(b) Let a be positive and b be negative. Find the curvature of the logarithmic spiral $\alpha(t) = (ae^{bt}\cos t, ae^{bt}\sin t)$ for $t \geq 0$.

8.4.2. Let $\gamma : I \longrightarrow \mathbb{R}^2$ be parametrized by arc length. Fix any unit vector $v \in \mathbb{R}^2$, and define a function

$$\theta : I \longrightarrow \mathbb{R}$$

by the conditions

$$\cos(\theta(s)) = \langle T(s), v \rangle, \qquad \sin(\theta(s)) = -\langle N(s), v \rangle.$$

Thus θ is the angle that the curve γ makes with the fixed direction v. Show that $\theta' = \kappa$. Thus our notion of curvature does indeed measure the rate at which γ is turning.

8.5 Space Curves: Curvature and Torsion

Now we discuss space curves similarly to the discussion of plane curves at the end of the previous section. Let $\gamma : I \longrightarrow \mathbb{R}^3$ be parametrized by arc length s. Its **tangent vector** $T(s)$ is

$$T = \gamma'.$$

So to first order, the curve is moving in the T-direction. Whenever T' is nonzero, the curve's **curvature** $\kappa(s)$ and **normal vector** $N(s)$ are defined by the conditions

$$T' = \kappa N, \quad \kappa > 0.$$

(Be aware that although the same equation $T' = \kappa N$ appeared in the context of plane curves, something different is happening now. For plane curves, N was defined as the 90-degree counterclockwise rotation of T, and the condition $\langle T, T \rangle = 1$ forced T' to be normal to T and hence some scalar multiple of N. The scalar was then given the name κ, and κ could be positive, negative, or zero depending on whether to second order the curve was bending toward N, away from N, or not at all. But now, for space curves, the conditions $T' = \kappa N$ and $\kappa > 0$ define both N and κ, assuming that $T' \neq \mathbf{0}$. Again by Lemma 8.4.1(a), T' is normal to T, and so N is normal to T, but now it makes no sense to speak of N being counterclockwise to T, and now κ is positive.) Assume that T' is always nonzero. Then the curve's **binormal vector** is

$$B = T \times N.$$

Thus, the Frenet frame $\{T, N, B\}$ is a positive basis of $\mathbb{R}^3$ consisting of orthogonal unit vectors.

We want to differentiate T, N, and B. The derivatives resolve into components,

$$T' = \langle T', T \rangle T + \langle T', N \rangle N + \langle T', B \rangle B,$$
$$N' = \langle N', T \rangle T + \langle N', N \rangle N + \langle N', B \rangle B,$$
$$B' = \langle B', T \rangle T + \langle B', N \rangle N + \langle B', B \rangle B.$$

The definition

$$T' = \kappa N$$

shows that the top row inner products are

$$\langle T', T \rangle = 0, \quad \langle T', N \rangle = \kappa, \quad \langle T', B \rangle = 0.$$

And since N and B are unit vectors, the other two diagonal inner products also vanish by Lemma 8.4.1(a),

$$\langle N', N \rangle = \langle B', B \rangle = 0.$$

Lemma 8.4.1(b) shows that the first inner product of the second row is the negative of the second inner product of the first row,

$$\langle N', T \rangle = -\langle T', N \rangle = -\kappa,$$

and so only the third inner product of the second row is a new quantity,

$$N' = -\kappa T + \tau B \quad \text{for the scalar function } \tau = \langle N', B \rangle.$$

The function τ is the **torsion** of γ. It can be positive, negative, or zero, depending on whether to third order the curve is twisting out of the (T, N)-plane toward B, away from B, or not at all.. Similarly, the first and second inner products of the third row are the negatives of the third inner products of the first and second rows,

$$\langle B', T \rangle = -\langle T', B \rangle = 0, \quad \langle B', N \rangle = -\langle N', B \rangle = -\tau.$$

All of the derivatives computed so far can be gathered into the **Frenet equations**,

$$\begin{bmatrix} T' \\ N' \\ B' \end{bmatrix} = \begin{bmatrix} 0 & \kappa & 0 \\ -\kappa & 0 & \tau \\ 0 & -\tau & 0 \end{bmatrix} \begin{bmatrix} T \\ N \\ B \end{bmatrix}.$$

The geometric idea is that as we move along the curve, the bending of the first natural coordinate determines the second natural coordinate; the second natural coordinate bends away from the first as much as the first is bending toward it, in order to preserve the ninety-degree angle between them; the remaining bending of the second coordinate is toward or away from the third remaining orthogonal coordinate, which bends away from or toward from the second coordinate at the same rate, in order to preserve the ninety-degree angle between them.

The relations $\gamma' = T$ and $\gamma'' = T' = \kappa N$ and $\gamma''' = (\kappa N)' = \kappa' N + \kappa N'$, and the second Frenet equation $N' = -\kappa T + \tau B$ combine to show that

$$\begin{bmatrix} \gamma' \\ \gamma'' \\ \gamma''' \end{bmatrix} = \begin{bmatrix} 1 & 0 & 0 \\ 0 & \kappa & 0 \\ -\kappa^2 & \kappa' & \kappa\tau \end{bmatrix} \begin{bmatrix} T \\ N \\ B \end{bmatrix}.$$

This relation shows that the local canonical form of a such a curve is, up to third order,

$$\gamma(s_0 + s) \approx \gamma(s_0) + s\gamma'(s_0) + \frac{1}{2}s^2\gamma''(s_0) + \frac{1}{6}s^3\gamma'''(s_0)$$

$$= \gamma(s_0) + sT + \frac{1}{2}s^2\kappa N + \frac{1}{6}s^3(-\kappa^2 T + \kappa' N + \kappa\tau B)$$

$$= \gamma(s_0) + \left(s - \frac{\kappa^2}{6}s^3\right)T + \left(\frac{\kappa}{2}s^2 + \frac{\kappa'}{6}s^3\right)N + \frac{\kappa\tau}{6}s^3 B.$$

In planar cross sections:

- In the (T, N)-plane the curve is locally $(s, (\kappa/2)s^2)$, a parabola opening upward at the origin (see Figure 8.11, viewing the curve down the positive B-axis).
- In the (T, B)-plane the curve is locally $(s, (\kappa\tau/6)s^3)$, a cubic curve inflecting at the origin, rising from left to right if $\tau > 0$ and falling if $\tau < 0$ (see Figure 8.12, viewing the figure up the negative N-axis).
- In the (N, B)-plane the curve is locally $((\kappa/2)s^2, (\kappa\tau/6)s^3)$, a curve in the right half-plane with a cusp at the origin (see Figure 8.13, viewing the curve down the positive T-axis).

The relation of the curve to all three local coordinate axes is shown in Figure 8.14.

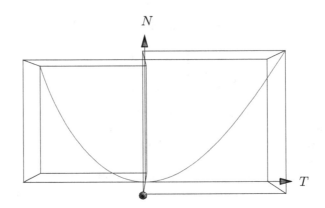

Figure 8.11. Space curve in local coordinates, from above

Let α be a regular curve, not necessarily parametrized by arc length. We want formulas for its curvature and torsion. Let γ be the reparametrization of α by arc length, so that $\alpha = \gamma \circ \ell$ where ℓ is the arc length of α. By the chain rule,

$$\alpha' = (\gamma' \circ \ell)\ell',$$
$$\alpha'' = (\gamma' \circ \ell)\ell'' + (\gamma'' \circ \ell)\ell'^2,$$
$$\alpha''' = (\gamma' \circ \ell)\ell''' + 3(\gamma'' \circ \ell)\ell'\ell'' + (\gamma''' \circ \ell)\ell'^3.$$

These relations and the earlier expressions of γ' and γ'' in terms of the Frenet frame combine to give

$$
\begin{bmatrix} \alpha' \\ \alpha'' \\ \alpha''' \end{bmatrix} = \begin{bmatrix} \ell' & 0 & 0 \\ \ell'' & \ell'^2 & 0 \\ \ell''' & 3\ell'\ell'' & \ell'^3 \end{bmatrix} \begin{bmatrix} \gamma' \circ \ell \\ \gamma'' \circ \ell \\ \gamma''' \circ \ell \end{bmatrix} = \begin{bmatrix} \ell' & 0 & 0 \\ \ell'' & \ell'^2 & 0 \\ \ell''' & 3\ell'\ell'' & \ell'^3 \end{bmatrix} \begin{bmatrix} 1 & 0 & 0 \\ 0 & \kappa & 0 \\ -\kappa^2 & \kappa' & \kappa\tau \end{bmatrix} \begin{bmatrix} T \\ N \\ B \end{bmatrix}.
$$

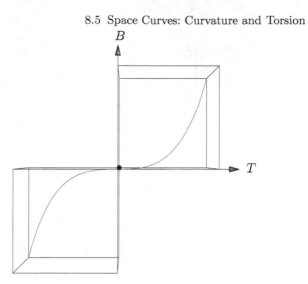

Figure 8.12. Space curve in local coordinates, from the side

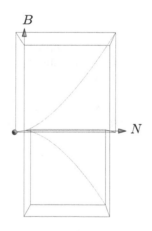

Figure 8.13. Space curve in local coordinates, from the front

Thus $\alpha' \times \alpha'' = \ell'T \times (*T + \ell'^2\kappa N) = \ell'^3\kappa B$, and since $\ell' = |\alpha'|$, this gives the curvature,

$$\kappa = \frac{|\alpha' \times \alpha''|}{|\alpha'|^3}.$$

Similarly, $\det(\alpha', \alpha'', \alpha''') = \ell'^6\kappa^2\tau$, giving the torsion,

$$\tau = \frac{\det(\alpha', \alpha'', \alpha''')}{|\alpha' \times \alpha''|^2}.$$

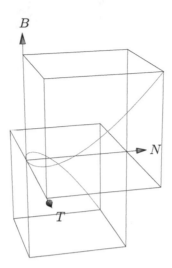

Figure 8.14. Space curve in local coordinates

As mentioned, the counterpart of Proposition 8.4.2 for space curves is considerably less obvious. Local measurements answer the global question whether we are moving on a sphere.

Theorem 8.5.1. *Let $\gamma : I \longrightarrow \mathbb{R}^3$ be regular, with curvature and torsion functions κ, τ never zero. Consider the reciprocal curvature and torsion functions,*

$$r = 1/\kappa, \quad t = 1/\tau.$$

Assume also that κ' never vanishes. Then

$$\gamma \text{ lies on a sphere} \quad \Longleftrightarrow \quad r^2 + (r't)^2 \text{ is constant.}$$

When these conditions hold, $r^2 + (r't)^2 = \rho^2$ where $\rho > 0$ is the radius of the sphere.

Proof. We may assume that γ is parametrized by arc length.

($\Longrightarrow$) As in the proof of Proposition 8.4.2, we zoom in on the global condition that γ lies on a sphere, differentiating repeatedly and using the Frenet frame. We are given that for some fixed point $p \in \mathbb{R}^3$ and some fixed radius $\rho > 0$,

$$|\gamma - p| = \rho.$$

And by the nature of the Frenet frame, $\gamma - p$ decomposes as

$$\gamma - p = \langle \gamma - p, T \rangle T + \langle \gamma - p, N \rangle N + \langle \gamma - p, B \rangle B. \tag{8.2}$$

Because $|\gamma - p|$ is constant, Lemma 8.4.1(a) gives $\langle \gamma - p, \gamma' \rangle = 0$; next, Lemma 8.4.1(b) and the fact that γ is parametrized by arc length combine to give $\langle \gamma - p, \gamma'' \rangle = -\langle \gamma', \gamma' \rangle = -1$; and now Lemma 8.4.1(b) and then Lemma 8.4.1(a) (again using the parametrization by arc length) give $\langle \gamma - p, \gamma''' \rangle = -\langle \gamma', \gamma'' \rangle = 0$. Since $\gamma' = T$ and $\gamma'' = \kappa N$ and $\gamma''' = -\kappa^2 T + \kappa' N + \kappa \tau B$, the first two calculations have shown that $\langle \gamma - p, T \rangle = 0$ and $\langle \gamma - p, N \rangle = -1/\kappa$ with $\kappa \neq 0$, and the third one therefore has shown that

$$0 = \langle \gamma - p, -\kappa^2 T + \kappa' N + \kappa \tau B \rangle = -\kappa'/\kappa + \kappa \tau \langle \gamma - p, B \rangle,$$

from which $\langle \gamma - p, B \rangle = \kappa'/(\kappa^2 \tau)$. Thus the description (8.2) of $\gamma - p$ in the Frenet frame is

$$\gamma - p = -(1/\kappa)N + \kappa'/(\kappa^2 \tau)B.$$

Because we have defined $r = 1/\kappa$, so that $r' = -\kappa'/\kappa^2$, and because $t = 1/\tau$, we have

$$\gamma - p = -rN - r'tB.$$

And thus $r^2 + (r't)^2 = \rho^2$.

($\Longleftarrow$) We expect that $\gamma = p - rN - r'tB$. So let $\delta = \gamma + rN + r'tB$ and compute δ' using the Frenet equations and various other results,

$$\delta' = T + r'N + r(-\kappa T + \tau B) + (r''t + r't')B - r't\tau N$$
$$= (1 - r\kappa)T + (r' - r't\tau)N + (r\tau + r''t + r't')B$$
$$= \left(\frac{r}{t} + r''t + r't' \right) B.$$

But $r^2 + (r't)^2$ is constant, so its derivative is zero,

$$0 = 2rr' + 2r't(r''t + r't') = 2r't\left(\frac{r}{t} + r''t + r't' \right).$$

Thus $\delta' = 0$ (here is where we use the hypothesis that κ' never vanishes: it prevents r' from vanishing) and so indeed δ is some fixed vector p. Thus $\gamma = p - rN + r'tB$ as expected, and $|\gamma - p|^2$ is the constant $r^2 + (r't)^2$. $\qquad \square$

Exercise

8.5.1. (a) Let a and b be positive. Compute the curvature κ and the torsion τ of the helix $\alpha(t) = (a\cos t, a\sin t, bt)$.
   (b) How do κ and τ behave if a is held constant and $b \to \infty$?
   (c) How do κ and τ behave if a is held constant and $b \to 0$?
   (d) How do κ and τ behave if b is held constant and $a \to \infty$?
   (e) How do κ and τ behave if b is held constant and $a \to 0$?

8.6 General Frenet Frames and Curvatures

This section extends the Frenet frame to any number of dimensions. As with plane curves and space curves, the basic idea is to take the derivatives of the curve and straighten them out, giving rise to a coordinate system of orthogonal unit vectors where each new direction takes one more derivative—and hence one more degree of the curve's behavior—into account. The result is a local coordinate system natural to the curve at each of its points.

Let $n \geq 2$ be an integer, and let

$$\alpha : I \longrightarrow \mathbb{R}^n$$

be a regular curve. For $t \in I$ define the first **Frenet vector** of α at t to be (suppressing the t from the notation for brevity)

$$F_1 = \alpha'/|\alpha'|.$$

Thus F_1 is a unit vector pointing in the same direction as the tangent vector of α at t.

Assuming that F_1' never vanishes and that $n \geq 3$, next define the first curvature $\kappa_1(t)$ of α at t and the second Frenet vector $F_2(t)$ of α at t by the conditions

$$F_1' = \kappa_1 F_2, \quad \kappa_1 > 0, \quad |F_2| = 1.$$

Since $|F_1| = 1$ for all t, it follows from Lemma 8.4.1(a) that $\langle F_2, F_1 \rangle = 0$.

Because $\langle F_2, F_1 \rangle = 0$, Lemma 8.4.1(b) gives $\langle F_2', F_1 \rangle = -\langle F_1', F_2 \rangle = -\kappa_1$. Assuming that $F_2' + \kappa_1 F_1$ never vanishes and that $n \geq 4$, define the second curvature $\kappa_2(t)$ and the third Frenet vector $F_3(t)$ by the conditions

$$F_2' = -\kappa_1 F_1 + \kappa_2 F_3, \quad \kappa_2 > 0, \quad |F_3| = 1.$$

Then $\langle F_3, F_1 \rangle = 0$, because $-\kappa_1 F_1$ is the F_1-component of F_2'. Again by Lemma 8.4.1(a), $\langle F_2', F_2 \rangle = 0$, so that (since also $\langle F_1, F_2 \rangle = 0$) $\langle F_3, F_2 \rangle = 0$.

In general, suppose that $2 \leq k \leq n-2$, and suppose that we have t-dependent orthogonal unit Frenet vectors $F_1, \ldots, F_k$ and t-dependent positive curvature functions $\kappa_1, \ldots, \kappa_{k-1}$ such that (defining $\kappa_0 F_0 = \mathbf{0}$ for convenience)

$$F_j' = -\kappa_{j-1} F_{j-1} + \kappa_j F_{j+1}, \quad j = 1, \ldots, k-1.$$

Since $\langle F_k, F_k \rangle = 1$, it follows by Lemma 8.4.1(a) that $\langle F_k', F_k \rangle = 0$. And since $\langle F_k, F_j \rangle = 0$ for $j = 1, \ldots, k-1$, it follows by Lemma 8.4.1(b) that for such j,

$$
\begin{aligned}
\langle F_k', F_j \rangle &= -\langle F_j', F_k \rangle \\
&= -\langle -\kappa_{j-1} F_{j-1} + \kappa_j F_{j+1}, F_k \rangle \\
&= \begin{cases} 0 & \text{if } j = 1, \ldots, k-2, \\ -\kappa_{k-1} & \text{if } j = k-1. \end{cases}
\end{aligned}
$$

So, assuming that $F'_k \neq -\kappa_{k-1}F_{k-1}$, define κ_k and F_{k+1} by the conditions

$$F'_k = -\kappa_{k-1}F_{k-1} + \kappa_k F_{k+1}, \quad \kappa_k > 0, \quad |F_{k+1}| = 1.$$

Then the relation $\kappa_k F_{k+1} = F'_k + \kappa_{k-1}F_{k-1}$ shows that $\langle F_{k+1}, F_j \rangle = 0$ for $j = 1, \ldots, k$. Use this process, assuming the nonvanishing that is needed, until κ_{n-2} and F_{n-1} have been defined. Thus if $n = 2$ then the process consists only of defining F_1; if $n = 3$ then the process also defines κ_1 and F_2; if $n = 4$ then the process further defines κ_2 and F_3; and so on.

Finally, define the nth Frenet vector F_n as the unique unit vector orthogonal to F_1 through F_{n-1} such that $\det(F_1, F_2, \ldots, F_n) > 0$, and then define the $(n-1)$st curvature κ_{n-1} by the condition

$$F'_{n-1} = -\kappa_{n-2}F_{n-2} + \kappa_{n-1}F_n.$$

The $(n-1)$st curvature need not be positive. By Lemma 8.4.1(b) yet again, we have $F'_n = -\kappa_{n-1}F_{n-1}$, and so the Frenet equations are

$$
\begin{bmatrix} F'_1 \\ F'_2 \\ F'_3 \\ \vdots \\ \vdots \\ F'_{n-1} \\ F'_n \end{bmatrix}
=
\begin{bmatrix}
0 & \kappa_1 & & & & & \\
-\kappa_1 & 0 & \kappa_2 & & & & \\
& -\kappa_2 & 0 & \kappa_3 & & & \\
& & \ddots & \ddots & \ddots & & \\
& & & \ddots & \ddots & \ddots & \\
& & & & -\kappa_{n-2} & 0 & \kappa_{n-1} \\
& & & & & -\kappa_{n-1} & 0
\end{bmatrix}
\begin{bmatrix} F_1 \\ F_2 \\ F_3 \\ \vdots \\ \vdots \\ F_{n-1} \\ F_n \end{bmatrix}.
$$

The first $n-1$ Frenet vectors and the first $n-2$ curvatures can also be obtained by applying the Gram–Schmidt process (see Exercise 2.2.16) to the vectors $\alpha', \ldots, \alpha^{(n-1)}$.

The Frenet vectors and the curvatures are independent of parametrization. To see this, let $\tilde{\alpha} : \tilde{I} \longrightarrow \mathbb{R}^n$ be a second curve equivalent to α. That is,

$$\alpha = \tilde{\alpha} \circ \phi$$

where $\phi : I \longrightarrow \tilde{I}$ is smooth and has a smooth inverse, and $\phi' > 0$ on I. By the chain rule,

$$\alpha'(t) = \tilde{\alpha}'(\tilde{t}) \cdot \phi'(t) \quad \text{where } \tilde{t} = \phi(t).$$

Thus $\alpha'(t)$ and $\tilde{\alpha}'(\tilde{t})$ point in the same direction (because $\phi'(t) > 0$), and so the corresponding first Frenet vectors are equal,

$$F_1(t) = \tilde{F}_1(\tilde{t}).$$

Since the curvatures and the rest of the Frenet vectors are described in terms of derivatives of the first Frenet vector with respect to its variable, it follows that the Frenet vectors and the curvatures are independent of parametrization, as claimed,

$$\widetilde{F}_i(\tilde{t}) = F_i(t) \quad \text{for } i = 1, \dots, n$$

and

$$\tilde{\kappa}_i(\tilde{t}) = \kappa_i(t) \quad \text{for } i = 1, \dots, n-1.$$

Since the curvatures describe the curve in local terms, they should be unaffected by passing the curve through a rigid motion. The remainder of this section establishes this invariance property of curvature, partly because doing so provides us an excuse to describe the rigid motions of Euclidean space.

Definition 8.6.1. *The square matrix $A \in M_n(\mathbb{R})$ is* **orthogonal** *if $A^t A = I$. That is, A is orthogonal if A is invertible and its transpose is its inverse. The set of $n \times n$ orthogonal matrices is denoted $O_n(\mathbb{R})$.*

It is straightforward to check (Exercise 8.6.2) that

- the identity matrix I is orthogonal,
- if A and B are orthogonal then so is the product AB,
- and if A is orthogonal then so is the inverse A^{-1}.

These three facts, along with the fact that matrix multiplication is associative, show that the orthogonal matrices form a *group* under matrix multiplication.

Some examples of orthogonal matrices are

$$\begin{bmatrix} 1 & 0 \\ 0 & -1 \end{bmatrix}, \quad \begin{bmatrix} \cos\theta & -\sin\theta \\ \sin\theta & \cos\theta \end{bmatrix} \quad \text{for every } \theta \in \mathbb{R}.$$

Orthogonal matrices are characterized by the property that they preserve inner products. That is, the following equivalence holds:

$$A \in O_n(\mathbb{R}) \iff \langle Ax, Ay \rangle = \langle x, y \rangle \text{ for all } x, y \in \mathbb{R}^n$$

(Exercise 8.6.2(a)). Consequently, multiplying vectors by an orthogonal matrix A preserves their lengths and the angles between them. Also, if $A \in M_n(\mathbb{R})$ is orthogonal then $\det A = \pm 1$ (Exercise 8.6.2(b)).

The orthogonal matrices of determinant 1 form the **special orthogonal group**, denoted $SO_n(\mathbb{R})$. These matrices not only preserve length and angle, but in addition they preserve orientation. Thus

$$A \in SO_n(\mathbb{R}) \iff \begin{cases} \langle Ax, Ay \rangle = \langle x, y \rangle, & x, y \in \mathbb{R}^n, \\ \det(Ax_1, \dots, Ax_n) = \det(x_1, \dots, x_n), & x_1, \dots, x_n \in \mathbb{R}^n. \end{cases}$$

It is straightforward to check that $SO_n(\mathbb{R})$ forms a *subgroup* of $O_n(\mathbb{R})$.

Definition 8.6.2. *A bijective mapping $R : \mathbb{R}^n \longrightarrow \mathbb{R}^n$ is called* **rigid** *if*

$$\langle R(x) - R(p), R(y) - R(p) \rangle = \langle x - p, y - p \rangle \quad \text{for all } p, x, y \in \mathbb{R}^n.$$

That is, rigid maps preserve the geometry of vector differences. The next proposition characterizes rigid mappings.

Proposition 8.6.3. *The mapping $R : \mathbb{R}^n \longrightarrow \mathbb{R}^n$ is rigid if and only if R takes the form $R(x) = Ax + b$ with $A \in O_n(\mathbb{R})$ and $b \in \mathbb{R}^n$.*

Proof. Verifying that every mapping $R(x) = Ax + b$ where $A \in O_n(\mathbb{R})$ and $b \in \mathbb{R}^n$ is rigid is Exercise 8.6.3.

Now let $R : \mathbb{R}^n \longrightarrow \mathbb{R}^n$ be rigid. Define a related mapping

$$S : \mathbb{R}^n \longrightarrow \mathbb{R}^n, \qquad S(x) = R(x) - R(0).$$

It suffices to show that $S(x) = Ax$ for some $A \in O_n(\mathbb{R})$. A small calculation shows that S preserves inner products: for every $x, y \in \mathbb{R}^n$,

$$\langle S(x), S(y) \rangle = \langle R(x) - R(0), R(y) - R(0) \rangle = \langle x - 0, y - 0 \rangle = \langle x, y \rangle.$$

Especially, if $\{e_1, \ldots, e_n\}$ is the standard basis of $\mathbb{R}^n$ then $\{S(e_1), \ldots, S(e_n)\}$ is again an orthonormal basis of $\mathbb{R}^n$. Furthermore, $\langle S(x), S(e_i) \rangle = \langle x, e_i \rangle$ for every $x \in \mathbb{R}^n$ and for $i = 1, \ldots, n$. That is,

$$S(x_1, \ldots, x_n) = x_1 S(e_1) + \cdots + x_n S(e_n).$$

This shows that $S(x) = Ax$ where A has columns $S(e_1), \ldots, S(e_n)$. Since $\langle S(e_i), S(e_j) \rangle = \langle e_i, e_j \rangle$ for $i, j \in \{1, \ldots, n\}$, in fact $A \in O_n(\mathbb{R})$, as desired. $\square$

Definition 8.6.4. *A* **congruence** *is a rigid map $R(x) = Ax + b$ where A is special orthogonal.*

With congruences understood, it is easy to show that they preserve curvatures. Consider a regular curve

$$\alpha : I \longrightarrow \mathbb{R}^n,$$

let $R(x) = Ax + b$ be a congruence, and define a second curve

$$\tilde{\alpha} : I \longrightarrow \mathbb{R}^n, \qquad \tilde{\alpha} = R \circ \alpha.$$

Then for every $t \in I$,

$$\tilde{\alpha}'(t) = R'(\alpha(t)) \cdot \alpha'(t) = A\alpha'(t).$$

Thus the first Frenet vectors of the two curves satisfy the relation

$$\tilde{F}_1 = AF_1,$$

and similarly for their derivatives,

$$\tilde{\kappa}_1 \tilde{F}_2 = \tilde{F}_1' = (AF_1)' = AF_1' = A\kappa_1 F_2 = \kappa_1 AF_2,$$

so that since $\tilde{\kappa}_1$ and κ_1 are positive and $|\tilde{F}_2| = 1 = |F_2| = |AF_2|$,

$$\tilde{\kappa}_1 = \kappa_1 \quad \text{and} \quad \tilde{F}_2 = AF_2.$$

Similarly,

$$\tilde{\kappa}_i = \kappa_i, \quad i = 1, \ldots, n-1$$

and

$$\widetilde{F}_i = AF_i, \quad i = 1, \ldots, n.$$

We need A to be special orthogonal rather than just orthogonal in order that this argument apply to the last Frenet vector and the last curvature. If A is orthogonal but not special orthogonal then $\widetilde{F}_n = -AF_n$ and $\tilde{\kappa}_{n-1} = -\kappa_{n-1}$.

Exercises

8.6.1. Are the following matrices orthogonal?

$$\begin{bmatrix} -\cos\theta & \sin\theta \\ \sin\theta & \cos\theta \end{bmatrix}, \quad \frac{1}{\sqrt{5}}\begin{bmatrix} 1 & 0 & 2 \\ 0 & \sqrt{5} & 0 \\ 2 & 0 & -1 \end{bmatrix}, \quad \begin{bmatrix} a & b \\ 0 & d \end{bmatrix}.$$

(b) Confirm that the identity matrix I is orthogonal, that if A and B are orthogonal then so is the product AB, and that if A is orthogonal then so is its inverse A^{-1}.

8.6.2. (a) Prove that a matrix $A \in M_n(\mathbb{R})$ is orthogonal if and only if $\langle Ax, Ay \rangle = \langle x, y \rangle$ for all $x, y \in \mathbb{R}^n$. (The fact that $\langle v, w \rangle = v^t w$ essentially gives ($\Longrightarrow$). For ($\Longleftarrow$), show that $A^t A$ has (i,j)th entry $\langle Ae_i, Ae_j \rangle$ for $i, j = 1, \ldots, n$, and recall that I_n is the matrix whose (i,j)th entry is δ_{ij}.)

(b) Prove that every matrix $A \in O_n(\mathbb{R})$ has determinant $\det A = \pm 1$.

8.6.3. Prove that every mapping $R(x) = Ax + b$ where $A \in O_n(\mathbb{R})$ and $b \in \mathbb{R}^n$ is rigid.

9

Integration of Differential Forms

The integration of differential forms over surfaces is characteristic of a fully developed mathematical theory: it starts from carefully preconfigured definitions and proceeds to one central theorem, whose proof is purely mechanical because of how the definitions are rigged. Furthermore, much of the work is algebraic, even though the theorem appears analytical. Since the motivation for the definitions is not immediately obvious, the early stages of working through such a body of material can feel unenlightening, but the payoff lies in the lucidity of the later arguments and the power of the end result. The main theorem here is often called Stokes's theorem, but in fact it is a generalization not only of the classical Stokes's theorem (which is not due to Stokes; he just liked to put it on his exams), but also of other nineteenth-century results called the divergence theorem (or Gauss's theorem) and Green's theorem, and even of the fundamental theorem of integral calculus. In fact, a better name for the theorem to be presented here is the general FTIC.

The definitions of a surface and of the integral of a function over a surface are given in Section 9.1. Formulas for particular integrals called flow and flux integrals are derived in Section 9.2. The theory to follow is designed partly to handle such integrals easily. The definitions of a differential form and of the integral of a differential form over a surface are given in Section 9.3, and the definitions are illustrated by examples in Sections 9.4 and 9.5. Sections 9.6 through 9.9 explain the algebraic rules of how to add differential forms and multiply them by scalars, how to multiply differential forms, how to differentiate them, and how to pass them through changes of variable. A change of variable theorem for differential forms follows automatically in Section 9.10. A construction of antiderivatives of forms is given in Section 9.11. Returning to surfaces, Sections 9.12 and 9.13 define a special class of surfaces called cubes, and a geometric boundary operator from cubes to cubes of lower dimension. The general FTIC is proved in Section 9.14. Section 9.15 sketches how it leads to another proof of the classical change of variable theorem. Finally, Section 9.16 explains how the classical vector integration theorems are

© Springer International Publishing AG 2016
J. Shurman, *Calculus and Analysis in Euclidean Space*,
Undergraduate Texts in Mathematics, DOI 10.1007/978-3-319-49314-5_9

special cases of the general FTIC, and Section 9.17 takes a closer look at some of the quantities that arise in this context.

9.1 Integration of Functions over Surfaces

Having studied integration over solid regions in $\mathbb{R}^n$, i.e., over subsets of $\mathbb{R}^n$ with positive n-dimensional volume, we face the new problem of how to integrate over surfaces of lower dimension in $\mathbb{R}^n$. For example, the circle in $\mathbb{R}^2$ is one-dimensional, and the torus surface in $\mathbb{R}^3$ is two-dimensional. Each of these sets has volume zero as a subset of its ambient space, in which it is curving around. In general, whatever the yet-undefined notion of a k-dimensional subset of $\mathbb{R}^n$ means, such objects will have volume zero when $k < n$, and so any attempt to integrate over them in the sense of Chapter 6 will give an integral of zero and a dull state of affairs. Instead, the idea is to *parametrize* surfaces in $\mathbb{R}^n$ and then define integration over a parametrized surface in terms of integration over a noncurved parameter space.

Definition 9.1.1 (Parametrized surface). *Let A be an open subset of $\mathbb{R}^n$. A k-surface in A is a smooth mapping*

$$\Phi : D \longrightarrow A,$$

where D is a compact connected subset of $\mathbb{R}^k$ whose boundary has volume zero. The set D is called the **parameter domain** *of Φ.*

See Figure 9.1. Here are some points to note about Definition 9.1.1:

- Recall that a subset A of $\mathbb{R}^n$ is called *open* if its complement is closed. The definitions in this chapter need the environment of an open subset rather than all of $\mathbb{R}^n$ in order to allow for functions that are not defined everywhere. For instance, the reciprocal modulus function

$$1/|\cdot| : \mathbb{R}^n - \{\mathbf{0}\} \longrightarrow \mathbb{R}$$

is defined only on surfaces that avoid the origin. In most of the examples, A will be all of $\mathbb{R}^n$, but Exercise 9.11.1 will touch on how the subject becomes more nuanced when it is not.
- Recall also that *compact* means closed and bounded. *Connected* means that D consists of only one piece, as discussed informally in Section 2.4. And as discussed informally in Section 6.5 and formally in Section 6.8, the boundary of a set consists of all points simultaneously near the set and near its complement—roughly speaking, its edge. Typically D will be some region that is easy to integrate over, such as a box, whose compactness, connectedness, and small boundary are self-evident.

- The word *smooth* in the definition means that the mapping Φ extends to some open superset of D in $\mathbb{R}^k$, on which it has continuous partial derivatives of all orders. Each such partial derivative is therefore again smooth. All mappings in this chapter are assumed to be smooth.
- When we compute, coordinates in parameter space will usually be written as $(u_1, \ldots, u_k)$, and coordinates in $\mathbb{R}^n$ as $(x_1, \ldots, x_n)$.
- It may be disconcerting that a surface is by definition a mapping rather than a set, but this is for good reason. Just as the integration of Chapter 6 was facilitated by distinguishing between functions and their outputs, the integration of this chapter is facilitated by viewing the surfaces over which we integrate as mappings rather than their images.
- A parametrized curve, as in Definition 8.2.1, is precisely a 1-surface.

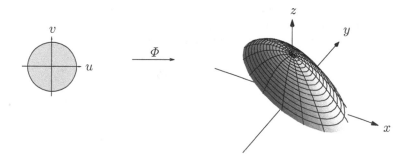

Figure 9.1. A surface

When $k = 0$, Definition 9.1.1 is a little tricky. By convention, $\mathbb{R}^0$ is the set of all points with no coordinates, each of the no coordinates being a real number. (Our definition of $\mathbb{R}^n$ at the beginning of Chapter 2 danced around this issue by requiring that n be positive.) There is exactly one such point, the point (). That is, $\mathbb{R}^0$ consists of a single point, naturally called $\mathbf{0}$ even though it is *not* (0). A 0-surface in $\mathbb{R}^n$ is thus a mapping

$$\Phi_p : \mathbb{R}^0 \longrightarrow \mathbb{R}^n, \qquad \Phi_p(\mathbf{0}) = p,$$

where p is some point in $\mathbb{R}^n$. In other words, Φ_p simply parametrizes the point p. At the other dimensional extreme, if $k = n$ then every compact connected subset D of $\mathbb{R}^n$ naturally defines a corresponding n-surface in $\mathbb{R}^n$ by trivially parametrizing itself,

$$\Delta : D \longrightarrow \mathbb{R}^n, \qquad \Delta(u) = u \text{ for all } u \in D.$$

Thus Definition 9.1.1 of a surface as a mapping is silly in the particular cases of $k = 0$ and $k = n$, when it amounts to parametrizing points using the empty point as a parameter domain, or parametrizing solids by taking them to be their own parameter domains and having the identity mapping map them to themselves. But for intermediate values of k, i.e., $0 < k < n$, we are going to integrate over k-dimensional subsets of $\mathbb{R}^n$ by traversing them, and parametrizing is the natural way to do so. Especially, a 1-surface is a parametrized curve, and a 2-surface is a parametrized surface in the usual sense of surface as in Figure 9.1.

Let A be an open subset of $\mathbb{R}^n$, let $\Phi : D \longrightarrow A$ be a k-surface in A, and let $f : A \longrightarrow \mathbb{R}$ be a smooth function. As mentioned above, if $k < n$ then the integral of f over $\Phi(D)$ in the sense of Chapter 6 is zero, because $\Phi(D)$ is of lower dimension than its ambient space $\mathbb{R}^n$. However, the integral of f over Φ can be defined more insightfully.

For each point u of the parameter domain D, the $n \times k$ derivative matrix $\Phi'(u)$ has as its columns vectors that are naturally viewed as tangent vectors to Φ at $\Phi(u)$, the jth column being tangent to the curve in Φ that arises from motion in the jth direction of the parameter domain. In symbols, the matrix is

$$\Phi'(u) = \begin{bmatrix} v_1 & \cdots & v_k \end{bmatrix}_{n \times k},$$

where each column vector v_j is

$$v_j = D_j \Phi(u) = \begin{bmatrix} D_j \Phi_1(u) \\ \vdots \\ D_j \Phi_n(u) \end{bmatrix}_{n \times 1}.$$

The parallelepiped spanned by these vectors (see Figure 9.2) has a naturally defined k-dimensional volume.

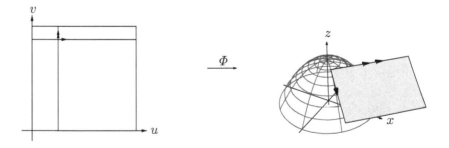

Figure 9.2. Tangent parallelepiped

Definition 9.1.2 (Volume of a parallelepiped). *Let $v_1, \ldots, v_k$ be vectors in $\mathbb{R}^n$. Let V be the $n \times k$ matrix with these vectors as its columns. Then the* k**-volume** *of the parallelepiped spanned by the $\{v_j\}$ is*

$$\text{vol}_k(\mathcal{P}(v_1, \ldots, v_k)) = \sqrt{\det(V^{\mathsf{T}} V)}. \tag{9.1}$$

In coordinates, this formula is

$$\text{vol}_k(\mathcal{P}(v_1, \ldots, v_k)) = \sqrt{\det\left([v_i \cdot v_j]_{i,j=1,\ldots,k}\right)}, \tag{9.2}$$

where $v_i \cdot v_j$ is the inner product of v_i and v_j.

The matrix V in this definition is $n \times k$, and its transpose V^{T} is $k \times n$, so neither of them need be square. But the product $V^{\mathsf{T}}V$ is square, $k \times k$, and this is the matrix whose determinant is being taken. Equation (9.2) follows immediately from (9.1), because

$$V^{\mathsf{T}} V = \begin{bmatrix} v_1^{\mathsf{T}} \\ \vdots \\ v_k^{\mathsf{T}} \end{bmatrix} \begin{bmatrix} v_1 & \cdots & v_k \end{bmatrix} = \begin{bmatrix} v_1 \cdot v_1 & \cdots & v_1 \cdot v_k \\ \vdots & \ddots & \vdots \\ v_k \cdot v_1 & \cdots & v_k \cdot v_k \end{bmatrix} = [v_i \cdot v_j]_{i,j=1,\ldots,k}.$$

For example, if $k = 1$ and $\gamma : [a, b] \longrightarrow \mathbb{R}^n$ is a 1-surface (i.e., a curve) in $\mathbb{R}^n$, then its derivative matrix at a point u of $[a, b]$ has one column,

$$\gamma'(u) = \begin{bmatrix} \gamma_1'(u) \\ \vdots \\ \gamma_n'(u) \end{bmatrix}.$$

Consequently, formula (9.2) is

$$\text{length}(\gamma'(u)) = \sqrt{\gamma'(u) \cdot \gamma'(u)}.$$

That is, Definition 9.1.2 for $k = 1$ specializes to the definition of $|\gamma'|$ as $\sqrt{\gamma' \cdot \gamma'}$ from Section 2.2. (Here and throughout this chapter, we drop the notational convention that curves named γ are parametrized by arc length; thus no assumption is present that $|\gamma'| = 1$.) At the other extreme, if $k = n$ then formula (9.1) is

$$\text{vol}_n(\mathcal{P}(v_1, \ldots, v_n)) = |\det(v_1, \ldots, v_n)|.$$

That is, Definition 9.1.2 for $k = n$ recovers the interpretation of $|\det|$ as volume from Section 3.8. When $k = 2$, formula (9.2) is

$$\begin{aligned}
\text{area}(\mathcal{P}(v_1, v_2)) &= \sqrt{|v_1|^2 |v_2|^2 - (v_1 \cdot v_2)^2} \\
&= \sqrt{|v_1|^2 |v_2|^2 (1 - \cos^2 \theta_{12})} \\
&= |v_1| |v_2| |\sin \theta_{12}|,
\end{aligned}$$

giving the familiar formula for the area of a parallelogram. When $k = 2$ and also $n = 3$, we can study the formula further by working in coordinates. Consider two vectors $u = (x_u, y_u, z_u)$ and $v = (x_v, y_v, z_v)$. An elementary calculation shows that the quantity under the square root in the previous display works out to

$$|u|^2 |v|^2 - (u \cdot v)^2 = |u \times v|^2.$$

So when $k = 2$ and $n = 3$, Definition 9.1.2 subsumes the familiar formula

$$\text{area}(\mathcal{P}(v_1, v_2)) = |v_1 \times v_2|.$$

Here is an argument that (9.2) is the appropriate formula for the k-dimensional volume of the parallelepiped spanned by the vectors $v_1, \ldots, v_k$ in $\mathbb{R}^n$. (The fact that the vectors are tangent vectors to a k-surface is irrelevant to this discussion.) Results from linear algebra guarantee that there exist vectors $v_{k+1}, \ldots, v_n$ in $\mathbb{R}^n$ such that

- each of v_{k+1} through v_n is a unit vector orthogonal to all the other v_j,
- $\det(v_1, \ldots, v_n) \geq 0$.

Recall the notation in Definition 9.1.2 that V is the $n \times k$ matrix with columns $v_1, \ldots, v_k$. Augment V to an $n \times n$ matrix W by adding the remaining v_j as columns too,

$$W = \begin{bmatrix} v_1 & \cdots & v_n \end{bmatrix} = \begin{bmatrix} V & v_{k+1} & \cdots & v_n \end{bmatrix}.$$

The scalar $\det(W)$ is the n-dimensional volume of the parallelepiped spanned by $v_1, \ldots, v_n$. But by the properties of v_{k+1} through v_n, this scalar should also be the k-dimensional volume of the the parallelepiped spanned by $v_1, \ldots, v_k$. That is, the natural definition is (using the second property of $v_1, \ldots, v_n$ for the second equality to follow)

$$\text{vol}_k(\mathcal{P}(v_1, \ldots, v_k)) = \det(W) = \sqrt{(\det W)^2} = \sqrt{\det(W^\mathsf{T}) \det(W)}$$
$$= \sqrt{\det(W^\mathsf{T} W)}.$$

The first property of $v_1, \ldots, v_n$ shows that

$$W^\mathsf{T} W = \begin{bmatrix} V^\mathsf{T} V & \mathbf{0}_{k \times (n-k)} \\ \mathbf{0}_{(n-k) \times k} & I_{n-k} \end{bmatrix},$$

so that $\det(W^\mathsf{T} W) = \det(V^\mathsf{T} V)$, and the natural definition becomes the desired formula,

$$\text{vol}_k(\mathcal{P}(v_1, \ldots, v_k)) = \sqrt{\det(V^\mathsf{T} V)}.$$

The argument here generalizes the ideas used in Section 3.10 to suggest a formula for the area of a 2-dimensional parallelogram in $\mathbb{R}^3$ as a 3×3 determinant. Thus the coordinate calculation sketched in the previous paragraph to recover the relation between parallelogram area and cross product length in $\mathbb{R}^3$ was unnecessary.

With k-dimensional volume in hand, we can naturally define the integral of a function over a k-surface.

Definition 9.1.3 (Integral of a function over a surface). *Let A be an open subset of $\mathbb{R}^n$. Let $\Phi : D \longrightarrow A$ be a k-surface in A. Let $f : \Phi(D) \longrightarrow \mathbb{R}$ be a function such that $f \circ \Phi$ is smooth. Then the* **integral of f over Φ** *is*

$$\int_\Phi f = \int_D (f \circ \Phi)\, \mathrm{vol}_k(\mathcal{P}(D_1\Phi, \ldots, D_k\Phi)).$$

In particular, the k-dimensional volume of Φ is

$$\mathrm{vol}_k(\Phi) = \int_\Phi 1 = \int_D \mathrm{vol}_k(\mathcal{P}(D_1\Phi, \ldots, D_k\Phi)).$$

By Definition 9.1.2, the k-volume factor in the surface integral is

$$\mathrm{vol}_k(\mathcal{P}(D_1\Phi, \ldots, D_k\Phi)) = \sqrt{\det(\Phi'^{\mathsf{T}}\Phi')} = \sqrt{\det([D_i\Phi \cdot D_j\Phi]_{i,j=1,\ldots,k})}.$$

The idea of Definition 9.1.3 is that as a parameter u traverses the parameter domain D, the composition $f \circ \Phi$ samples the function f over the surface, while the k-volume factor makes the integral the limit of sums of many f-weighted small tangent parallelepiped k-volumes over the surface rather than the limit of sums of many $(f \circ \Phi)$-weighted small box volumes over the parameter domain. (See Figure 9.3.) The k-volume factor itself is not small, as seen in Figure 9.2, but it is the ratio of the small parallelepiped k-volume to the small box volume shown in Figure 9.3.

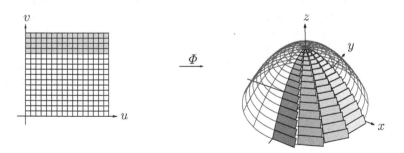

Figure 9.3. Integrating over a surface

For example, let r be a positive real number and consider a 2-surface in $\mathbb{R}^3$,

$$\Phi : [0, 2\pi] \times [0, \pi] \longrightarrow \mathbb{R}^3, \qquad \Phi(\theta, \varphi) = (r\cos\theta\sin\varphi, r\sin\theta\sin\varphi, r\cos\varphi).$$

This surface is the 2-sphere of radius r. Since the sphere is a surface of revolution, its area is readily computed by methods from a first calculus course, but we do so with the ideas of this section to demonstrate their use. The derivative vectors are

$$v_1 = \begin{bmatrix} -r\sin\theta\sin\varphi \\ r\cos\theta\sin\varphi \\ 0 \end{bmatrix}, \qquad v_2 = \begin{bmatrix} r\cos\theta\cos\varphi \\ r\sin\theta\cos\varphi \\ -r\sin\varphi \end{bmatrix},$$

and so the integrand of the surface area integral is

$$\sqrt{|v_1|^2|v_2|^2 - (v_1 \cdot v_2)^2} = \sqrt{r^4\sin^2\varphi} = r^2\sin\varphi$$

(note that $\sin\varphi \geq 0$ because $\varphi \in [0,\pi]$). Therefore the area is

$$\text{area}(\varPhi) = r^2 \int_{\theta=0}^{2\pi} \int_{\varphi=0}^{\pi} \sin\varphi = 4\pi r^2.$$

The fact that the sphere-area magnification factor $r^2\sin\varphi$ is the familiar volume magnification factor for spherical coordinates is clear geometrically: to traverse the sphere, the spherical coordinates θ and φ vary while r stays constant, and when r does vary, it moves orthogonally to the sphere-surface so that the incremental volume is the incremental surface-area times the incremental radius-change. Indeed, the vectors v_1 and v_2 from a few displays back are simply the second and third columns of the spherical change of variable derivative matrix. The reader can enjoy checking that the first column of the spherical change of variable derivative matrix is indeed a unit vector orthogonal to the second and third columns.

The integral in Definition 9.1.3 seems to depend on the surface $\varPhi$ as a parametrization rather than merely as a set, but in fact, the integral is unaffected by reasonable changes of parametrization, because of the change of variable theorem. To see this, let A be an open subset of $\mathbb{R}^n$, and let $\varPhi : D \longrightarrow A$ and $\varPsi : \tilde{D} \longrightarrow A$ be k-surfaces in A. Suppose that there exists a smoothly invertible mapping $T : D \longrightarrow \tilde{D}$ such that $\varPsi \circ T = \varPhi$. In other words, T is smooth, T is invertible, its inverse is also smooth, and the following diagram commutes (meaning that either path around the triangle yields the same result):

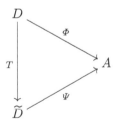

When such a mapping T exists, $\varPsi$ is called a **reparametrization** of $\varPhi$. Let $f : A \longrightarrow \mathbb{R}$ be any smooth function. Then the integral of f over the reparametrization $\varPsi$ of $\varPhi$ is

$$\int_{\tilde{D}}(f \circ \varPsi)\sqrt{\det(\varPsi'^{\mathsf{T}}\varPsi')}.$$

By the change of variable theorem, since $\tilde{D} = T(D)$, this integral is

$$\int_D (f \circ \Psi \circ T) \sqrt{\det \left((\Psi' \circ T)^\mathsf{T} (\Psi' \circ T) \right)} \, |\det(T')|.$$

But $|\det(T')| = \sqrt{\det(T')^2} = \sqrt{\det(T'^\mathsf{T}) \det(T')}$, so this becomes

$$\int_D (f \circ \Psi \circ T) \sqrt{\det \left(T'^\mathsf{T} (\Psi' \circ T)^\mathsf{T} (\Psi' \circ T) T' \right)},$$

and by the general matrix rule $B^\mathsf{T} A^\mathsf{T} A B = (AB)^\mathsf{T} AB$, this is in turn

$$\int_D (f \circ \Psi \circ T) \sqrt{\det \left(((\Psi' \circ T) T')^\mathsf{T} (\Psi' \circ T) T' \right)}.$$

Finally, since $\Psi \circ T = \Phi$, the chain rule shows that we have

$$\int_D (f \circ \Phi) \sqrt{\det \left(\Phi'^\mathsf{T} \Phi' \right)},$$

giving the integral of f over the original surface Φ, as desired.

Exercises

9.1.1. Consider two vectors $u = (x_u, y_u, z_u)$ and $v = (x_v, y_v, z_v)$. Calculate that $|u|^2 |v|^2 - (u \cdot v)^2 = |u \times v|^2$.

9.1.2. Consider two vectors $u = (x_u, y_u, z_u)$ and $v = (x_v, y_v, z_v)$. Calculate that the area of the parallelogram spanned by u and v is the square root of the sum of the squares of the areas of the parallelogram's shadows in the (x, y)-plane, the (y, z)-plane, and the (z, x)-plane.

9.1.3. Let $f(x, y, z) = x^2 + yz$.
   (a) Integrate f over the box $B = [0, 1]^3$.
   (b) Integrate f over the parametrized curve

$$\gamma : [0, 2\pi] \longrightarrow \mathbb{R}^3, \quad \gamma(t) = (\cos t, \sin t, t).$$

   (c) Integrate f over the parametrized surface

$$S : [0, 1]^2 \longrightarrow \mathbb{R}^3, \quad S(u, v) = (u + v, u - v, v).$$

   (d) Integrate f over the parametrized solid

$$V : [0, 1]^3 \longrightarrow \mathbb{R}^3, \quad V(u, v, w) = (u + v, v - w, u + w).$$

9.1.4. Find the surface area of the upper half of the cone at fixed angle φ from the z-axis, extended outward to radius a. That is, the surface is the image of the spherical coordinate mapping with φ fixed at some value between 0 and π as ρ varies from 0 to a and θ varies from 0 to 2π.

9.1.5. (a) Let $D \subset \mathbb{R}^k$ be a parameter domain, and let $f : D \longrightarrow \mathbb{R}$ be a smooth function. Recall from Exercise 2.4.3 that the graph of f is a subset of $\mathbb{R}^{k+1}$,

$$G(f) = \{(u, f(u)) : u \in D\}.$$

Note that f is a 1-surface in $\mathbb{R}$, while the surface that captures the idea of the graph of f as a k-surface in $\mathbb{R}^{k+1}$ is not f itself but rather

$$\Phi : D \longrightarrow \mathbb{R}^{k+1}, \qquad \Phi(u) = (u, f(u)).$$

Derive a formula for the k-dimensional volume of Φ. In particular, show that when $k = 2$, the formula is

$$\text{area}(\Phi) = \int_D \sqrt{1 + (D_1 f)^2 + (D_2 f)^2}.$$

(b) What is the area of the graph of the function $f : D \longrightarrow \mathbb{R}$ (where D is the unit disk in the plane) given by $f(x, y) = x^2 + y^2$?

9.2 Flow and Flux Integrals

Let A be an open subset of $\mathbb{R}^n$. A mapping $F : A \longrightarrow \mathbb{R}^n$ is also called a *vector field on A*. (The usage of *field* here is unrelated to the field axioms.) If $\gamma : I \longrightarrow A$ is a curve in A and u is a point of I, then the *flow of F along γ at u* is the scalar component of $F(\gamma(u))$ tangent to γ at $\gamma(u)$. If $\Phi : D \longrightarrow A$ is an $(n-1)$-surface in A and u is a point of D, then the *flux of F through Φ at u* is the scalar component of F normal to Φ at $\Phi(u)$. Surface integrals involving the flow or the flux of a vector field arise naturally. If F is viewed as a force field then its flow integrals, also called *line integrals*, measure the work of moving along curves γ in A. If F is viewed as a velocity field describing the motion of some fluid then its flux integrals measure the rate at which fluid passes through permeable membranes Φ in A. Each of the classical theorems of vector integral calculus to be proved at the end of this chapter involves a flow integral or a flux integral.

Flow and flux integrals have a more convenient form than the general integral of a function over a surface, in that the k-volume factor from Definition 9.1.3 (an unpleasant square root) cancels, and what remains is naturally expressed in terms of determinants of the derivatives of the component functions of Φ. These formulas rapidly become complicated, so the point of this section is only to see what form they take.

Working first in two dimensions, consider a vector field,

$$F = (F_1, F_2) : \mathbb{R}^2 \longrightarrow \mathbb{R}^2,$$

and a curve,

$$\gamma = (\gamma_1, \gamma_2) : [a, b] \longrightarrow \mathbb{R}^2.$$

Assuming that the derivative γ' is always nonzero but not assuming that γ is parametrized by arc length, the unit tangent vector to γ at the point $\gamma(u)$, pointing in the direction of the traversal, is

$$\widehat{T}(\gamma(u)) = \frac{\gamma'(u)}{|\gamma'(u)|}.$$

Note that the denominator is the length factor in Definition 9.1.3. The parallel component of $F(\gamma(u))$ along $\widehat{T}(\gamma(u))$ has magnitude $(F \cdot \widehat{T})(\gamma(u))$. (See Exercise 2.2.15.) Therefore the net flow of F along γ in the direction of traversal is $\int_\gamma F \cdot \widehat{T}$. By Definition 9.1.3, this **flow integral** is

$$\int_\gamma F \cdot \widehat{T} = \int_{u=a}^b F(\gamma(u)) \cdot \frac{\gamma'(u)}{|\gamma'(u)|} |\gamma'(u)| = \int_{u=a}^b F(\gamma(u)) \cdot \gamma'(u), \qquad (9.3)$$

and the length factor has canceled. In coordinates, the flow integral is

$$\int_\gamma F \cdot \widehat{T} = \int_{u=a}^b \left((F_1 \circ \gamma)\gamma_1' + (F_2 \circ \gamma)\gamma_2' \right)(u). \qquad (9.4)$$

On the other hand, for every vector $(x, y) \in \mathbb{R}^2$, define $(x, y)^\times = (-y, x)$. (This seemingly ad hoc procedure of negating one of the vector entries and then exchanging them will be revisited soon as a particular manifestation of a general idea.) The unit normal vector to the curve γ at the point $\gamma(u)$, at angle $\pi/2$ counterclockwise from $\widehat{T}(\gamma(u))$, is

$$\widehat{N}(\gamma(u)) = \frac{\gamma'(u)^\times}{|\gamma'(u)|}.$$

Therefore the net flux of F through γ counterclockwise to the direction of traversal is the **flux integral**

$$\int_\gamma F \cdot \widehat{N} = \int_{u=a}^b F(\gamma(u)) \cdot \gamma'(u)^\times, \qquad (9.5)$$

or, in coordinates,

$$\int_\gamma F \cdot \widehat{N} = \int_{u=a}^b \left((F_2 \circ \gamma)\gamma_1' - (F_1 \circ \gamma)\gamma_2' \right)(u). \qquad (9.6)$$

Next let $n = 3$ and modify the vector field F suitably to

$$F = (F_1, F_2, F_3) : \mathbb{R}^3 \longrightarrow \mathbb{R}^3.$$

The intrinsic expression (9.3) for the flow integral of F along a curve γ remains unchanged in $\mathbb{R}^3$, making the 3-dimensional counterpart of (9.4) in coordinates obvious,

$$\int_\gamma F \cdot \widehat{T} = \int_{u=a}^b \left((F_1 \circ \gamma)\gamma_1' + (F_2 \circ \gamma)\gamma_2' + (F_3 \circ \gamma)\gamma_3' \right)(u).$$

As for the flux integral, consider a 2-surface in $\mathbb{R}^3$,

$$\Phi = (\Phi_1, \Phi_2, \Phi_3) : D \longrightarrow \mathbb{R}^3.$$

Assuming that the two columns $D_1\Phi$ and $D_2\Phi$ of the derivative matrix Φ' are always linearly independent, a unit normal to the surface Φ at the point $\Phi(u)$ (where now $u = (u_1, u_2)$) is obtained from their cross product,

$$\widehat{N}(\Phi(u)) = \frac{D_1\Phi(u) \times D_2\Phi(u)}{|D_1\Phi(u) \times D_2\Phi(u)|}.$$

By property CP6 of the cross product, the denominator in this expression is the area of the parallelogram spanned by $D_1\Phi(u)$ and $D_2\Phi(u)$, and this is the area factor in Definition 9.1.3 of the surface integral. Therefore this factor cancels in the flux integral of F through Φ in the $\widehat{N}$-direction,

$$\int_\Phi F \cdot \widehat{N} = \int_{u \in D} F(\Phi(u)) \cdot (D_1\Phi(u) \times D_2\Phi(u)), \qquad (9.7)$$

or, in coordinates,

$$\int_\Phi F \cdot \widehat{N} = \int_{u \in D} \begin{pmatrix} (F_1 \circ \Phi)(D_1\Phi_2 \, D_2\Phi_3 - D_1\Phi_3 \, D_2\Phi_2) \\ +(F_2 \circ \Phi)(D_1\Phi_3 \, D_2\Phi_1 - D_1\Phi_1 \, D_2\Phi_3) \\ +(F_3 \circ \Phi)(D_1\Phi_1 \, D_2\Phi_2 - D_1\Phi_2 \, D_2\Phi_1) \end{pmatrix}(u). \qquad (9.8)$$

Whereas the 2-dimensional flow and flux integrands and the 3-dimensional flow integrand involved derivatives γ'_j of the 1-surface γ, the integrand here contains the determinants of all 2×2 subblocks of the 3×2 derivative matrix of the 2-surface Φ,

$$\Phi' = \begin{bmatrix} D_1\Phi_1 & D_2\Phi_1 \\ D_1\Phi_2 & D_2\Phi_2 \\ D_1\Phi_3 & D_2\Phi_3 \end{bmatrix}.$$

The subdeterminants give a hint about the general picture. Nonetheless, (9.8) is forbidding enough that we should pause and think before trying to compute more formulas.

For general n, formula (9.3) for the flow integral of a vector field along a curve generalizes transparently,

$$\int_\gamma F \cdot \widehat{T} = \int_{u=a}^b ((F \circ \gamma) \cdot \gamma')(u) = \int_{u=a}^b \left(\sum_{i=1}^n (F_i \circ \gamma)\gamma'_i \right)(u). \qquad (9.9)$$

But the generalization of formulas (9.5) through (9.8) to a formula for the flux integral of a vector field in $\mathbb{R}^n$ through an $(n-1)$-surface is not so obvious. Based on (9.7), the intrinsic formula should be

$$\int_\Phi F \cdot \widehat{N} = \int_{u \in D} ((F \circ \Phi) \cdot (D_1\Phi \times \cdots \times D_{n-1}\Phi))(u), \qquad (9.10)$$

where the $(n-1)$-fold cross product on $\mathbb{R}^n$ is analogous to the 2-fold cross product on $\mathbb{R}^3$ from Section 3.10. That is, the cross product should be orthogonal to each of the multiplicand-vectors, its length should be their $(n-1)$-dimensional volume, and when the multiplicands are linearly independent, they should combine with their cross product to form a positive basis of $\mathbb{R}^n$.

Such a cross product exists by methods virtually identical to those of Section 3.10. What is special to three dimensions is that the cross product is binary, i.e., it is a twofold product. In coordinates, a mnemonic formula for the cross product in $\mathbb{R}^3$, viewing the vectors as columns, is

$$v_1 \times v_2 = \det \begin{bmatrix} & & e_1 \\ v_1 & v_2 & e_2 \\ & & e_3 \end{bmatrix}.$$

This formula appeared in row form in Section 3.10, and it makes the corresponding formula for the cross product of $n-1$ vectors in $\mathbb{R}^n$ inevitable,

$$v_1 \times \cdots \times v_{n-1} = \det \begin{bmatrix} & & & e_1 \\ v_1 & \cdots & v_{n-1} & \vdots \\ & & & e_n \end{bmatrix}. \tag{9.11}$$

For example, a single vector $v = (x, y)$ in $\mathbb{R}^2$ has a sort of cross product,

$$v^\times = \det \begin{bmatrix} x & e_1 \\ y & e_2 \end{bmatrix} = (-y, x)$$

This is the formula that appeared with no explanation as part of the flux integral in $\mathbb{R}^2$. That is, the generalization (9.10) of the 3-dimensional flux integral to higher dimensions also subsumes the 2-dimensional case. Returning to $\mathbb{R}^n$, the cross product of the vectors $D_1\Phi(u),\ldots,D_{n-1}\Phi(u)$ is

$$(D_1\Phi \times \cdots \times D_{n-1}\Phi)(u) = \det \begin{bmatrix} & & & e_1 \\ D_1\Phi(u) & \cdots & D_{n-1}\Phi(u) & \vdots \\ & & & e_n \end{bmatrix}.$$

This determinant can be understood better by considering the data in the matrix as rows. Recall that for $i = 1,\ldots,n$, the ith row of the $n \times (n-1)$ derivative matrix Φ' is the derivative matrix of the ith component function of Φ,

$$\Phi_i'(u) = \begin{bmatrix} D_1\Phi_i(u) & \cdots & D_{n-1}\Phi_i(u) \end{bmatrix}.$$

In terms of these component function derivatives, the general cross product is

$$(D_1\Phi \times \cdots \times D_{n-1}\Phi)(u) = \det \begin{bmatrix} \Phi'_1(u) & e_1 \\ \vdots & \vdots \\ \Phi'_n(u) & e_n \end{bmatrix} = (-1)^{n-1} \det \begin{bmatrix} e_1 & \Phi'_1(u) \\ \vdots & \vdots \\ e_n & \Phi'_n(u) \end{bmatrix}$$

$$= (-1)^{n-1}\Big(\det \begin{bmatrix} \Phi'_2(u) \\ \Phi'_3(u) \\ \Phi'_4(u) \\ \vdots \\ \Phi'_n(u) \end{bmatrix} e_1 - \det \begin{bmatrix} \Phi'_1(u) \\ \Phi'_3(u) \\ \Phi'_4(u) \\ \vdots \\ \Phi'_n(u) \end{bmatrix} e_2 + \det \begin{bmatrix} \Phi'_1(u) \\ \Phi'_2(u) \\ \Phi'_4(u) \\ \vdots \\ \Phi'_n(u) \end{bmatrix} e_3 + \cdots \Big)$$

$$= (-1)^{n-1} \sum_{i=1}^{n} (-1)^{i-1} \det \begin{bmatrix} \Phi'_1(u) \\ \vdots \\ \Phi'_{i-1}(u) \\ \Phi'_{i+1}(u) \\ \vdots \\ \Phi'_n(u) \end{bmatrix} e_i.$$

Thus finally, the general flux integral in coordinates is

$$\int_\Phi F \cdot \widehat{N} = (-1)^{n-1} \int_{u \in D} \Big(\sum_{i=1}^{n} (-1)^{i-1} (F_i \circ \Phi) \det \begin{bmatrix} \Phi'_1 \\ \vdots \\ \Phi'_{i-1} \\ \Phi'_{i+1} \\ \vdots \\ \Phi'_n \end{bmatrix} \Big)(u). \qquad (9.12)$$

The integrand here contains the determinants of all $(n-1) \times (n-1)$ subblocks of the $n \times (n-1)$ derivative matrix of the $(n-1)$-surface Φ. The best way to understand the notation of (9.12) is to derive (9.6) and (9.8) from it by setting $n = 2$ and then $n = 3$.

We end this section by mentioning one more integral. Let $k = 2$ and let $n = 4$, and consider a 2-surface in $\mathbb{R}^4$,

$$\Phi = (\Phi_1, \Phi_2, \Phi_3, \Phi_4) : D \longrightarrow \mathbb{R}^4.$$

Note that Φ' is a 4×2 matrix,

$$\Phi' = \begin{bmatrix} \Phi'_1 \\ \Phi'_2 \\ \Phi'_3 \\ \Phi'_4 \end{bmatrix} = \begin{bmatrix} D_1\Phi_1 & D_2\Phi_1 \\ D_1\Phi_2 & D_2\Phi_2 \\ D_1\Phi_3 & D_2\Phi_3 \\ D_1\Phi_4 & D_2\Phi_4 \end{bmatrix},$$

so that any two of its rows form a square matrix. Consider also any six smooth functions

$$F_{1,2}, F_{1,3}, F_{1,4}, F_{2,3}, F_{2,4}, F_{3,4} : \mathbb{R}^4 \longrightarrow \mathbb{R}.$$

Then we can define an integral,

$$
\int_{u \in D} \begin{pmatrix} (F_{1,2} \circ \Phi) \det \begin{bmatrix} \Phi_1' \\ \Phi_2' \end{bmatrix} + (F_{1,3} \circ \Phi) \det \begin{bmatrix} \Phi_1' \\ \Phi_3' \end{bmatrix} + (F_{1,4} \circ \Phi) \det \begin{bmatrix} \Phi_1' \\ \Phi_4' \end{bmatrix} \\ + (F_{2,3} \circ \Phi) \det \begin{bmatrix} \Phi_2' \\ \Phi_3' \end{bmatrix} + (F_{2,4} \circ \Phi) \det \begin{bmatrix} \Phi_2' \\ \Phi_4' \end{bmatrix} + (F_{3,4} \circ \Phi) \det \begin{bmatrix} \Phi_3' \\ \Phi_4' \end{bmatrix} \end{pmatrix} (u).
$$

$$(9.13)$$

Since the surface Φ is not 1-dimensional, this is not a flow integral. And since Φ is not $(n-1)$-dimensional, it is not a flux integral either. Nonetheless, since the integrand contains the determinants of all 2×2 subblocks of the 4×2 derivative matrix of the 2-surface Φ, it is clearly cut from the same cloth as the flow and flux integrands of this section. The ideas of this chapter will encompass this integral and many others in the same vein.

As promised at the beginning of this section, the k-volume factor has canceled in flow and flux integrals, and the remaining integrand features determinants of the derivatives of the component functions of the surface of integration. Rather than analyze such cluttered integrals, the method of this chapter is to abstract their key properties into symbol-patterns, and then work with the patterns algebraically instead. An analysis tracking all the details of the original setup would be excruciating to follow, not to mention being unimaginable to recreate ourselves. Instead, we will work insightfully, economy of ideas leading to ease of execution. Since the definitions to follow do indeed distill the essence of vector integration, they will enable us to think fluently about the phenomena that we encounter. This is real progress in methodology, much less laborious than the classical approach. Indeed, having seen the modern argument, it is unimaginable to *want* to recreate the older one.

Exercises

9.2.1. Show that the n-dimensional cross product defined by a formula in (9.11) satisfies the property

$$\langle v_1 \times \cdots \times v_{n-1}, w \rangle = \det(v_1, \ldots, v_{n-1}, w) \quad \text{for all } w \in \mathbb{R}^n.$$

As in Section 3.10, this property characterizes the cross product uniquely. Are there significant differences between deriving the properties of the cross product from its characterization (cf. Proposition 3.10.2) in n dimensions rather than in 3?

9.2.2. Derive equations (9.6) and (9.8) from equation (9.12).

9.3 Differential Forms Syntactically and Operationally

We need objects to integrate over surfaces, objects whose integrals encompass at least the general flow integral (9.9) and flux integral (9.12) of the previous section. Let A be an open subset of $\mathbb{R}^n$. The objects are called **differential forms of order k on A** or simply **k-forms on A**. Thus a k-form ω is some sort of mapping

$$\omega : \{k\text{-surfaces in } A\} \longrightarrow \mathbb{R}.$$

Naturally, the value $\omega(\Phi)$ will be denoted $\int_\Phi \omega$. The definition of a k-form will come in two parts. The first is syntactic: it doesn't say what a k-form *is* as a function of k-surfaces, only what kind of *name* a k-form can have. This definition requires some preliminary vocabulary: an **ordered k-tuple from** $\{1,\ldots,n\}$ is a vector

$$(i_1,\ldots,i_k) \text{ with each } i_j \in \{1,\ldots,n\}.$$

For example, the ordered 3-tuples from $\{1,2\}$ are

$$(1,1,1), \ (1,1,2), \ (1,2,1), \ (1,2,2), \ (2,1,1), \ (2,1,2), \ (2,2,1), \ (2,2,2).$$

A sum over the ordered k-tuples from $\{1,\ldots,n\}$ means simply a sum of terms with each term corresponding to a distinct k-tuple. Thus we may think of an ordered k-tuple $(i_1,\ldots,i_k)$ as a sort of multiple index or multiple subscript, and for this reason we often will abbreviate it to I. These multiple subscripts will figure prominently throughout this chapter, so you should get comfortable with them. Exercise 9.3.1 provides some practice.

Definition 9.3.1 (Syntax of differential forms). *Let A be an open subset of $\mathbb{R}^n$. A 0-form on A is a smooth function $f : A \longrightarrow \mathbb{R}$. For $k \geq 1$, a k-form on A is an element of the form*

$$\sum_{i_1,\ldots,i_k=1}^n f_{(i_1,\ldots,i_k)} \, \mathrm{d}x_{i_1} \wedge \cdots \wedge \mathrm{d}x_{i_k},$$

or

$$\sum_I f_I \, \mathrm{d}x_I,$$

where each $I = (i_1,\ldots,i_k)$ is an ordered k-tuple from $\{1,\ldots,n\}$ and each f_I is a smooth function $f_I : A \longrightarrow \mathbb{R}$.

Make the convention that the empty set $I = \varnothing$ is the only ordered 0-tuple from $\{1,\ldots,n\}$, and that the corresponding empty product $\mathrm{d}x_\varnothing$ is 1. Then the definition of a k-form for $k \geq 1$ in Definition 9.3.1 also makes sense for $k = 0$, and it subsumes the special definition that was given for $k = 0$.

For example, a differential form for $n = 3$ and $k = 1$ is

$$e^{x+y+z} \, \mathrm{d}x + \sin(yz) \, \mathrm{d}y + x^2 z \, \mathrm{d}z,$$

and a differential form for $n = 2$ and $k = 2$ is

$$y \, \mathrm{d}x \wedge \mathrm{d}x + e^x \, \mathrm{d}x \wedge \mathrm{d}y + y \cos x \, \mathrm{d}y \wedge \mathrm{d}x,$$

with the missing $dy \wedge dy$ term tacitly understood to have the zero function as its coefficient-function $f_{(2,2)}(x, y)$, and hence to be zero itself. The expression

$$\frac{1}{x}\,dx$$

is a 1-form on the open subset $A = \{x \in \mathbb{R} : x \neq 0\}$ of $\mathbb{R}$, but it is not a 1-form on all of $\mathbb{R}$. The hybrid expression

$$z\,dx \wedge dy + e^x\,dz$$

is not a differential form, because it mixes an order-2 term and an order-1 term.

Before completing the definition of differential form, we need one more piece of terminology. If M is an $n \times k$ matrix and $I = (i_1, \dots, i_k)$ is an ordered k-tuple from $\{1, \dots, n\}$, then M_I denotes the square $k \times k$ matrix comprising the Ith rows of M. For example, if

$$M = \begin{bmatrix} 1 & 2 \\ 3 & 4 \\ 5 & 6 \end{bmatrix},$$

and if $I = (3, 1)$, then

$$M_I = \begin{bmatrix} 5 & 6 \\ 1 & 2 \end{bmatrix}.$$

The second part of the definition of a k-form explains how to integrate it over a k-surface. In this definition, a differential form in the sense of Definition 9.3.1 is called a syntactic differential form.

Definition 9.3.2 (Integration of differential forms). *Let A be an open subset of $\mathbb{R}^n$. For $k = 0$, a syntactic 0-form $\omega = f$ on A gives rise to a function of 0-surfaces in A, also called ω,*

$$\omega : \{0\text{-surfaces in } A\} \longrightarrow \mathbb{R},$$

defined by the rule that for every point $p \in A$,

$$\omega(\Phi_p) = f(p).$$

That is, integrating ω over a one-point surface consists simply in evaluating f at the point. For $k \geq 1$, a syntactic k-form $\omega = \sum_I f_I dx_I$ on A gives rise to a function of k-surfaces in A, also called ω,

$$\omega : \{k\text{-surfaces in } A\} \longrightarrow \mathbb{R},$$

defined by the rule that for every k-surface $\Phi : D \longrightarrow A$,

$$\omega(\Phi) = \int_D \sum_I (f_I \circ \Phi) \det \Phi'_I. \tag{9.14}$$

For all k, the integral of ω over Φ is defined to be $\omega(\Phi)$,

$$\int_\Phi \omega = \omega(\Phi).$$

Formula (9.14), defining $\omega(\Phi)$, is the key for everything to follow in this chapter. It defines an integral over the image $\Phi(D)$, which may have volume zero in $\mathbb{R}^n$, by *pulling back*—this term will later be defined precisely—to an integral over the parameter domain D, which is a full-dimensional set in $\mathbb{R}^k$ and hence has positive k-dimensional volume.

Under Definition 9.3.2, the integral of a differential form over a surface depends on the surface as a mapping, i.e., as a parametrization. However, it is a straightforward exercise to show that that the multivariable change of variable theorem implies that the integral is unaffected by reasonable changes of parametrization.

Returning to formula (9.14): despite looking like the flux integral (9.12), it may initially be impenetrable to the reader who (like the author) does not assimilate notation quickly. The next two sections will illustrate the formula in specific instances, after which its general workings should be clear. Before long, you will have an operational understanding of the definition.

Operational understanding should be complemented by structural understanding. The fact that the formal consequences of Definitions 9.3.1 and 9.3.2 subsume the main results of classical integral vector calculus still doesn't explain these ad hoc definitions conceptually. For everything to play out so nicely, the definitions must somehow be natural rather than merely clever, and a structural sense of why they work so well might let us extend the ideas to other contexts rather than simply tracking them. Indeed, differential forms fit into a mathematical structure called a *cotangent bundle*, with each differential form being a *section* of the bundle. The construction of the cotangent bundle involves the *dual space* of the *alternation* of a *tensor product*, all of these formidable-sounding technologies being utterly Platonic mathematical objects. However, understanding this language requires an investment in ideas and abstraction, and in the author's judgment the startup cost is much higher without some experience first. Hence the focus of the chapter is purely operational. Since formula (9.14) may be opaque to the reader for now, the first order of business is to render it transparent by working easy concrete examples.

Exercises

9.3.1. Write out all ordered k-tuples from $\{1,\ldots,n\}$ in the cases $n = 4$, $k = 1$; $n = 3$, $k = 2$. In general, how many ordered k-tuples $I = (i_1,\ldots,i_k)$ from $\{1,\ldots,n\}$ are there? How many of these are **increasing**, meaning that $i_1 < \cdots < i_k$? Write out all increasing k-tuples from $\{1,2,3,4\}$ for $k = 1,2,3,4$.

9.3.2. An expression $\omega = \sum_I f_I \, dx_I$ in which the sum is over only increasing k-tuples from $\{1, \ldots, n\}$ is called a **standard presentation** of ω. Write out explicitly what a standard presentation for a k-form on $\mathbb{R}^4$ looks like for $k = 0, 1, 2, 3, 4$.

9.4 Examples: 1-Forms

A k-form is a function of k-surfaces. That is, one can think of a k-form ω as a set of instructions: given a k-surface Φ, ω carries out some procedure on Φ to produce a real number, $\int_\Phi \omega$.

For example, let

$$\omega = x \, dy \quad \text{and} \quad \lambda = y \, dz,$$

both 1-forms on $\mathbb{R}^3$. A 1-surface in $\mathbb{R}^3$ is a curve,

$$\gamma = (\gamma_1, \gamma_2, \gamma_3) : [a, b] \longrightarrow \mathbb{R}^3,$$

with 3×1 derivative matrix

$$\gamma' = \begin{bmatrix} \gamma_1' \\ \gamma_2' \\ \gamma_3' \end{bmatrix}.$$

For every such curve, ω is the instructions *integrate $\gamma_1 \gamma_2'$ over the parameter domain* $[a, b]$, and similarly λ instructs to integrate $\gamma_2 \gamma_3'$. You should work through applying formula (9.14) to ω and λ to see how it produces these directions. Note that x and y are being treated as functions on $\mathbb{R}^3$—for example,

$$x(a, b, c) = a \quad \text{for all } (a, b, c),$$

so that $x \circ \gamma = \gamma_1$.

To see ω and λ work on a specific curve, consider the helix

$$H : [0, 2\pi] \longrightarrow \mathbb{R}^3, \qquad H(t) = (a \cos t, a \sin t, bt).$$

Its derivative matrix is

$$H'(t) = \begin{bmatrix} -a \sin t \\ a \cos t \\ b \end{bmatrix} \quad \text{for all } t \in [0, 2\pi].$$

Thus by (9.14),

$$\int_H \omega = \int_{t=0}^{2\pi} a \cos t \cdot a \cos t = \pi a^2 \quad \text{and} \quad \int_H \lambda = \int_{t=0}^{2\pi} a \sin t \cdot b = 0.$$

Looking at the projections of the helix in the (x, y)-plane and the (y, z)-plane suggests that these are the right values for $\int_H x \, dy$ and $\int_H y \, dz$ if we interpret the symbols $x \, dy$ and $y \, dz$ as in one-variable calculus. (See Figure 9.4.)

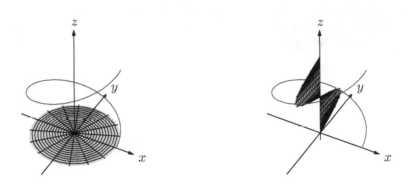

Figure 9.4. Integrating 1-forms over a helix

For another example, let
$$\omega = \mathrm{d}x,$$
a 1-form on $\mathbb{R}^3$, and consider any curve
$$\gamma : [a, b] \longrightarrow \mathbb{R}^3, \quad \gamma(t) = (\gamma_1(t), \gamma_2(t), \gamma_3(t)).$$
Then
$$\int_\gamma \omega = \int_a^b (1 \circ \gamma) \cdot \gamma_1' = \int_a^b \gamma_1' = \gamma_1(b) - \gamma_1(a).$$
A change of notation makes this example more telling. Rewrite the component functions of the curve as x, y, and z,
$$\gamma : [a, b] \longrightarrow \mathbb{R}^3, \quad \gamma(t) = (x(t), y(t), z(t)).$$
So now x is not a function on $\mathbb{R}^3$ as in the previous example, but a function on $[a, b]$. The integral can be rewritten as follows:

For curves $\gamma = (x, y, z) : [a, b] \longrightarrow \mathbb{R}^3$, $\quad \displaystyle\int_\gamma \mathrm{d}x = x(b) - x(a)$.

That is, *the form $\mathrm{d}x$ does indeed measure change in x along curves.* As a set of instructions, it simply says to evaluate the x-coordinate difference from the initial point on the curve to the final point. Returning to the helix H, it is now clear with no further work that
$$\int_H \mathrm{d}x = 0, \qquad \int_H \mathrm{d}y = 0, \qquad \int_H \mathrm{d}z = 2\pi b.$$
It would be good practice with formula (9.14) to confirm these values.

To generalize the previous example, let A be an open subset of $\mathbb{R}^n$, let $f : A \longrightarrow \mathbb{R}$ be any smooth function, and associate a 1-form ω to f,

$$\omega = D_1 f \, dx_1 + \cdots + D_n f \, dx_n.$$

Then for every curve $\gamma : [a, b] \longrightarrow A$,

$$\int_\gamma \omega = \int_a^b (D_1 f \circ \gamma)\gamma_1' + \cdots + (D_n f \circ \gamma)\gamma_n'$$

$$= \int_a^b (f \circ \gamma)' \qquad \text{by the chain rule in coordinates}$$

$$= (f \circ \gamma)\Big|_a^b$$

$$= f(\gamma(b)) - f(\gamma(a)).$$

That is, *the form ω measures change in f along curves.* Indeed, ω is classically called the *total differential* of f. It is tempting to give ω the name df, i.e., to define

$$df = D_1 f \, dx_1 + \cdots + D_n f \, dx_n.$$

Soon we will do so as part of a more general definition.

(Recall the chain rule: If $A \subset \mathbb{R}^n$ is open, then for every smooth $\gamma : [a, b] \longrightarrow A$ and $f : A \longrightarrow \mathbb{R}$,

$$(f \circ \gamma)'(t) = f'(\gamma(t))\gamma'(t)$$

$$= \big[D_1 f(\gamma(t)) \cdots D_n f(\gamma(t)) \big] \begin{bmatrix} \gamma_1'(t) \\ \vdots \\ \gamma_n'(t) \end{bmatrix}$$

$$= \sum_{i=1}^n D_i f(\gamma(t))\gamma_i'(t)$$

$$= \Big[\sum_{i=1}^n (D_i f \circ \gamma)\gamma_i' \Big](t),$$

so indeed $(f \circ \gamma)' = \sum_{i=1}^n (D_i f \circ \gamma)\gamma_i'$.)

Continuing to generalize, consider now a 1-form that does not necessarily arise from differentiation,

$$\omega = F_1 \, dx_1 + \cdots + F_n \, dx_n.$$

For every curve $\gamma : [a, b] \longrightarrow \mathbb{R}^n$ the integral of ω over γ is

$$\int_\gamma \omega = \int_{u=a}^b \Big(\sum_{i=1}^n (F_i \circ \gamma)\gamma_i' \Big)(u),$$

and this is the general flow integral (9.9) of the vector field $(F_1, \ldots, F_n)$ along γ. That is, the flow integrals from Section 9.2 are precisely the integrals of 1-forms.

Exercises

9.4.1. Let $\omega = x\,dy - y\,dx$, a 1-form on $\mathbb{R}^2$. Evaluate $\int_\gamma \omega$ for the following curves.

    (a) $\gamma : [-1,1] \longrightarrow \mathbb{R}^2$, $\gamma(t) = (t^2 - 1, t^3 - t)$;

    (b) $\gamma : [0,2] \longrightarrow \mathbb{R}^2$, $\gamma(t) = (t, t^2)$.

9.4.2. Let $\omega = z\,dx + x^2\,dy + y\,dz$, a 1-form on $\mathbb{R}^3$. Evaluate $\int_\gamma \omega$ for the following two curves.

    (a) $\gamma : [-1,1] \longrightarrow \mathbb{R}^3$, $\gamma(t) = (t, at^2, bt^3)$;

    (b) $\gamma : [0,2\pi] \longrightarrow \mathbb{R}^3$, $\gamma(t) = (a\cos t, a\sin t, bt)$.

9.4.3. (a) Let $\omega = f\,dy$ where $f : \mathbb{R}^2 \longrightarrow \mathbb{R}$ depends only on y. That is, $f(x,y) = \varphi(y)$ for some $\varphi : \mathbb{R} \longrightarrow \mathbb{R}$. Show that for every curve $\gamma = (\gamma_1, \gamma_2) : [a,b] \longrightarrow \mathbb{R}^2$,

$$\int_\gamma \omega = \int_{\gamma_2(a)}^{\gamma_2(b)} \varphi.$$

    (b) Let $\omega = f\,dx + g\,dy$ where f depends only on x and g depends only on y. Show that $\int_\gamma \omega = 0$ whenever $\gamma : [a,b] \longrightarrow \mathbb{R}^2$ is a *closed* curve, meaning that $\gamma(b) = \gamma(a)$.

9.5 Examples: 2-Forms on $\mathbb{R}^3$

To get a more complete sense of what formula (9.14) is doing, we need to study a case with $k > 1$, i.e., integration on surfaces of more than one dimension. Fortunately, the case $n = 3$, $k = 2$ is rich enough in geometry to understand in general how k-forms on n-space work.

Consider Figure 9.5. The figure shows a 2-surface in $\mathbb{R}^3$,

$$\Phi = (\Phi_1, \Phi_2, \Phi_3) : D \longrightarrow \mathbb{R}^3.$$

The parameter domain D has been partitioned into subrectangles, and the image $\Phi(D)$ has been divided up into subpatches by mapping the grid lines in D over to it via Φ. The subrectangle J of D maps to the subpatch B of $\Phi(D)$, which in turn has been projected down to its shadow $B_{(1,2)}$ in the (x,y)-plane. The point (u_J, v_J) resides in J, and its image under Φ is $\Phi(u_J, v_J) = (x_B, y_B, z_B)$.

Note that $B_{(1,2)} = (\Phi_1, \Phi_2)(J)$. Rewrite this as

$$B_{(1,2)} = \Phi_{(1,2)}(J).$$

That is, $B_{(1,2)}$ is the image of J under the $(1,2)$ component functions of Φ. If J is small then results on determinants give

$$\text{area}(B_{(1,2)}) \approx |\det \Phi'_{(1,2)}(u_J, v_J)|\,\text{area}(J).$$

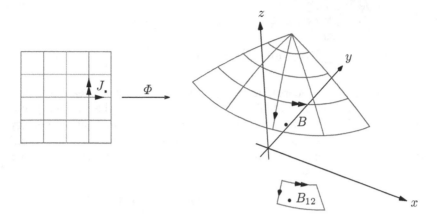

Figure 9.5. 2-surface in 3-space

Thus, *the magnification factor between subrectangles of D and (x,y)-projected subpatches of $\Phi(D)$ is (up to sign) the factor* $\det \Phi'_I$ *from formula* (9.14) *for $I = (1,2)$.* The sign is somehow keeping track of the orientation of the projected patch, which would be reversed under projection onto the (y,x)-plane. (See Figure 9.6.)

Figure 9.6. Projected patch and its reversal

Let $\omega = f\,dx \wedge dy$, a 2-form on $\mathbb{R}^3$, where $f : \mathbb{R}^3 \longrightarrow \mathbb{R}$ is a smooth function. By (9.14) and Riemann sum approximation,

$$\int_{\Phi} \omega = \int_{D} (f \circ \Phi) \det \Phi'_{(1,2)}$$
$$\approx \sum_{J} (f \circ \Phi)(u_J, v_J) \det \Phi'_{(1,2)}(u_J, v_J) \mathrm{area}(J)$$
$$\approx \sum_{B} f(x_B, y_B, z_B)\big(\pm \mathrm{area}(B_{(1,2)})\big).$$

This calculation gives a geometric interpretation of what it means to integrate $f \, dx \wedge dy$ over Φ: to evaluate $\int_{\Phi} f \, dx \wedge dy$, traverse the set $\Phi(D)$ and measure projected, oriented area in the (x,y)-plane, weighted by the density function f. The interpretation is analogous for forms with $dy \wedge dz$, and so on.

For an illustrative example, consider the forms $dx \wedge dy$, $dz \wedge dx$, and $dy \wedge dz$ integrated over the arch surface

$$\Phi : [-1,1] \times [0,1] \longrightarrow \mathbb{R}^3, \qquad \Phi(u,v) = (u, v, 1 - u^2).$$

(See Figure 9.7.) The (x,y)-shadows of B_1, B_2 have the same areas as J_1, J_2 and positive orientation, so $\int_{\Phi} dx \wedge dy$ should be equal to $\mathrm{area}(D)$, i.e., 2. (See the left half of Figure 9.8.) The (z,x)-shadows of B_1, B_2 have area zero, so $\int_{\Phi} dz \wedge dx$ should be an emphatic 0. (See the right half of Figure 9.8.) The (y,z)-shadows of B_1, B_2 have the same area but opposite orientations, so $\int_{\Phi} dy \wedge dz$ should be 0 by some cancellation on opposite sides of the (y,z)-plane or equivalently, cancellation in the u-direction of the parameter domain. (See Figure 9.9.)

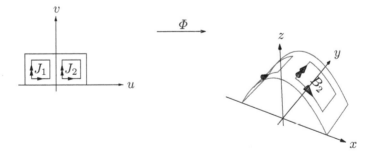

Figure 9.7. An arch

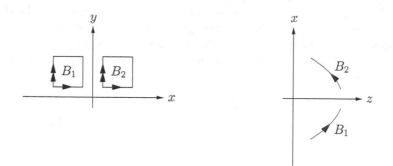

Figure 9.8. (x, y)-shadows and (z, x)-shadows

Figure 9.9. (y, z)-shadows

Integrating with formula (9.14) confirms this intuition. Since

$$\Phi'(u, v) = \begin{bmatrix} 1 & 0 \\ 0 & 1 \\ -2u & 0 \end{bmatrix},$$

we have

$$\int_\Phi \mathrm{d}x \wedge \mathrm{d}y = \int_D \det \Phi'_{(1,2)} = \int_{v=0}^1 \int_{u=-1}^1 \det \begin{bmatrix} 1 & 0 \\ 0 & 1 \end{bmatrix} = 2,$$

and similarly

$$\int_\Phi \mathrm{d}z \wedge \mathrm{d}x = \int_D \det \Phi'_{(3,1)} = \int_{v=0}^1 \int_{u=-1}^1 \det \begin{bmatrix} -2u & 0 \\ 1 & 0 \end{bmatrix} = \int_v \int_u 0 = 0,$$

$$\int_\Phi \mathrm{d}y \wedge \mathrm{d}z = \int_D \det \Phi'_{(2,3)} = \int_{v=0}^1 \int_{u=-1}^1 \det \begin{bmatrix} 0 & 1 \\ -2u & 0 \end{bmatrix} = \int_v \int_u 2u = 0.$$

Note how the first integral reduces to integrating 1 over the parameter domain, the second integral vanishes because its integrand is zero, and the third integral vanishes because of cancellation in the u-direction. All three of these behaviors confirm our geometric insight into how forms should behave.

Since the differential form $dx \wedge dy$ measures projected area in the (x, y)-plane, the integral

$$\int_\Phi z \, dx \wedge dy$$

should give the volume under the arch. And indeed formula (9.14) gives

$$\int_\Phi z \, dx \wedge dy = \int_{(u,v) \in D} (1 - u^2) \cdot 1,$$

which is the volume. Specifically, the integral is

$$\int_\Phi z \, dx \wedge dy = \int_{v=0}^1 \int_{u=-1}^1 (1 - u^2) = 1 \cdot (2 - u^3/3 \Big|_{-1}^1) = 4/3.$$

Similarly, since $dy \wedge dz$ measures oriented projected area in the (y, z)-plane, integrating the differential form $x \, dy \wedge dz$ should also give the volume under the arch. Here the interesting feature is that for $x > 0$, the form will multiply the positive distance from the (y, z)-plane to the arch by positive (y, z)-area, while for $x < 0$, the form will multiply the negative distance from the plane to the arch by negative (y, z)-area, again measuring a positive quantity. To see explicitly that the integral is again 4/3, compute

$$\int_\Phi x \, dy \wedge dz = \int_{v=0}^1 \int_{u=-1}^1 u \cdot 2u = 1 \cdot (2/3)u^3 \Big|_{-1}^1 = 4/3.$$

With these examples, the meaning of a k-form $\omega = f \, dx_I$ on n-space is fairly clear:

> *Integrating ω over a surface $\Phi : D \longrightarrow \mathbb{R}^n$ means traversing the set $\Phi(D)$ and measuring oriented, k-dimensional volume of the projection of $\Phi(D)$ into k-space $\mathbb{R}^I$, weighted by the density function f.*

This interpretation explains the results from integrating various 1-forms over the helix in the previous section. Those integrals deserve reviewing in light of this interpretation.

As the last example of this section, consider a 2-form on $\mathbb{R}^3$,

$$\omega = F_1 \, dx_2 \wedge dx_3 + F_2 \, dx_3 \wedge dx_1 + F_3 \, dx_1 \wedge dx_2.$$

For every 2-surface $\Phi : D \longrightarrow \mathbb{R}^3$ the integral of ω over Φ is

$$\int_\Phi \omega = \int_{u \in D} \begin{pmatrix} (F_1 \circ \Phi)(D_1\Phi_2 \, D_2\Phi_3 - D_1\Phi_3 \, D_2\Phi_2) \\ +(F_2 \circ \Phi)(D_1\Phi_3 \, D_2\Phi_1 - D_1\Phi_1 \, D_2\Phi_3) \\ +(F_3 \circ \Phi)(D_1\Phi_1 \, D_2\Phi_2 - D_1\Phi_2 \, D_2\Phi_1) \end{pmatrix} (u),$$

and this is the flux integral (9.8) of the vector field (F_1, F_2, F_3) through Φ. A straightforward generalization of this example shows that the general integral of an $(n-1)$-form over an $(n-1)$-surface in $\mathbb{R}^n$ is the general flux integral (9.12). That is, the flux integrals from Section 9.2 are precisely the integrals of $(n-1)$-forms.

Along with the last example of the previous section, this raises the following question: why bother with k-forms for values of k other than 1 and $n - 1$, and maybe also 0 and n? The answer is that the amalgamation of k-forms for all values of k has a coherent algebraic structure, making the whole easier to study than its parts. The remainder of the chapter is largely an elaboration of this point.

After this discussion of the mechanics and meaning of integrating forms, you should be ready to prove a result that has already been mentioned: integration of forms reduces to ordinary integration when $k = n$, and integration of forms is unaffected by reasonable changes of parametrization. These points are covered in the next set of exercises.

Exercises

9.5.1. Let a be a positive number. Consider a 2-surface in $\mathbb{R}^3$,

$$\Phi : [0, a] \times [0, \pi] \longrightarrow \mathbb{R}^3, \qquad \Phi(r, \theta) = (r \cos \theta, r \sin \theta, r^2).$$

Sketch this surface, noting that θ varies from 0 to π, not from 0 to 2π. Try to determine $\int_\Phi dx \wedge dy$ by geometric reasoning, and then check your answer using (9.14) to evaluate the integral. Do the same for $dy \wedge dz$ and $dz \wedge dx$. Do the same for $z\, dx \wedge dy - y\, dz \wedge dx$.

9.5.2. Let $\omega = x\, dy \wedge dz + y\, dx \wedge dy$, a 2-form on $\mathbb{R}^3$. Evaluate $\int_\Phi \omega$ when Φ is the 2-surface (a) $\Phi : [0, 1] \times [0, 1] \longrightarrow \mathbb{R}^3$, $\Phi(u, v) = (u + v, u^2 - v^2, uv)$; (b) $\Phi : [0, 2\pi] \times [0, 1] \longrightarrow \mathbb{R}^3$, $\Phi(u, v) = (v \cos u, v \sin u, u)$.

9.5.3. Consider a 2-form on $\mathbb{R}^4$,

$$\begin{aligned} \omega = {} & F_{1,2}\, dx_1 \wedge dx_2 + F_{1,3}\, dx_1 \wedge dx_3 + F_{1,4}\, dx_1 \wedge dx_4 \\ & + F_{2,3}\, dx_2 \wedge dx_3 + F_{2,4}\, dx_2 \wedge dx_4 + F_{3,4}\, dx_3 \wedge dx_4. \end{aligned}$$

Show that for every 2-surface $\Phi : D \longrightarrow \mathbb{R}^4$, the integral of ω over Φ is given by formula (9.13) from near the end of Section 9.2.

9.5.4. This exercise proves that integration of k-forms on $\mathbb{R}^n$ reduces to standard integration when $k = n$

Let $D \subset \mathbb{R}^n$ be compact and connected. Define the corresponding natural parametrization, $\Delta : D \longrightarrow \mathbb{R}^n$, by $\Delta(u_1, \ldots, u_n) = (u_1, \ldots, u_n)$. (This is how to turn a set in $\mathbb{R}^n$, where we can integrate functions, into the corresponding surface, where we can integrate n-forms.) Let $\omega = f\,dx_1 \wedge \cdots \wedge dx_n$, an n-form on $\mathbb{R}^n$. Use (9.14) to show that

$$\int_\Delta \omega = \int_D f.$$

Your solution should use the basic properties of Δ but not the highly substantive change of variable theorem. Note that in particular if $f = 1$, then $\omega = dx_1 \wedge \cdots \wedge dx_n$ and $\int_\Delta \omega = \mathrm{vol}(D)$, explaining why in this case ω is called the **volume form**.

Thus in $\mathbb{R}^n$, we may from now on blur the distinction between integrating the function f over a set and integrating the n-form $\omega = f\,dx_I$ over a surface, provided that $I = (1,\ldots,n)$ (i.e., the dx_i factors appear in canonical order), and provided that the surface is parametrized trivially.

9.5.5. This exercise proves that because of the change of variable theorem, the integration of differential forms is invariant under orientation-preserving reparametrizations of a surface.

Let A be an open subset of $\mathbb{R}^n$. Let $\Phi : D \longrightarrow A$ and $\Psi : \widetilde{D} \longrightarrow A$ be k-surfaces in A. Suppose that there exists a smoothly invertible mapping $T : D \longrightarrow \widetilde{D}$ such that $\Psi \circ T = \Phi$. In other words, T is smooth, T is invertible, its inverse is also smooth, and the following diagram commutes:

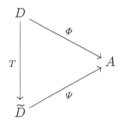

If $\det T' > 0$ on D then the surface Ψ is called an **orientation-preserving reparametrization** of Φ, while if $\det T' < 0$ on D then Ψ is an **orientation-reversing reparametrization** of Φ.

(a) Let Ψ be a reparametrization as just defined. Let $S = T^{-1} : \widetilde{D} \longrightarrow D$, a smooth mapping. Starting from the relation $(S \circ T)(u) = \mathrm{id}(u)$ for all $u \in D$ (where id is the identity mapping on D), differentiate, use the chain rule, and take determinants to show that $\det T'(u) \neq 0$ for all $u \in D$.

(b) Assume now that the reparametrization Ψ is orientation-preserving. For every $n \times k$ matrix M and every ordered k-tuple I from $\{1,\ldots,n\}$, recall that M_I denotes the $k \times k$ matrix comprising the Ith rows of M. If N is a $k \times k$ matrix, prove the equality

$$(MN)_I = M_I N.$$

In words, this says that

the Ith rows of (M times N) are (the Ith rows of M) times N.

(Suggestion: Do it first for the case $I = i$, that is, I denotes a single row.)

(c) Use the chain rule and part (b) to show that for every I,

$$\det \Phi_I'(u) = \det \Psi_I'(T(u)) \det T'(u) \quad \text{for all } u \in D.$$

(d) Let $\omega = f(x)\, dx_I$, a k-form on A. Show that

$$\int_\Psi \omega = \int_{T(D)} (f \circ \Psi) \det \Psi_I'.$$

Explain why the change of variable theorem shows that

$$\int_\Psi \omega = \int_D \left((f \circ \Psi) \det \Psi_I' \right) \circ T \cdot \det T'.$$

Explain why this shows that

$$\int_\Psi \omega = \int_\Phi \omega.$$

What would the conclusion be for orientation-reversing Ψ?

(e) Do the results from (d) remain valid if ω has the more general form $\omega = \sum_I f_I dx_I$?

9.6 Algebra of Forms: Basic Properties

One advantage of forms over earlier setups of vector integral calculus is that one can do much of the necessary work with them algebraically. That is, crucial properties will follow from purely rule-driven symbolic manipulation rather than geometric intuition or close analysis.

Let A be an open subset of $\mathbb{R}^n$. Since k-forms on A are functions (functions of k-surfaces), they come with an inherent notion of equality. The meaning of

$$\omega_1 = \omega_2$$

is that $\omega_1(\Phi) = \omega_2(\Phi)$ for all k-surfaces Φ in A. In particular, the meaning of $\omega = 0$ is that $\omega(\Phi) = 0$ for all Φ, where the first 0 is a form, while the second is a real number. Addition of k-forms is defined naturally,

$$(\omega_1 + \omega_2)(\Phi) = \omega_1(\Phi) + \omega_2(\Phi) \quad \text{for all } \omega_1,\, \omega_2,\, \Phi,$$

where the first "+" lies between two forms, the second between two real numbers. Similarly, the definition of scalar multiplication is

$$(c\omega)(\Phi) = c(\omega(\Phi)) \quad \text{for all } c,\, \omega,\, \Phi.$$

The addition of forms here is compatible with the twofold use of summation in the definition of forms and how they integrate. Addition and scalar multiplication of forms inherit all the vector space properties from corresponding properties of addition and multiplication in the real numbers, showing that the set of all k-forms on A forms a vector space. Proving familiar-looking facts about addition and scalar multiplication of forms reduces quickly to citing the analogous facts in $\mathbb{R}$. For example, $(-1)\omega = -\omega$ for every k-form ω (where the second minus sign denotes additive inverse), because for every k-surface Φ,

$$(\omega + (-1)\omega)(\Phi) = \omega(\Phi) + ((-1)\omega)(\Phi) = \omega(\Phi) + (-1)(\omega(\Phi)) = 0,$$

the last equality holding since $(-1)x = -x$ for all real numbers x.

Forms have other algebraic properties that are less familiar. For example, on $\mathbb{R}^2$, $dy \wedge dx = -dx \wedge dy$. This rule follows from the skew symmetry of the determinant: for any 2-surface $\Phi : D \longrightarrow \mathbb{R}^2$,

$$(dy \wedge dx)(\Phi) = \int_D \det \Phi'_{(2,1)} = -\int_D \det \Phi'_{(1,2)} = -(dx \wedge dy)(\Phi).$$

More generally, given two k-tuples I and J from $\{1, \dots, n\}$, $dx_J = -dx_I$ if J is obtained from I by an odd number of transpositions. Thus for example,

$$dz \wedge dy \wedge dx = -dx \wedge dy \wedge dz$$

since $(3, 2, 1)$ is obtained from $(1, 2, 3)$ by swapping the first and third entries. Showing this reduces again to the skew symmetry of the determinant. As a special case, $dx_I = 0$ whenever the k-tuple I has two matching entries. This rule holds because exchanging those matching entries has no effect on I but gives the negative of dx_I, and so $dx_I = -dx_I$, forcing $dx_I = 0$. One can also verify directly that $dx_I = 0$ if I has matching entries by referring back to the fact that the determinant of a matrix with matching rows vanishes.

Using these rules ($dy \wedge dx = -dx \wedge dy$, $dx \wedge dx = 0$, and their generalizations), one quickly convinces oneself that every k-form can be written

$$\omega = \sum_I f_I \, dx_I \quad \text{(sum only over increasing } I\text{)},$$

where a k-tuple $I = (i_1, \dots, i_k)$ is called *increasing* if $i_1 < \cdots < i_k$, as mentioned in Exercise 9.3.1. This is the standard presentation for ω mentioned in Exercise 9.3.2. It is not hard to show that the standard presentation for ω is unique. In particular, ω is identically zero as a function of surfaces if and only if ω has standard presentation 0.

The next few sections will define certain operations on forms and develop rules of algebra for manipulating the forms under these operations. Like other rules of algebra, they will be unfamiliar at first and deserve to be scrutinized critically, but eventually they should become second nature and you should find yourself skipping steps fluently.

Exercise

9.6.1. Show that if ω is a k-form on $\mathbb{R}^n$ that satisfies $\omega = -\omega$, then $\omega = 0$.

9.7 Algebra of Forms: Multiplication

Given a k-tuple and an ℓ-tuple, both from $\{1,\ldots,n\}$,

$$I = (i_1,\ldots,i_k) \quad \text{and} \quad J = (j_1,\ldots,j_\ell),$$

define their concatenation (I,J), a $(k+\ell)$-tuple from $\{1,\ldots,n\}$, in the obvious way,

$$(I,J) = (i_1,\ldots,i_k,j_1,\ldots,j_\ell).$$

Also, if $f,g : A \longrightarrow \mathbb{R}$ are functions on an open subset of $\mathbb{R}^n$ then their product fg is the function

$$fg : A \longrightarrow \mathbb{R}, \quad (fg)(x) = f(x)g(x).$$

Definition 9.7.1 (Wedge product). *Let A be an open subset of $\mathbb{R}^n$. If $\omega = \sum_I f_I\,dx_I$ and $\lambda = \sum_J g_J\,dx_J$ are respectively a k-form and an ℓ-form on A, then their* **wedge product** *$\omega \wedge \lambda$ is a $(k+\ell)$-form on A,*

$$\omega \wedge \lambda = \sum_{I,J} f_I g_J\,dx_{(I,J)}.$$

That is, the wedge product is formed by following the usual distributive law and wedge-concatenating the dx-terms.

For convenient notation, let $\Lambda^k(A)$ denote the vector space of k-forms on A. Thus the wedge product is a mapping,

$$\wedge : \Lambda^k(A) \times \Lambda^\ell(A) \longrightarrow \Lambda^{k+\ell}(A).$$

For example, a wedge product of a 1-form and a 2-form on $\mathbb{R}^3$ is

$$(f_1\,dx + f_2\,dy + f_3\,dz) \wedge (g_1\,dy \wedge dz + g_2\,dz \wedge dx + g_3\,dx \wedge dy)$$
$$= f_1 g_1\,dx \wedge dy \wedge dz + f_1 g_2\,dx \wedge dz \wedge dx + f_1 g_3\,dx \wedge dx \wedge dy$$
$$+ f_2 g_1\,dy \wedge dy \wedge dz + f_2 g_2\,dy \wedge dz \wedge dx + f_2 g_3\,dy \wedge dx \wedge dy$$
$$+ f_3 g_1\,dz \wedge dy \wedge dz + f_3 g_2\,dz \wedge dz \wedge dx + f_3 g_3\,dz \wedge dx \wedge dy$$
$$= (f_1 g_1 + f_2 g_2 + f_3 g_3)\,dx \wedge dy \wedge dz.$$

This example shows that the wedge product automatically encodes the inner product in $\mathbb{R}^3$, and the idea generalizes easily to $\mathbb{R}^n$. For another example, a wedge product of two 1-forms on $\mathbb{R}^3$ is

$$(x_u\,dx + y_u\,dy + z_u\,dz) \wedge (x_v\,dx + y_v\,dy + z_v\,dz)$$
$$= (y_u z_v - z_u y_v)\,dy \wedge dz + (z_u x_v - x_u z_v)\,dz \wedge dx + (x_u y_v - y_u x_v)\,dx \wedge dy.$$

Comparing this to the formula for the cross product in Section 3.10 shows that the wedge product automatically encodes the cross product. Similarly, a wedge product of two 1-forms on $\mathbb{R}^2$ is

$$(a\,dx + b\,dy) \wedge (c\,dx + d\,dy) = (ad - bc)\,dx \wedge dy,$$

showing that the wedge product encodes the 2×2 determinant as well. Lemma 9.9.2 to follow will show that it encodes the general $n \times n$ determinant.

Naturally the wedge in Definition 9.7.1 is the same as the one in Definition 9.3.1. There is no conflict in now saying that the two wedges are the same, since each wedge in the earlier definition sits between two 1-forms, and the definition attached no meaning to the wedge symbol. Definition 9.3.1 also juxtaposes functions (0-forms) and dx_I terms (k-forms) without putting a wedge between them, and it is still unclear what sort of multiplication that juxtaposition connotes. In fact, it is also a wedge product, but when we wedge-multiply a 0-form and a k-form, we usually suppress the wedge. A basic property of the wedge, its skew symmetry, will explain why in a moment.

Proposition 9.7.2 (Properties of the wedge product). *Let A be an open subset of $\mathbb{R}^n$. The wedge product has the following properties.*

(1) *The wedge product distributes over form addition: for all $\omega \in \Lambda^k(A)$ and $\lambda_1, \lambda_2 \in \Lambda^\ell(A)$,*

$$\omega \wedge (\lambda_1 + \lambda_2) = \omega \wedge \lambda_1 + \omega \wedge \lambda_2.$$

(2) *The wedge product is associative: for all $\omega \in \Lambda^k(A)$, $\lambda \in \Lambda^\ell(A)$, and $\mu \in \Lambda^m(A)$,*

$$(\omega \wedge \lambda) \wedge \mu = \omega \wedge (\lambda \wedge \mu).$$

(3) *The wedge product is skew symmetric: for all $\omega \in \Lambda^k(A)$ and $\lambda \in \Lambda^\ell(A)$,*

$$\lambda \wedge \omega = (-1)^{k\ell} \omega \wedge \lambda.$$

The proof is an exercise. The unfamiliar (and hence interesting) property is the third one. The essence of its proof is to show that for every k-tuple I and every ℓ-tuple J,

$$dx_J \wedge dx_I = (-1)^{k\ell}\,dx_I \wedge dx_J.$$

This formula follows from counting transpositions.

Note that the skew symmetry of the wedge product reduces to symmetry (i.e., commutativity) when either of the forms being multiplied is a 0-form. The symmetry is why one generally doesn't bother writing the wedge when a 0-form is involved. In fact, the wedge symbol is unnecessary in all cases, and typically in multivariable calculus one sees, for example,

$$dx\,dy\,dz \quad \text{rather than} \quad dx \wedge dy \wedge dz.$$

Indeed, we could use mere juxtaposition to denote form-multiplication, but because this new multiplication obeys unfamiliar rules, we give it a new symbol to remind us of its novel properties as we study it.

Also, the special case of multiplying a constant function c and a k-form ω is consistent with scalar multiplication of c (viewed now as a real number) and ω. Thus all of our notions of multiplication are compatible.

Exercises

9.7.1. Find a wedge product of two differential forms that encodes the inner product of $\mathbb{R}^4$.

9.7.2. Find a wedge product of three differential forms that encodes the 3×3 determinant.

9.7.3. Prove the properties of the wedge product.

9.7.4. Prove that $(\omega_1 + \omega_2) \wedge \lambda = \omega_1 \wedge \lambda + \omega_2 \wedge \lambda$ for all $\omega_1, \omega_2 \in \Lambda^k(A)$ and $\lambda \in \Lambda^\ell(A)$. (Use skew symmetry, distributivity, and skew symmetry again.)

9.8 Algebra of Forms: Differentiation

Definition 9.8.1 (Derivative of a differential form). *Let A be an open subset of $\mathbb{R}^n$. For each integer $k \geq 0$ define the derivative mapping,*

$$d : \Lambda^k(A) \longrightarrow \Lambda^{k+1}(A),$$

by the rules

$$df = \sum_{i=1}^{n} D_i f \, dx_i \quad \text{for a 0-form } f,$$

$$d\omega = \sum_I df_I \wedge dx_I \quad \text{for a k-form } \omega = \sum_I f_I \, dx_I.$$

For example, we saw in Section 9.4 that for a function f, the 1-form

$$df = D_1 f \, dx_1 + \cdots + D_n f \, dx_n$$

is the form that measures change in f along curves. To practice this new kind of function-differentiation in a specific case, define the function

$$\pi_1 : \mathbb{R}^3 \longrightarrow \mathbb{R}$$

to be projection onto the first coordinate,

$$\pi_1(x, y, z) = x \quad \text{for all } (x, y, z) \in \mathbb{R}^3.$$

Then by the definition of the derivative,

$$d\pi_1 = D_1\pi_1 \, dx + D_2\pi_1 \, dy + D_3\pi_1 \, dz = dx. \tag{9.15}$$

This calculation is purely routine. In practice, however, one often blurs the distinction between the name of a function and its output, for instance speaking of *the function x^2* rather than *the function $f : \mathbb{R} \longrightarrow \mathbb{R}$ where $f(x) = x^2$* or *the squaring function on $\mathbb{R}$*. Such loose nomenclature is usually harmless enough and indeed downright essential in any explicit calculation in which we compute using a function's values. But if we blur the distinction here between the function π_1 and its output x then the calculation of $d\pi_1$ in (9.15) can be rewritten as

$$dx = dx. \quad (!)$$

This is not tautological: the two sides have different meanings. The left side is the operator d acting on the projection function x, while the right side is a single entity, the 1-form denoted dx. The equation is better written

$$d(x) = dx.$$

However it is written, this equality ensures that there is no possible conflict between naming the differential operator d and using this same letter as part of the definition of differential form.

Similarly, for a function $f : \mathbb{R} \longrightarrow \mathbb{R}$ of one variable, the definition of d immediately says that

$$df = \frac{df}{dx}\, dx,$$

where the single, indivisible symbol df/dx is the Leibniz notation for the derivative of f. This relation, which is sometimes presented in first-semester calculus with nebulous meanings attached to df and dx, and which can**NOT** be proved by cancellation, is now a relation between 1-forms that follows from the definition of d. The moral is that the operator d has been so named to make such vague, undefined formulas into definitions and theorems. For more examples of differentiation, if

$$\omega = x\, dy - y\, dx$$

then according to Definition 9.8.1,

$$d\omega = (D_1 x\, dx + D_2 x\, dy) \wedge dy - (D_1 y\, dx + D_2 y\, dy) \wedge dx = 2\, dx \wedge dy.$$

And if

$$\omega = x\, dy \wedge dz + y\, dz \wedge dx + z\, dx \wedge dy$$

then

$$d\omega = 3\, dx \wedge dy \wedge dz.$$

The differentiation operator d commutes with sums and scalar multiples. That is, if ω_1, ω_2 are k-forms and c is a constant then

$$d(c\omega_1 + \omega_2) = c\, d\omega_1 + d\omega_2.$$

More interesting are the following two theorems about form differentiation.

Theorem 9.8.2 (Product rule for differential forms). *Let A be an open subset of $\mathbb{R}^n$. Let ω and λ be respectively a k-form and an ℓ-form on A. Then*

$$d(\omega \wedge \lambda) = d\omega \wedge \lambda + (-1)^k \omega \wedge d\lambda.$$

Proof. Start with the case of 0-forms f and g. Then

$$
\begin{aligned}
\mathrm{d}(fg) &= \sum_{i=1}^{n} D_i(fg)\,\mathrm{d}x_i \\
&= \sum_{i=1}^{n} (D_i f\, g + f D_i g)\,\mathrm{d}x_i \\
&= \left(\sum_{i=1}^{n} D_i f\,\mathrm{d}x_i\right) g + f\left(\sum_{i=1}^{n} D_i g\,\mathrm{d}x_i\right) \\
&= \mathrm{d}f\, g + f\,\mathrm{d}g.
\end{aligned}
$$

Next consider a k-form and an ℓ-form with one term each, $f_I\,\mathrm{d}x_I$ and $g_J\,\mathrm{d}x_J$. Then

$$
\begin{aligned}
\mathrm{d}(f_I\,\mathrm{d}x_I \wedge g_J\,\mathrm{d}x_J) &= \mathrm{d}(f_I g_J\,\mathrm{d}x_I \wedge \mathrm{d}x_J) && \text{by definition of multiplication} \\
&= \mathrm{d}(f_I g_J) \wedge \mathrm{d}x_I \wedge \mathrm{d}x_J && \text{by definition of d} \\
&= (\mathrm{d}f_I g_J + f_I \mathrm{d}g_J) \wedge \mathrm{d}x_I \wedge \mathrm{d}x_J && \text{by the result for 0-forms} \\
&= \mathrm{d}f_I(g_J \wedge \mathrm{d}x_I) \wedge \mathrm{d}x_J && \text{by distributivity} \\
&\quad + f_I(\mathrm{d}g_J \wedge \mathrm{d}x_I) \wedge \mathrm{d}x_J && \text{and associativity of } \wedge \\
&= \mathrm{d}f_I \wedge (-1)^{0 \cdot k}(\mathrm{d}x_I \wedge g_J) \wedge \mathrm{d}x_J && \\
&\quad + f_I(-1)^{1 \cdot k}(\mathrm{d}x_I \wedge \mathrm{d}g_J) \wedge \mathrm{d}x_J && \text{by skew symmetry} \\
&= \mathrm{d}(f_I \wedge \mathrm{d}x_I) \wedge g_J\mathrm{d}x_J && \text{by associativity and symmetry} \\
&\quad + (-1)^k f_I\mathrm{d}x_I \wedge \mathrm{d}(g_J \wedge \mathrm{d}x_J) && \text{and definition of d.}
\end{aligned}
$$

Finally, in the general case, $\omega = \sum_I \omega_I$ and $\lambda = \sum_J \lambda_J$, where each ω_I is equal to $f_I\,\mathrm{d}x_I$ and each λ_J is equal to $g_J\,\mathrm{d}x_J$, quoting the one-term result at the third equality,

$$
\begin{aligned}
\mathrm{d}(\omega \wedge \lambda) &= \mathrm{d}\left(\sum_I \omega_I \wedge \sum_J \lambda_J\right) = \sum_{I,J} \mathrm{d}(\omega_I \wedge \lambda_J) \\
&= \sum_{I,J}(\mathrm{d}\omega_I \wedge \lambda_J + (-1)^k \omega_I \wedge \mathrm{d}\lambda_J) \\
&= \mathrm{d}\sum_I \omega_I \wedge \sum_J \lambda_J + (-1)^k \sum_I \omega_I \wedge \mathrm{d}\sum_J \lambda_J \\
&= \mathrm{d}\omega \wedge \lambda + (-1)^k \omega \wedge \mathrm{d}\lambda.
\end{aligned}
$$

$\square$

Because the last step in this proof consisted only in pushing sums tediously through the other operations, typically it will be omitted from now on, and proofs will be carried out for the case of one-term forms.

Consider a function $f(x, y)$ on $\mathbb{R}^2$. Its derivative is

$$df = D_1 f(x,y)\,dx + D_2 f(x,y)\,dy,$$

and its second derivative is in turn

$$d^2 f = d(df) = d(D_1 f(x,y)\,dx) + d(D_2 f(x,y)\,dy)$$
$$= D_{11} f(x,y)\,dx \wedge dx + D_{12} f(x,y)\,dy \wedge dx$$
$$+ D_{21} f(x,y)\,dx \wedge dy + D_{22} f(x,y)\,dy \wedge dy.$$

The $dx \wedge dx$ term and the $dy \wedge dy$ term are both 0. And the other two terms sum to 0, because the mixed partial derivatives $D_{12}f(x,y)$ and $D_{21}f(x,y)$ are equal while $dy \wedge dx$ and $dx \wedge dy$ are opposite. Overall, then,

$$d^2 f = 0.$$

This phenomenon of the second derivative vanishing is completely general.

Theorem 9.8.3 (Nilpotence of d). *Let A be an open subset of $\mathbb{R}^n$. Then $d^2 \omega = 0$ for every form $\omega \in \Lambda^k(A)$, where d^2 means $d \circ d$. In other words,*

$$d^2 = 0.$$

Proof. For a 0-form f,

$$df = \sum_{i=1}^{n} D_i f\,dx_i,$$

and so

$$d^2 f = d(df) = \sum_{i=1}^{n} d(D_i f) \wedge dx_i = \sum_{i,j} D_{ij} f\,dx_j \wedge dx_i.$$

All terms with $i = j$ cancel because $dx_i \wedge dx_i = 0$, and the rest of the terms cancel pairwise because for $i \neq j$, $D_{ji}f = D_{ij}f$ (equality of mixed partial derivatives) and $dx_i \wedge dx_j = -dx_j \wedge dx_i$ (skew symmetry of the wedge product). Thus

$$d^2 f = 0.$$

Also, for a k-form dx_I with constant coefficient function 1,

$$d(dx_I) = d(1dx_I) = (d1) \wedge dx_I = 0.$$

Next, for a one-term k-form $\omega = f\,dx_I$,

$$d\omega = df \wedge dx_I,$$

and so by the first two calculations,

$$d^2 \omega = d(df \wedge dx_I) = d^2 f \wedge dx_I + (-1)^1 df \wedge d(dx_I) = 0 + 0 = 0.$$

For a general k-form, pass sums and d^2s through each other.   □

A form ω is called

$$\textbf{exact if } \omega = d\lambda \text{ for some form } \lambda$$

and

$$\textbf{closed if } d\omega = 0.$$

Theorem 9.8.3 shows that:

Every exact form is closed.

The converse question, whether every closed form is exact, is more subtle. We will discuss it in Section 9.11.

Exercises

9.8.1. Let $\omega = f\,dx + g\,dy + h\,dz$. Show that

$$d\omega = (D_2 h - D_3 g)\,dy \wedge dz + (D_3 f - D_1 h)\,dz \wedge dx + (D_1 g - D_2 f)\,dx \wedge dy.$$

9.8.2. Let $\omega = f\,dy \wedge dz + g\,dz \wedge dx + h\,dx \wedge dy$. Evaluate $d\omega$.

9.8.3. Differential forms of orders $0, 1, 2, 3$ on $\mathbb{R}^3$ are written

$$\begin{aligned}
\omega_0 &= \phi, \\
\omega_1 &= f_1\,dx + f_2\,dy + f_3\,dz, \\
\omega_2 &= g_1\,dy \wedge dz + g_2\,dz \wedge dx + g_3\,dx \wedge dy, \\
\omega_3 &= h\,dx \wedge dy \wedge dz.
\end{aligned}$$

(a) For a 0-form ϕ, what are the coefficients f_i of $d\phi$ in terms of ϕ?

(b) For a 1-form ω_1, what are the coefficients g_i of $d\omega_1$ in terms of the coefficients f_i of ω_1?

(c) For a 2-form ω_2, what is the coefficient h of $d\omega_2$ in terms of the coefficients g_i of ω_2?

9.8.4. Classical vector analysis features the operator

$$\nabla = (D_1, D_2, D_3),$$

where the D_i are familiar partial derivative operators. Thus, for a function $\phi : \mathbb{R}^3 \longrightarrow \mathbb{R}$,

$$\nabla\phi = (D_1\phi, D_2\phi, D_3\phi).$$

Similarly, for a mapping $F = (f_1, f_2, f_3) : \mathbb{R}^3 \longrightarrow \mathbb{R}^3$, $\nabla \times F$ is defined in the symbolically appropriate way, and for a mapping $G = (g_1, g_2, g_3) : \mathbb{R}^3 \longrightarrow \mathbb{R}^3$, so is $\langle \nabla, G \rangle$. Write down explicitly the vector-valued mapping $\nabla \times F$ and the function $\langle \nabla, G \rangle$ for F and G as just described. The vector-valued mapping $\nabla\phi$ is the **gradient** of ϕ from Section 4.8,

$$\operatorname{grad}\phi = \nabla\phi.$$

The vector-valued mapping $\nabla \times F$ is the **curl** of F,

$$\operatorname{curl} F = \nabla \times F.$$

And the scalar-valued function $\langle \nabla, G \rangle$ is the **divergence** of G,

$$\operatorname{div} G = \langle \nabla, G \rangle.$$

9.8.5. Continuing with the notation of the previous two problems, introduce correspondences between the classical scalar–vector environment and the environment of differential forms, as follows. Let

$$\vec{ds} = (dx, dy, dz),$$
$$\vec{dn} = (dy \wedge dz, dz \wedge dx, dx \wedge dy),$$
$$dV = dx \wedge dy \wedge dz.$$

Let id be the mapping that takes each function $\phi : \mathbb{R}^3 \longrightarrow \mathbb{R}$ to itself, but with the output-copy of ϕ viewed as a 0-form. Let $\cdot\vec{ds}$ be the mapping that takes each vector-valued mapping $F = (f_1, f_2, f_3)$ to the 1-form

$$F \cdot \vec{ds} = f_1\, dx + f_2\, dy + f_3\, dz.$$

Let $\cdot\vec{dn}$ be the mapping that takes each vector-valued mapping $G = (g_1, g_2, g_3)$ to the 2-form

$$G \cdot \vec{dn} = g_1\, dy \wedge dz + g_2\, dz \wedge dx + g_3\, dx \wedge dy.$$

And let dV be the mapping that takes each function h to the 3-form

$$h\, dV = h\, dx \wedge dy \wedge dz.$$

Combine the previous problems to verify that the following diagram commutes, meaning that either path around each square yields the same result. (Do each square separately, e.g., for the middle square start from an arbitrary (f_1, f_2, f_3) with no assumption that it is the gradient of some function ϕ.)

$$
\begin{array}{ccccccc}
\phi & \xrightarrow{\;\text{grad}\;} & (f_1, f_2, f_3) & \xrightarrow{\;\text{curl}\;} & (g_1, g_2, g_3) & \xrightarrow{\;\text{div}\;} & h \\[4pt]
\Big\downarrow{\scriptstyle \text{id}} & & \Big\downarrow{\scriptstyle \cdot\vec{ds}} & & \Big\downarrow{\scriptstyle \cdot\vec{dn}} & & \Big\downarrow{\scriptstyle dV} \\[4pt]
\phi & \xrightarrow{\;d\;} & \begin{array}{l} f_1\, dx \\ +f_2\, dy \\ +f_3\, dz \end{array} & \xrightarrow{\;d\;} & \begin{array}{l} g_1\, dy \wedge dz \\ +g_2\, dz \wedge dx \\ +g_3\, dx \wedge dy \end{array} & \xrightarrow{\;d\;} & h\, dx \wedge dy \wedge dz
\end{array}
$$

Thus the form-differentiation operator d, specialized to three dimensions, unifies the classical gradient, divergence, and curl operators.

9.8.6. Two of these operators are zero:

$$\text{curl} \circ \text{grad}, \quad \text{div} \circ \text{curl}, \quad \text{div} \circ \text{grad}.$$

Explain, using the diagram from the preceding exercise and the nilpotence of d. For a function $\phi : \mathbb{R}^3 \longrightarrow \mathbb{R}$, write out the **harmonic equation** (or **Laplace's equation**), which does not automatically hold for all ϕ but turns out to be an interesting condition,

$$\text{div}(\text{grad}\,\phi) = 0.$$

9.9 Algebra of Forms: The Pullback

Recall the change of variable theorem from Chapter 6: given a change of variable mapping now called T (rather than Φ as in Chapter 6) and given a function f on the range space of T, the appropriate function to integrate over the domain is obtained by composing with T and multiplying by an absolute determinant factor,

$$\int_{T(D)} f = \int_D (f \circ T) \cdot |\det T'|.$$

A generalization to forms of the notion of composing with T lets us similarly transfer forms—rather than functions—from the range space of a mapping T to the domain. This generalization will naturally include a determinant factor that is no longer encumbered by absolute value signs. The next section will show that integration of differential forms is inherently invariant under change of variable.

We start with some examples. The familiar polar coordinate mapping from (r,θ)-space to (x,y)-space is

$$(x,y) = T(r,\theta) = (r\cos\theta, r\sin\theta).$$

Using this formula, and thinking of T as mapping from (r,θ)-space *forward* to (x,y)-space, every form on (x,y)-space can naturally be converted *back* into a form on (r,θ)-space, simply by substituting $r\cos\theta$ for x and $r\sin\theta$ for y. If the form on (x,y)-space is named λ then the form on (r,θ)-space is denoted $T^*\lambda$. For example, the 2-form that gives area on (x,y)-space,

$$\lambda = \mathrm{d}x \wedge \mathrm{d}y,$$

has a naturally corresponding 2-form on (r,θ)-space,

$$T^*\lambda = \mathrm{d}(r\cos\theta) \wedge \mathrm{d}(r\sin\theta).$$

Working out the derivatives and then the wedge shows that

$$T^*\lambda = (\cos\theta\,dr - r\sin\theta\,d\theta) \wedge (\sin\theta\,dr + r\cos\theta\,d\theta)$$
$$= r\,dr \wedge d\theta.$$

Thus (now dropping the wedges from the notation), this process has converted $dx\,dy$ into $r\,dr\,d\theta$ as required by the change of variable theorem.

For another example, continue to let T denote the polar coordinate mapping, and consider a 1-form on (x, y)-space (for $(x, y) \neq (0, 0)$),

$$\omega = \frac{x\,dy - y\,dx}{x^2 + y^2}.$$

The corresponding 1-form on (r, θ)-space (for $r > 0$) is

$$T^*\omega = \frac{r\cos\theta\,d(r\sin\theta) - r\sin\theta\,d(r\cos\theta)}{(r\cos\theta)^2 + (r\sin\theta)^2}.$$

Here the differentiations give

$$d(r\sin\theta) = \sin\theta\,dr + r\cos\theta\,d\theta, \quad d(r\cos\theta) = \cos\theta\,dr - r\sin\theta\,d\theta,$$

and so the form on (r, θ)-space is

$$T^*\omega = \frac{r\cos\theta(\sin\theta\,dr + r\cos\theta\,d\theta) - r\sin\theta(\cos\theta\,dr - r\sin\theta\,d\theta)}{r^2} = d\theta.$$

This result suggests that integrating ω over a curve in (x, y)-space will return the change in angle along the curve. For example, integrating ω counterclockwise over the unit circle should return 2π.

Geometrically, let $\gamma : I \longrightarrow \mathbb{R}^2 - \{\mathbf{0}\}$ be a parametrized curve, let $p = (x, y) = \gamma(t)$ be a point on the curve, and view the unary cross product $(x, y)^\times = (-y, x)$ as a vector originating at p, pointing in the direction of increasing polar angle θ. The tangent vector $\gamma'(t) = (x'(t), y'(t))$ has component length along the unary cross product vector as follows,

$$\frac{\langle (x', y'), (-y, x) \rangle}{|(-y, x)|} = \frac{xy' - yx'}{\sqrt{x^2 + y^2}}.$$

(See Figure 9.10.) To infinitesimalize this, multiply it by dt, and then, to make the resulting form measure infinitesimal change in the polar angle θ along the curve, we also need to divide by the distance from the origin to get altogether $(x\,dy - y\,dx)/(x^2 + y^2)$.

For a third example, again start with the 1-form

$$\omega = \frac{x\,dy - y\,dx}{x^2 + y^2},$$

but this time consider a different change of variable mapping,

$$(x, y) = T(u, v) = (u^2 - v^2, 2uv).$$

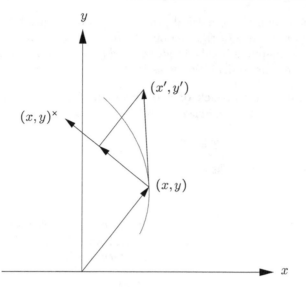

Figure 9.10. Angular component of the tangent vector

The 1-form on (u,v)-space (for $(u,v) \neq (0,0)$) corresponding to ω is now

$$T^*\omega = \frac{(u^2 - v^2)\,\mathrm{d}(2uv) - 2uv\,\mathrm{d}(u^2 - v^2)}{(u^2 - v^2)^2 + (2uv)^2}.$$

The derivatives are

$$\mathrm{d}(2uv) = 2(v\,\mathrm{d}u + u\,\mathrm{d}v), \quad \mathrm{d}(u^2 - v^2) = 2(u\,\mathrm{d}u - v\,\mathrm{d}v),$$

and so

$$T^*\omega = 2\frac{(u^2 - v^2)(v\,\mathrm{d}u + u\,\mathrm{d}v) - 2uv(u\,\mathrm{d}u - v\,\mathrm{d}v)}{(u^2 + v^2)^2}$$

$$= 2\frac{((u^2 - v^2)v - 2u^2v)\,\mathrm{d}u + ((u^2 - v^2)u + 2uv^2)\,\mathrm{d}v}{(u^2 + v^2)^2}$$

$$= 2\frac{u\,\mathrm{d}v - v\,\mathrm{d}u}{u^2 + v^2}.$$

Thus $T^*\omega$ is essentially the original form, except that it is doubled, and now it is a form on (u,v)-space. The result of the calculation stems from the fact that T is the complex square mapping, which doubles angles. The original form ω, which measures change of angle in (x,y)-space, has transformed back to the form that measures twice the change of angle in (u,v)-space. Integrating $T^*\omega$ along a curve γ in (u,v)-space that misses the origin returns twice the change in angle along this curve, and this is the change in angle along the image-curve $T \circ \gamma$ in (x,y)-space.

Given a mapping, the natural process of changing variables in a differential form on the range of the mapping to produce a differential form on the domain of the mapping is called *pulling the differential form back* through the mapping. The general definition is as follows.

Definition 9.9.1 (Pullback of a differential form). *Let k be a nonnegative integer. Let A be an open subset of $\mathbb{R}^n$, and let B be an open subset of $\mathbb{R}^m$. Let*

$$T = (T_1, \ldots, T_m) : A \longrightarrow B$$

be a smooth mapping. Then T gives rise to a **pullback** *mapping of k-forms in the other direction,*

$$T^* : \Lambda^k(B) \longrightarrow \Lambda^k(A).$$

Let the coordinates on $\mathbb{R}^n$ be $(x_1, \ldots, x_n)$, and let the coordinates on $\mathbb{R}^m$ be $(y_1, \ldots, y_m)$. For each k-tuple $I = (i_1, \ldots, i_k)$ from $\{1, \ldots, m\}$, let $\mathrm{d}T_I$ denote $\mathrm{d}T_{i_1} \wedge \cdots \wedge \mathrm{d}T_{i_k}$. Then the pullback of a k-form on B,

$$\omega = \sum f_I \, \mathrm{d}y_I,$$

is

$$T^* \omega = \sum_I (f_I \circ T) \, \mathrm{d}T_I.$$

Since each T_{i_j} is a function on A, each $\mathrm{d}T_{i_j}$ is a 1-form on A, and the definition makes sense. As usual, when $k = 0$, the empty products $\mathrm{d}y_I$ and $\mathrm{d}T_I$ are interpreted as 1, and the pullback is simply composition,

$$T^* f = f \circ T.$$

As the examples before the definition have shown, computing pullbacks is easy and purely mechanical: given a form ω in terms of y's and $\mathrm{d}y$'s, its pullback $T^* \omega$ comes from replacing each y_i in ω by the expression $T_i(x_1, \ldots, x_n)$ and then working out the resulting d's and wedges.

The fact that pulling the form $\mathrm{d}x \wedge \mathrm{d}y$ back through the polar coordinate mapping produced the factor r from the change of variable theorem is no coincidence.

Lemma 9.9.2 (Wedge–determinant lemma). *Define an n-form-valued function Δ on n-tuples of n-vectors as follows. For n vectors in $\mathbb{R}^n$,*

$$a_1 = (a_{11}, a_{12}, \ldots, a_{1n}),$$
$$a_2 = (a_{21}, a_{22}, \ldots, a_{2n}),$$
$$\vdots$$
$$a_n = (a_{n1}, a_{n2}, \ldots, a_{nn}),$$

create the corresponding 1-forms,

$$\omega_1 = a_{11}\,dx_1 + a_{12}\,dx_2 + \cdots + a_{1n}\,dx_n,$$
$$\omega_2 = a_{21}\,dx_1 + a_{22}\,dx_2 + \cdots + a_{2n}\,dx_n,$$
$$\vdots$$
$$\omega_n = a_{n1}\,dx_1 + a_{n2}\,dx_2 + \cdots + a_{nn}\,dx_n,$$

and then define

$$\Delta(a_1, a_2, \ldots, a_n) = \omega_1 \wedge \omega_2 \wedge \cdots \wedge \omega_n.$$

Then

$$\Delta(a_1, a_2, \ldots, a_n) = \det(a_1, a_2, \ldots, a_n)\,dx_1 \wedge \cdots \wedge dx_n.$$

That is, $\Delta = \det \cdot dx_{(1,\ldots,n)}$.

We have already seen this result for $n = 2$ in Section 9.7 and for $n = 3$ in Exercise 9.7.2.

Proof. The only increasing n-tuple from $\{1, \ldots, n\}$ is $(1, \ldots, n)$. As a product of n 1-forms on $\mathbb{R}^n$, $\Delta(a_1, a_2, \ldots, a_n)$ is an n-form on $\mathbb{R}^n$, and therefore it is a scalar-valued function $\delta(a_1, a_2, \ldots, a_n)$ times $dx_{(1,\ldots,n)}$. The relation

$$\delta(a_1, a_2, \ldots, a_n)\,dx_{(1,\ldots,n)} = \omega_1 \wedge \omega_2 \wedge \cdots \wedge \omega_n,$$

where ω_i is the inner product $a_i \cdot (dx_1, \ldots, dx_n)$ for each i, combines with various properties of the wedge product to show that the following three conditions hold:

- The function δ is linear in each of its vector variables, e.g.,

$$\delta(a_1, a_2 + \tilde{a}_2, \ldots, a_n) = \delta(a_1, a_2, \ldots, a_n) + \delta(a_1, \tilde{a}_2, \ldots, a_n)$$

and

$$\delta(a_1, ca_2, \ldots, a_n) = c\,\delta(a_1, a_2, \ldots, a_n).$$

- The function δ is skew-symmetric, i.e., transposing two of its vector variables changes its sign.
- The function δ is normalized, i.e., $\delta(e_1, e_2, \ldots, e_n) = 1$.

The determinant is the unique function satisfying these three conditions, so $\delta = \det$. $\qquad\square$

Theorem 9.9.3 (Pullback–determinant theorem). *Let A be an open subset of $\mathbb{R}^n$, and let B be an open subset of $\mathbb{R}^m$. Let $T : A \longrightarrow B$ be a smooth mapping. Let $\mathbb{R}^n$ have coordinates $(x_1, \ldots, x_n)$, and let $\mathbb{R}^m$ have coordinates $(y_1, \ldots, y_m)$. Let $I = (i_1, \ldots, i_n)$ be an n-tuple from $\{1, \ldots, m\}$. Then*

$$T^*dy_I = \det T'_I\,dx_1 \wedge \cdots \wedge dx_n.$$

Proof. By definition,

$$T^* dy_I = dT_I = dT_{i_1} \wedge \cdots \wedge dT_{i_n}$$
$$= (D_1 T_{i_1} dx_1 + \cdots + D_n T_{i_1} dx_n)$$
$$\wedge (D_1 T_{i_2} dx_1 + \cdots + D_n T_{i_2} dx_n)$$
$$\vdots$$
$$\wedge (D_1 T_{i_n} dx_1 + \cdots + D_n T_{i_n} dx_n).$$

The right side is precisely $\Delta(T'_{i_1}, T'_{i_2}, \ldots, T'_{i_n})$, so the lemma completes the proof.   □

In particular, when $m = n$ and $I = (1, \ldots, n)$, the theorem says that

$$T^* (dy_1 \wedge \cdots \wedge dy_n) = \det T' \, dx_1 \wedge \cdots \wedge dx_n,$$

confirming the polar coordinate example early in this section. Similarly, if T is the spherical coordinate mapping,

$$T(\rho, \theta, \phi) = (\rho \cos \theta \sin \phi, \rho \sin \theta \sin \phi, \rho \cos \phi),$$

then the theorem tells us that

$$T^* (dx \wedge dy \wedge dz) = -\rho^2 \sin \phi \, d\rho \wedge d\theta \wedge d\phi.$$

You may want to verify this directly to get a better feel for the pullback and the lemma. In general, the pullback–determinant theorem can be a big time-saver for computing pullbacks when the degree of the form equals the dimension of the domain space. Instead of multiplying out lots of wedge products, simply compute the relevant subdeterminant of a derivative matrix.

What makes the integration of differential forms invariant under change of variable is that the pullback operator commutes with everything else in sight.

Theorem 9.9.4 (Properties of the pullback). *Let A be an open subset of $\mathbb{R}^n$, and let B be an open subset of $\mathbb{R}^m$. Let $T = (T_1, \ldots, T_m) : A \longrightarrow B$ be a smooth mapping. Then:*

(1) For all $\omega_1, \omega_2, \omega \in \Lambda^k(B)$ and $c \in \mathbb{R}$,

$$T^* (\omega_1 + \omega_2) = T^* \omega_1 + T^* \omega_2,$$
$$T^* (c\omega) = c T^* \omega.$$

(2) For all $\omega \in \Lambda^k(B)$ and $\lambda \in \Lambda^\ell(B)$,

$$T^* (\omega \wedge \lambda) = (T^* \omega) \wedge (T^* \lambda).$$

(3) For all $\omega \in \Lambda^k(B)$,

$$T^* (d\omega) = d(T^* \omega).$$

That is, the pullback is linear, the pullback is multiplicative (meaning that it preserves products), and the pullback of the derivative is the derivative of the pullback. The results in the theorem can be expressed in commutative diagrams, as in Exercise 9.8.5. Part (2) says that the following diagram commutes:

$$
\begin{array}{ccc}
\Lambda^k(B) \times \Lambda^\ell(B) & \xrightarrow{\;(T^*,T^*)\;} & \Lambda^k(A) \times \Lambda^\ell(A) \\
{\scriptstyle \wedge}\downarrow & & \downarrow{\scriptstyle \wedge} \\
\Lambda^{k+\ell}(B) & \xrightarrow{\;\;T^*\;\;} & \Lambda^{k+\ell}(A),
\end{array}
$$

and part (3) says that the following diagram commutes:

$$
\begin{array}{ccc}
\Lambda^k(B) & \xrightarrow{\;T^*\;} & \Lambda^k(A) \\
{\scriptstyle d}\downarrow & & \downarrow{\scriptstyle d} \\
\Lambda^{k+1}(B) & \xrightarrow{\;T^*\;} & \Lambda^{k+1}(A).
\end{array}
$$

All of this is especially gratifying because the pullback itself is entirely natural. Furthermore, the proofs are straightforward: all we need to do is compute, apply definitions, and recognize definitions. The only obstacle is that the process requires patience.

Proof. (1) Is immediate from the definition.

(2) For one-term forms $f \, dy_I$ and $g \, dy_J$,

$$
\begin{aligned}
T^*(f \, dy_I \wedge g \, dy_J) &= T^*(fg \, dy_{(I,J)}) && \text{by definition of multiplication} \\
&= (fg) \circ T \, dT_{(I,J)} && \text{by definition of the pullback} \\
&= f \circ T \, dT_I \wedge g \circ T \, dT_J && \text{since } (fg) \circ T = (f \circ T)(g \circ T) \\
&= T^*(f \, dy_I) \wedge T^*(g \, dy_J) && \text{by definition of the pullback.}
\end{aligned}
$$

The result on multiterm forms follows from this and (1).

(3) For a 0-form $f : \mathbb{R}^m \longrightarrow \mathbb{R}$, compute that

$$
T^*(df) = T^*\Big(\sum_{i=1}^m D_i f \, dy_i\Big) \qquad \text{applying the definition of d}
$$

$$
= \sum_{i=1}^m (D_i f \circ T) \, dT_i \qquad \begin{array}{l}\text{applying the definition}\\\text{of the pullback}\end{array}
$$

$$
= \sum_{i=1}^m D_i f \circ T \cdot \sum_{j=1}^n D_j T_i \, dx_j \qquad \text{applying the definition of d}
$$

$$
= \sum_{j=1}^n \Big[\sum_{i=1}^m (D_i f \circ T) \cdot D_j T_i\Big] dx_j \qquad \text{interchanging the sums}
$$

$$
= \sum_{j=1}^n D_j(f \circ T) \, dx_j \qquad \text{recognizing the chain rule}
$$

$$= d(f \circ T) \qquad \text{recognizing the definition of d}$$
$$= d(T^* f) \qquad \text{recognizing the pullback.}$$

For a one-term k-form $f \, dy_I$ we have $d(f \, dy_I) = df \wedge dy_I$, so by (2) and the result for 0-forms,

$$
\begin{aligned}
T^*(d(f \, dy_I)) &= T^*(df \wedge dy_I) & &\text{applying the definition of d} \\
&= T^* df \wedge T^* dy_I & &\text{since pullback and wedge commute} \\
&= d(T^* f) \wedge T^* dy_I & &\text{by the just-established result} \\
&= d(f \circ T) \wedge dT_I & &\text{by definition of the pullback, twice} \\
&= d(f \circ T \, dT_I) & &\text{recognizing the definition of d} \\
&= d(T^*(f \, dy_I)) & &\text{recognizing the pullback.}
\end{aligned}
$$

The multiterm result follows from this and (1). $\qquad\qquad\qquad\qquad\qquad$ $\square$

The pullback also behaves naturally with respect to composition.

Theorem 9.9.5 (Contravariance of the pullback). *Let A be an open subset of $\mathbb{R}^n$, let B be an open subset of $\mathbb{R}^m$, and let C be an open subset of $\mathbb{R}^\ell$. Let $T : A \longrightarrow B$ and $S : B \longrightarrow C$ be smooth mappings. Then for every form $\omega \in \Lambda^k(C)$,*

$$(S \circ T)^* \omega = (T^* \circ S^*) \omega.$$

This peculiar-looking result—that the pullback of a composition is the composition of the pullbacks, but in reverse order—is grammatically inevitable. Again, a commutative diagram expresses the idea:

$$
\Lambda^k(C) \xrightarrow{\ S^*\ } \Lambda^k(B) \xrightarrow{\ T^*\ } \Lambda^k(A).
$$
$$
\underbrace{\qquad\qquad\qquad\qquad}_{(S \circ T)^*}
$$

Proof. For a 0-form $f : C \longrightarrow \mathbb{R}$, the result is simply the associativity of composition,

$$(S \circ T)^* f = f \circ (S \circ T) = (f \circ S) \circ T = T^*(S^* f) = (T^* \circ S^*) f.$$

Let $(z_1, \ldots, z_\ell)$ be coordinates on $\mathbb{R}^\ell$. Every one-term 1-form dz_q (where q is an integer from $\{1, \ldots, \ell\}$) can be viewed as $d(z_q)$, with d the differentiation operator and z_q the qth projection function. Thus

$$
\begin{aligned}
(S \circ T)^* dz_q &= d((S \circ T)^* z_q) & &\text{since derivative commutes with pullback} \\
&= d((T^* \circ S^*) z_q) & &\text{from just above, since } z_q \text{ is a function} \\
&= d(T^*(S^* z_q)) & &\text{by definition of composition} \\
&= T^*(d(S^* z_q)) & &\text{since derivative commutes with pullback} \\
&= T^*(S^* dz_q) & &\text{since derivative commutes with pullback} \\
&= (T^* \circ S^*) dz_q & &\text{by definition of composition.}
\end{aligned}
$$

Since every k-form is a sum of wedge products of 0-forms and 1-forms, and since the pullback passes through sums and products, the general case follows.

□

Recapitulating this section: To pull a differential form back though a map is to change variables in the form naturally. Because the wedge product has the determinant wired into it, so does the pullback. Because the pullback is natural, it commutes with addition, scalar multiplication, wedge multiplication, and differentiation of forms, and it anticommutes with composition of forms. That is, everything that we are doing is preserved under change of variables.

The results of this section are the technical heart of this chapter. The reader is encouraged to contrast their systematic algebraic proofs with the tricky analytic estimates in the main proofs of Chapter 6. The work of this section will allow the pending proof of the general fundamental theorem of integral calculus to be carried out by algebra, an improvement over handwaving geometry or tortuous analysis. The classical integration theorems of the nineteenth century will follow without recourse to the classical procedure of cutting a big curvy object into many pieces and then approximating each small piece by a straight piece instead. The classical procedure is either imprecise or byzantine, but for those willing to think algebraically, the modern procedure is accurate and clear.

We end this section by revisiting the third example from its beginning. Recall that we considered the 1-form

$$\omega = \frac{x\,dy - y\,dx}{x^2 + y^2}$$

and the complex square mapping

$$(x, y) = T(u, v) = (u^2 - v^2, 2uv),$$

and we computed that the pullback $T^*\omega$ was twice ω, but written in (u, v)-coordinates. Now we obtain the same result more conceptually in light of the results of this section. The idea is that since ω measures change in angle, which doubles under the complex square mapping, the result will be obvious in polar coordinates, and furthermore, the pullback behaves so well under changes of variable that the corresponding result for Cartesian coordinates will follow easily as well. Thus, consider the polar coordinate mapping

$$\Phi : \mathbb{R}_{>0} \times \mathbb{R} \longrightarrow \mathbb{R}^2 \backslash \{(0,0)\}, \qquad \Phi(r, \theta) = (r\cos\theta, r\sin\theta) = (u, v).$$

In polar coordinates, the complex square mapping can be reexpressed as

$$S : \mathbb{R}_{>0} \times \mathbb{R} \longrightarrow \mathbb{R}_{>0} \times \mathbb{R}, \qquad S(r, \theta) = (r^2, 2\theta) = (\tilde{r}, \tilde{\theta}).$$

And the polar coordinate mapping also applies to the polar coordinates that are output by the complex square mapping,

$$\Phi : \mathbb{R}_{>0} \times \mathbb{R} \longrightarrow \mathbb{R}^2 \backslash \{(0,0)\}, \qquad \Phi(\tilde{r}, \tilde{\theta}) = (\tilde{r} \cos \tilde{\theta}, \tilde{r} \sin \tilde{\theta}) = (x, y).$$

Thus we have a commutative diagram

$$
\begin{array}{ccc}
\mathbb{R}_{>0} \times \mathbb{R} & \xrightarrow{\ \Phi\ } & \mathbb{R}^2 \backslash \{(0,0)\} \\
{\scriptstyle S}\big\downarrow & & \big\downarrow {\scriptstyle T} \\
\mathbb{R}_{>0} \times \mathbb{R} & \xrightarrow{\ \Phi\ } & \mathbb{R}^2 \backslash \{(0,0)\}.
\end{array}
$$

In terms of differential forms and pullbacks we have the resulting diagram

$$
\begin{array}{ccc}
\Lambda^1(\mathbb{R}_{>0} \times \mathbb{R}) & \xleftarrow{\ \Phi^*\ } & \Lambda^1(\mathbb{R}^2 \backslash \{(0,0)\}) \\
{\scriptstyle S^*}\big\uparrow & & \big\uparrow {\scriptstyle T^*} \\
\Lambda^1(\mathbb{R}_{>0} \times \mathbb{R}) & \xleftarrow{\ \Phi^*\ } & \Lambda^1(\mathbb{R}^2 \backslash \{(0,0)\}).
\end{array}
$$

Now to find $T^*\omega$, where $\omega = (x \, dy - y \, dx)/(x^2 + y^2)$, recall that ω pulls back through the polar coordinate mapping to $d\tilde{\theta}$, and recall that $\tilde{\theta} = 2\theta$. Thus we have in the second diagram

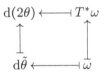

$$
\begin{array}{ccc}
d(2\theta) & \longleftarrow & T^*\omega \\
\big\uparrow & & \big\uparrow \\
d\tilde{\theta} & \longleftarrow & \omega
\end{array}
$$

Since $d(2\theta) = 2 \, d\theta$, the sought-for pullback $T^*\omega$ must be the (u,v)-form that pulls back through the polar coordinate mapping to $2 \, d\theta$. And so $T^*\omega$ should be the double of ω, but with u and v in place of x and y,

$$T^*\omega = 2 \frac{u \, dv - v \, du}{u^2 + v^2}.$$

This is the value of $T^*\omega$ that we computed mechanically at the beginning of this section. Indeed, note that this second derivation of $T^*\omega$ makes no reference whatsoever to the formula $T(u,v) = (u^2 - v^2, 2uv)$, only to the fact that in polar coordinates the complex square mapping squares the radius and doubles the angle.

Similarly, we can use these ideas to pull the area-form $\lambda = dx \wedge dy$ back through T. Indeed, $dx \wedge dy$ pulls back through the polar coordinate mapping to $\tilde{r} \, d\tilde{r} \wedge d\tilde{\theta}$, which pulls back through S to $r^2 \, d(r^2) \wedge d(2\theta) = 4r^3 \, dr \wedge d\theta$. Thus we have a commutative diagram

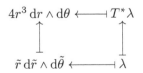

$$
\begin{array}{ccc}
4r^3 \, dr \wedge d\theta & \longleftarrow & T^*\lambda \\
\big\uparrow & & \big\uparrow \\
\tilde{r} \, d\tilde{r} \wedge d\tilde{\theta} & \longleftarrow & \lambda
\end{array}
$$

So $T^*\lambda$ must pull back through the polar coordinate mapping to $4r^3\,dr \wedge d\theta$. Since the area-form $du \wedge dv$ pulls back to $r\,dr \wedge d\theta$, the answer is the area form $du \wedge dv$ multiplied by $4r^2$ in (u,v)-coordinates. That is, since r in (u,v)-coordinates is $\sqrt{u^2 + v^2}$,

$$T^*\lambda = T^*(dx \wedge dy) = 4(u^2 + v^2)\,du \wedge dv.$$

This formula for $T^*\lambda$ can be verified directly by purely mechanical computation.

Exercises

9.9.1. Define $S : \mathbb{R}^2 \longrightarrow \mathbb{R}^2$ by $S(u,v) = (u + v, uv) \overset{\text{call}}{=} (x,y)$. Let $\omega = x^2\,dy + y^2\,dx$ and $\lambda = xy\,dx$, forms on (x,y)-space.

(a) Compute $\omega \wedge \lambda$, $S'(u,v)$, and (use the pullback–determinant theorem) $S^*(\omega \wedge \lambda)$.

(b) Compute $S^*\omega$, $S^*\lambda$, and $S^*\omega \wedge S^*\lambda$. How do you check the last of these? Which of the three commutative diagrams from this section is relevant here?

(c) Compute $d\omega$ and $S^*(d\omega)$.

(d) Compute $d(S^*\omega)$. How do you check this? Which commutative diagram is relevant?

(e) Define $T : \mathbb{R}^2 \longrightarrow \mathbb{R}^2$ by $T(s,t) = (s - t, se^t) \overset{\text{call}}{=} (u,v)$. Compute $T^*(S^*\lambda)$.

(f) What is the composite mapping $S \circ T$? Compute $(S \circ T)^*\lambda$. How do you check this, and which commutative diagram is relevant?

9.9.2. Recall the two forms from the beginning (and the end) of this section,

$$\omega = \frac{x\,dy - y\,dx}{x^2 + y^2}, \qquad \lambda = dx \wedge dy.$$

Consider a mapping from the nonzero points of (u,v)-space to nonzero points of (x,y)-space.

$$(x,y) = T(u,v) = \left(\frac{u}{u^2 + v^2}, \frac{-v}{u^2 + v^2} \right).$$

As at the end of this section, in light of the fact that T is the complex reciprocal mapping, determine what $T^*\omega$ and $T^*\lambda$ must be. If you wish, confirm your answers by computing them mechanically as at the beginning of this section.

9.9.3. Consider a differential form on the punctured (x,y)-plane,

$$\mu = \frac{x\,dx + y\,dy}{\sqrt{x^2 + y^2}}.$$

(a) Pull μ back through the polar coordinate mapping from the end of this section,

$$(x, y) = \Phi(\tilde{r}, \tilde{\theta}) = (\tilde{r}\cos\tilde{\theta}, \tilde{r}\sin\tilde{\theta}).$$

In light of the value of the pullback, what must be the integral $\int_\gamma \mu$ where γ is a parametrized curve in the punctured (x, y)-plane?

(b) In light of part (a), pull μ back through the complex square mapping from this section,

$$(x, y) = T(u, v) = (u^2 - v^2, 2uv),$$

using diagrams rather than relying heavily on computation. Check your answer by computation if you wish.

(c) Similarly to part (a), pull μ back through the complex reciprocal mapping from the previous exercise,

$$(x, y) = T(u, v) = \left(\frac{u}{u^2 + v^2}, \frac{-v}{u^2 + v^2}\right).$$

using diagrams. Check your answer by computation if you wish.

(d) Let k be an integer. The relation $x + iy = (u + iv)^k$ determines (x, y) as a function $T(u, v)$. Pull the forms ω and λ from the previous exercise and the form μ from this exercise back through T, with no reference to any explicit formula for T. The results should in particular reproduce your previous answers for $k = 2$ and $k = -1$.

9.9.4. Let $A = \mathbb{R}^3 - \{0\}$. Let r be a fixed positive real number. Consider a 2-surface in A,

$$\Phi : [0, 2\pi] \times [0, \pi] \longrightarrow A, \quad \Phi(\theta, \varphi) = (r\cos\theta\,\sin\varphi, r\sin\theta\,\sin\varphi, r\cos\varphi).$$

Consider also a 2-form on A,

$$\omega = -(x/r)\,dy \wedge dz - (y/r)\,dz \wedge dx - (z/r)\,dx \wedge dy.$$

Compute the derivative matrix $\Phi'(\theta, \varphi)$, and use the pullback–determinant theorem three times to compute the pullback $\Phi^*\omega$. Compare your answer to the integrand of the surface integral near the end of Section 9.1 used to compute the volume of the sphere of radius r. (It follows that ω is the area-form for the particular surface Φ in this exercise, but *not* that ω is a general area-form for all surfaces.)

9.10 Change of Variable for Differential Forms

The definition of integration and the algebra of forms combine to make a change of variable theorem for differential forms a triviality. First, a theorem of independent interest allows us to replace any integral of a differential form over a parametrized surface with an integral over the trivial parametrization of the surface's parameter domain.

Theorem 9.10.1 (Pullback theorem). *Let A be an open subset of $\mathbb{R}^n$. Let ω be a k-form on A and let $\Phi : D \longrightarrow A$ be a k-surface in A. Define a k-surface in $\mathbb{R}^k$,*

$$\Delta^D : D \longrightarrow \mathbb{R}^k, \qquad \Delta^D(u) = u \text{ for all } u \in D.$$

Then

$$\int_\Phi \omega = \int_{\Delta^D} \Phi^* \omega.$$

Proof. As usual, just do the case of a one-term form, $\omega = f\,\mathrm{d}x_I$. Then

$$
\begin{aligned}
\int_\Phi f\,\mathrm{d}x_I &= \int_D (f \circ \Phi) \det \Phi_I' && \text{by definition, as in (9.14)} \\
&= \int_{\Delta^D} (f \circ \Phi) \det \Phi_I'\,\mathrm{d}u_1 \wedge \cdots \wedge \mathrm{d}u_k && \text{by Exercise 9.5.4} \\
&= \int_{\Delta^D} (f \circ \Phi) \Phi^* \mathrm{d}x_I && \text{by Theorem 9.9.3} \\
&= \int_{\Delta^D} \Phi^*(f\,\mathrm{d}x_I) && \text{by definition of pullback.}
\end{aligned}
$$

$\square$

The general change of variable theorem for differential forms follows immediately from the pullback theorem and the contravariance of the pullback.

Theorem 9.10.2 (Change of variable for differential forms). *Let A be an open subset of $\mathbb{R}^n$, and let B be an open subset of $\mathbb{R}^m$. Let $T : A \longrightarrow B$ be a smooth mapping. For every k-surface in A, $\Phi : D \longrightarrow A$, the composition $T \circ \Phi : D \longrightarrow B$ is thus a k-surface in B. Let ω be a k-form on B. Then*

$$\int_{T \circ \Phi} \omega = \int_\Phi T^* \omega.$$

Proof. Let $\Delta^D : D \longrightarrow \mathbb{R}^k$ be as above. Then

$$\int_{T \circ \Phi} \omega = \int_{\Delta^D} (T \circ \Phi)^* \omega = \int_{\Delta^D} \Phi^*(T^* \omega) = \int_\Phi T^* \omega.$$

$\square$

The pullback theorem is essentially equivalent to the definition of integration once one has the pullback–determinant theorem. Thus, a logically equivalent route to ours through this material is to define integration of a k-form in k-space as ordinary integration, and integration of a k-form in n-space for $k < n$ via the pullback. Doing so would have been a little tidier (there would not be two notions of integration when $k = n$ whose compatibility needs to be verified), but the approach here has the advantage that one can start integrating immediately before developing all the algebra.

Exercise

9.10.1. Let $T : \mathbb{R}^2 \longrightarrow \mathbb{R}^2$ be given by $T(x_1, x_2) = (x_1^2 - x_2^2, 2x_1 x_2) \overset{\text{call}}{=} (y_1, y_2)$. Let γ be the curve $\gamma : [0, 1] \longrightarrow \mathbb{R}^2$ given by $\gamma(t) = (1, t)$ mapping the unit interval into (x_1, x_2)-space, and let $T \circ \gamma$ be the corresponding curve mapping into (y_1, y_2)-space. Let $\omega = y_1 \, dy_2$, a 1-form on (y_1, y_2)-space.

(a) Compute $T \circ \gamma$, and then compute $\int_{T \circ \gamma} \omega$ using formula (9.14).

(b) Compute $T^*\omega$, the pullback of ω by T.

(c) Compute $\int_\gamma T^*\omega$ using formula (9.14). What theorem says that the answer here is the same as (a)?

(d) Let $\lambda = dy_1 \wedge dy_2$, the area form on (y_1, y_2)-space. Compute $T^*\lambda$.

(e) A rectangle in the first quadrant of (x_1, x_2)-space,

$$R = \{(x_1, x_2) : a_1 \le x_1 \le b_1, a_2 \le x_2 \le b_2\},$$

gets taken to some indeterminate patch $B = T(R)$ by T. Find the area of B, $\int_B \lambda$, using (d). (This exercise abuses notation slightly, identifying R with its natural parametrization and B with the corresponding surface $T \circ R$.)

(f) Why does this exercise require that R lie in the first quadrant? Can the restriction be weakened?

9.11 Closed Forms, Exact Forms, and Homotopy

Let ω be a differential form. Recall the terminology that

$$\omega \text{ is } exact \text{ if } \omega = d\lambda \text{ for some } \lambda$$

and

$$\omega \text{ is } closed \text{ if } d\omega = 0.$$

The nilpotence of d (the rule $d^2 = 0$ from Theorem 9.8.3) shows that every exact form is closed. We now show that under certain conditions, the converse is true as well, i.e., under certain conditions a closed differential form can be antidifferentiated.

A *homotopy* of a set is a process of deforming the set to a single point, the deformation taking place entirely within the original set. For example, consider the open ball

$$A = \{x \in \mathbb{R}^n : |x| < 1\}.$$

A mapping that shrinks the ball to its center as one unit of time elapses is

$$h : [0, 1] \times A \longrightarrow A, \qquad h(t, x) = tx.$$

The idea geometrically is that at time $t = 1$, h is the identity mapping so that $h(1, A) = A$, while at any intermediate time $t \in (0, 1)$, $h(t, A) = tA$ is a scaled-down copy of the ball, and finally at time $t = 0$, $h(0, A) = \{0\}$ and the ball has shrunk to its center. (So here we have let time flow from $t = 1$ to $t = 0$ for convenience.)

However, the geometric story just told is slightly misleading. We could replace the ball A in the previous example by all of Euclidean space $\mathbb{R}^n$, and the map

$$h : [0,1] \times \mathbb{R}^n \longrightarrow \mathbb{R}^n, \qquad h(t,x) = tx$$

would still contract $\mathbb{R}^n$ to $\{\mathbf{0}\}$ in the sense that each point $x \in \mathbb{R}^n$ is moved by h to $\mathbf{0}$ as t varies from 1 to 0. However, at any intermediate time $t \in (0,1)$, $h(t,\mathbb{R}^n) = t\mathbb{R}^n = \mathbb{R}^n$ is still all of Euclidean space. Although every point of $\mathbb{R}^n$ is moved steadily by h to $\mathbf{0}$, h does not shrink the set $\mathbb{R}^n$ as a whole until the very end of the process, when space collapses instantaneously to a point. Each point x of $\mathbb{R}^n$ is taken close to the origin once the time t is close enough to 0, but the required smallness of t depends on x; for no positive t, however close to 0, is all of $\mathbb{R}^n$ taken close to the origin simultaneously. The relevant language here is that homotopy is a convergent process that need not be uniformly convergent, analogously to how a continuous function need not be uniformly continuous. The mental movie that we naturally have of a set shrinking to a point depicts a uniformly convergent process, and so it doesn't fully capture homotopy.

For another example, consider the annulus

$$A = \{x \in \mathbb{R}^2 : 1 < |x| < 2\}.$$

Plausibly there is no homotopy of the annulus, meaning that the annulus cannot be shrunk to a point by a continuous process that takes place entirely within the annulus. But proving that there is no homotopy of the annulus is not trivial. We will return to this point in Exercise 9.11.1.

The formal definition of a homotopy is as follows.

Definition 9.11.1 (Homotopy, contractible set). *Let A be an open subset of $\mathbb{R}^n$. Let ε be a positive number and let*

$$B = (-\varepsilon, 1 + \varepsilon) \times A,$$

an open subset of $\mathbb{R}^{n+1}$. A **homotopy** *of A is a smooth mapping*

$$h : B \longrightarrow A$$

such that for some point p of A,

$$\left\{ \begin{matrix} h(0,x) = p \\ h(1,x) = x \end{matrix} \right\} \quad \textit{for all } x \in A.$$

An open subset A of $\mathbb{R}^n$ that has a homotopy is called **contractible**.

Again, the idea is that B is a sort of cylinder over A, and that at one end of the cylinder the homotopy gives an undisturbed copy of A, while by the other end of the cylinder the homotopy has compressed A down to a point.

This section proves the following result.

Theorem 9.11.2 (Poincaré). *Let A be a contractible subset of $\mathbb{R}^n$, and let $k \geq 1$ be an integer. Then every closed k-form on A is exact.*

To prepare for the proof of theorem, we consider a cylinder over A,

$$B = (-\varepsilon, 1 + \varepsilon) \times A,$$

but for now we make no reference to the pending homotopy that will have B as its domain. Recall that the differentiation operator d increments the degree of a differential form. Now, by contrast, we define a linear operator that takes differential forms on B and returns differential forms of one degree lower on A. Let the coordinates on B be $(t, x) = (t, x_1, \ldots, x_n)$ with t viewed as the zeroth coordinate.

Definition 9.11.3. *For each positive integer k, define a linear mapping of differential forms,*

$$c : \Lambda^k(B) \longrightarrow \Lambda^{k-1}(A), \quad k = 1, 2, 3, \ldots,$$

as follows: c acts on a one-term form that contains dt by integrating its component function in the t-direction and suppressing its dt, and c annihilates differential forms that don't contain dt. That is, letting I denote $(k-1)$-tuples and J denote k-tuples, all tuples being from $\{1, \ldots, n\}$,

$$c\left(\sum_I g_I(t, x)\, dt\, dx_I + \sum_J g_J(t, x)\, dx_J\right) = \sum_I \left(\int_{t=0}^1 g_I(t, x)\right) dx_I.$$

With c in hand, we have two degree-preserving mappings from differential forms on B to differential forms on A, the compositions of c and the differentiation operator d in either order,

$$cd, \ dc : \Lambda^k(B) \longrightarrow \Lambda^k(A), \quad k = 1, 2, 3, \ldots.$$

However, note that cd proceeds from $\Lambda^k(B)$ to $\Lambda^k(A)$ via $\Lambda^{k+1}(B)$, while dc proceeds via $\Lambda^{k-1}(A)$. To analyze the two compositions, compute first that for a one-term differential form that contains dt,

$$(cd)(g(t, x)\, dt\, dx_I) = c\left(\sum_{i=1}^n D_i g(t, x)\, dx_i\, dt\, dx_I\right)$$

$$= c\left(-\sum_{i=1}^n D_i g(t, x)\, dt\, dx_{(i,I)}\right)$$

$$= -\sum_{i=1}^n \left(\int_{t=0}^1 D_i g(t, x)\right) dx_{(i,I)},$$

while, using the fact that x_i-derivatives pass through t-integrals for the third equality to follow,

$$(dc)(g(t,x)\,dt\,dx_I) = d\left(\left(\int_{t=0}^1 g(t,x)\right)dx_I\right)$$

$$= \sum_{i=1}^n D_i\left(\int_{t=0}^1 g(t,x)\right)dx_{(i,I)}$$

$$= \sum_{i=1}^n \left(\int_{t=0}^1 D_i g(t,x)\right)dx_{(i,I)}.$$

Thus $cd + dc$ annihilates forms that contain dt. On the other hand, for a one-term differential form without dt,

$$(cd)(g(t,x)\,dx_J) = c\left(D_0 g(t,x)\,dt\,dx_J + \sum_{j=1}^n D_j g(t,x)\,dx_{(j,J)}\right)$$

$$= \left(\int_{t=0}^1 D_0 g(t,x)\right)dx_J$$

$$= (g(1,x) - g(0,x))\,dx_J,$$

while

$$(dc)(g(t,x)\,dx_J) = d(0) = 0.$$

That is, $cd + dc$ replaces each coefficient function $g(t,x)$ in forms without dt by $g(1,x) - g(0,x)$, a function of x only.

To notate the effect of $cd + dc$ more tidily, define the two natural mappings from A to the cross sections of B where the pending homotopy of A will end and where it will begin,

$$\beta_0, \ \beta_1 : A \longrightarrow B, \qquad \left\{\begin{array}{l}\beta_0(x) = (0,x)\\ \beta_1(x) = (1,x)\end{array}\right\}.$$

Because β_0 and β_1 have ranges where t is constant, and because they don't affect x, their pullbacks,

$$\beta_0^*, \ \beta_1^* : \Lambda^k(B) \longrightarrow \Lambda^k(A), \quad k = 0,1,2,\ldots,$$

act correspondingly by replacing t with a constant and dt with 0 while preserving x and dx,

$$\beta_0^*(g(t,x)\,dt\,dx_I) = 0, \qquad \beta_1^*(g(t,x)\,dt\,dx_I) = 0$$

and

$$\beta_0^*(g(t,x)\,dx_J) = g(0,x)\,dx_J, \qquad \beta_1^*(g(t,x)\,dx_J) = g(1,x)\,dx_J.$$

It follows that our calculations can be rephrased as **Poincaré's identity**,

$$(cd + dc)\lambda = (\beta_1^* - \beta_0^*)\lambda, \quad \lambda \in \Lambda^k(B), \ k = 1,2,3,\ldots.$$

With Poincaré's identity established, we prove Poincaré's theorem.

Proof (of Theorem 9.11.2). We have an open subset A of $\mathbb{R}^n$, a point p of A, a cylinder $B = (-\varepsilon, 1 + \varepsilon) \times A$ for some positive number ε, and a homotopy

$$h : B \longrightarrow A.$$

So also we have the corresponding pullback

$$h^* : \Lambda^k(A) \longrightarrow \Lambda^k(B), \quad k = 0, 1, 2, \ldots.$$

Let $k \geq 1$, and consider a closed form $\omega \in \Lambda^k(A)$. Then $h^*\omega \in \Lambda^k(B)$ and $ch^*\omega \in \Lambda^{k-1}(A)$. We show that $ch^*\omega$ is an antiderivative of ω by computing the quantity $(cd + dc)h^*\omega$ in two ways. First, because the pullback and boundary operators commute and because $d\omega = 0$,

$$(cd + dc)h^*\omega = ch^*d\omega + dch^*\omega = d(ch^*\omega).$$

Second, by Poincaré's identity and the contravariance of the pullback,

$$(cd + dc)h^*\omega = (\beta_1^* - \beta_0^*)h^*\omega = ((h \circ \beta_1)^* - (h \circ \beta_0)^*)\omega.$$

But $(h \circ \beta_1)(x) = h(1, x) = x$ and $(h \circ \beta_0)(x) = h(0, x) = p$, i.e., $h \circ \beta_1$ is the identity mapping and $h \circ \beta_0$ is a constant mapping, so that $(h \circ \beta_1)^*$ has no effect on ω, while $(h \circ \beta_0)^*$ annihilates the dx's of ω (which are present because $k \geq 1$), thus annihilating ω. In sum, the second computation gives ω. So the computations combine to give

$$d(ch^*\omega) = \omega.$$

That is, ω is exact, as desired.   □

Note that this process of antidifferentiating ω by taking $ch^*\omega$ moves from A up to the larger space B and then back down to A. In terms of algebra, the process inserts t's into ω by pulling it back through the homotopy and then strips them out in a different way by applying the c operator.

We end this section with an example. Consider any closed form on $\mathbb{R}^2$,

$$\omega = f(x, y) \, dx + g(x, y) \, dy, \qquad D_2 f = D_1 g.$$

Pull ω back through the homotopy $h(t, x, y) = (tx, ty)$ of $\mathbb{R}^2$ to get

$$h^*\omega = f(tx, ty) \, d(tx) + g(tx, ty) \, d(ty)$$
$$= (xf(tx, ty) + yg(tx, ty)) \, dt + tf(tx, ty) \, dx + tg(tx, ty) \, dy.$$

Apply c to $h^*\omega$ in turn to get

$$ch^*\omega = \int_{t=0}^1 (xf(tx, ty) + yg(tx, ty)).$$

This function must have derivative ω. To verify that it does, compute that its first partial derivative is

$$D_1 ch^*\omega(x,y) = \int_{t=0}^1 \big(f(tx,ty) + xD_1(f(tx,ty)) + yD_1(g(tx,ty))\big).$$

By the chain rule and then by the fact that $D_1 g = D_2 f$, the first partial derivative is therefore

$$D_1 ch^*\omega(x,y) = \int_{t=0}^1 \big(f(tx,ty) + xD_1 f(tx,ty)t + yD_1 g(tx,ty)t\big)$$

$$= \int_{t=0}^1 f(tx,ty) + \int_{t=0}^1 t(xD_1 f(tx,ty) + yD_2 f(tx,ty)).$$

The last integral takes the form $\int_{t=0}^1 u\,v'$ where $u(t) = t$ and $v(t) = f(tx,ty)$. And so finally, integrating by parts gives

$$D_1 ch^*\omega(x,y) = \int_{t=0}^1 f(tx,ty) + tf(tx,ty)\Big|_{t=0}^1 - \int_{t=0}^1 f(tx,ty)$$

$$= f(x,y).$$

Similarly $D_2 ch^*\omega(x,y) = g(x,y)$, so that indeed

$$d(ch^*\omega) = f(x,y)\,dx + g(x,y)\,dy = \omega.$$

Exercises

9.11.1. (a) Here is a special case of showing that a closed form is exact without recourse to Poincaré's theorem. A function $f : \mathbb{R}^3 \longrightarrow \mathbb{R}$ is called **homogeneous of degree** k if

$$f(tx, ty, tz) = t^k f(x,y,z) \quad \text{for all } t \in \mathbb{R} \text{ and } (x,y,z) \in \mathbb{R}^3.$$

Such a function must satisfy **Euler's identity,**

$$xD_1 f + yD_2 f + zD_3 f = kf.$$

Suppose that $\omega = f_1\,dx + f_2\,dy + f_3\,dz$ is a closed 1-form whose coefficient functions are all homogeneous of degree k where $k \geq 0$. Show that $\omega = d\phi$ where

$$\phi = \frac{1}{k+1}(xf_1 + yf_2 + zf_3).$$

(Suggestion: first check only the dx term of $d\phi$, remembering that ω is closed. The other two terms will work out similarly by symmetry.)

(b) Here is a closed form that is not exact. Let

$$\omega = \frac{x\,dy - y\,dx}{x^2 + y^2},$$

a 1-form on the punctured plane $A = \mathbb{R}^2 - \{(0,0)\}$. Show that ω is closed. Compute that integrating ω around the counterclockwise unit circle,

$$\gamma : [0, 2\pi] \longrightarrow A, \qquad \gamma(t) = (\cos t, \sin t),$$

gives a nonzero answer. Explain why this shows that there is no 0-form (i.e., function) θ on the punctured plane such that $\omega = d\theta$.

(c) Use part (b) to show that there cannot exist a homotopy of the punctured plane. How does this nonexistence relate to the example of the annulus at the beginning of this section?

9.11.2. (a) Let $\omega = f(x, y) \, dx \wedge dy$ be a form on $\mathbb{R}^2$, so that $d\omega = 0$. Find and confirm an antiderivative of ω.

(b) Let $\omega = f(x, y, z) \, dy \wedge dz + g(x, y, z) \, dz \wedge dx + h(x, y, z) \, dx \wedge dy$ be a closed form on $\mathbb{R}^3$. (Here h does not denote a homotopy.) Find an antiderivative of ω.

9.12 Cubes and Chains

Sections 9.7 through 9.9 introduced algebraic operators on differential forms: the wedge product, the derivative, and the pullback. The next section will introduce a geometric operator on surfaces. The first thing to do is specialize the definition of a surface a bit. As usual, let $[0, 1]$ denote the unit interval. For $k \geq 0$, the unit k-box is the Cartesian product

$$[0, 1]^k = [0, 1] \times \cdots \times [0, 1] = \{(u_1, \ldots, u_k) : u_i \in [0, 1] \text{ for } i = 1, \ldots, k\}.$$

As mentioned in Section 9.3, when $k = 0$ this means the one-point set whose point is ().

Definition 9.12.1 (Singular cube, standard cube). *Let A be an open subset of $\mathbb{R}^n$. A* **singular k-cube** *in A is a surface whose parameter domain is the unit k-box,*

$$\Phi : [0, 1]^k \longrightarrow A.$$

In particular, the **standard k-cube** *is*

$$\Delta^k : [0, 1]^k \longrightarrow \mathbb{R}^k, \qquad \Delta^k(u) = u \text{ for all } u \in [0, 1]^k.$$

As with Definition 9.1.1 of a surface, now a cube is by definition a mapping, and in particular, a 0-cube is the parametrization of a point. In practice, we often blur the distinction between a mapping and its image, and under this blurring the word *cube* now encompasses noncubical objects such as a torus-surface (which is a singular 2-cube in $\mathbb{R}^3$) and a solid sphere (a singular 3-cube in $\mathbb{R}^3$). The next definition allows us to consider more than one cube at a time. The purpose is to integrate over several cubes in succession, integrating over each of them a prescribed number of times.

Definition 9.12.2 (Chain). *Let A be an open subset of $\mathbb{R}^n$. A k-chain in A is a finite formal linear combination*

$$\mathcal{C} = \sum_s \nu_s \Phi_{(s)},$$

where each ν_s is an integer and each $\Phi_{(s)}$ is a singular k-cube in A. (The surface subscript is in parentheses only to distinguish it from a component function subscript.)

For example, if Φ, Ψ, and Γ are singular k-cubes in $\mathbb{R}^n$ then

$$2\Phi - 3\Psi + 23\Gamma$$

is a k-chain in $\mathbb{R}^n$. This k-chain is *not* the singular k-cube that maps points u to $2\Phi(u) - 3\Psi(u) + 23\Gamma(u)$ in $\mathbb{R}^n$. The term *formal linear combination* in the definition means that we don't actually carry out any additions and scalings. Rather, the coefficients ν_s are to be interpreted as integration multiplicities. A k-chain, like a k-form, is a set of instructions.

Definition 9.12.3 (Integral of a k-form over a k-chain in n-space). *Let A be an open subset of $\mathbb{R}^n$. Let*

$$\mathcal{C} = \sum_s \nu_s \Phi_{(s)}$$

be a k-chain in A, and let ω be a k-form on A. Then the integral of ω over $\mathcal{C}$ is

$$\int_{\mathcal{C}} \omega = \sum_s \nu_s \int_{\Phi_{(s)}} \omega.$$

This definition can be written more suggestively as

$$\int_{\sum \nu_s \Phi_{(s)}} \omega = \sum_s \nu_s \int_{\Phi_{(s)}} \omega.$$

Although $\mathcal{C}$ is a formal linear combination, the operations on the right of the equality are literal addition and multiplication in $\mathbb{R}$. For example, let a and b be points in $\mathbb{R}^n$, and let Φ_a and Φ_b be the corresponding 0-cubes. Then for every 0-form on $\mathbb{R}^n$, $\omega = f : \mathbb{R}^n \longrightarrow \mathbb{R}$,

$$\int_{\Phi_b - \Phi_a} \omega = f(b) - f(a).$$

One can define predictable rules for addition and scalar multiplication (integer scalars) of chains, all of which will pass through the integral sign tautologically. Especially, the change of variable theorem for differential forms extends from integrals over surfaces to integrals over chains,

$$\int_{T \circ \mathcal{C}} \omega = \int_{\mathcal{C}} T^* \omega.$$

We will quote this formula in the proof of the general FTIC.

Also, if C is a chain in A and $T : A \longrightarrow B$ is a mapping, then we can naturally compose them to get a chain in B by passing sums and constant multiples through T. That is,

$$\text{if } C = \sum_s \nu_s \Phi_{(s)} \text{ then } T \circ C = \sum_s \nu_s (T \circ \Phi_{(s)}).$$

Exercises

9.12.1. Let A be an open subset of $\mathbb{R}^n$. Consider the inner-product-like function (called a *pairing*)

$$\langle \ , \ \rangle : \{k\text{-chains in } A\} \times \{k\text{-forms on } A\} \longrightarrow \mathbb{R}$$

defined by the rule

$$\langle C, \omega \rangle = \int_C \omega \quad \text{for all suitable } k\text{-chains } C \text{ and } k\text{-forms } \omega.$$

Show that this inner product is bilinear, meaning that for all suitable chains C and C_i, all suitable forms ω and ω_i, and all constants c_i,

$$\left\langle \sum_i c_i C_i, \omega \right\rangle = \sum_i c_i \langle C_i, \omega \rangle$$

and

$$\left\langle C, \sum_i c_i \omega_i \right\rangle = \sum_i c_i \langle C, \omega_i \rangle.$$

It makes no sense to speak of symmetry of this pairing, because the arguments cannot be exchanged.

Do you think the pairing is *nondegenerate*, meaning that for every fixed chain C, if $\langle C, \omega \rangle = 0$ for all forms ω then C must be 0, and for every fixed form ω, if $\langle C, \omega \rangle = 0$ for all chains C then ω must be 0?

9.12.2. Let A be an open subset of $\mathbb{R}^n$, let B be an open subset of $\mathbb{R}^m$, and let $k \geq 0$. Every smooth mapping $T : A \longrightarrow B$ gives rise via composition to a corresponding *pushforward* mapping from k-surfaces in A to k-surfaces in B,

$$T_* : \{k\text{-surfaces in } A\} \longrightarrow \{k\text{-surfaces in } B\}, \quad T_* \Phi = T \circ \Phi.$$

In more detail, since a k-surface in A takes the form $\Phi : D \longrightarrow A$ where $D \subset \mathbb{R}^k$ is a parameter domain, the pushforward mapping is

$$(\Phi : D \longrightarrow A) \overset{T_*}{\longmapsto} (T \circ \Phi : D \longrightarrow B).$$

Using the pairing-notation of the previous exercise, which result from earlier in this chapter can be renotated as

$$\langle T_* \Phi, \omega \rangle = \langle \Phi, T^* \omega \rangle \quad \text{for all suitable } \Phi \text{ and } \omega?$$

Note that the renotation shows that the pushforward and pullback are like a pair of adjoint operators in the sense of linear algebra.

9.13 Geometry of Chains: The Boundary Operator

This section defines an operator that takes k-chains to $(k-1)$-chains. The idea is to traverse the edge of each singular k-cube in the chain, with suitable multiplicity and orientation. The following definition gives three rules that say how to do so. The first rule reduces taking the boundary of a k-chain to taking the boundary of its constituent singular k-cubes. The second rule reduces taking the boundary of a singular k-cube to taking the boundary of the standard k-cube. The third rule, giving the procedure for taking the boundary of the standard k-cube, is the substance of the definition. It is best understood by working through specific cases.

Definition 9.13.1 (Boundary). *Let A be an open subset of $\mathbb{R}^n$. For each $k \geq 1$, define the* **boundary mapping**

$$\partial : \{k\text{-chains in } A\} \longrightarrow \{(k-1)\text{-chains in } A\}$$

by the following properties:

(1) For every k-chain $\sum \nu_s \Phi_{(s)}$,

$$\partial \left(\sum \nu_s \Phi_{(s)} \right) = \sum \nu_s \partial \Phi_{(s)}.$$

(2) For every singular k-cube Φ,

$$\partial \Phi = \Phi \circ \partial \Delta^k.$$

(The composition here is of the sort defined at the end of the previous section.)

(3) Define mappings from the standard $(k-1)$-cube to the faces of the standard k-cube as follows: for every $i \in \{1, \ldots, n\}$ and $\alpha \in \{0, 1\}$, the mapping to the face where the ith coordinate equals α is

$$\Delta_{i,\alpha}^k : [0,1]^{k-1} \longrightarrow [0,1]^k,$$

given by

$$\Delta_{i,\alpha}^k (u_1, \ldots, u_{k-1}) = (u_1, \ldots, u_{i-1}, \alpha, u_i, \ldots, u_{k-1}).$$

Then

$$\partial \Delta^k = \sum_{i=1}^{k} \sum_{\alpha=0}^{1} (-1)^{i+\alpha} \Delta_{i,\alpha}^k. \tag{9.16}$$

In property (2) the composition symbol "$\circ$" has been generalized a little from its ordinary usage. Since $\partial \Delta^k$ is a chain $\sum \mu_s \Psi_{(s)}$, the composition $\Phi \circ \partial \Delta^k$ is defined as the corresponding chain $\sum \mu_s \Phi \circ \Psi_{(s)}$. The compositions in the sum make sense, because by property (3), each $\Psi_{(s)}$ maps $[0,1]^{k-1}$ into $[0,1]^k$. To remember the definition of $\Delta_{i,\alpha}^k$ in (9.16), read its name as:

Of k variables, set the ith to α,

or just *set the ith variable to α*. The idea of formula (9.16) is that for each of the directions in k-space ($i = 1, \ldots, k$), the standard k-cube has two faces with normal vectors in the ith direction ($\alpha = 0, 1$), and we should take these two faces with opposite orientations in order to make both normal vectors point outward. Unlike differentiation, which increments the degree of the form it acts on, the boundary operator decrements chain dimension.

For example, the boundary of the standard 1-cube is given by (9.16),

$$\partial \Delta^1 = -\Delta^1_{1,0} + \Delta^1_{1,1}.$$

That is, the boundary is the right endpoint of $[0, 1]$ with a plus and the left endpoint with a minus. (See Figure 9.11. The figures for this section show the *images* of the various mappings involved, with symbols added as a reminder that the images are being traversed by the mappings.) One consequence of this is that the familiar formula from the one-variable fundamental theorem of integral calculus,

$$\int_0^1 f' = f(1) - f(0),$$

is now expressed suggestively in the notation of differential forms as

$$\int_{\Delta^1} \mathrm{d}f = \int_{\partial \Delta^1} f.$$

As for the boundary of a singular 1-cube $\gamma : [0, 1] \longrightarrow \mathbb{R}^n$ (i.e., a curve in space) with $\gamma(0) = a$ and $\gamma(1) = b$, property (2) of the boundary definition gives

$$\partial \gamma = \gamma \circ \partial \Delta^1 = -\gamma \circ \Delta^1_{1,0} + \gamma \circ \Delta^1_{1,1}.$$

Thus the boundary is the curve's endpoint b with a plus and the start-point a with a minus. The last example of Section 9.4 now also takes on a more suggestive expression,

$$\int_\gamma \mathrm{d}f = \int_{\partial \gamma} f.$$

Figure 9.11. Standard 1-cube and its boundary

The boundary of the standard 2-cube is again given by (9.16),

$$\partial \Delta^2 = -\Delta^2_{1,0} + \Delta^2_{1,1} + \Delta^2_{2,0} - \Delta^2_{2,1}.$$

This chain traverses the boundary square of $[0,1]^2$ once counterclockwise. (See Figure 9.12.) Next consider a singular 2-cube that parametrizes the unit disk,

$$\Phi : [0,1]^2 \longrightarrow \mathbb{R}^2, \qquad \Phi(r,\theta) = (r\cos 2\pi\theta, r\sin 2\pi\theta).$$

By property (2), $\partial\Phi = \Phi \circ \partial\Delta^2$. This chain traverses the boundary circle once counterclockwise, two radial traversals cancel, and there is a degenerate mapping to the centerpoint. (See Figure 9.13.) Changing to $\Phi(r,\theta) = (r\cos 2\pi\theta, -r\sin 2\pi\theta)$ also parametrizes the unit disk, but now $\partial\Phi$ traverses the boundary circle clockwise.

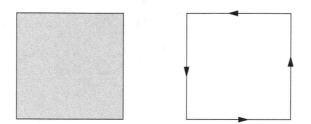

Figure 9.12. Standard 2-cube and its boundary

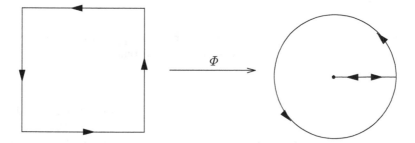

Figure 9.13. Boundary of a singular 2-cube

The boundary of the standard 3-cube is, by (9.16),

$$\partial\Delta^3 = -\Delta^3_{1,0} + \Delta^3_{1,1} + \Delta^3_{2,0} - \Delta^3_{2,1} - \Delta^3_{3,0} + \Delta^3_{3,1}.$$

This chain traverses the faces of $[0,1]^3$, oriented positively if we look at them from outside the solid cube. (See Figure 9.14.)

The second boundary of the standard 2-cube works out by cancellation to

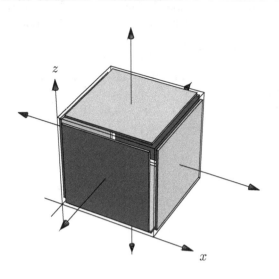

Figure 9.14. Boundary of the standard 3-cube

$$\partial^2 \Delta^2 = 0.$$

(See the left side of Figure 9.15.) And the second boundary of the standard 3-cube similarly is

$$\partial^2 \Delta^3 = 0.$$

(See the right side of Figure 9.15.) These two examples suggest that the notational counterpart to the nilpotence of d is also true,

$$\partial^2 = 0.$$

The nilpotence of ∂ is indeed a theorem, and it is readily shown by a double sum calculation in which terms cancel pairwise. (See Exercise 9.13.8.) But it will also follow immediately from the main theorem of the chapter, the general FTIC, which states that in a precise sense, the differentiation operator d and the boundary operator ∂ are complementary. Their complementary nature is why they are notated so similarly.

Because integration is invariant under reparametrization, you needn't be too formal in computing boundaries once you understand how they work on standard cubes. The boundary of the unit square (the 2-cube), for example, is adequately described as its edge traversed counterclockwise at unit speed, and so the boundary of every singular 2-cube Φ from the unit square into $\mathbb{R}^n$ is simply the restriction of Φ to the edge of the square with appropriate traversal, or any orientation-preserving reparametrization thereof. In particular, every

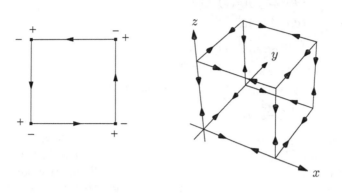

Figure 9.15. Second boundaries

rectangle in $\mathbb{R}^2$ can be obtained by scaling and translating the unit square in an orientation-preserving fashion, so the boundary of such a rectangle is, as one would hope, its edge, counterclockwise. More generally, a singular 2-cube in $\mathbb{R}^3$ is a sort of parametrized membrane floating in space, and its boundary is just its edge, traversed in the direction inherited from the parametrization, as we saw for the disk. Without the parametrization, neither direction of traversing the membrane's edge in $\mathbb{R}^n$ for $n > 2$ is naturally preferable to the other. Similarly in $\mathbb{R}^3$, the boundary of the unit cube is its six faces, oriented to look positive from outside the cube. In other words, an acceptable coordinate system for a boundary face of the cube is two orthonormal vectors whose cross product is an outward unit normal to the cube. The boundary of every singular 3-cube $\Phi : [0,1]^3 \longrightarrow \mathbb{R}^3$ is the restriction of Φ to the boundary faces of $[0,1]^3$.

For example, consider the surface

$$\Phi : [0,a] \times [0,2\pi] \times [0,b] \longrightarrow \mathbb{R}^3$$

given by the cylindrical coordinate mapping,

$$\Phi(r,\theta,z) = (r\cos\theta, r\sin\theta, z).$$

Although the parametrizing box is not literally $[0,1]^3$, we grant ourselves license to treat the upper limits of the parameters as 1 in determining the signs in the formula

$$\partial\Phi = \Phi \circ \left(-\Delta^3_{1,0} + \Delta^3_{1,a} + \Delta^3_{2,0} - \Delta^3_{2,2\pi} - \Delta^3_{3,0} + \Delta^3_{3,b}\right).$$

Here we also grant ourselves license to use chain-addition inside the parentheses rather than compose Φ six times. The boundary components, unsigned, are

$$(\Phi \circ \Delta_{1,0}^3)(\theta, z) = (0, 0, z),$$
$$(\Phi \circ \Delta_{1,a}^3)(\theta, z) = (a \cos \theta, a \sin \theta, z),$$
$$(\Phi \circ \Delta_{2,0}^3)(r, z) = (r, 0, z),$$
$$(\Phi \circ \Delta_{2,2\pi}^3)(r, z) = (r, 0, z),$$
$$(\Phi \circ \Delta_{3,0}^3)(r, \theta) = (r \cos \theta, r \sin \theta, 0),$$
$$(\Phi \circ \Delta_{3,b}^3)(r, \theta) = (r \cos \theta, r \sin \theta, b).$$

The first component maps to the z-axis from 0 to b, which is trivial as a 2-surface in the sense that integrating any 2-form over it will give 0. The second component maps to the vertical outside of the cylinder (the label on the can), and the positive sign that it carries connotes that the associated normal vector at each point of the vertical outside of the cylinder points outward. The third and fourth components map to a solid $a \times b$ rectangle in the (x, z)-plane, inside the solid cylinder; these are not trivial as 2-surfaces, but the components carry opposite signs and so they cancel. The last two components map to the bottom and the top of the cylinder, and the signs that they carry connote that in each case the natural normal vector points outward. Thus the boundary of the cylinder is as expected.

For another example, let B_3 denote the solid unit ball in $\mathbb{R}^3$. Let a, b, c be positive numbers, and consider the surface that dilates the ball to the associated solid ellipsoid

$$\Phi : B_3 \longrightarrow \mathbb{R}^3, \qquad \Phi(x, y, z) = (ax, by, cz).$$

Since the parameter domain of Φ is not a box, Φ is not a singular 3-cube even under the looser grammar that we have granted ourselves. Thus, to compute the boundary of Φ formally, we should preparametrize B_3 from a box using the spherical coordinate system, $\Psi : [0, 1] \times [0, 2\pi] \times [0, \pi] \longrightarrow B_3$, and then understand that $\partial \Phi$ really means $\partial(\Phi \circ \Psi) = \Phi \circ \Psi \circ \partial \Delta^3$, where the notation Δ^3 is being stretched a little as in the previous example, because the parameter domain of Ψ isn't literally $[0, 1]^3$. Inevitably, the boundary of the ball works out to be its spherical skin, although it is unfortunately oriented so that the natural normal vector points inward in consequence of our spherical coordinate system reversing orientation. (See Exercise 9.13.3.) Consequently the boundary of the ellipsoid is its skin as well.

Exercises

9.13.1. Define a singular k-cube called the **simplex**, $\Phi : [0, 1]^k \longrightarrow \mathbb{R}^k$, by

$$\Phi(u_1, \ldots, u_k) = \left(u_1, (1 - u_1) u_2, (1 - u_1)(1 - u_2) u_3, \ldots, \prod_{i=1}^{k-1} (1 - u_i) u_k \right).$$

(a) Let $(x_1, \ldots, x_k) = \Phi(u_1, \ldots, u_k)$. Show that $\sum_{i=1}^{k} x_i = 1 - \prod_{i=1}^{k}(1 - u_i)$.
(b) Show that the image of Φ lies in the set (also called the simplex)

$$S = \{(x_1, \ldots, x_k) : x_1 \geq 0, \ldots, x_k \geq 0, \sum_{i=1}^{k} x_i \leq 1\}.$$

(In fact, the image is all of the simplex, but showing this would take us too far afield.)

(c) For each of the values $k = 1, 2, 3$, do the following. Calculate $\partial \Phi$ (the result is a $(k-1)$-chain). Graph $\partial \Phi$ by graphing each $(k-1)$-cube in the chain and indicating its coefficient $(+1$ or $-1)$ beneath the graph. Each graph should show $[0,1]^{k-1}$ and $\mathbb{R}^k$.

9.13.2. Describe the boundary of the hemispherical shell $H : D \longrightarrow \mathbb{R}^3$ where D is the unit disk in $\mathbb{R}^2$ and $H(x,y) = (x, y, \sqrt{1 - x^2 - y^2})$. (You might parametrize D from $[0,1]^2$ and then compute the boundary of the composition, or you might simply push ∂D from this section through H.)

9.13.3. Describe the boundary of the solid unit upper hemisphere

$$\mathbb{H} = \{(x, y, z) \in \mathbb{R}^3 : x^2 + y^2 + z^2 \leq 1, z \geq 0\}.$$

(Since $\mathbb{H}$ is being described as a set, parametrize it.)

9.13.4. Describe the boundary of the paraboloid $\Phi : D \longrightarrow \mathbb{R}^3$ where again D is the unit disk in $\mathbb{R}^2$ and

$$\Phi(u, v) = (u, v, u^2 + v^2).$$

9.13.5. Describe the boundary of $\Phi : [0, 2\pi] \times [0, \pi] \longrightarrow \mathbb{R}^3$ where

$$\Phi(\theta, \phi) = (\cos\theta \sin\phi, \sin\theta \sin\phi, \cos\phi).$$

(Before going straight to calculations, it will help to understand the geometry of the problem, especially the interpretation of θ and ϕ in the image-space $\mathbb{R}^3$.)

9.13.6. Describe the boundary of $\Phi : [0, 1] \times [0, 2\pi] \times [0, \pi] \longrightarrow \mathbb{R}^3$ where

$$\Phi(\rho, \theta, \phi) = (\rho\cos\theta \sin\phi, \rho\sin\theta \sin\phi, \rho\cos\phi).$$

(Again, first make sure that you understand the geometry of the problem, especially the interpretation of the parametrizing variables in the image-space.) How does this exercise combine with the result $\partial^2 = 0$ to bear on Exercise 9.13.5?

9.13.7. Fix constants $0 < a < b$. Describe the boundary of $\Phi : [0, 2\pi] \times [0, 2\pi] \times [0, 1] \longrightarrow \mathbb{R}^3$ where $\Phi(u, v, t) = ((b + at\cos v)\cos u, (b + at\cos v)\sin u, at\sin v)$. (First understand the geometry, especially the interpretation of u, v, and t in the image-space.)

9.13.8. This exercise gives a self-contained proof that the double boundary operator is identically zero. It suffices to show this for the double boundary on the standard k-cube, where $k \geq 2$.

(a) Explain why the double boundary is

$$\partial^2 \Delta^k = \sum_{i=1}^{k} \sum_{\alpha=0}^{1} \sum_{j=1}^{k-1} \sum_{\beta=0}^{1} (-1)^{i+j+\alpha+\beta} \Delta_{i,\alpha}^{k} \circ \Delta_{j,\beta}^{k-1}.$$

(b) Show that if $i \leq j$ then we have

$$\Delta_{i,\alpha}^{k} \circ \Delta_{j,\beta}^{k-1}(u_1, \ldots, u_{k-2}) = (u_1, \ldots, u_{i-1}, \alpha, u_i, \ldots, u_{j-1}, \beta, u_j, \ldots, u_{k-2}),$$

with α in the ith slot and β in the $(j+1)$st slot, whereas if $i > j$ then we have

$$\Delta_{i,\alpha}^{k} \circ \Delta_{j,\beta}^{k-1}(u_1, \ldots, u_{k-2})(u_1, \ldots, u_{j-1}, \beta, u_j, \ldots, u_{i-2}, \alpha, u_{i-1}, \ldots, u_{k-2}),$$

with β in the jth slot and α in the ith slot. Thus the double boundary of the standard k-cube consists of two sums, written as formal sums of functions of the variables $u_1, \ldots, u_{k-2}$,

$$\partial^2 \Delta = \sum_{i=1}^{k-1} \sum_{j=i}^{k-1} (-1)^{i+j+\alpha+\beta} (u_1, \ldots, u_{i-1}, \alpha, u_i, \ldots, u_{j-1}, \beta, u_j, \ldots, u_{k-2})$$

$$+ \sum_{i=1}^{k} \sum_{j=1}^{i-1} (-1)^{i+j+\alpha+\beta} (u_1, \ldots, u_{j-1}, \beta, u_j, \ldots, u_{i-2}, \alpha, u_{i-1}, \ldots, u_{k-2}).$$

(c) Explain why the second double sum can instead be written as

$$\sum_{j=1}^{k-1} \sum_{i=j+1}^{k} (-1)^{i+j+\alpha+\beta} (u_1, \ldots, u_{j-1}, \beta, u_j, \ldots, u_{i-2}, \alpha, u_{i-1}, \ldots, u_{k-2}).$$

(d) Convince yourself that it is valid to replace i by $i+1$ in this new second sum, and that doing so gives

$$-\sum_{j=1}^{k-1} \sum_{i=j}^{k-1} (-1)^{i+j+\alpha+\beta} (u_1, \ldots, u_{j-1}, \beta, u_j, \ldots, u_{i-1}, \alpha, u_i, \ldots, u_{k-2}),$$

now with α in the $(i+1)$st slot.

(e) Convince yourself that it is valid to exchange the roles of i and j, and to exchange the roles of α and β, and that doing so gives

$$-\sum_{i=1}^{k-1} \sum_{j=i}^{k-1} (-1)^{i+j+\alpha+\beta} (u_1, \ldots, u_{i-1}, \alpha, u_i, \ldots, u_{j-1}, \beta, u_j, \ldots, u_{k-2}).$$

This cancels the first sum, so we are done.

9.14 The General Fundamental Theorem of Integral Calculus

As mentioned in the previous section, the algebraic encoding d of the derivative (an analytic operator) and the algebraic encoding ∂ of the boundary (a geometric operator) are complementary with respect to integration:

Theorem 9.14.1 (General FTIC). *Let A be an open subset of $\mathbb{R}^n$. Let C be a k-chain in A, and let ω be a $(k-1)$-form on A. Then*

$$\int_{\mathcal{C}} d\omega = \int_{\partial \mathcal{C}} \omega. \tag{9.17}$$

Before proving the theorem, we study two examples. First, suppose that $k = n = 1$, and that the 1-chain $\mathcal{C}$ is a singular 1-cube $\Phi : [0, 1] \longrightarrow \mathbb{R}$ taking 0 and 1 to some points a and b. Then the theorem says that for every suitable smooth function f,

$$\int_a^b f'(x)\, dx = f(b) - f(a).$$

This is the one-variable fundamental theorem of integral calculus. Thus, whatever else we are doing, we are indeed generalizing it.

Second, to study a simple case involving more than one variable, suppose that $\mathcal{C} = \Delta^2$ (the standard 2-cube) and $\omega = f(x, y)\, dy$ for some smooth function $f : [0, 1]^2 \longrightarrow \mathbb{R}$. The derivative on the left side of (9.17) works out to

$$d\omega = D_1 f(x, y)\, dx \wedge dy,$$

Exercise 9.5.4 says that we may drop the wedges from the integral of this 2-form over the full-dimensional surface Δ^2 in 2-space to obtain a Chapter 6 function-integral, and so the left side of (9.17) works out to

$$\int_{\Delta^2} d\omega = \int_{\Delta^2} D_1 f(x, y)\, dx \wedge dy = \int_{[0,1]^2} D_1 f.$$

Meanwhile, on the right side of (9.17), the boundary $\partial \Delta^2$ has four pieces, but on the two horizontal pieces dy is zero because y is constant. Thus only the integrals over the two vertical pieces contribute, giving

$$\int_{\partial \Delta^2} \omega = \int_{u=0}^1 f(1, u) - \int_{u=0}^1 f(0, u) = \int_{u=0}^1 f(1, u) - f(0, u).$$

By the one-variable fundamental theorem, the integrand is

$$f(1, u) - f(0, u) = \int_{t=0}^1 D_1 f(t, u),$$

and so by Fubini's theorem, the integral is

$$\int_{u=0}^1 \int_{t=0}^1 D_1 f(t, u) = \int_{[0,1]^2} D_1 f.$$

Thus both sides of (9.17) work out to $\int_{[0,1]^2} D_1 f$, making them equal, as desired, and the general FTIC holds in this case. The first step of its proof is essentially the same process as in this example.

Proof. Recall that we want to establish formula (9.17), $\int_C d\omega = \int_{\partial C} \omega$, where C is a k-chain and ω is a $(k-1)$-form. Begin with the special case that C is the standard k-cube,

$$C = \Delta^k,$$

and ω takes the form $\omega = f(x)\, dx_1 \wedge \cdots \wedge \widehat{dx_j} \wedge \cdots \wedge dx_k$, where $x = (x_1, \ldots, x_k)$ and the $\frown$ means to omit the term. Thus

$$\omega = f(x)\, dx_J \quad \text{where } J = (1, \ldots, \widehat{j}, \ldots, k).$$

To evaluate the left side $\int_C d\omega$ of (9.17), we need to compute $d\omega$. In this special case,

$$d\omega = D_j f(x)\, dx_j \wedge dx_J = (-1)^{j-1} D_j f\, dx_{(1,\ldots,k)},$$

and so by Exercise 9.5.4, the left side reduces to the function-integral of the jth partial derivative over the unit box,

$$\int_{\Delta^k} d\omega = (-1)^{j-1} \int_{\Delta^k} D_j f\, dx_{(1,\ldots,k)} = (-1)^{j-1} \int_{[0,1]^k} D_j f. \tag{9.18}$$

To evaluate the right side $\int_{\partial C} \omega$ of (9.17), we need to examine the boundary

$$\partial \Delta^k = \sum_{i=1}^{k} \sum_{\alpha=0}^{1} (-1)^{i+\alpha} \Delta^k_{i,\alpha},$$

where $\Delta^k_{i,\alpha}(u_1, \ldots, u_{k-1}) = (u_1, \ldots, u_{i-1}, \alpha, u_i, \ldots, u_{k-1})$. Note that

$$(\Delta^k_{i,\alpha})' = \left[\begin{array}{ccc|ccc}
1 & 0 \cdots 0 & 0 \cdots 0 \\
0 & 1 \cdots 0 & 0 \cdots 0 \\
\vdots & \vdots \ddots \vdots & \vdots \quad \vdots \\
0 & 0 \cdots 1 & 0 \cdots 0 \\
\hline
0 & 0 \cdots 0 & 0 \cdots 0 \\
0 & 0 \cdots 0 & 1 \cdots 0 \\
\vdots & \vdots \quad \vdots & \vdots \ddots \vdots \\
0 & 0 \cdots 0 & 0 \cdots 1
\end{array} \right].$$

This derivative matrix is $k \times (k-1)$, consisting of the identity matrix except that zeros have been inserted at the ith row, displacing everything from there downward. Meanwhile, recall that $J = (1, \ldots, \widehat{j}, \ldots, k)$, where the omitted index j is fixed throughout this calculation. It follows that as the index i of summation varies, the determinant of the Jth rows of the matrix is

$$\det(\Delta^k_{i,\alpha})'_J = \begin{cases} 1 & \text{if } i = j, \\ 0 & \text{if } i \neq j. \end{cases}$$

That is, the integral of $\omega = f(x)\,dx_J$ can be nonzero only for the two terms in the boundary chain $\partial\Delta^k$ with $i = j$, parametrizing the two boundary faces whose normal vectors point in the direction missing from dx_J:

$$\int_{\partial\Delta^k} f(x)\,dx_J = \int_{(-1)^{j+1}(\Delta^k_{j,1}-\Delta^k_{j,0})} f(x)\,dx_J$$

$$= (-1)^{j+1}\int_{[0,1]^{k-1}}(f\circ\Delta^k_{j,1})\cdot 1 - (f\circ\Delta^k_{j,0})\cdot 1.$$

Here the last equality follows from the definition of integration over chains and the defining formula (9.14). For every point $u = (u_1,\dots,u_{k-1})\in[0,1]^{k-1}$, the integrand can be rewritten as an integral of the jth partial derivative by the one-variable fundamental theorem of integral calculus,

$$(f\circ\Delta^k_{j,1} - f\circ\Delta^k_{j,0})(u)$$

$$= f(u_1,\dots,u_{j-1},1,u_j,\dots,u_{k-1}) - f(u_1,\dots,u_{j-1},0,u_j,\dots,u_{k-1})$$

$$= \int_{t\in[0,1]} D_j f(u_1,\dots,u_{j-1},t,u_j,\dots,u_{k-1}).$$

Therefore, the right side of (9.17) is

$$\int_{\partial\Delta^k}\omega = (-1)^{j+1}\int_{u\in[0,1]^{k-1}}\int_{t\in[0,1]} D_j f(u_1,\dots,u_{j-1},t,u_j,\dots,u_{k-1}).$$

By Fubini's theorem this is equal to the right side of (9.18), and so the general FTIC is proved in the special case.

The rest of the proof is handled effortlessly by the machinery of forms and chains. A general $(k-1)$-form on $[0,1]^k$ is

$$\omega = \sum_{j=1}^{k}\omega_j,\quad \text{each }\omega_j = f_j(x)\,dx_1\wedge\cdots\wedge\widehat{dx_j}\wedge\cdots\wedge dx_k.$$

Each ω_j is a form of the type covered by the special case, and $d\omega = \sum_j d\omega_j$. So, continuing to integrate over the standard k-cube, and citing the special case just shown for the crucial third equality,

$$\int_{\Delta^k} d\omega = \int_{\Delta^k}\sum_j d\omega_j = \sum_j\int_{\Delta^k} d\omega_j$$

$$= \sum_j\int_{\partial\Delta^k}\omega_j = \int_{\partial\Delta^k}\sum_j\omega_j = \int_{\partial\Delta^k}\omega.$$

Thus the theorem holds for a general form when $\mathcal{C} = \Delta^k$.

For a singular k-cube Φ in A and for every $(k-1)$-form ω on A, we now have

$$\int_{\Phi} d\omega = \int_{\Delta^k} \Phi^*(d\omega) \qquad \text{by the pullback theorem}$$

$$= \int_{\Delta^k} d(\Phi^*\omega) \qquad \text{since derivative commutes with pullback}$$

$$= \int_{\partial\Delta^k} \Phi^*\omega \qquad \text{since the result holds on } \Delta^k$$

$$= \int_{\Phi \circ \partial \Delta^k} \omega \qquad \begin{array}{l}\text{by the change of variable theorem for}\\ \text{differential forms, extended to chains}\end{array}$$

$$= \int_{\partial\Phi} \omega \qquad \text{by definition of boundary.}$$

So the result holds for singular cubes.

Finally, for a k-chain $C = \sum_s \nu_s \Phi_{(s)}$ in A and for every $(k-1)$-form ω on A,

$$\int_C d\omega = \int_{\sum_s \nu_s \Phi_{(s)}} d\omega = \sum_s \nu_s \int_{\Phi_{(s)}} d\omega = \sum_s \nu_s \int_{\partial\Phi_{(s)}} \omega,$$

with the third equality due to the result for singular cubes, and the calculation continues

$$\sum_s \nu_s \int_{\partial\Phi_{(s)}} \omega = \int_{\sum_s \nu_s \partial\Phi_{(s)}} \omega = \int_{\partial(\sum_s \nu_s \Phi_{(s)})} \omega = \int_{\partial C} \omega.$$

This completes the proof. $\qquad\qquad\qquad\qquad\qquad\qquad\qquad\qquad\qquad\qquad\square$

The beauty of this argument is that the only analytic results that it uses are the one-variable FTIC and Fubini's theorem, and the only geometry that it uses is the definition of the boundary of a standard k-cube. All the twisting and turning of k-surfaces and their boundaries in n-space is filtered out automatically by the algebra of differential forms.

Computationally, the general FTIC will sometimes give you a choice between evaluating two integrals, one of which may be easier to work. Note that the integral of lower dimension may not be the preferable one, however; for example, integrating over a solid 3-cube may be quicker than integrating over the six faces of its boundary.

Conceptually the general FTIC is exciting because it allows the possibility of evaluating an integral over a region by antidifferentiating and then integrating only over the boundary of the region instead.

Exercises

9.14.1. Similarly to the second example before the proof of the general FTIC, show that the theorem holds when $C = \Delta^3$ and $\omega = f(x, y, z)\,dz \wedge dx$.

9.14.2. Prove as a corollary to the general FTIC that $\partial^2 = 0$, in the sense that $\int_{\partial^2 C} \omega = 0$ for all forms ω.

9.14.3. Let $\mathcal{C}$ be a k-chain in $\mathbb{R}^n$, $f : \mathbb{R}^n \longrightarrow \mathbb{R}$ a function, and ω a $(k-1)$-form on $\mathbb{R}^n$. Use the general FTIC to prove a generalization of the formula for integration by parts,

$$\int_{\mathcal{C}} f \, d\omega = \int_{\partial\mathcal{C}} f\omega - \int_{\mathcal{C}} df \wedge \omega.$$

9.14.4. Let Φ be a 4-chain in $\mathbb{R}^4$ with boundary $\partial\Phi$. Suitably specialize the general FTIC to prove the identity

$$\int_{\partial\Phi} f_1 \, dy \wedge dz \wedge dw + f_2 \, dz \wedge dw \wedge dx + f_3 \, dw \wedge dx \wedge dy + f_4 \, dx \wedge dy \wedge dz$$

$$= \int_{\Phi} (D_1 f_1 - D_2 f_2 + D_3 f_3 - D_4 f_4) \, dx \wedge dy \wedge dz \wedge dw.$$

Here the order of the variables is (x, y, z, w).

9.15 Classical Change of Variable Revisited

The most technical argument in these notes is the proof of the classical change of variable theorem (Theorem 6.7.1) in Sections 6.8 and 6.9. The analytic results contributing to the proof were the one-variable change of variable theorem and Fubini's theorem, and of these, the one-variable change of variable theorem is a consequence of the one-variable FTIC. Meanwhile, the analytic results contributing to the proof of the general FTIC were the one-variable FTIC and Fubini's theorem. Thus the proofs of the multivariable classical change of variable theorem and of the general FTIC rely on the same analysis. However, the proof of the general FTIC was easy. Now, with the general FTIC in hand, we revisit the classical change of variable theorem, sketching the light, graceful proof that it deserves in turn.

The first issue to address is that the classical change of variable theorem has been quoted in this chapter, and so if we now propose to revisit its proof then we must take care not to argue in a circle. In fact, our only uses of the classical change of variable theorem in this chapter were to prove that integrals of functions over surfaces are independent of reparametrization (the end of Section 9.1) and that integrals of differential forms over surfaces are independent of orientation-preserving reparametrization (Exercise 9.5.5). The proof of the general FTIC requires neither the classical change of variable theorem nor independence of parametrization. Thus this chapter could have proceeded without the classical change of variable theorem, but then requiring us to remember that all of its results were provisionally parametrization-dependent. A schematic layout of the ideas is shown in Figure 9.16.

Nonetheless, even the parametrization-dependent general FTIC, which we may grant ourselves without the classical change of variable theorem, is a powerful result, and in particular it leads to the conceptually different proof of the classical change of variable theorem. Once the theorem is proved, we

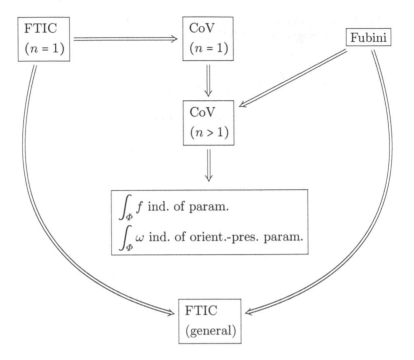

Figure 9.16. Layout of the main results as established so far

may conclude that this chapter's results are independent of parametrization after all. Being patient gives us the same results more easily. The provisional new layout of the ideas is shown in Figure 9.17. The improved organization is clear.

Let J be a box in $\mathbb{R}^n$, and consider a smooth change of variable mapping

$$\Phi : J \longrightarrow \mathbb{R}^n.$$

(See Figure 9.18.) Assume that

$$\det \Phi' > 0 \quad \text{everywhere on } J.$$

To prove the classical change of variable theorem, we need to show that the following formula holds for every smooth function $f : \Phi(J) \longrightarrow \mathbb{R}$:

$$\int_{\Phi(J)} f = \int_J (f \circ \Phi) \cdot \det \Phi'.$$

View the mapping Φ as a singular n-cube in $\mathbb{R}^n$. (Since J need not be the unit box, the definition of a singular n-cube is being extended here slightly to allow any box as the domain. The boundary operator extends correspondingly, as discussed at the end of Section 9.13.) Consider the trivial parametrization of the image of the cube,

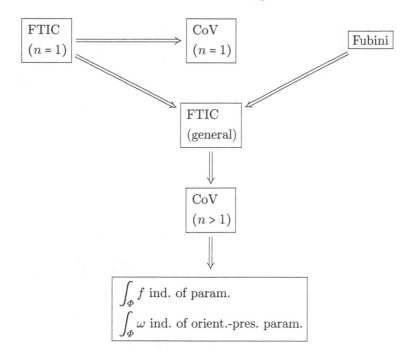

Figure 9.17. Provisional layout of the main results after this section

$$\Delta^{\Phi(J)} : \Phi(J) \longrightarrow \mathbb{R}^n, \qquad \Delta^{\Phi(J)}(x) = x \text{ for all } x \in \Phi(J).$$

Let Δ^J be the trivial parametrization of J. In the language of differential forms, the formula that we need to prove is

$$\int_{\Delta^{\Phi(J)}} \omega = \int_{\Delta^J} \Phi^* \omega \quad \text{where } \omega = f(x)\, dx. \tag{9.19}$$

Here $x = (x_1, \ldots, x_n)$ and $dx = dx_1 \wedge \cdots \wedge dx_n$, and the pullback on the right side of the equality is $\Phi^* \omega = (f \circ \Phi)(x) \det \Phi'(x)\, dx$. (Note that applying the pullback theorem (Theorem 9.10.1) reduces the desired formula to

$$\int_{\Delta^{\Phi(J)}} \omega = \int_{\Phi} \omega,$$

i.e., to independence of parametrization, the one result in this chapter that relied on the classical change of variable theorem.) The starting idea of this section is to try to derive (9.19) from the general FTIC.

To see how this might be done, begin by reviewing the derivation of the one-variable change of variable theorem from the one-variable FTIC, displaying the calculation in two parts,

$$\int_{\phi(a)}^{\phi(b)} f = \int_{\phi(a)}^{\phi(b)} F' = F(\phi(b)) - F(\phi(a)) \tag{9.20}$$

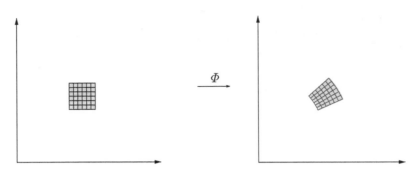

Figure 9.18. The singular cube Φ

and

$$\int_a^b (f \circ \phi) \cdot \phi' = \int_a^b (F \circ \phi)' = (F \circ \phi)(b) - (F \circ \phi)(a). \tag{9.21}$$

Since the right sides are equal, so are the left sides, giving the theorem. Here the first version of the one-variable FTIC (Theorem 6.4.1) provides the antiderivative $F = \int_{\phi(a)}^x f$ of f.

Now, starting from the integral on the left side of the desired equality (9.19), attempt to pattern-match the calculation (9.20) without yet worrying about whether the steps are justified or even meaningful,

$$\int_{\Delta^{\Phi(J)}} \omega = \int_{\Delta^{\Phi(J)}} d\lambda = \int_{\partial \Delta^{\Phi(J)}} \lambda. \tag{9.22}$$

Similarly, the integral on the right side of (9.19) looks like the integral at the beginning of the calculation (9.21), so pattern-match again,

$$\int_{\Delta^J} \Phi^* \omega = \int_{\Delta^J} d(\Phi^* \lambda) = \int_{\partial \Delta^J} \Phi^* \lambda. \tag{9.23}$$

Thus it suffices to show that the right sides are equal,

$$\int_{\partial \Delta^{\Phi(J)}} \lambda = \int_{\partial \Delta^J} \Phi^* \lambda.$$

This formula looks like the desired (9.19) but with $(n-1)$-dimensional integrals of $(n-1)$-forms. Perhaps we are discovering a proof of the multivariable change of variable theorem by induction on the number of variables. But we need to check whether the calculation is sensible.

Just as the one-variable calculation rewrote f as F', the putative multivariable calculation has rewritten ω as $d\lambda$, but this needs justification. Recall that $\omega = f(x)\,dx$. Although $\Phi(J)$ is not a box, an application of Theorem 6.4.1 to the first variable shows that in the small, f takes the form

$$f(x_1, x_2, \ldots, x_n) = D_1 F(x_1, x_2, \ldots, x_n).$$

Consequently the λ in our calculation can be taken as

$$\lambda = F(x)\,dx_2 \wedge \cdots \wedge dx_n,$$

provided that whatever we are doing is on a small enough scale. So now we assume that the box J is small enough that the argument of this paragraph applies at each point of the nonbox $\Phi(J)$. We can do this by partitioning the original box J finely enough into subboxes J' and then carrying out the proof for each subbox. Alternatively, by Proposition 6.9.3 we may assume that f is identically 1 and then take $F(x) = x_1$. Or, to avoid any specific calculation we may assume that the box J is small enough that $\Phi(J)$ is contractible, and then ω has an antiderivative λ by Poincaré's theorem, Theorem 9.11.2. Once we have λ, the objects in (9.23) are noncontroversial and the steps are clear, except perhaps the tacit exchange of the derivative and the pullback in the first step of pattern-matching. The remaining issue is what to make of the symbol-pattern $\int_{\Delta^{\Phi(J)}} d\lambda = \int_{\partial\Delta^{\Phi(J)}} \lambda$ in (9.22). Recall that $\Delta^{\Phi(J)}$ is the trivial parametrization of $\Phi(J)$. However, in dimension $n > 1$, $\Phi(J)$ is not a box, so $\Delta^{\Phi(J)}$ is not a cube, and so $\partial\Delta^{\Phi(J)}$ has no meaning. Even if we know the topological boundary of $\Phi(J)$ (the points arbitrarily close to $\Phi(J)$ and to its complement), the topological boundary inherits no canonical traversal from the trivial parametrization. The calculation is not sensible.

A 1999 article by Peter Lax in the *American Mathematical Monthly* shows how to solve this problem. Recall that we are working with a mapping

$$\Phi : J \longrightarrow \mathbb{R}^n.$$

The box J is compact, and hence so is its continuous image $\Phi(J)$. Therefore some large box B contains them both. If J is small enough then because $\det \Phi' > 0$ on J, it follows from some analysis that Φ extends to a mapping

$$\Psi : B \longrightarrow \mathbb{R}^n$$

such that

- Ψ is the original Φ on J,
- Ψ takes the complement of J in B to the complement of $\Phi(B)$ in B,
- Ψ is the identity mapping on the boundary of B.

(See Figure 9.19.) Furthermore, the n-form ω on the original $\Phi(J)$ can be modified into a form ω on the larger set B such that

- ω is the original ω on $\Phi(J)$,
- $\omega = 0$ essentially everywhere off the original $\Phi(J)$.

And now that the nonbox $\Phi(J)$ has been replaced by the box B, the calculation of the antiderivative form λ such that $\omega = d\lambda$ works in the large.

Let Δ^B denote the trivial parametrization of B. Then the properties of Ψ and ω show that the desired equality (9.19) has become

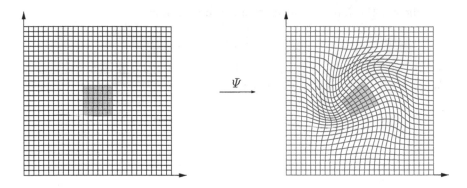

Figure 9.19. The extension of Φ to B

$$\int_{\Delta^B} \omega = \int_{\Delta^B} \Psi^* \omega,$$

the integrals on both sides now being taken over the same box B. Again pattern-matching the one-variable proof shows that the integral on the left side is

$$\int_{\Delta^B} \omega = \int_{\Delta^B} d\lambda = \int_{\partial \Delta^B} \lambda$$

and the integral on the right side is

$$\int_{\Delta^B} \Psi^* \omega = \int_{\Delta^B} d(\Psi^* \lambda) = \int_{\partial \Delta^B} \Psi^* \lambda,$$

where everything here makes sense. Thus the problem is reduced to proving that

$$\int_{\partial \Delta^B} \lambda = \int_{\partial \Delta^B} \Psi^* \lambda.$$

And now the desired equality is immediate: since Ψ is the identity mapping on the boundary of B, the pullback Ψ^* in the right-side integral of the previous display does nothing, and the two integrals are equal. (See Exercise 9.15.1 for a slight variant of this argument.) The multivariable argument has ended exactly as the one-variable argument did. We did not need to argue by induction after all.

In sum, the general FTIC lets us side-step the traditional proof of the classical change of variable theorem, by expanding the environment of the problem to a larger box and then reducing the scope of the question to the larger box's boundary. On the boundary there is no longer any difference between the two quantities that we want to be equal, and so we are done.

The reader may well object that the argument here is only heuristic, and that there is no reason to believe that its missing technical details will be any less onerous than those of the usual proof the classical change of variable theorem. The difficulty of the usual proof is that it involves nonboxes, while the analytic details of how this argument proceeds from the nonbox $\Phi(J)$ to a box B were not given. Along with the extensions of Φ and ω to B being invoked, the partitioning of J into small enough subboxes was handwaved. Furthermore, the change of variable mapping Φ is assumed here to be smooth, whereas in Theorem 6.7.1 it need only be $\mathcal{C}^1$. But none of these matters is serious. A second article by Lax, written in response to such objections, shows how to take care of them. Although some analysis is admittedly being elided here, the new argument nonetheless feels more graceful to the author of these notes than the older one.

Exercise

9.15.1. Show that in the argument at the end of this section, we could instead reason about the integral on the right side that

$$\int_{\Delta^B} \Psi^* \omega = \int_\Psi d\lambda = \int_{\partial \Psi} \lambda.$$

Thus the problem is reduced to proving that $\int_{\partial \Delta^B} \lambda = \int_{\partial \Psi} \lambda$. Explain why the desired equality is immediate.

9.16 The Classical Theorems

The classical integration theorems of vector calculus arise from specializing n and k in the general FTIC. As already noted, the values $n = k = 1$ give the one-variable FTIC,

$$\int_a^b \frac{df}{dx}\, dx = f(b) - f(a).$$

If $k = 1$ but n is left arbitrary then the result is familiar from Section 9.4. For a curve $\gamma : [0, 1] \longrightarrow \mathbb{R}^n$, let $a = \gamma(0)$ and $b = \gamma(1)$. Then

$$\int_\gamma \frac{\partial f}{\partial x_1}\, dx_1 + \cdots + \frac{\partial f}{\partial x_n}\, dx_n = f(b) - f(a).$$

Setting $n = 2$, $k = 2$ gives **Green's theorem**: Let A be an open subset of $\mathbb{R}^2$. For every singular 2-cube Φ in A and functions $f, g : A \longrightarrow \mathbb{R}$,

$$\iint_\Phi \left(\frac{\partial g}{\partial x} - \frac{\partial f}{\partial y} \right) dx \wedge dy = \int_{\partial \Phi} f\, dx + g\, dy.$$

The double integral sign is used on the left side of Green's theorem to emphasize that the integral is two-dimensional. Naturally the classical statement doesn't refer to a singular cube or include a wedge. Instead, the idea classically is to view Φ as a set in the plane and require a traversal of $\partial \Phi$ (also

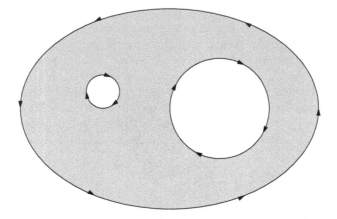

Figure 9.20. Traversing the boundary in Green's theorem

viewed as a set) such that Φ is always to the left as one moves along $\partial\Phi$. Other than this, the boundary integral is independent of how the boundary is traversed because the whole theory is invariant under orientation-preserving reparametrization. (See Figure 9.20.)

Green's theorem has two geometric interpretations. To understand them, first let $A \subset \mathbb{R}^2$ be open and think of a vector-valued mapping $\vec{F} : A \longrightarrow \mathbb{R}^2$ as defining a fluid flow in A. Define two related scalar-valued functions on A,

$$\operatorname{curl} \vec{F} = D_1 F_2 - D_2 F_1 \qquad \text{and} \qquad \operatorname{div} \vec{F} = D_1 F_1 + D_2 F_2.$$

These are two-dimensional versions of the quantities from exercises 9.8.4 and 9.8.5. Now consider a point p in A. Note that $\operatorname{curl} \vec{F}(p)$ and $\operatorname{div} \vec{F}(p)$ depend only on the derivatives of $\vec{F}$ at p, not on $\vec{F}(p)$ itself. So replacing $\vec{F}$ by $\vec{F} - \vec{F}(p)$, we may assume that $\vec{F}(p) = \mathbf{0}$, i.e., the fluid flow is stationary at p. Recall that $D_1 F_2$ is the rate of change of the vertical component of F with respect to change in the horizontal component of its input, and $D_2 F_1$ is the rate of change of the horizontal component of F with respect to change in the vertical component of its input. The left side of Figure 9.21 shows a scenario in which the two terms $D_1 F_2$ and $-D_2 F_1$ of $(\operatorname{curl} \vec{F})(p)$ are positive. The figure illustrates why $\operatorname{curl} \vec{F}$ is interpreted as measuring the vorticity of $\vec{F}$ at p, its tendency to rotate a paddle wheel at p counterclockwise. Similarly, $D_1 F_1$ is the rate of change of the horizontal component of F with respect to change in the horizontal component of its input, and $D_2 F_2$ is the rate of change of the vertical component of F with respect to change in the vertical component of its input. The right side of Figure 9.21 shows a scenario in which the terms of $(\operatorname{div} \vec{F})(p)$ are positive. The figure illustrates why $\operatorname{div} \vec{F}$ is viewed as measuring the extent to which fluid is spreading out from p, i.e., how much fluid is being pumped into or drained out of the system at the point. Specifically, the left side of the figure shows the vector field

$$\vec{F}(x,y) = (-y,x)$$

whose curl and divergence at the origin are

$$(\text{curl}\,\vec{F})(\mathbf{0}) = 2, \qquad (\text{div}\,\vec{F})(\mathbf{0}) = 0,$$

and the right side shows (with some artistic license taken to make the figure legible rather than accurate) the vector field

$$\vec{F}(x,y) = (x,y)$$

whose curl and divergence at the origin are

$$(\text{curl}\,\vec{F})(\mathbf{0}) = 0, \qquad (\text{div}\,\vec{F})(\mathbf{0}) = 2.$$

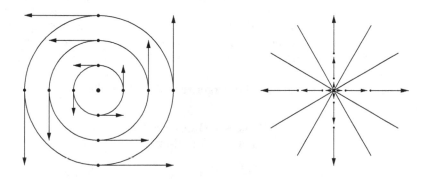

Figure 9.21. Positive curl and positive divergence

For the two geometric interpretations of Green's theorem, introduce the notation

$$dA = dx \wedge dy, \qquad \overrightarrow{ds} = (dx, dy), \qquad \overrightarrow{dn} = (dy, -dx).$$

The form-vectors $\overrightarrow{ds}$ and $\overrightarrow{dn}$ on $\partial\Phi$ are viewed respectively as differential increment around the boundary and differential outward normal (see Exercise 9.16.1), while dA is differential area. Then setting $\vec{F} = (f,g)$ and $\vec{F} = (g,-f)$ respectively shows that Green's theorem says that

$$\iint_{\Phi} \text{curl}\,\vec{F}\,dA = \int_{\partial\Phi} \vec{F}\cdot\overrightarrow{ds} \qquad \text{and} \qquad \iint_{\Phi} \text{div}\,\vec{F}\,dA = \int_{\partial\Phi} \vec{F}\cdot\overrightarrow{dn}.$$

The resulting two interpretations are

the net counterclockwise vorticity of $\vec{F}$ throughout Φ
equals the net flow of $\vec{F}$ counterclockwise around $\partial\Phi$

and

> the net positive rate of creation of fluid by $\vec{F}$ throughout Φ
> equals the net flux of $\vec{F}$ outward through $\partial\Phi$.

These interpretations appeal strongly to physical intuition.

We can also bring dimensional analysis to bear on the integrals in Green's theorem. Again view the vector field $\vec{F}$ as a velocity field describing a fluid flow. Thus each component function of $\vec{F}$ carries units of length over time (for instance, m/s). The partial derivatives that make up $\operatorname{curl}\vec{F}$ and $\operatorname{div}\vec{F}$ are derivatives with respect to space-variables, so the curl and the divergence carry units of reciprocal time (1/s). The units of the area-integral on the left side of Green's theorem are thus area over time $(1/\text{s}\cdot m^2 = m^2/\text{s})$, as are the units of the path-integral on the right side $(\text{m/s}\cdot\text{m} = m^2/\text{s}$ as well). Thus both integrals measure area per unit of time. If the fluid is incompressible then area of fluid is proportional to mass of fluid, and so both integrals essentially measure fluid per unit of time: the amount of fluid being created throughout the region per unit of time, and the amount of fluid passing through the boundary per unit of time; or the amount of fluid circulating throughout the region per unit of time, and the amount of fluid flowing along the boundary per unit of time.

The physical interpretations of divergence and curl will be discussed more carefully in the next section.

Setting $n = 3$, $k = 2$ gives **Stokes's theorem**: Let A be an open subset of $\mathbb{R}^3$. For a singular 2-cube Φ in A and functions $f, g, h : A \longrightarrow \mathbb{R}$,

$$\iint_\Phi \left(\frac{\partial h}{\partial y} - \frac{\partial g}{\partial z}\right) \mathrm{d}y \wedge \mathrm{d}z + \left(\frac{\partial f}{\partial z} - \frac{\partial h}{\partial x}\right) \mathrm{d}z \wedge \mathrm{d}x + \left(\frac{\partial g}{\partial x} - \frac{\partial f}{\partial y}\right) \mathrm{d}x \wedge \mathrm{d}y$$

$$= \int_{\partial\Phi} f \,\mathrm{d}x + g \,\mathrm{d}y + h \,\mathrm{d}z.$$

Introduce the notation

$$\overrightarrow{\mathrm{d}s} = (\mathrm{d}x, \mathrm{d}y, \mathrm{d}z) \qquad \text{and} \qquad \overrightarrow{\mathrm{d}n} = (\mathrm{d}y \wedge \mathrm{d}z, \mathrm{d}z \wedge \mathrm{d}x, \mathrm{d}x \wedge \mathrm{d}y),$$

and for a vector-valued mapping $\vec{F} : \mathbb{R}^3 \longrightarrow \mathbb{R}^3$ define

$$\operatorname{curl}\vec{F} = (D_2 F_3 - D_3 F_2, D_3 F_1 - D_1 F_3, D_1 F_2 - D_2 F_1).$$

Then setting $\vec{F} = (f, g, h)$ shows that Stokes's theorem is

$$\iint_\Phi \operatorname{curl}\vec{F}\cdot\overrightarrow{\mathrm{d}n} = \int_{\partial\Phi}\vec{F}\cdot\overrightarrow{\mathrm{d}s}.$$

As with Green's theorem, the classical statement doesn't refer to a singular cube or include a wedge. Instead, Φ is an orientable two-dimensional set in space, and its boundary $\partial\Phi$ is traversed counterclockwise about its normal vectors. The integrals in the previous display are both independent of how Φ and $\partial\Phi$ are parametrized, provided that the geometry is as just described.

To interpret Stokes's theorem, think of a mapping $\vec{F} : \mathbb{R}^3 \longrightarrow \mathbb{R}^3$ as describing a fluid flow in space. The mapping $\operatorname{curl} \vec{F}$ is interpreted as measuring the local vorticity of $\vec{F}$ around each positive coordinate direction. The form-vector $\overrightarrow{dn}$ on Φ is viewed as differential outward normal, while $\overrightarrow{ds}$ on $\partial\Phi$ is viewed as differential increment around the boundary. Thus the interpretation of Stokes's theorem is a 3-dimensional version of the first interpretation of Green's theorem,

> the net tangent vorticity of $\vec{F}$ throughout Φ
> equals the net flow of $\vec{F}$ around $\partial\Phi$.

Setting $n = 3$, $k = 3$ gives the **divergence theorem** (or **Gauss's theorem**): Let A be an open subset of $\mathbb{R}^3$. For a singular 3-cube Φ in A and functions $f, g, h : A \longrightarrow \mathbb{R}$,

$$\iiint_\Phi \left(\frac{\partial f}{\partial x} + \frac{\partial g}{\partial y} + \frac{\partial h}{\partial z} \right) dx \wedge dy \wedge dz = \iint_{\partial\Phi} f \, dy \wedge dz + g \, dz \wedge dx + h \, dx \wedge dy.$$

Introduce the notation

$$dV = dx \wedge dy \wedge dz,$$

and for a vector-valued mapping $\vec{F} : \mathbb{R}^3 \longrightarrow \mathbb{R}^3$ define

$$\operatorname{div} \vec{F} = D_1 F_1 + D_2 F_2 + D_3 F_3.$$

Then setting $\vec{F} = (f, g, h)$ shows that the divergence theorem is

$$\iiint_\Phi \operatorname{div} \vec{F} \, dV = \iint_{\partial\Phi} \vec{F} \cdot \overrightarrow{dn}.$$

Thus the interpretation of the divergence theorem is a 3-dimensional version of the second interpretation of Green's theorem,

> the net positive creation of fluid by $\vec{F}$ throughout Φ
> equals the net flux of $\vec{F}$ outward through $\partial\Phi$.

Again, the classical theorem views Φ and $\partial\Phi$ as sets, as long as whatever parametrization of $\partial\Phi$ is used to compute the right-side integral has the same orientation as the boundary of the parametrization of Φ used to compute the left-side integral.

Exercises

9.16.1. (a) Let $\gamma : [0,1] \longrightarrow \mathbb{R}^2$, $t \mapsto \gamma(t)$ be a curve, and recall the form-vectors on $\mathbb{R}^2$ $\overrightarrow{ds} = (dx, dy)$, $\overrightarrow{dn} = (dy, -dx)$. Compute the pullbacks $\gamma^*(\overrightarrow{ds})$ and $\gamma^*(\overrightarrow{dn})$ and explain why these are interpreted as differential tangent and normal vectors to γ.

(b) Let $\gamma : [0,1] \longrightarrow \mathbb{R}^3$, $t \mapsto \gamma(t)$ be a curve and $\Phi : [0,1]^2 \longrightarrow \mathbb{R}^3$, $(u,v) \mapsto \Phi(u,v)$ a surface, and recall the form-vectors on $\mathbb{R}^3$ $\overrightarrow{ds} = (dx, dy, dz)$, $\overrightarrow{dn} = (dy \wedge dz, dz \wedge dx, dx \wedge dy)$. Compute the pullbacks $\gamma^*(\overrightarrow{ds})$ and $\Phi^*(\overrightarrow{dn})$ and explain why these are interpreted respectively as differential tangent vector to γ and differential normal vector to Φ.

9.16.2. Use Green's theorem to show that for a planar region Φ,

$$\mathrm{area}(\Phi) = \int_{\partial\Phi} x\,dy = -\int_{\partial\Phi} y\,dx.$$

Thus one can measure the area of a planar set by traversing its boundary. (This principle was used to construct ingenious area-measuring machines called *planimeters* before Green's theorem was ever written down.)

9.16.3. Let H be the upper unit hemispherical shell,

$$H = \{(x,y,z) \in \mathbb{R}^3 : x^2 + y^2 + z^2 = 1, z \geq 0\}.$$

Define a vector-valued function on $\mathbb{R}^3$,

$$F(x,y,z) = (x + y + z, xy + yz + zx, xyz).$$

Use Stokes's theorem to calculate $\iint_H \mathrm{curl}\,F \cdot \overrightarrow{dn}$.

9.16.4. Use the divergence theorem to evaluate

$$\int_{\partial\mathbb{H}} x^2\,dy \wedge dz + y^2\,dz \wedge dx + z^2\,dx \wedge dy,$$

where $\partial\mathbb{H}$ is the boundary of the solid unit hemisphere

$$\mathbb{H} = \{(x,y,z) \in \mathbb{R}^3 : x^2 + y^2 + z^2 \leq 1, z \geq 0\}.$$

(Thus $\partial\mathbb{H}$ is the union of the unit disk in the (x,y)-plane and the unit upper hemispherical shell.) Feel free to cancel terms by citing symmetry if you're confident of what you're doing.

9.16.5. Let g and h be functions on $\mathbb{R}^3$. Recall the operator $\nabla = (D_1, D_2, D_3)$, which takes scalar-valued functions to vector-valued functions. As usual, define the Laplacian operator to be $\Delta = D_{11} + D_{22} + D_{33}$. From an earlier exercise, $\Delta = \mathrm{div} \circ \mathrm{grad}$.
  (a) Prove that $\mathrm{div}\,(g\,\nabla h) = g\,\Delta h + \nabla g \cdot \nabla h$.
  (b) If D is a closed compact subset of $\mathbb{R}^3$ with positively oriented boundary ∂D, prove that

$$\iiint_D (g\,\Delta h + \nabla g \cdot \nabla h)\,dV = \iint_{\partial D} g\,\nabla h \cdot \overrightarrow{dn}.$$

(Here n is the unit outward normal to D and $\nabla h \cdot n$ is the directional derivative of h in the direction of n.) Interchange g and h and subtract the resulting formula from the first one to get

$$\iiint_D (g\,\Delta h - h\,\Delta g)\,\mathrm{d}V = \iint_{\partial D} (g\,\nabla h - h\,\nabla g)\cdot \overrightarrow{\mathrm{d}n}.$$

These two formulas are **Green's identities**.

(c) Assume that h is harmonic, meaning that it satisfies the harmonic equation $\Delta h = 0$.

Take $g = h$ and use Green's first identity to conclude that if $h = 0$ on the boundary ∂D then $h = 0$ on all of D.

Take $g = 1$ and use Green's second identity to show that

$$\iint_{\partial D} \nabla h \cdot \overrightarrow{\mathrm{d}n} = 0.$$

What does this say about harmonic functions and flux?

9.17 Divergence and Curl in Polar Coordinates

The picture-explanations given in the previous section to interpret the divergence and the curl are not entirely satisfying. Working with the polar coordinate system further quantifies the ideas and makes them more coherent by applying to both operators in the same way.

Rather than study the divergence and the curl of a vector field $\widetilde{F}$ at a general point p, we may study the divergence and the curl of the modified vector field

$$F(x) = \widetilde{F}(x+p) - \widetilde{F}(p)$$

at the convenient particular point $\mathbf{0}$, at which the value of F is $\mathbf{0}$ as well. That is, we may normalize the point p to be $\mathbf{0}$ by prepending a translation of the domain, and we also may normalize $F(\mathbf{0})$ to $\mathbf{0}$ by postpending a translation of the range. With this in mind, let $A \subset \mathbb{R}^2$ be an open set that contains the origin, and let F be a continuous vector field on A that is stationary at the origin,

$$F = (f_1, f_2) : A \longrightarrow \mathbb{R}^2, \qquad F(\mathbf{0}) = \mathbf{0}.$$

At every point other than the origin, F resolves into a radial component and an angular component. Specifically,

$$F = F_r + F_\theta,$$

where

$$F_r = f_r \hat{r}, \qquad f_r = F \cdot \hat{r}, \qquad \hat{r} = (\cos\theta, \sin\theta) = (x,y)/|(x,y)|,$$
$$F_\theta = f_\theta \hat{\theta}, \qquad f_\theta = F \cdot \hat{\theta}, \qquad \hat{\theta} = \hat{r}^\times = (-\sin\theta, \cos\theta) = (-y,x)/|(x,y)|.$$

(Recall that the unary cross product $(x, y)^\times = (-y, x)$ in $\mathbb{R}^2$ rotates vectors 90 degrees counterclockwise.) Here f_r is positive if F_r points outward and negative if F_r points inward, and f_θ is positive if F_θ points counterclockwise and negative if F_θ points clockwise. Since $F(\mathbf{0}) = \mathbf{0}$, the resolution of F into radial and angular components extends continuously to the origin, $f_r(\mathbf{0}) = f_\theta(\mathbf{0}) = 0$, so that $F_r(\mathbf{0}) = F_\theta(\mathbf{0}) = \mathbf{0}$ even though $\hat{r}$ and $\hat{\theta}$ are undefined at the origin.

The goal of this section is to express the divergence and the curl of F at the origin in terms of the polar coordinate system derivatives that seem naturally suited to describe them, the radial derivative of the scalar radial component of F,

$$D_r f_r(\mathbf{0}) = \lim_{r \to 0^+} \frac{f_r(r \cos\theta, r \sin\theta)}{r},$$

and the radial derivative of the scalar angular component of F,

$$D_r f_\theta(\mathbf{0}) = \lim_{r \to 0^+} \frac{f_\theta(r \cos\theta, r \sin\theta)}{r}.$$

However, matters aren't as simple here as one might hope. For one thing, the limits are stringent in the sense that they must always exist and take the same values regardless of how θ behaves as $r \to 0^+$. Also, although F is differentiable at the origin if its vector radial and angular components F_r and F_θ are differentiable at the origin, the converse is not true. So first we need sufficient conditions for the converse, i.e., sufficient conditions for the components to be differentiable at the origin. Necessary conditions are always easier to find, so Proposition 9.17.1 will do so, and then Proposition 9.17.2 will show that the necessary conditions are sufficient. The conditions in question are the **Cauchy–Riemann equations**,

$$D_1 f_1(\mathbf{0}) = D_2 f_2(\mathbf{0}),$$
$$D_1 f_2(\mathbf{0}) = -D_2 f_1(\mathbf{0}).$$

When the Cauchy–Riemann equations hold, we can describe the divergence and the curl of F at the origin in polar terms, as desired. This will be the content of Theorem 9.17.3.

Before we proceed to the details, a brief geometric discussion of the Cauchy–Riemann equations may be helpful. The equation $D_1 f_1 = D_2 f_2$ describes the left side of Figure 9.22, in which the radial component of F on the horizontal axis is growing at the same rate as the radial component on the vertical axis. Similarly, the equation $D_2 f_1 = -D_1 f_2$ describes the right side of the figure, in which the angular component on the vertical axis is growing at the same rate as the angular component on the horizontal axis. Combined with differentiability at the origin, these two conditions will imply that moving outward in any direction, the radial component of F is growing at the same rate as it is on the axes, and similarly for the angular component. Thus the two limits that define the radial derivatives of the radial and angular components of F at $\mathbf{0}$ (these were displayed in the previous paragraph) are indeed independent of θ. An example of this situation, with radial and angular components both present, is shown in Figure 9.23.

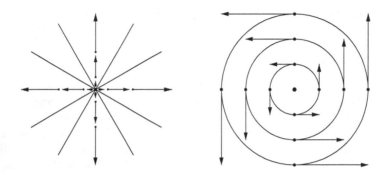

Figure 9.22. Geometry of the Cauchy–Riemann equations individually

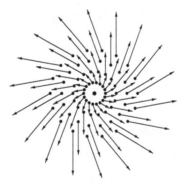

Figure 9.23. Geometry of the Cauchy–Riemann equations together

As mentioned, the necessity of the Cauchy–Riemann equations is the natural starting point.

Proposition 9.17.1 (Polar differentiability implies differentiability and the Cauchy–Riemann equations). *Let $A \subset \mathbb{R}^2$ be an open set that contains the origin, and let F be a continuous vector field on A that is stationary at the origin,*

$$F = (f_1, f_2) : A \longrightarrow \mathbb{R}^2, \qquad F(0) = 0.$$

Assume that the vector radial and angular components F_r and F_θ of F are differentiable at the origin. Then F is differentiable at the origin, and the Cauchy–Riemann equations hold at the origin.

For example, the vector field $F(x, y) = (x, 0)$ is differentiable at the origin, but since $D_1 f_1(0) = 1$ and $D_2 f_2(0) = 0$, it does not satisfy the Cauchy–Riemann equations, and so the derivatives of the radial and angular components of F at the origin do not exist.

Proof. As already noted, the differentiability of F at the origin is immediate, because $F = F_r + F_\theta$ and the sum of differentiable mappings is again differentiable. We need to establish the Cauchy–Riemann equations.

The radial component F_r is stationary at the origin, and we are given that it is differentiable at the origin. By the componentwise nature of differentiability, the first component $F_{r,1}$ of F_r is differentiable at the origin, and so necessarily both partial derivatives of $F_{r,1}$ exist at 0. Since $F_{r,1}$ vanishes on the y-axis, the second partial derivative is 0. Thus the differentiability criterion for the first component of F_r is

$$F_{r,1}(h, k) - h D_1 F_{r,1}(0) = o(h, k).$$

To further study the condition in the previous display, use the formula

$$F_r(x, y) = \begin{cases} \frac{f_r(x,y)}{|(x,y)|}(x, y) & \text{if } (x, y) \neq 0, \\ 0 & \text{if } (x, y) = 0 \end{cases}$$

to substitute $h f_r(h, k)/|(h, k)|$ for $F_{r,1}(h, k)$. Also, because F_θ is angular, $F_{\theta,1}$ vanishes on the x-axis, and so $D_1 F_{\theta,1}(0) = 0$; thus, since $f_1 = F_{r,1} + F_{\theta,1}$, we may substitute $D_1 f_1(0)$ for $D_1 F_{r,1}(0)$ as well. Altogether the condition becomes

$$h(f_r(h, k)/|(x, y)| - D_1 f_1(0)) = o(h, k).$$

A similar argument using the second component $F_{r,2}$ of F_r shows that

$$k(f_r(h, k)/|(x, y)| - D_2 f_2(0)) = o(h, k).$$

And so we have shown that the first Cauchy–Riemann equation holds and a little more,

$$\lim_{(h,k) \to 0} \frac{f_r(h, k)}{|(h, k)|} = D_1 f_1(0) = D_2 f_2(0).$$

For the second Cauchy–Riemann equation we could essentially repeat the argument just given, but a quicker way is to consider the radial component of the vector field $-F^\times = f_\theta \hat{r} - f_r \hat{\theta}$,

$$(-F^\times)_r(x, y) = \begin{cases} \frac{f_\theta(x,y)}{|(x,y)|}(x, y) & \text{if } (x, y) \neq 0, \\ 0 & \text{if } (x, y) = 0. \end{cases}$$

This radial component is differentiable at the origin since it is a rotation of the angular component of the original F, which we are given to be differentiable at the origin. And $-F^\times = (f_2, -f_1)$ in Cartesian coordinates, so as just argued,

$$\lim_{(h,k)\to 0} \frac{f_\theta(h,k)}{|(h,k)|} = D_1 f_2(0) = -D_2 f_1(0).$$

This last display encompasses the second Cauchy–Riemann equation at the origin.

Note that the argument has used the full strength of the hypotheses, i.e., it has used the differentiability at the origin of each component function of F_r and each component function of F_θ. □

As mentioned, the converse to Proposition 9.17.1 holds too.

Proposition 9.17.2 (Differentiability and the Cauchy–Riemann equations imply polar differentiability). *Let $A \subset \mathbb{R}^2$ be an open set that contains the origin, and let F be a continuous vector field on A that is stationary at the origin,*

$$F = (f_1, f_2) : A \longrightarrow \mathbb{R}^2, \qquad F(0) = 0.$$

Assume that F is differentiable at the origin, and assume that the Cauchy–Riemann equations hold at the origin. Then the vector radial and angular components F_r and F_θ are differentiable at the origin.

Proof. Let $a = D_1 f_1(0)$ and let $b = D_1 f_2(0)$. By the Cauchy–Riemann equations, also $a = D_2 f_2(0)$ and $b = -D_2 f_1(0)$, so that the Jacobian matrix of F at 0 is

$$F'(0) = \begin{bmatrix} a & -b \\ b & a \end{bmatrix}.$$

The condition that F is differentiable at 0 is

$$F(h,k) - (ah - bk, bh + ak) = o(h,k).$$

Decompose the quantity in the previous display into radial and angular components,

$$F(h,k) - (ah - bk, bh + ak) = \big(F_r(h,k) - a(h,k)\big) + \big(F_\theta(h,k) - b(-k,h)\big).$$

Since the components are at most as long as the vector,

$$F_r(h,k) - a(h,k) = o(h,k) \qquad \text{and} \qquad F_\theta(h,k) - b(-k,h) = o(h,k).$$

That is, F_r and F_θ are differentiable at the origin with respective Jacobian matrices

$$F_r'(0) = \begin{bmatrix} a & 0 \\ 0 & a \end{bmatrix} \qquad \text{and} \qquad F_\theta'(0) = \begin{bmatrix} 0 & -b \\ b & 0 \end{bmatrix}.$$

This completes the proof. □

Now we can return to the divergence and the curl.

Theorem 9.17.3 (Divergence and curl in polar coordinates). *Let $A \subset \mathbb{R}^2$ be a region of $\mathbb{R}^2$ containing the origin, and let F be a continuous vector field on A that is stationary at the origin,*

$$F = (f_1, f_2) : A \longrightarrow \mathbb{R}^2, \qquad F(0) = 0.$$

Assume that F is differentiable at the origin and that the Cauchy–Riemann equations hold at the origin. Then the radial derivatives of the scalar radial and angular components of F at the origin,

$$D_r f_r(0) = \lim_{r \to 0^+} \frac{f_r(r\cos\theta, r\sin\theta)}{r}$$

and

$$D_r f_\theta(0) = \lim_{r \to 0^+} \frac{f_\theta(r\cos\theta, r\sin\theta)}{r},$$

both exist independently of how θ behaves as r shrinks to 0. Furthermore, the divergence of F at the origin is twice the radial derivative of the radial component,

$$(\operatorname{div} F)(0) = 2D_r f_r(0),$$

and the curl of F at the origin is twice the radial derivative of the angular component,

$$(\operatorname{curl} F)(0) = 2D_r f_\theta(0).$$

Proof. By Proposition 9.17.2, the angular and radial components of F are differentiable at the origin, so that the hypotheses of Proposition 9.17.1 are met. The first limit in the statement of the theorem was calculated in the proof of Proposition 9.17.1,

$$D_r f_r(0) = \lim_{(h,k) \to 0} \frac{f_r(h,k)}{|(h,k)|} = D_1 f_1(0) = D_2 f_2(0).$$

This makes the formula for the divergence immediate,

$$(\operatorname{div} F)(0) = D_1 f_1(0) + D_2 f_2(0) = 2D_r f_r(0).$$

Similarly, again recalling the proof of Proposition 9.17.1,

$$D_r f_\theta(0) = \lim_{(h,k) \to 0} \frac{f_\theta(h,k)}{|(h,k)|} = D_1 f_2(0) = -D_2 f_1(0),$$

so that

$$(\operatorname{curl} F)(0) = D_1 f_2(0) - D_2 f_1(0) = 2D_r f_\theta(0).$$

$\square$

If F is a velocity field then the limit in the formula

$$(\operatorname{curl} F)(0) = 2 \lim_{r \to 0^+} \frac{f_\theta(r\cos\theta, r\sin\theta)}{r}$$

has the interpretation of the angular velocity of F at the origin. That is:

> When the Cauchy–Riemann equations hold, the curl is twice the angular velocity.

Indeed, the angular velocity ω away from the origin is by definition the rate of increase of the polar angle θ with the motion of F. This is not the counterclockwise component f_θ, but rather $\omega = f_\theta/r$, i.e., ω is the function called g_θ in the proof of Proposition 9.17.1. To understand this, think of a uniformly spinning disk such as a record on a turntable. At each point except the center, the angular velocity is the same. But the speed of motion is not constant over the disk, it is the angular velocity times the distance from the center. That is, the angular velocity is the speed divided by the radius, as claimed. In these terms, the proof showed that the angular velocity ω extends continuously to 0, and that $(\operatorname{curl} F)(0)$ is twice the extended value $\omega(0)$.

Also, if F is a velocity field then the right side of the formula

$$(\operatorname{div} F)(0) = 2 \lim_{r \to 0^+} \frac{f_r(r\cos\theta, r\sin\theta)}{r}$$

has the interpretation of the flux density of F at the origin. That is:

> When the Cauchy–Riemann equations hold, the divergence is the flux density.

To understand this, think of a planar region of incompressible fluid about the origin, and let r be a positive number small enough that the fluid fills the area inside the circle of radius r. Suppose that new fluid is being added throughout the interior of the circle, at rate c per unit of area. Thus fluid is being added to the area inside the circle at total rate $\pi r^2 c$. Here c is called the flux density over the circle, and it is measured in reciprocal time units, while the units of $\pi r^2 c$ are area over time. Since the fluid is incompressible, $\pi r^2 c$ is also the rate at which fluid is passing normally outward through the circle. And since the circle has circumference $2\pi r$, fluid is therefore passing normally outward through each point of the circle with radial velocity

$$f_r(r\cos\theta, r\sin\theta) = \frac{\pi r^2 c}{2\pi r} = \frac{rc}{2}.$$

Consequently,

$$2 \cdot \frac{f_r(r\cos\theta, r\sin\theta)}{r} = c.$$

Now let r shrink to 0. The left side of the display goes to the divergence of F at 0, and the right side becomes the continuous extension to radius 0 of the flux density over the circle of radius r. That is, the divergence is the flux density when fluid is being added at a single point.

Exercises

9.17.1. Put $\mathbb{R}^2$ into correspondence with the complex number field $\mathbb{C}$ as follows:

$$\begin{bmatrix} x \\ y \end{bmatrix} \longleftrightarrow x + iy.$$

Show that the correspondence extends to

$$\begin{bmatrix} a & -b \\ b & a \end{bmatrix}\begin{bmatrix} x \\ y \end{bmatrix} \longleftrightarrow (a + ib)(x + iy).$$

Show also that the correspondence preserves absolute value, i.e.,

$$\left|\begin{bmatrix} x \\ y \end{bmatrix}\right| = |x + iy|,$$

where the first absolute value is on $\mathbb{R}^2$ and the second one on $\mathbb{C}$.

9.17.2. Let $A \subset \mathbb{R}^2$ be an open set that contains the origin, and let $F : A \longrightarrow \mathbb{R}^2$ be a vector field on A that is stationary at the origin. Define a complex-valued function of a complex variable corresponding to F,

$$f(x + iy) = f_1(x, y) + if_2(x, y), \quad (x, y) \in A.$$

Then f is called **complex-differentiable at** 0 if the following limit exists:

$$\lim_{\Delta z \to 0} \frac{f(z + \Delta z) - f(z)}{\Delta z}.$$

The limit is denoted $f'(z)$.

(a) Suppose that f is complex-differentiable at 0. Compute $f'(z)$ first by letting Δz go to 0 along the x-axis, and again by letting Δz go to 0 along the y-axis. Explain how your calculation shows that the Cauchy–Riemann equations hold at 0.

(b) Show also that if f is complex differentiable at 0 then F is vector differentiable at $\mathbf{0}$, meaning differentiable in the usual sense. Suppose that f is complex-differentiable at 0, and that $f'(0) = re^{i\theta}$. Show that

$$(\operatorname{div} F)(\mathbf{0}) = 2r\cos\theta, \qquad (\operatorname{curl} F)(\mathbf{0}) = 2r\sin\theta.$$

(c) Suppose that F is vector-differentiable at $\mathbf{0}$ and that the Cauchy–Riemann equations hold at $\mathbf{0}$. Show that f is complex-differentiable at 0.

Correction to: Calculus and Analysis in Euclidean Space

Correction to:
J. Shurman, *Calculus and Analysis in Euclidean Space*,
Undergraduate Texts in Mathematics,
https://doi.org/10.1007/978-3-319-49314-5

The original version of the book was inadvertently published with a few typesetting errors, which have now been corrected.

The updated version of the book can be found at
https://doi.org/10.1007/978-3-319-49314-5

© Springer International Publishing AG 2019
J. Shurman, *Calculus and Analysis in Euclidean Space,*
Undergraduate Texts in Mathematics, https://doi.org/10.1007/978-3-319-49314-5_10

Index

Printed in the USA
CPSIA information can be obtained
at www.ICGtesting.com
LVHW012339310823
756928LV00008B/171

9 783319 493138